W9-AXY-821

Ocean Studies
Introduction to Oceanography

Second Edition

Joseph M. Moran, Editor

Education Program

American Meteorological Society

The American Meteorological Society Education Program

The American Meteorological Society (AMS), founded in 1919, is a **scientific and professional** society. Interdisciplinary in its scope, the Society actively promotes the development and dissemination of information on the atmospheric and related oceanic and hydrologic sciences. AMS has more than 10,000 professional members from more than 100 countries and over 135 corporate and institutional members representing 40 countries.

The Education Program is the initiative of the American Meteorological Society fostering the teaching of the atmospheric and related oceanic and hydrologic sciences at the precollege level and in community college, college and university programs. It is a unique partnership between scientists and educators at all levels with the ultimate goals of (1) attracting young people to further studies in science, mathematics and technology, and (2) promoting public scientific literacy. This is done via the development and dissemination of scientifically authentic, up-to-date, and instructionally sound learning and resource materials for teachers and students.

AMS Ocean Studies is an introductory undergraduate oceanography course offered partially via the Internet in partnership with college and university faculty. **AMS Ocean Studies** provides students with a comprehensive study of the principles of oceanography while simultaneously providing pedagogically appropriate investigations and applications focusing on web-delivered real-world current data. It provides real experiences demonstrating the value of computers and electronic access to time-sensitive data and information.

Ocean Studies: Introduction to Oceanography / Joseph M. Moran, Editor — 2nd Edition
ISBN-10 1-878220-90-X   ISBN-13 978-1-878220-90-5

Copyright © 2008 by the American Meteorological Society

All rights reserved. No part of this publication may be reproduced, stored in a retrieval system, or transmitted, in any form or by any means, electronic, mechanical, photocopying, recording or otherwise. without the prior written permission of the publisher.

Published by the American Meteorological Society
45 Beacon Street, Boston, MA 02108

Printed in the United States of America

The previous edition of this book was published under the title Online Ocean Studies.

Cover Photo © Nathaniel Young/Acclaim Images Stock Photography. (Note: the curvature in the horizon seen in the image is due to distortion produced by the 15mm fisheye lens used.)

BRIEF CONTENTS

PREFACE

CHAPTER 1:   OCEAN IN THE EARTH SYSTEM   1

CHAPTER 2:   OCEAN BASINS AND PLATE TECTONICS   33

CHAPTER 3   PROPERTIES OF OCEAN WATER   61

CHAPTER 4   MARINE SEDIMENTS   87

CHAPTER 5   THE ATMOSPHERE AND OCEAN   113

CHAPTER 6   OCEAN CURRENTS   145

CHAPTER 7   OCEAN WAVES AND TIDES   171

CHAPTER 8   THE DYNAMIC COAST   199

CHAPTER 9   MARINE ECOSYSTEMS   233

CHAPTER 10   LIFE IN THE OCEAN   261

CHAPTER 11   THE OCEAN, ATMOSPHERE, AND CLIMATE

                  VARIABILITY   293

CHAPTER 12   THE OCEAN AND CLIMATE CHANGE   317

CHAPTER 13   THE FUTURE OF OCEAN SCIENCE   353

CHAPTER 14   OCEAN STEWARDSHIP   377

CHAPTER 15   OCEAN PROBLEMS AND POLICY   401

APPENDIX I   CONVERSION FACTORS   423

APPENDIX II   OCEAN TIMELINE   425

GLOSSARY   435

INDEX   453

CONTENTS

CHAPTER 1   OCEAN IN THE EARTH SYSTEM   1

Case-in-Point 1
Driving Question 2
Earth as a System 3
      Hydrosphere 3
      Atmosphere 6
      Geosphere 8
      Biosphere 9
Biogeochemical Cycles 12
The Ocean in the Global Water Cycle 14
Observing the Ocean 17
      In Situ Monitoring of the Ocean's Depths 17
      Remote Sensing by Satellite 18
Modeling the Ocean 21
Humans and the Ocean 22
Conclusions 23
Basic Understandings/Review/Critical Thinking 23
ESSAY: What Killed the Dinosaurs? 27
ESSAY: Where Did the Water Come From? 29
ESSAY: Co-Evolution of the Ocean, Atmosphere, and Life 30

CHAPTER 2   OCEAN BASINS AND PLATE TECTONICS   33

Case-in-Point 33
Driving Question 35
Distribution of the World Ocean 35
Oceanic Crust and Continental Crust 36
      Earth Materials 36
      Rock Cycle 37
Ocean Bottom Profile 38
      Continental Margins 38
      Ocean Basins 41
Plate Tectonics and Ocean Basin Features 41
      Evidence for Plate Tectonics 41
      Divergent Plate Boundaries 44
      Convergent Plate Boundaries 46
      Transform Plate Boundaries 47
      Mantle Convection and Sea Level 48

Marine Volcanism 48
Hydrothermal Vents 49
Spreading and Closing Cycles 50
Conclusions 53
Basic Understandings/Review/Critical Thinking 53
ESSAY: Investigating the Ocean Bottom 56
ESSAY: Hotspot Volcanism and the Hawaiian Islands 59

CHAPTER 3   PROPERTIES OF OCEAN WATER   61

Case-in-Point 61
Driving Question 62
The Water Molecule and Hydrogen Bonding 62
        Water as Ice, Liquid, and Vapor 63
        Temperature and Heat 64
        Changes in Phase of Water 65
        Specific Heat of Water 66
        Maritime Influence on Climate 67
Chemical Properties of Seawater 68
        Water as a Solvent 68
        Sea Salts 68
        Variations in Salinity 71
        Dissolved Gases 71
        Seawater pH 73
        Ocean Acidification 74
Physical Properties of Seawater 75
        Water Density and Temperature 75
        Pressure 77
        Sea Ice 77
        Sound Transmission 78
Conclusions 79
Basic Understandings/Review/Critical Thinking 79
ESSAY: Desalination 83
ESSAY: Sea Ice Terminology 85

CHAPTER 4   MARINE SEDIMENTS   87

Case-in-Point 87
Driving Question 88
Classification of Marine Sediment by Size 89
        Size and Sorting 89
        Terminal Velocity 90
Classification of Marine Sediments by Source 91
        Lithogenous Sediment 91

Biogenous Sediment 94
Hydrogenous Sediment 96
Cosmogenous Sediment 97
Marine Sedimentary Deposits 97
Continental-Margin Deposits 97
Deep-Ocean Deposits 99
Marine Sedimentary Rock 101
Resources of the Seafloor 102
Oil and Natural Gas 102
Mineral Resources 102
Exclusive Economic Zone 103
Conclusions 104
Basic Understandings/Review/Critical Thinking 105
ESSAY: Heinrich Events 108
ESSAY: Burgess Shale: A Glimpse into Ancient Marine
Life 110

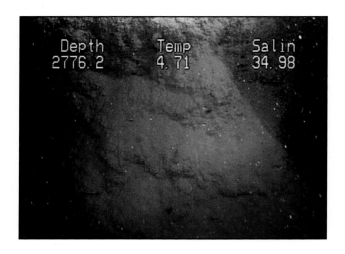

CHAPTER 5   THE ATMOSPHERE AND OCEAN   113

Case-in-Point 113
Driving Question 114
Weather and Climate 115
Heating and Cooling Earth's Surface 115
Solar Radiation 115
Solar Radiation Budget 119
Solar Radiation and the Ocean 120
Infrared Radiation and the Greenhouse Effect 121
Heating Imbalances: Earth's Surface versus Atmosphere 123
Latent Heating 124
Sensible Heating 126
Heating Imbalances: Tropics versus High Latitudes 127
Heat Transport by Air Mass Exchange 127
Heat Transport by Storms 128
Heat Transport by Ocean Circulation 129
Circulation of the Atmosphere: The Forces 129
Pressure Gradient Force 129
Coriolis Effect 130
Circulation of the Atmosphere: Patterns of Motion 131
Planetary-Scale Circulation 131
Synoptic-Scale Weather Systems 133
Conclusions 135
Basic Understandings/Review/Critical Thinking 135
ESSAY: Location at Sea, A Historical Perspective 139
ESSAY: The Stratospheric Ozone Shield and Marine Life 141

Case-in-Point 145
Driving Question 147
Ocean's Vertical Structure 147
Ocean in Motion: The Forces 149
    Wind-Driven Currents and Ekman Transport 149
    Geostrophic Flow 150
Wind-Driven Surface Currents 151
    Subtropical and Sub-Polar Gyres 152
    Equatorial Currents 153
    Boundary Currents 154
    Ocean Rings 155
    Upwelling and Downwelling 157
Monitoring the Ocean Depths 159
Thermohaline Circulation 160
    Formation of Deep Water 160
    Water Masses 161
    Implications for Climate 162
Conclusions 163
Basic Understandings/Review/Critical Thinking 163
ESSAY: Global Positioning System 166
ESSAY: Profiling the Ocean Depths 168
ESSAY: Bottles and Rubber Duckies, Tracking Currents
    with Flotsam and Jetsam 170

CHAPTER 7   OCEAN WAVES AND TIDES   171

Case-in-Point 171
Driving Question 172
Wind-Driven Waves 173
    Wind-Wave Generation 173
    Deep-Water and Shallow-Water Waves 175
    Seiche 176
    Wave Mediated Atmosphere-Ocean Transfer 178
Internal Waves 178
Ocean Tides 178
    Tide-Generating Forces 179
    Types of Tides 180
    Tides in Ocean Basins 182
    Tidal Currents 183
    Observing and Predicting Tides 184
    Open-Ocean Tides 185
Tsunamis 186
Conclusions 190
Basic Understandings/Review/Critical Thinking 190

ESSAY: The State of the Sea 193
ESSAY: Monitoring Sea Level from Space 196
ESSAY: Power Generation from Ocean Tides and Waves 198

CHAPTER 8   THE DYNAMIC COAST   199

Case-in-Point 199
Driving Question 201
Coastline Formation 202
Coastal Features 204
    Beaches 204
    Barrier Islands 206
    Rip Currents 207
    Salt Marshes and Wetlands 208
    Human Alterations 208
Estuaries 210
Coastal Storms and Storm Surge 211
Tropical Cyclones 214
    Hurricane Characteristics 216
    Where and When 216
    Hurricane Life Cycle 218
    Hurricane Hazards 219
    Evacuation 220
Extratropical Cyclones 222
Conclusions 223
Basic Understandings/Review/Critical Thinking 224
ESSAY: The Great Lakes and the Ocean 227
ESSAY: Moving the Cape Hatteras Lighthouse 232

CHAPTER 9   MARINE ECOSYSTEMS   233

Case-in-Point 233
Driving Question 235
Requirements for Marine Life 235
Structure of Marine Ecosystems 236
    Producers 236
    Consumers 238
    Decomposers 239
    Trophic Structure of Ecosystems 239
    Bioaccumulation 240
Ecosystem Processes 241
    Energy for Growth and Reproduction 241
    Production in the Photic Zone 242
    Nutrients and Trace Elements as Limiting

    Factors 244
        Microbial Marine Ecosystems 244
Ocean's Role in the Global Carbon Cycle 246
        Physical Pump 246
        Biological Pump 247
Ecosystem Observations and Models 249
Conclusions 250
Basic Understandings/Review/Critical Thinking 250
ESSAY: Ocean Iron Fertilization and Climate Change 254
ESSAY: Methane Hydrates, Future Energy Source 256
ESSAY: Ocean Color and Marine Productivity 259

CHAPTER 10   LIFE IN THE OCEAN 261

Case-in-Point 261
Driving Question 262
Marine Habitats 262
        Oceanic Life Zones 263
        Plankton in the Pelagic Zone 264
        Nekton in the Pelagic Zone 265
Life Strategies and Adaptations 266
        Vertical Migration 266
        Light and Vision 266
        Sound 267
        Feeding Strategies 268
Life at the Ocean's Edge 268
        Intertidal Zone 269
        Sea Grass Beds and Salt Marshes 271
        Kelp Forests 272
        Coral Reefs 273
        Benthic Feeding Habits 276
        Life on the Deep-Sea Floor 276
Marine Animals 277
        Fishes 277
        Marine Mammals 280
        Marine Reptiles 281
        Sea Birds 282
Conclusions 283
Basic Understandings/Review/Critical Thinking 283
ESSAY: Life and Sea Ice 287
ESSAY: Dead Zones 289
ESSAY: Marine Sanctuaries and Reserves 291

CHAPTER 11   THE OCEAN, ATMOSPHERE, AND CLIMATE VARIABILITY   293

Case-in-Point 293
Driving Question 294
Earth's Climate System 295
    Climate Controls 295
    Role of the Ocean 295
Tropical Pacific Ocean/Atmosphere 297
    Historical Perspective 297
    Neutral Conditions in the Tropical Pacific 299
    El Niño, The Warm Phase 300
    The 1997-98 El Niño 302
    La Niña, The Cold Phase 304
    Predicting and Monitoring El Niño and La Niña 305
    Frequency of El Niño and La Niña 307
North Atlantic Oscillation 308
Arctic Oscillation 310
Pacific Decadal Oscillation 310
Conclusions 310
Basic Understandings/Review/Critical Thinking 311
ESSAY: Sea Surface Temperature and Drought in Sub-Saharan
    Africa 314
ESSAY: El Niño in the Past 316

CHAPTER 12   THE OCEAN AND CLIMATE CHANGE   317

Case-in-Point 317
Driving Question 318
The Climate Record 318
    Marine Sediments and Climate 319
    Other Proxy Climatic Data Sources 320
    Geologic Time 321
    Past Two Million Years 323
    Instrument-Based Temperature Trends 325
Lessons of the Climate Past 327
Factors Contributing to Climate Change 327
    Climate and Plate Tectonics 328
    Climate and Solar Variability 329
    Climate and Earth's Orbit 330
    Climate and Volcanoes 332
    Climate and Earth's Surface Properties 333
    Climate and Human Activity 333
The Climate Future 335
    Global Climate Models 335
    Enhanced Greenhouse Effect and Global Warming 336

Impact of Climate Change on the Ocean 337
     Sea Level Fluctuations 337
     Arctic Sea Ice Cover 340
     Marine Life 342
Conclusions 343
Basic Understandings/Review/Critical Thinking 343
ESSAY: Climate Rhythms in Glacial Ice Cores 347
ESSAY: The Drying of the Mediterranean Sea 349
ESSAY: Sea Level Rise and Saltwater Intrusion 351

CHAPTER 13   THE FUTURE OF OCEAN SCIENCE   353

Case-in-Point 353
Driving Question 355
Investigating the Ocean 355
     Voyages of Exploration 355
     Challenger Expedition (1872-1876) 358
Modern Ocean Studies 359
     Technological Innovations 359
     Remote Sensing 362
     Scientific Ocean Drilling 363
     Ships of Opportunity 363
     International Cooperation 364
Emerging Ocean-Sensing Technologies 364
     Autonomous Instrumented Platforms and Vehicles 364
     Ocean Floor Observatories 366
     Computers and Numerical Models 368
Challenges in Ocean-Sensing Technologies 368
Conclusions 370
Basic Understandings/Review/Critical Thinking 370
ESSAY: Monitoring the Ocean with Animal-Borne Instruments 374

CHAPTER 14   OCEAN STEWARDSHIP   377

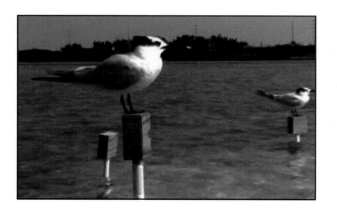

Case-in-Point 377
Driving Question 378
Stewardship of Ocean Life 379
Fisheries and Sustainable Exploitation 379
     Overfishing 380
     Maximum Sustainable Yield 382
     Ecologically Sustainable Yield 383
     Bycatch 385
     Restoring Fisheries 386
     Habitat Destruction and Restoration 387
     Recreational Fisheries 388

Protecting Endangered Marine Species 389
    Sea Turtles 389
    Whales 390
    Water Birds 392
Mariculture 393
Marine Exotic Species 394
Conclusions 395
Basic Understandings/Review/Critical Thinking 395
ESSAY: Determining the Age of a Fish 398
ESSAY: Loss and Restoration of Coastal Wetlands 399

CHAPTER 15   OCEAN PROBLEMS AND POLICY   401

Case-in-Point 401
Driving Question 402
Milestones in Ocean Governance 402
    Freedom of the Seas 402
    Antarctic Treaty 404
Human Impact in the Coastal Zone 404
    Human Population Trends 404
    Environmental Pollution 405
    Coastal Zone Management 406
Oil Spills 406
Dams and Marine Habitats 409
Restoring Chesapeake Bay 411
Waste Disposal in the Ocean 413
Deep-Ocean Carbon Storage 414
Obstacles to Ocean Policy Making 416
Conclusions 416
Basic Understandings/Review/Critical Thinking 417
ESSAY: Pathogens in the Coastal Zone 420
ESSAY: Predicting Oil-Spill Trajectories 422

Appendix I: Conversion Factors   423

Appendix II: Ocean Timeline   425

Glossary   435

Index   453

Preface

Welcome to *Ocean Studies*! You are about to embark on an analysis of the world ocean and the role of the ocean in the Earth system. *Ocean Studies* is a major initiative of the American Meteorological Society (AMS) and the National Oceanic and Atmospheric Administration (NOAA) Cooperative Program for Earth System Education (AMS/NOAA CPESE). *Ocean Studies* explores the ocean in the Earth system with special emphasis on (1) the flow and transformations of water and energy into and out of the ocean, (2) physical and chemical properties of seawater, (3) ocean circulation, (4) marine life, its habitats and adaptations, (5) interactions between the ocean and the other components of the Earth system (i.e., hydrosphere, atmosphere, geosphere, cryosphere, and biosphere), and (6) the human/societal impacts on and response to those interactions. The purpose of this book is to provide you with background information on the physical, chemical, geological, and biological foundations of oceanography. This information will assist your work on twice-weekly *Investigations* whose components are available in the companion *Ocean Studies Investigations Manual* and the *Ocean Studies Website*.

You will explore twelve principal themes plus three optional themes that are arranged by chapter, each corresponding to one week of the *Ocean Studies* course. Themes are organized so that concepts build logically upon one another as the ocean and its role in the Earth system are demonstrated to follow patterns described by physical laws. *Investigations*, partially delivered via the Internet and focused on some aspect of the ocean in the Earth system, are tied directly to each chapter. The first chapter introduces the Earth system and examines the ocean's place in the Earth system. The second chapter focuses on the characteristics of the ocean basin that are largely the products of plate tectonics. Chapter 3 deals with the unique physical and chemical properties of seawater and Chapter 4 covers the origin and distribution of sediment in the ocean. Chapter 5 investigates air-sea interactions and the flow of heat energy in the Earth-atmosphere-ocean system. The next three chapters cover the dynamic ocean: surface and deep-ocean currents (Chapter 6), waves and tides (Chapter 7), and shoreline processes (Chapter 8). Chapters 9 and 10 examine marine ecosystems and life in the ocean. The next two chapters explore the ocean's role in short-term climate

variability (Chapter 11) and long-term climate change (Chapter 12). Optional chapters consider the future of ocean science (Chapter 13), ocean stewardship (Chapter 14), and public policy and the ocean (Chapter 15).

Each chapter opens with a *Case-in-Point*, an authentic event or issue that highlights or applies one or more of the main concepts introduced in the chapter. In essence, the *Case-in-Point* previews the chapter and is intended to engage reader interest in the topic early on. Chapter 2, for example, opens with a discussion of the impacts of massive volcanic eruptions on the Earth system. The *Case-in-Point* is followed by a *Driving Question*, a broad-based query that links chapter concepts and provides a central focus from the beginning of the chapter. Content is science-rich and informs additional driving questions. Each chapter closes with a list of *Basic Understandings*, review questions, and critical thinking questions. *Essays* at the end of each chapter address in some depth a specific topic that builds on a concept introduced in the narrative. Examples include *Co-Evolution of the Ocean, Atmosphere, and Life*, *Desalination*, *Burgess Shale: A Glimpse into Ancient Marine Life*, *Global Positioning System*, *The State of the Sea*, *Moving the Cape Hatteras Lighthouse*, and *Monitoring the Ocean with Animal-Borne Instruments*. All bold-faced terms are defined in the *Glossary* at the back of the book.

Ocean Studies is pedagogically guided by an educational approach that seeks to engage learners in exploring their world by investigating meaningful questions. *Ocean Studies* plus its companion *Investigations Manual* and *Website* incorporates driving questions, scientific inquiry, collaboration, technology, and artifacts. Each investigation has printed and electronic components that make use of environmental data available on the Internet. Investigations promote critical thinking as participants engage in observation, data analysis, inference, and prediction. The course presents opportunities for students to collaborate with their instructor and fellow students as together they negotiate understanding. Application of information-age technology provides the student with experience in retrieving and analyzing real-world data (some in real-time) and sharing interpretations. Throughout the course, students assemble learning materials (*artifacts*) for assessment purposes.

This second edition has greater emphasis on the ocean in the Earth system, the ocean in Earth's climate system, plus methods of in situ and remote sensing of the ocean. New, expanded, or significantly revised topics include marine volcanism, hydrothermal vents, ocean acidification, thermohaline circulation, tsunamis, beaches and barrier islands, tropical cyclones, harmful algal blooms, global climate change, Arctic sea ice, and deep-sea cabled observatories. *Case-in-Points* and Essays have been added to Chapters 13, 14, and 15. All chapters have review and critical thinking questions. New full-color photographs and line art have been added to the textbook.

Ocean Studies learning materials are the products of collaboration among many individuals with extensive scientific backgrounds and teaching experience. The first edition of this textbook was derived from a manuscript co-authored by M. Grant Gross of Washington College (MD) and Elizabeth Gross of the Scientific Committee on Oceanic Research, International Council for Science. Joseph M. Moran of the AMS Education Program was managing editor for the first edition and overall editor for this second edition. For both editions, textbook development was a team effort that benefited greatly from suggestions, constructive criticisms, and editing provided by Ira W. Geer, Bernard A. Blair, Elizabeth W. Mills, and Thomas P. Kiley, Jr. of the AMS Education Program, Robert S. Weinbeck of SUNY College at Brockport and the AMS Education Program, David R. Smith and Andrew C. Muller of the U.S. Naval Academy, Edward J. Hopkins of the University of Wisconsin-Madison, James A. Brey of the AMS Education Program and the University of Wisconsin-Fox Valley, H. Joseph Niebauer of the University of Wisconsin-Madison, and Ronald D. Stieglitz and Ashley L. Boivin of the University of Wisconsin-Green Bay. We are grateful for the interest, encouragement, and assistance provided by John H. Dunnigan, Assistant Administrator for NOAA's National Ocean Service, John Oliver, Deputy Assistant Administrator for Operations for NOAA's National Marine Fisheries Service, and Peg Steffen, Educational Coordinator, NOAA's National Ocean Service. Much thanks to Stephen Gill, Bruce Moravchik, and Carol Kavanagh of NOAA's National Ocean Service, and Becky Allee, Kristen Koch and Heather Stirratt of NOAA's National Marine Fisheries Service. Special thanks are extended to Paul E. Robbins for his thorough, insightful review of the second edition manuscript, and to Joellen L. Russell of University of Arizona for her constructive comments.

Norman J. Frisch of Brockport, NY did an excellent job of turning line drawings into final art. Bernard Blair of the AMS Education Program met the numerous technical challenges in converting the original manuscript into this book with his usual skill, fine attention to detail, dedication, and perseverance. Special thanks are extended to the group of outstanding K-12 teachers who serve as AMS Educational Resource Agents (AERAs) for providing valuable advice and encouragement during the development, national implementation, and revision of *Ocean Studies* learning materials.

A note concerns the use of units in *Ocean Studies*. Generally, the International System of Units (abbreviated SI, for Systèm Internationale d'Unitès) is employed with equivalent English or other units following in parentheses. Exceptions are units used by convention or convenience in oceanography (e.g., pressure is given in units of decibars). Also, the equivalence between units is given in context; that is, where general estimates are given, approximate values are shown for all units. Conversion factors are in Appendix I and an ocean timeline is in Appendix II.

Ocean Studies is a major initiative of AMS/NOAA CPESE, a program designed to enhance public understanding of the fluid Earth system emphasizing the atmospheric, oceanic, and hydrologic sciences and to promote activity that will contribute to greater human resource diversity in the nation's scientific workforce. Through CPESE, the AMS assists NOAA in the advancement of its goals directed toward environmental assessment and prediction, protection of life and property, and the fostering of global environmental stewardship. NOAA's success in meeting its mission objectives is highly dependent upon synergistic relationships between it and the users of its products and services. CPESE nurtures this synergy through precollege teacher, introductory undergraduate and general educational activity. Fundamental to CPESE are (1) *breadth*, demonstrating the comprehensive need for describing and predicting changes in the Earth's environment and conserving and wisely managing the nation's coastal and marine resources; (2) *visibility*, increasing pubic awareness of the ways environmental assessment, prediction, and stewardship touch the lives of all Americans every day; and (3) *diversity*, promoting educational activity and outreach to attract members of groups underrepresented in science, technology, engineering and mathematics to study and consider careers in those fields, including those for which NOAA has employment needs and opportunities. For additional information on CPESE and the AMS Education Program, go to *http://www.ametsoc.org/amsedu*.

Ira W. Geer
AMS Education Program

CHAPTER 1

OCEAN IN THE EARTH SYSTEM

Case-in-Point
Driving Question
Earth as a System
        Hydrosphere
        Atmosphere
        Geosphere
        Biosphere
Biogeochemical Cycles
The Ocean in the Global Water Cycle
Observing the Ocean
        In Situ Monitoring of the Ocean's Depths
        Remote Sensing by Satellite
Modeling the Ocean
Humans and the Ocean
Conclusions
Basic Understandings/Review/Critical Thinking
ESSAY: What killed the Dinosaurs?
ESSAY: Where Did the Water Come From?
ESSAY: Co-Evolution of the Ocean, Atmosphere, and Life

Columbia River plume front. At certain phases of the tide, the boundary between the river and ocean water is visible as a long foam line between brownish water from the river and more grayish or bluish water from the ocean. [Courtesy of NOAA/NWFSC]

Case in Point

On 26 December 2004, a succession of tsunami waves devastated coastal areas surrounding the Indian Ocean. The death toll of about 230,000 was the greatest ever recorded due to a tsunami. At least 1 million people were made homeless. The extraordinary loss of life was attributed to the combination of high population density along the coast plus the lack of any warning. About 85% of all tsunamis take place in the Pacific Ocean where a tsunami wave warning system operates but there was no similar system in the Indian Ocean.

A tsunami is a rapidly propagating shallow-water ocean wave that develops when a submarine earthquake, landslide, or volcanic eruption disturbs deep ocean water and is known to build to tremendous heights in coastal areas (Chapter 7). A powerful earthquake was responsible for the December 2004 tsunami. In the eastern Indian Ocean about 100 km (62 mi) off the west coast of Sumatra,

Indonesia, one tectonic plate (the India plate) plunges beneath another tectonic plate (the Burma plate). This was the site of a magnitude 9.3 earthquake. The Burma plate shifted westward and upward about 15 m (50 ft) raising a portion of the seafloor, disturbing the overlying seawater, and generating tsunami waves. Waves spread eastward to Sumatra and radiated outward across the Indian Ocean and beyond.

As is typical with tsunamis in the open ocean, waves traveled at 500 to 1000 km per hr (300 to 600 mph) with a height of only about 0.5 m (1.5 ft). But as the tsunami waves approached the shallow coastal waters, the speed slowed, and wave heights built setting the stage for disaster as the tsunami waves pushed inland. In Sumatra's Aceh Province, the first region struck by the tsunami, the maximum wave height exceeded 30 m (100 ft), almost the height of a 10-story building (Figure 1.1).

FIGURE 1.1
Satellite images of Aceh Province, Indonesia before (left) and after (right) the 26 December 2004 tsunami destroyed coastal villages. Note areas denuded of vegetation along the coast. Left image taken by Landsat-7 in June 2001 and right image acquired on 12 January 2005 by ASTER (Advanced Spaceborne Thermal Emission and Reflection Radiometer). The location is approximately 4.8 degrees N, 95.4 degrees E and represents an area of about 14.3 km by 9.1 km. [Courtesy of NASA/GSFC/METI/ERSDAC/JAROS and U.S./Japan ASTER Science Team.]

Understanding how the December 2004 tsunami disaster occurred is key to developing effective planning and a warning system that will mediate the effects of any future tsunami. But to achieve this goal calls for a perspective that takes into account oceanographic and geological processes plus human settlement patterns, that is, an *Earth system perspective*.

Driving Question:
What is the relationship between the ocean and Earth system?

This book examines Earth's ocean and the energy and processes responsible for formation of its basins, the supply of seawater and dissolved salts, the circulation of its waters, and the abundant life it supports. We also consider the ocean's interactions with the continents, atmosphere, the rocks and sediments that form the ocean floor, and living organisms. By studying the ocean in this way, we are adopting an Earth system perspective, viewing the planet as a set of interacting subsystems. Thus, we examine the hydrosphere (Earth's water and ice), atmosphere (its gaseous envelope), geosphere (Earth's solid surface), and biosphere (all living organisms). In this opening chapter we introduce the Earth system and briefly describe Earth's various interacting subsystems with special emphasis on the ocean.

In short, the Earth system perspective guides our investigation of the ocean. Space explorers use this same systems approach in studying the other planets of the solar system. We also examine the flow and transformations of matter and energy within and among Earth's subsystems. We stress the transport and cycling of water, salts, carbon, and oxygen as we seek to understand how the ocean functions and how it influences our lives. Furthermore, the systems approach is valuable in studying how the planet responds to large-scale environmental change. An example is presented in the first Essay at the end of this chapter.

In this opening chapter, we survey some of the advances in direct (in situ) and remote sensing of the ocean made possible by modern technology (e.g., Argo floats, Earth-orbiting satellites). We introduce the contributions that specialized electronic sensors, computers and numerical models are making in the collection, analysis, and interpretation of environmental data. Finally, we briefly examine how human activity influences the ocean and how the ocean influences humanity.

Earth as a System

What is the Earth system and more fundamentally, what is a system? A **system** is an interacting set of components that behave in an orderly way according to the laws of nature. One familiar example of a system is the human body, which consists of various subsystems including the nervous, respiratory, and reproductive systems plus energy and matter input/output. In a healthy person, these subsystems function internally and interact with one another in regular and predictable ways. Based on extensive

observations and understanding of a system, scientists can predict how the system and its components are likely to respond to changing conditions. This predictive ability is important, for example, in dealing with the complexities of global climate change and its potential impacts on Earth's subsystems (Chapter 12).

The Earth system consists of four major interacting subsystems: hydrosphere, atmosphere, geosphere, and biosphere. Here we briefly examine each subsystem, its composition, basic properties, and some of its interactions with other components of the Earth system. The view of Planet Earth in Figure 1.2, resembling a "blue marble," shows all the major subsystems of the Earth system. The ocean, the most prominent feature, appears blue; clouds mostly obscure the ice sheets that cover much of Greenland and Antarctica; and the atmosphere is made visible by swirling storm clouds over the Pacific near Mexico and the middle of the Atlantic Ocean. Viewed edgewise, the atmosphere appears as a thin, bluish layer. Land (part of the geosphere) is mostly green because of vegetative cover (biosphere). The dominant color of Earth is blue because the ocean covers more than two-thirds of its surface; in fact, often Earth is referred to as the "blue planet" or "water planet."

HYDROSPHERE

The **hydrosphere** encompasses water in all three phases (i.e., ice, liquid, and vapor) that continually cycles from one reservoir to another within the Earth system. (We discuss the global water cycle in more detail later in this chapter.) Water is unique among the chemical components of the Earth system in that it is the only naturally occurring substance that co-exists in all three phases at normal temperatures and pressures near Earth's surface. The ocean, by far the largest reservoir of water in the hydrosphere, covers about 70.8% of the planet's surface and has an average depth of about 3.8 km (2.4 mi) but accounts for only 0.02% of Earth's mass. About 96.4% of the hydrosphere is ocean salt water; other saline bodies of water account for 0.6%. The next largest reservoir in the hydrosphere is glacial ice, most of which covers much of Antarctica and Greenland. Ice and snow make up 2.1% of water in the hydrosphere. Considerably smaller quantities of water occur on the land surface (lakes, rivers), in the subsurface (soil moisture, groundwater), the atmosphere (water vapor, clouds, precipitation), and biosphere (plants, animals). The possible origins of water on Earth are described in this chapter's second Essay.

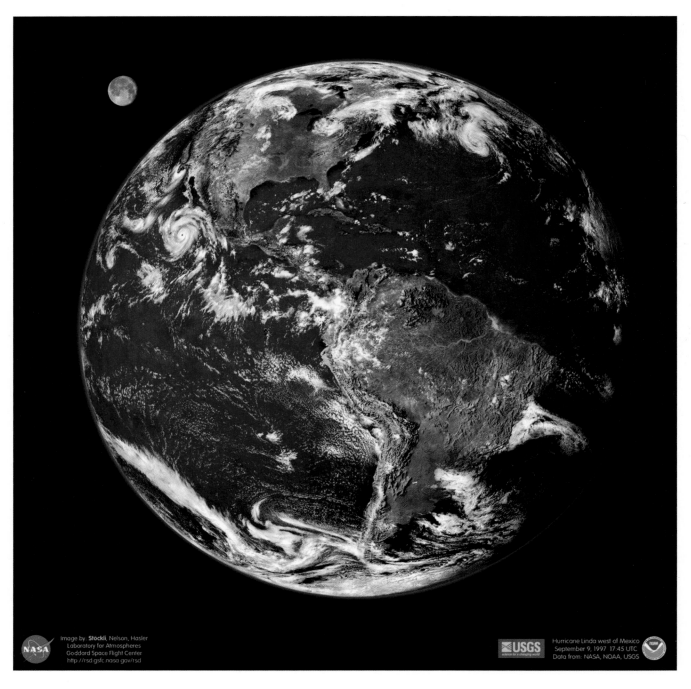

FIGURE 1.2
Planet Earth, viewed from space, appears as a "blue marble," with its surface mostly ocean water and partially obscured by swirling cloud masses. The moon, appearing in the upper left limb of the Earth, is the planet's only natural satellite and exerts a major influence on the ocean through tides. [Courtesy of NASA, Goddard Space Flight Center]

The ocean and atmosphere are coupled such that winds drive surface ocean currents. Wind-driven currents are restricted to a surface ocean layer typically about 100 m (300 ft) deep and take a few months to years to cross an ocean basin (Chapter 6). Deep-ocean currents, at depths greater than 100 m (300 ft), are much more sluggish and more challenging to study than surface currents because of the considerable difficulties in making measurements at great depths. Movements of deep-ocean waters are caused primarily by small differences in water density (mass per unit volume) arising from small differences in water temperature and salinity (a measure of dissolved salt content). Cold water, being denser than warm water, tends to sink whereas warm water, being less dense, is buoyed upward by (or floats on) colder water. Likewise, saltier water is denser than less salty water and tends to sink whereas less salty water is buoyed upward. The combination of temperature and salinity determines whether a water mass remains at its original depth or sinks to the bottom. Even though deep currents are relatively slow, they keep ocean waters well mixed so that the ocean has a nearly uniform chemical composition (Chapter 3).

The densest ocean waters form in polar or nearby subpolar regions. Salty waters become even saltier where sea ice forms at high latitudes because growing ice crystals exclude dissolved salts. Chilling of this salty water near Greenland and Iceland and in the Norwegian and Labrador Seas further increases its density so that it sinks and forms a bottom current that flows southward under equatorial surface waters and into the South Atlantic as far south as Antarctica. Here, deep water from the North Atlantic mixes with deep water around Antarctica (Chapter 6). Branches of that cold bottom current then spread northward into the Atlantic, Indian, and Pacific basins. Eventually, the water slowly diffuses to the surface, mainly in the Pacific, and then starts its journey on the surface through the islands of Indonesia, across the Indian Ocean, around South Africa, and into the tropical Atlantic. There, intense heating and evaporation make the water hot and salty. This surface water is then transported northward in the Gulf Stream thereby completing the cycle. This *meridional overturning circulation* (MOC) and its transport of heat energy and salt is an important control of climate (Chapter 6).

The frozen portion of the hydrosphere, known as the **cryosphere**, encompasses massive glacial ice sheets, mountain glaciers, ice in permanently frozen ground (*permafrost*), and the pack ice and bergs floating at sea. All of these ice types except pack ice (frozen sea water) are fresh water. A **glacier** is a mass of ice that flows internally under the influence of gravity. In places, the Greenland and Antarctic ice sheets are up to 3 km (1.8 mi) thick. The Antarctic ice sheet contains 90% of the ice in the Earth system. Much smaller glaciers (tens to hundreds of meters thick) primarily occupy the highest mountain valleys on all continents. At present, glacial ice covers about 10% of the planet's land area but at times during the past 1.7 million years, glacial ice expanded over as much as 30% of the land

surface, primarily in the Northern Hemisphere. At the peak of the last glacial advance, about 20,000 to 18,000 years ago, the Laurentide ice sheet covered much of what is now Canada and the northern tier states of the United States. At the same time, a smaller ice sheet buried the British Isles and portions of northwest Europe. Meanwhile, mountain glaciers worldwide thickened and expanded.

Glaciers form where annual snowfall exceeds annual snowmelt. As snow accumulates, the pressure of the new snow converts underlying snow to ice. As the ice forms, it preserves traces of the original seasonal layers of snow and traps gas bubbles. Chemical analysis of the ice layers and air bubbles in the ice provides clues to climatic conditions at the time the original snow fell (Chapter 12). Ice cores extracted from the Greenland and Antarctic ice sheets yield information on changes in Earth's climate and atmospheric composition extending back in time hundreds of thousands of years—to about 650,000 years ago in Antarctica.

Under the influence of gravity, glacial ice flows slowly from sources at higher latitudes or higher elevations (where some winter snow survives the summer) to lower latitudes or lower elevations, where the ice either melts or flows into the nearby ocean. Around Antarctica, streams of glacial ice flow out to the ocean. Ice, being less dense than seawater, floats, forming ice shelves (typically about 500 m or 1600 ft thick). Thick masses of ice break off the shelf edge, forming flat-topped icebergs that are carried by surface ocean currents around Antarctica (Figure 1.3). Likewise, irregularly shaped icebergs break off the glacial ice streams of Greenland and flow out into the North Atlantic Ocean. In 1912, the newly launched luxury liner, *RMS Titanic*, struck a Greenland iceberg southeast of Newfoundland and sank with the loss of more than 1500 lives. Most sea ice surrounding Antarctica forms each winter through freezing of surface seawater. During summer most of the sea ice around Antarctica melts whereas in the Arctic Ocean sea ice can persist for several years before flowing out through Fram Strait into the Greenland Sea and eventually melting. This "multi-year" ice loses salt content with age, so that Eskimos harvest this older, less salty ice for drinking water.

The hydrosphere is dynamic; water moves continually although at different rates through different parts of the Earth system. Nonetheless, the ocean is the ultimate destination of all water moving on or beneath the land surface. Water flowing in river or stream channels may take a few weeks to reach the ocean. Groundwater typically moves at a very slow pace through fractures

16 September 2000   4 November 2001   12 November 2001

FIGURE 1.3
A massive iceberg (42 km by 17 km or 26 mi by 10.5 mi) is shown breaking off Pine Island Glacier, West Antarctica (75 degrees S, 102 degrees W) in early November 2001 along a large fracture that formed across the glacier in mid 2000. Images of the glacier were obtained by the Multi-angle Imaging SpectroRadiometer (MISR) instrument onboard NASA's Terra spacecraft. Pine Island Glacier is the largest discharger of ice in Antarctica and the continent's fastest moving glacier. [Courtesy of NASA]

and tiny openings in subsurface rock and sediment and feeds into rivers, lakes, or directly into the ocean. Water in large, deep lakes also moves slowly, in some cases taking centuries to reach the ocean.

How long is water frozen into glaciers? Glaciers normally expand (thicken and advance) and shrink (thin and retreat) slowly in response to changes in climate (long-term average temperature and snowfall). Mountain glaciers respond to climate change on time scales of a decade or so. Until recently, scientists had assumed that the response time for the Greenland and Antarctic ice sheets is measured in millennia. However, in 2007 scientists reported that two outlet glaciers that drain the Greenland ice sheet can undergo significant changes in discharge in only a few years. This finding was confirmed by measurements of changes in ice surface elevation by sensors onboard NASA's Ice, Cloud, and Land Elevation Satellite (ICESat). This unexpectedly rapid discharge is likely due to the flow of large ice streams over subglacial water. Hence, outlet glaciers behave more like mountain glaciers and this raises questions regarding the long-term stability of polar ice sheets (Chapter 12).

ATMOSPHERE

Earth's **atmosphere** is a relatively thin envelope of gases and tiny suspended particles surrounding the planet. Compared to Earth's diameter, the atmosphere is like the thin skin of an apple accounting for only about 0.07% of the mass of the Earth system. But the thin atmospheric skin is essential for life and the orderly functioning of physical and biological processes on Earth. Unlike the nearly uncompressible ocean water, air is compressible, so that air density decreases with increasing altitude above Earth's surface. About half of the atmosphere's mass is concentrated within about 5.5 km (3.4 mi) of Earth's surface and 99% of its mass occurs below an altitude of 32 km (20 mi). At an altitude of about 1000 km (620 mi), Earth's atmosphere merges with the highly rarefied interplanetary gases, hydrogen and helium.

Based on the average vertical temperature profile, the atmosphere is divided into four layers (Figure 1.4). The **troposphere** (averaging about 10 km or 6 mi thick) is where the atmosphere interfaces with the hydrosphere, geosphere, and biosphere and where most

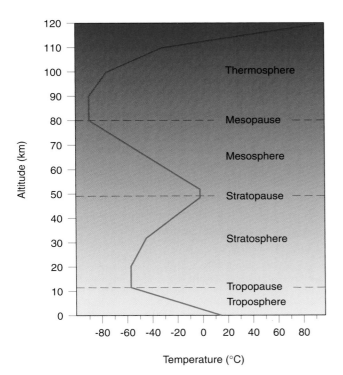

FIGURE 1.4
Based on variations in average temperature with altitude, the atmosphere is divided into the troposphere, stratosphere, mesosphere, and thermosphere.

weather takes place. In the troposphere, the average air temperature drops with increasing altitude so that it is usually colder on mountaintops than in lowlands. The troposphere contains 75% of the atmosphere's mass and 99% of its water. The *stratosphere* (10 to 50 km, 6 to 30 mi above Earth's surface) contains the *ozone shield*, which protects organisms from exposure to potentially lethal levels of solar ultraviolet radiation. Above the stratosphere is the *mesosphere* where the average temperature generally decreases with altitude and above that is the *thermosphere* where the average temperature increases with altitude but is particularly sensitive to variations in incoming solar radiation.

Nitrogen (N_2) and oxygen (O_2), the chief atmospheric gases, are mixed in uniform proportions up to an altitude of about 80 km (50 mi). Not counting water vapor (which has a highly variable concentration),

nitrogen occupies 78.08% by volume of the lower atmosphere, and oxygen is 20.95% by volume. The next most abundant gases are argon (0.93%) and carbon dioxide (0.038%). Many other gases occur in the atmosphere in trace concentrations, including ozone (O_3) and methane (CH_4) (Table 1.1). Unlike nitrogen and oxygen, the percent volume of some of these trace gases varies with time and location.

In addition to gases, minute solid and liquid particles, collectively called **aerosols**, are suspended in the atmosphere. A flashlight beam in a darkened room reveals an abundance of tiny dust particles floating in the air. Individually, most atmospheric aerosols are too small to be visible but in aggregates, such as water droplets and ice crystals composing clouds, they may be visible. Most aerosols occur in the lower atmosphere, near their sources on Earth's surface; they are derived from wind erosion of soil, ocean spray, forest fires, volcanic eruptions, industrial chimneys, and the exhaust of motor vehicles. Although the concentration of aerosols in the atmosphere is relatively small, they participate in some important processes. Aerosols function as nuclei that promote the formation of clouds, essential for the global water cycle. And some aerosols (e.g., volcanic dust, sulfurous particles) influence air temperatures by interacting with incoming solar radiation.

The significance of an atmospheric gas is not necessarily related to its concentration. Some atmospheric components that are essential for life occur in very low concentrations. For example, most water vapor is confined

TABLE 1.1
Gases Composing Dry Air in the Lower Atmosphere (below 80 km)

Gas	% by Volume	Parts per Million
Nitrogen (N_2)	78.08	780,840.0
Oxygen (O_2)	20.95	209,460.0
Argon (A)	0.93	9,340.0
Carbon dioxide (CO_2)	0.03835	383.5
Neon (Ne)	0.0018	18.0
Helium (He)	0.00052	5.2
Methane (CH_4)	0.00014	1.4
Krypton (Kr)	0.00010	1.0
Nitrous oxide (N_2O)	0.00005	0.5
Hydrogen (H)	0.00005	0.5
Xenon (Xe)	0.000009	0.09
Ozone (O_3)	0.000007	0.07

to the lowest kilometer or so of the atmosphere and is never more than about 4% by volume even in the most humid places on Earth (e.g., over tropical rainforests and seas). But without water vapor, the planet would have no water cycle, no rain or snow, no ocean, and no fresh water. Also, without water vapor, Earth would be much too cold for most forms of life to exist. Although comprising only 0.038% of the lower atmosphere, carbon dioxide (CO_2) is essential for photosynthesis. Without carbon dioxide, green plants and the food webs they support could not exist. Although the atmospheric concentration of ozone (O_3) is minute, the chemical reactions responsible for its formation (from oxygen) and dissociation (to oxygen) in the stratosphere (mostly at altitudes between 30 and 50 km) shield organisms on Earth's surface from potentially lethal intensities of solar ultraviolet radiation.

The atmosphere is dynamic; that is, the atmosphere is always circulating in response to differences in rates of heating and cooling within the Earth system. On an average annual basis, Earth's surface experiences net radiational heating (more heating than cooling mainly due to the sun) and the atmosphere undergoes net radiational cooling (to space). Also, net radiational heating occurs in the tropics, while net radiational cooling characterizes higher latitudes. Variations in heating and cooling give rise to temperature gradients, that is, differences in temperature from one location to another. In response to *temperature gradients*, the atmosphere (and ocean) circulates and redistributes heat within the Earth system. Heat is conveyed from where it is warmer to where it is colder: from the Earth's surface to atmosphere and from the tropics to higher latitudes. As discussed in detail in Chapter 5, the global water cycle and accompanying phase changes of water play an important role in this planetary-scale transport of heat energy.

GEOSPHERE

The **geosphere** is the solid portion of the planet consisting of rocks, minerals, and sediments. Most of Earth's interior cannot be observed directly—the deepest mines and oil wells do not penetrate the solid Earth to any great depth. Most of what is known about the composition and physical properties of Earth's interior comes from studying seismic waves generated by earthquakes and explosions. In addition, meteorites provide valuable clues regarding the chemical composition of Earth's interior. From study of the behavior of vibrations that penetrate the planet, geologists have determined that Earth's interior consists of four spherical shells: crust, mantle, and outer

and inner core (Figure 1.5). Earth's interior is mostly solid and accounts for much of the mass of the Earth system. The outermost solid skin of the planet, called the *crust*, ranges in thickness from only about 8 km (5 mi) under the ocean to about 70 km (45 mi) in some mountain belts. We live on the crust and it is the source of almost all rock, mineral, and fuel (e.g., coal, oil, and natural gas) resources that are essential for our industrial-based economy. The rigid uppermost portion of the *mantle* plus the overlying crust constitutes Earth's **lithosphere**, averaging about 100 km (62 mi) thick. Two sets of geological processes continually modify the lithosphere: surface geological processes and internal geological processes.

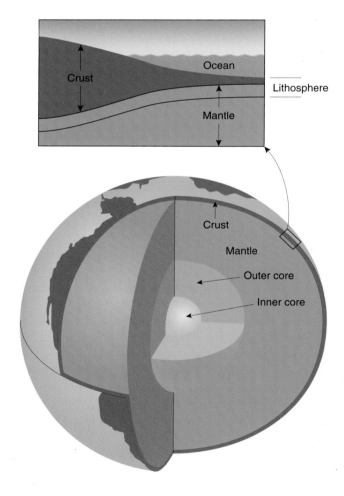

FIGURE 1.5
Earth's interior is divided into the crust, mantle, and outer and inner core. The lithosphere is the rigid upper portion of the mantle plus the overlying crust. (Drawing is not to scale.)

Surface geological processes encompass weathering and erosion taking place at the interface between the lithosphere (mainly the crust) and the other Earth subsystems. **Weathering** entails the physical disintegration, chemical decomposition, or solution of exposed rock. Rock fragments produced by weathering are known as *sediments*. Water plays an important role in weathering by dissolving soluble rock and minerals and participating in chemical reactions that decompose rock. Water's unusual physical property of expanding (by 9%) when freezing can produce pressure that fragments rock if the water saturates the tiny cracks and pore spaces in the rock and the temperature drops below 0°C (32°F). More likely, however, the water is not so confined and fragmentation is due to stress caused by the growth of ice lenses within the rock.

The ultimate weathering product is *soil*, a mixture of organic (humus) and inorganic matter (sediment) on Earth's land surface that supports rooted plants and supplies mineral nutrients and water for plants. Soils derive from the weathering of bedrock or sediment and vary widely in texture (particle size). A typical soil is 50% open space (pores) that is occupied by air and water in roughly equal proportions. Plants also participate in weathering through the physical action of their growing roots and the carbon dioxide they release to the soil.

Erosion is the removal and transport of sediments by gravity, moving water, glaciers, and wind. Running water and glaciers are pathways in the global water cycle. Erosive agents transport sediments from source regions (usually highlands) to low-lying depositional environments (e.g., ocean, lakes). Weathering aids erosion by reducing massive rock to particles that are sufficiently small to be transported by agents of erosion. Erosion aids weathering by removing sediment and exposing fresh surfaces of rock to the atmosphere and weathering processes. Together, weathering and erosion reduce the elevation of the land.

Internal geological processes counter surface geological processes by uplifting the land through tectonic activity, including volcanism and mountain building. Most tectonic activity occurs at the boundaries between lithospheric plates. The lithosphere is broken into a dozen massive plates (and many smaller ones) that are slowly driven (typically less than 20 cm per year) across the face of the globe by huge convection currents in Earth's mantle. Continents are carried on the moving plates and, as we will see in Chapter 2, ocean basins are formed by seafloor spreading.

Plate tectonics probably has operated on the planet for at least 3 billion years, with continents periodically assembling into supercontinents and then splitting into smaller segments (Chapter 2). The most recent supercontinent, called *Pangaea* (Greek for "all land"), broke apart about 200 million years ago and its constituent landmasses, the continents of today, slowly moved to their present locations. Plate tectonics explains such seemingly strange discoveries as glacial sediments in the Sahara Desert and fossil coral reefs indicative of tropical climates in Wisconsin. Such discoveries reflect climatic conditions hundreds of millions of years ago when the continents were at different latitudes than they are today.

Geological processes occurring at boundaries between plates produce large-scale landscape and ocean bottom features, including mountain ranges, volcanoes, deep-sea trenches, and the ocean basins themselves. Enormous stresses develop at plate boundaries, bending and fracturing bedrock over broad areas. Hot molten rock material, known as **magma**, wells up from deep in the crust or upper mantle and migrates along rock fractures. Some magma pushes into the upper portion of the crust where it cools and solidifies into massive bodies of rock that form the core of mountain ranges (e.g., Sierra Nevada). Some magma feeds volcanoes or flows through fractures and spreads over Earth's surface as lava flows that cool and solidify (e.g., Columbia Plateau in the Pacific Northwest). At spreading plate boundaries on the sea floor, upward flowing magma solidifies into new oceanic crust (Chapter 2). Plate tectonics and associated volcanism are important in geochemical cycling and release water vapor, carbon dioxide, and other gases to the atmosphere and ocean.

Volcanic activity is not confined to plate boundaries. Some volcanic activity occurs at great distances from plate boundaries and is due to hot spots in the mantle (Chapter 2). A **hot spot** is a long-lived source of magma caused by rising plumes of hot material originating in the mantle (*mantle plumes*). Where a plate is situated over a hot spot, magma may break through the crust and form a volcano. The "Big Island" of Hawaii is volcanically active because it sits over a hot spot located in the mantle under the Pacific plate. A hot spot underlying Yellowstone National Park is the source of heat for geyser eruptions (including Old Faithful). Further complicating matters, however, both lithospheric plates and hot spots move.

BIOSPHERE

All living organisms on Earth are components of the **biosphere** (Figure 1.6). They range in size from

FIGURE 1.6
Earth's biosphere viewed by instruments flown onboard NASA's SeaWiFS (Sea-viewing Wide Field-of-view Sensor) on the SeaStar satellite launched in August 1997. Biological productivity is color-coded and highest where it is dark green and lowest where it is violet. White indicates snow and ice covered areas. [Provided by the SeaWiFS Project, NASA/Goddard Space Flight Center and ORBIMAGE.]

microscopic single-celled bacteria to the largest plants and animals that ever lived (e.g., redwood trees and blue whales). Bacteria and other one-celled organisms dominate the biosphere, both on land and in the ocean. The average animal in the ocean is the size of a mosquito. Large, multi-cellular organisms (including humans) are relatively rare on Earth.

Organisms on land or in the atmosphere live close to Earth's surface. However, marine organisms occur throughout the ocean depths and even inhabit rock fractures, volcanic vents, and mud on the ocean floor. Certain organisms live in so-called *extreme environments* at temperatures and pressures previously thought impossible for life. In fact, some scientists estimate that the mass of organisms living in fractured rocks on and below the ocean floor may vastly exceed the mass of organisms living on or above it. Most of these deep-dwelling organisms remain a mystery.

Photosynthesis and cellular respiration are essential for life near the surface of the Earth and exemplify the interaction of the biosphere with the other subsystems of the Earth system. **Photosynthesis** is the process whereby green plants use light energy from the sun to combine carbon dioxide from the atmosphere with water to produce sugars, a form of carbohydrate containing a relatively large amount of energy. Oxygen (O_2) is an important byproduct

of photosynthesis. Animals that consume plants harvest some of that energy. Other animals consume those animals and energy progresses up the food chain. Through **cellular respiration**, an organism processes food and liberates energy in a form that can be used for maintenance, growth, and reproduction. Thereby, carbon dioxide, water, and heat energy are released (cycled) within the Earth system.

Sunlight is the principal source of energy for most organisms living on land or in the ocean's surface waters. However, for specialized organisms inhabiting the darkness of the ocean depths and rock fractures on the ocean floor, chemical energy rather than sunlight drives biological processes. Through a process known as **chemosynthesis**, these marine organisms derive energy from substances such as hydrogen sulfide (H_2S) that originate in Earth's interior (Chapter 9).

Dependency of organisms on one another (e.g., as a source of food) and on their physical and chemical environment (e.g., for water, oxygen, carbon dioxide, and habitat) is embodied in the concept of ecosystem. The biosphere is composed of **ecosystems**, communities of plants and animals that interact with one another, together with the physical conditions and chemical substances in a specific geographical area. Deserts, tropical rain forests, tundra, estuaries, marshes, lakes, streams, and coral reefs are examples of natural ecosystems. Most people live in highly modified terrestrial ecosystems such as cities, towns, farms, or ranches.

An ecosystem is home to producers (plants), consumers (animals), and decomposers (bacteria, fungi). *Producers* (also called *autotrophs* for "self-nourishing") form the base of most ecosystems. Using solar energy, their photosynthetic pigments form energy-rich carbohydrates. Consumers that depend directly or indirectly on plants for their food are called *heterotrophs*. Animals feeding directly on plants are called *herbivores*; those that prey on other animals are called carnivores and animals that consume both plants and animals are *omnivores*. After death, the remains of organisms are broken down by decomposers, usually bacteria and fungi, which cycle nutrients back to the environment.

Feeding relationships, called a **food chain**, can be quite simple. In a hypothetical land-based (or terrestrial) food chain, plants (primary producers) are eaten by deer (herbivores), which in turn are eaten by wolves (carnivores) or humans (mostly omnivores). In a food chain, each stage is called a *trophic level* (or feeding level). On average, only about 10% of the energy available at one trophic level is transferred to the next higher trophic level. *Biomass*, the total weight or mass of organisms, is more readily measured than energy so that scientists describe the transfer of energy in food chains in terms of so many grams or kilograms of biomass. Thus 100 g of plants are required to produce 10 g of deer, which in turn produces 1 g of wolf. Terrestrial and marine food chains are often more complex than our plants-deer-wolves-humans example. With some notable exceptions, marine and terrestrial organisms usually eat many different kinds of food, and in turn, are eaten by a host of other consumers. These more complicated feeding relationships constitute a *food web* (Figure 1.7).

An example of an ecosystem that is particularly important in the coastal zone is an estuary, where the hydrosphere, lithosphere, and biosphere interact in special ways. An estuary forms where fresh and salt water mix usually at the mouths of rivers and in tidal marshes and bays. Water in an estuary undergoes daily tidal oscillations (i.e., periodic rise and fall of sea level in response to the gravitational attraction of the moon and sun). Organisms living in an *estuary* are adapted to frequent fluctuations in currents, temperature, salinity, and the concentration of suspended sediment. Among the nation's best-known estuaries are Chesapeake Bay (largest in the U.S.), San Francisco Bay, and Puget Sound (Washington).

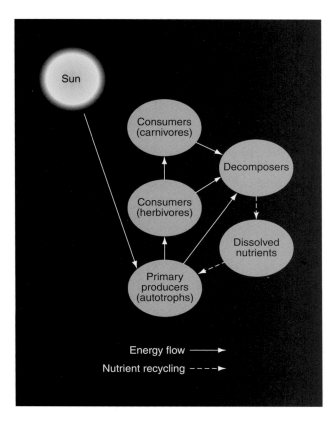

FIGURE 1.7
Schematic diagram of a marine food web in which solar radiation powers photosynthesis and energy is conveyed to successively higher trophic (feeding) levels.

Estuaries are among the most productive ecosystems on the planet because of a special combination of biological and physical characteristics. They receive a continual supply of nutrients and organic matter delivered by both rivers and ocean tidal currents. Water circulates in an estuary in a way that traps and re-circulates nutrients and detritus (dead or partially decomposed remains of plants and animals). These conditions support luxuriant plant growth (e.g., phytoplankton, marsh grass) as well as large populations of animals that feed on detritus. The abundant food supply coupled with the unique environmental conditions of an estuary favor development and protection of juvenile fish. Low salinity and shallow water deter many ocean predators that would feed on juvenile fish. Estuaries provide habitat favorable for oysters, mussels, clams, lobsters, shrimp, and snails. These organisms, in turn, are an abundant food source for fish, birds, and humans. Estuaries are also home to juvenile *anadromous fish* (fish that swim from the sea to fresh water upriver to spawn) such as striped bass and salmon. We have more about estuaries in Chapter 8.

Through the vast expanse of geologic time, the biosphere co-evolved with the ocean and atmosphere. For more on this topic, refer to this chapter's third Essay.

Biogeochemical Cycles

A *biogeochemical cycle* consists of pathways along which solid, liquid, and gaseous materials move among the various reservoirs of the Earth system. Accompanying this flow of materials is the movement and transformation of energy. Examples of biogeochemical cycles are the water cycle, carbon cycle, rock cycle, and oxygen cycle. The Earth system is an open (or flow-through) system for energy where *energy* is defined as the capacity for doing work. The Earth system receives energy from the sun and from Earth's interior while emitting energy in the form of infrared radiation to space. Within the Earth system, energy is neither created nor destroyed although it is converted from one form to another. This is the *law of energy conservation* (also known as the *first law of thermodynamics*).

The Earth system is essentially closed for matter; that is, it neither gains nor loses matter over time (except for meteorites and asteroids). All biogeochemical cycles obey the *law of conservation of matter*, which states that matter can be neither created nor destroyed, but can change in chemical or physical form. When a log burns in a fireplace, a portion of the log is converted to ash (and heat energy), and the rest goes up the chimney as carbon dioxide, water vapor, creosote and heat. In terms of accountability, all losses from one reservoir in a cycle can be accounted for as gains in other reservoirs of the cycle. Stated succinctly, for any reservoir

$$Input = Output + Storage$$

The amount of some substance stored within a reservoir of a biogeochemical cycle depends on the rates at which the material is cycled into and out of the reservoir. *Cycling rate* is defined as the amount of material that moves from one reservoir to another within a specified period of time. If the input rate exceeds the output rate, the amount in the reservoir (storage) increases. If the input rate is less than the output rate, the amount decreases. Over the long term, the cycling rates of materials among the various global reservoirs have been relatively stable; that is, equilibrium tends to prevail between the rates of input and output.

Closely related to cycling rate is residence time. **Residence time** is the average length of time for a substance in a reservoir to be replaced completely, that is,

$$\text{Residence time} = \frac{(\text{amount in reservoir})}{(\text{rate of addition or removal})}$$

The residence time of a water molecule in the various reservoirs of the hydrosphere varies from only about 10 days in the atmosphere to tens of thousands of years or longer in glacial ice sheets. Residence time of dissolved constituents of seawater ranges from 100 years for aluminum to 260 million years for sodium.

Consider the global cycling of carbon as an illustration of a biogeochemical cycle (Figure 1.8). Through photosynthesis, carbon dioxide (CO_2) cycles from the atmosphere into green plants where carbon is incorporated into sugar ($C_6H_{12}O_6$). Plants use sugar to manufacture other organic compounds including fats, proteins, and other carbohydrates. As a byproduct of cellular respiration, plants and animals transform a portion of the carbon in these organic compounds into carbon dioxide that is released to the atmosphere. The same cycle occurs in the ocean when carbon dioxide is cycled into and out of marine organisms through photosynthesis and respiration. In addition to the uptake of CO_2 via photosynthesis, marine organisms also use carbon for calcium carbonate ($CaCO_3$) to make hard, protective shells. Furthermore, decomposer organisms (e.g., bacteria) both on land and in the ocean act on the remains of dead plants and animals, releasing CO_2 to the atmosphere and ocean through respiration.

When marine organisms die their shells and skeletons settle to the ocean bottom. Over long periods of time, these organic remains accumulate, are compressed by their own weight and the weight of other sediments, and gradually transform into solid, carbonate rock. Common carbonate rocks are limestone ($CaCO_3$) and dolostone ($CaMg(CO_3)_2$). Subsequently, tectonic processes uplift these rocks and expose them to physical and chemical weathering processes. For example, atmospheric CO_2 dissolves in rainwater producing carbonic acid (H_2CO_3) that, in turn, dissolves carbonate rock (e.g., limestone) releasing CO_2. As part of the global water cycle, rivers and streams transport these weathering products to the sea where they settle out of suspension or precipitate as sediments that accumulate on the ocean floor. Over the millions of years that constitute geologic time, weathering and erosion of carbon-containing rocks have significantly altered the concentration of carbon dioxide in the atmosphere.

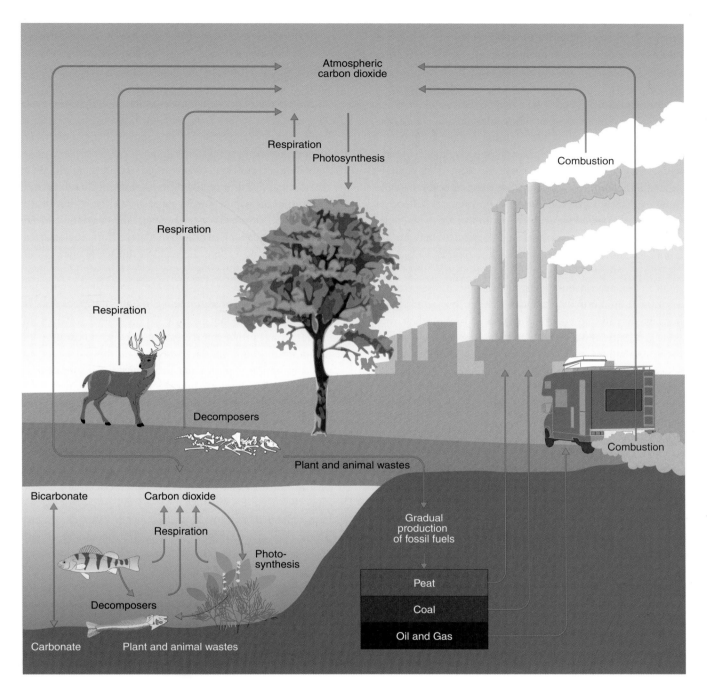

FIGURE 1.8
Schematic representation of the global carbon cycle.

About 280 to 345 million years ago, during the geologic time interval known as the Carboniferous Period, trillions of metric tons of organic remains (detritus) accumulated on the ocean bottom and in low-lying swampy terrain on land. The supply of detritus was so great that decomposer organisms could not keep pace. In some marine environments, plant and animal remains were converted to oil and natural gas. In swampy terrain, heat and pressure from accumulating organic debris concentrated carbon, converting the remains of luxuriant swamp forests into thick layers of coal. Today, when we burn coal, oil, and natural gas, collectively called *fossil fuels*, we are tapping energy that was originally locked in vegetation through photosynthesis hundreds of millions of years ago. During combustion, carbon from these fossil fuels combines with oxygen in the air to form carbon dioxide which escapes to the atmosphere.

Another important biogeochemical cycle operating in the Earth system is the global water cycle, which is closely linked to all other biogeochemical cycles. Reservoirs in the water cycle (ocean, atmosphere, lithosphere, living organisms) are also reservoirs in the other cycles. Furthermore, water is an important mode of transport in biogeochemical cycles. In the nitrogen cycle, for example, intense heating of air associated with lightning combines atmospheric nitrogen (N_2), oxygen (O_2), and moisture to form droplets of extremely dilute nitric acid (HNO_3) that are washed by rain to the soil. In the process, nitric acid converts to nitrate (NO_3^-), an important plant nutrient that can be taken up by plants through their root system. Plants convert nitrate to ammonia (NH_3), which is incorporated into a variety of compounds including amino acids, proteins, and DNA. On the other hand, both nitrate and ammonia readily dissolve in water so that heavy rains can deplete soil of these important nutrients and wash them into waterways.

The Ocean in the Global Water Cycle

We can reasonably assume that the total amount of water in the Earth system is neither increasing nor decreasing although natural processes continually generate and break-down water. Volcanic activity is more or less continuous on Earth and adds to the supply of water. Water vapor accounts for perhaps half of all gases emitted during a volcanic eruption; at least some of this water originally was sequestered in magma and solid rock. A minute amount of water is contributed to Earth by meteorites and other extra-terrestrial debris continually bombarding the upper atmosphere. At the same time, intense solar radiation entering the upper atmosphere converts (*photodissociates*) a small amount of water vapor into its constituent hydrogen and oxygen atoms, which may escape to space. Also, water reacts chemically with other substances and thereby is locked up in various compounds. Annually, the addition of water from volcanic eruptions roughly equals the loss of water through photodissociation of water vapor and chemical reactions. This balance of give and take has prevailed on Earth for perhaps hundreds of millions of years.

The fixed quantity of water in the Earth's system is distributed in all three phases among oceanic, terrestrial (land-based), atmospheric, and biospheric reservoirs. The ceaseless movement of water among its various reservoirs at the planetary scale is known as the **global water cycle** (Figure 1.9). In brief, water vaporizes from ocean and land to the atmosphere where winds can transport water vapor thousands of kilometers. Clouds form and rain, snow and other forms of precipitation fall from clouds to Earth's surface and recharge the ocean and the terrestrial reservoirs of water. From terrestrial reservoirs, water seeps and flows back to the ocean. The continuity of the global water cycle is captured in a verse from Ecclesiastes: "Every river flows into the sea, but the sea is not yet full. The waters return to where the rivers began and starts all over again."

Transfer of water between Earth's surface and the atmosphere is the key pathway in the global water cycle. Water from Earth's surface cycles into the atmosphere via evaporation, sublimation, and transpiration. Ultimately, solar radiation supplies the heat energy for these phase changes of water and powers the global water cycle. **Evaporation** is the process whereby water changes from a liquid to a vapor. Water evaporates from the surface of bodies of water including the ocean, lakes and rivers as well as from soil and the damp surfaces of plant leaves and stems. About 85% of the total annual evaporation in the Earth system takes place at the ocean surface so that the ocean is the principal source of water in the atmosphere. During **sublimation** water changes directly from a solid to a vapor without first becoming liquid. Through sublimation, snow banks shrink and patches of ice on sidewalks and roads disappear even while the air temperature remains below freezing.

Transpiration is the process whereby water that is taken up from the soil by plant roots eventually escapes as vapor through the tiny pores (called stomates) on the underside of green leaves. On land during the growing season, transpiration is considerable and is often more important than direct evaporation of water in delivering water vapor to the atmosphere. A single hectare (2.5 acres) of corn typically transpires 28,000 to 38,000 liters (7400 to 10,000 gallons) of water per day. Transpiration accounts for about 10% of the water vapor component of the atmosphere.

Water moves from the atmosphere to land and ocean via condensation, deposition, and precipitation. **Condensation** is the process whereby water changes phase from vapor to liquid (in the form of small droplets).

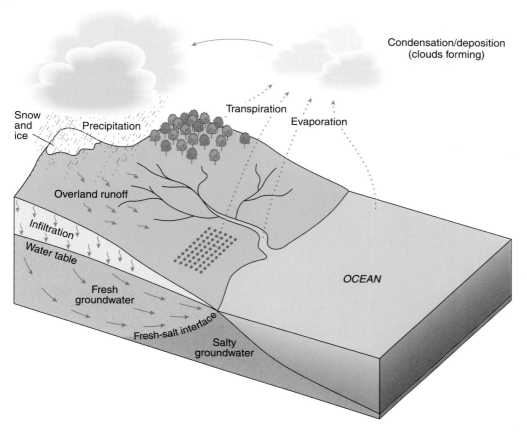

FIGURE 1.9
Schematic representation of the global water cycle.

Water droplets forming on the outside surface of a cold can of soda on a warm, humid day is an example of condensation of water vapor. **Deposition** is the process whereby water changes directly from vapor to solid (ice crystals) without first becoming a liquid. Appearance of frost on an automobile windshield is an example of deposition of water vapor. Condensation or deposition within the atmosphere produces clouds, only a small fraction of which produce precipitation. **Precipitation** is water in liquid or frozen form (i.e., rain, drizzle, snow, ice pellets, or hail) that falls from clouds and reaches Earth's surface.

Significantly, evaporation (or sublimation) followed by condensation (or deposition) purifies water. As water vaporizes (evaporation, transpiration, or sublimation), all suspended and dissolved substances such as sea salts are left behind. Through this natural cleansing mechanism, ocean water that originally was too salty to drink eventually falls as freshwater precipitation, replenishing reservoirs on Earth's surface. Purification of water through phase changes is known as **distillation**. Although precipitation is fresh water, it is not free of all dissolved or suspended materials. Condensation and deposition take place on tiny aerosols suspended in the atmosphere, slightly altering the chemical composition of cloud and precipitation particles. Also, as precipitation falls through the atmosphere, it dissolves or captures gases or suspended particles that also change its composition. (This is the origin of acid rain.)

Return of water from the atmosphere to Earth's surface via condensation, deposition, and precipitation completes an essential sub-cycle in the global water cycle. To learn more about the atmosphere-Earth's surface sub-cycle of the global water cycle, compare the movement of water between the continents and the atmosphere with that between the ocean and atmosphere. The balance sheet for inputs and outputs of water to and from the various global reservoirs is the *global water budget* (Table 1.2).

Over the course of a year, the total volume of water that falls as precipitation (rain plus melted snow) on land exceeds the total volume of water that vaporizes (via evaporation, transpiration, and sublimation) from land by about one-third. (This imbalance occurs because landmasses favor certain precipitation-forming mechanisms.) Over the same period, the total volume of water falling as precipitation on the ocean is less than the total volume of water that evaporates from the ocean. (Evaporation is more important because the ocean surface supplies a nearly limitless supply of water vapor.) The global water budget thus indicates an annual net gain of water mass on the continents and an annual net loss of water mass from the ocean. The annual excess of water on the continents about equals the annual deficit from the ocean. But year after year the continents do not get any

TABLE 1.2
Global Water Budget

Source	Cubic meters per yr	Gallons per yr
Precipitation on the ocean	$+3.24 \times 10^{14}$	$+85.5 \times 10^{15}$
Evaporation from the ocean	$\underline{3.60 \times 10^{14}}$	$\underline{95.2 \times 10^{15}}$
Net loss from the ocean	0.36×10^{14}	09.7×10^{15}
Precipitation on land	$+0.98 \times 10^{14}$	$+26.1 \times 10^{15}$
Evapotranspiration from land	$\underline{0.62 \times 10^{14}}$	$\underline{16.4 \times 10^{15}}$
Net gain on land	$+0.36 \times 10^{14}$	$+09.7 \times 10^{15}$

wetter and the ocean basins are not drying up because the excess water on land drips, seeps, and flows back to the sea, thus completing the global water cycle. The net flow of water from land to sea also implies a net flow of water in the atmosphere from sea to land.

The flow of excess surface and subsurface water from the continents to the ocean has important implications for the composition of seawater and the global distribution of water pollutants. The ocean is the ultimate destination for all substances dissolved or suspended in surface or subsurface waters. This is one (but not the only) source of salt in seawater. The ocean is also the ultimate destination of contaminants discharged into waterways (e.g., rivers, streams, canals). These contaminants primarily end up in estuaries and other coastal waters, which are also the most productive portion of the ocean. Not surprisingly, considerable debate centers on the capacity of the ocean to assimilate waste—especially toxic and hazardous industrial waste.

Precipitation reaching the land surface can follow one of several pathways. Some precipitated water vaporizes (evaporates or sublimates) directly back into the atmosphere and some is temporarily stored in lakes, snow and ice fields, or glaciers. Some either flows on the surface as rivers or streams (*runoff component*) or seeps into the ground as soil moisture or groundwater

(*infiltration component*). The amount of water that infiltrates the ground compared to the amount that runs off depends on rainfall intensity, vegetation, topography, and physical properties of the land surface. For example, rain falling on frozen ground or city streets mostly runs off whereas rain falling on unfrozen sandy soil readily soaks into the ground.

During the growing season, plant roots take up some soil moisture and almost all of that water (98%) transpires back to the atmosphere. Water that seeps to greater depths may completely fill the spaces between particles of soil or sediment or the fractures within rock, constituting *groundwater*. In most environments, groundwater flows very slowly in the subsurface from recharge areas at Earth's surface toward discharge areas including wells, springs, rivers, lakes, and the ocean. Where the groundwater reservoir is located well below surface water reservoirs, water may seep out of rivers and lakes and recharge the groundwater reservoir.

Rivers and streams plus their tributaries drain a fixed geographical area known as a *drainage basin* (or watershed). The quantity and quality of water flowing in a river depends on the climate, topography, geology, and land use in the drainage basin. A drainage basin may also include lakes or glaciers, temporary impoundments of surface water.

Observing the Ocean

Scientists observe the ocean not only out of curiosity but also to better understand the ocean's role in the Earth system. Scientists want to know, for example, the physical and biological factors governing the distribution of marine life and how the ocean influences seasonal and long-term variability in climate. Answers to these and other questions require observational data on the ocean's properties and processes. Today, scientists observe the ocean using both in situ and remote sensing techniques. With an *in situ* measurement, the sensor is immersed in the medium that is being monitored. *Remote sensing* refers to acquisition of data on the properties of some object without the sensor being in direct physical contact with the object.

IN SITU MONITORING OF THE OCEAN'S DEPTHS

While data collected remotely via sensors onboard Earth-orbiting satellites are extremely valuable, oceanographic ships, instrumented buoys, floats, and gliders, piloted submersibles, autonomous instrumented platforms and vehicles, and undersea observatories are in situ sources of essential ocean data for surveys and field experiments (Chapter 13). A great deal of ocean research has been and is still done from ships (Figure 1.10). It is the only way to get out on and stay at sea to investigate what cannot be detected remotely. Furthermore, satellite-borne monitoring instruments, such as radar, can directly observe only the ocean's surface because water is nearly opaque to electromagnetic radiation. Therefore, other techniques are necessary to examine the ocean below the surface. Instruments lowered from ships are used to sample ocean water at depth. And instruments moored on the sea floor monitor properties of the ocean beneath the surface waters. As we will see in subsequent chapters, a variety of in situ instruments and techniques have contributed substantially to our understanding of the ocean. Consider some examples.

One in situ method uses the speed of sound waves in water to measure ocean-water temperature and its variation through time. Ocean water is highly transparent to sound, just as the atmosphere is nearly transparent to visible light. A sound pulse from a transmitter on one side of the ocean can be detected by a sensitive receiver thousands of kilometers away on the other side of the ocean. Whales, for example, take advantage of this property of seawater to communicate long distances across an ocean basin, to attract mates and to locate food.

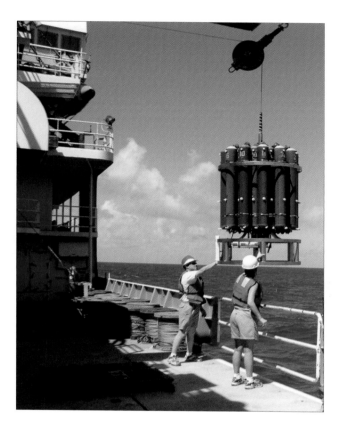

FIGURE 1.10
Launch of a CTD over the side of the R/V Thompson. The CTD measures conductivity (salinity), temperature, and depth of the water. [NOAA Ocean Explorer]

Sound travels faster in warm water than in cold water. Thus measuring the speed of sound in seawater can be used to determine the average water temperature between the transmitter and the receiver. Furthermore, variations in sound speed between many transmitters and receivers can be combined to obtain a three-dimensional representation of seawater temperature. This technique, called *acoustic thermometry*, is similar in concept to the X-ray scans used to examine the internal organs of humans. We have more to say about acoustic thermometry in Chapter 3.

A **profiling float** is an instrument package that measures vertical profiles of ocean water temperature and salinity plus current velocity (Figure 1.11). In 1998, scientists from more than 30 nations plus the European Union began deploying Argo floats worldwide. (*Argo* is the name of the ship whose captain was the Greek mythological figure Jason.) The goal was to deploy initially 3000 free-drifting floats providing coverage of one sensor per 3 degrees latitude and longitude. That goal was realized on

FIGURE 1.11
Launch of an Argo float from a German research ship. This instrument is designed to take profiles of temperature and salinity to a depth of 2000 m. [Courtesy of the Argo Project.]

1 November 2007. Typically, an Argo float is programmed for a 10-day cycle during which it sinks to a depth of 1000 m (3300 ft) where it drifts for approximately 9 days before sinking to a maximum depth of 2000 m (6600 ft). From that depth, sensors measure temperature and conductivity (a measure of salinity) through ocean layers as the float ascends to the surface. At the surface, data and the float's location are transmitted to a communications satellite and made available to the scientific community and the public via the Internet within 24 hours.

Already, the Argo float has proven its value by increasing the accuracy of estimates of the heat storage in the ocean, an important factor in predicting the climate future and changes in sea level (Chapter 12). These data have also made possible development of more realistic coupled ocean/atmosphere models used for seasonal climate forecasts. Finally, Argo float data provide insights on the dynamics of air-sea interaction during hurricanes and tropical storms. We have more to say about Argo floats in Chapter 6.

REMOTE SENSING BY SATELLITE

An important source of remotely sensed ocean data is Earth-orbiting satellites. Earth-orbiting satellites routinely monitor the ocean's surface waters, the atmosphere, and other components of the Earth system. Powerful computers collect, process, and analyze enormous quantities of satellite-acquired environmental data. In only minutes, sensors onboard an ocean-observing satellite collect as much data as an ocean-research vessel operating at sea continuously for a decade or longer. Instruments

observing Earth from orbiting spacecraft measure selected wavelengths (or frequencies) of electromagnetic radiation reflected or emitted by the various components of the Earth system. **Electromagnetic radiation** (or simply radiation) describes both a form of energy and a means of energy transfer. Forms of radiation include gamma rays, X-rays, ultraviolet (UV) radiation, visible light, infrared (IR) radiation, microwaves, and radio waves. Together, these forms of radiation make up the **electromagnetic spectrum** (Figure 1.12). All types of radiation travel as waves at the speed of light and the different segments of the electromagnetic spectrum are differentiated by wavelength or frequency. *Wavelength* is the distance between successive wave crests or troughs whereas *frequency* is the number of wave crests or troughs passing a point during a period of time, usually a second (Figure 1.13).

The clear atmosphere is essentially transparent to visible light and is selectively transparent by wavelength to other types of radiation such as infrared. Satellite-borne sensors monitor these forms of radiation to gather information on atmospheric processes and properties. Ocean water is much less transparent to electromagnetic radiation than is the atmosphere so that remote sensing by satellite is essentially limited to obtaining data on surface or near-surface ocean processes and properties.

The earliest ocean observations from space came from sensors on meteorological satellites orbited in the 1960s. Beginning in 1978, satellites were launched specifically to monitor the ocean. Now instruments flown on Earth-orbiting satellites routinely provide global images of ocean conditions, which are typically summarized and updated every few days. Satellite-borne sensors are either passive or active. Passive sensors measure radiation coming from the ocean surface, that is, visible solar radiation reflected by the ocean surface and invisible infrared radiation emitted by the ocean surface. Among the ocean properties measured by passive radiation sensors are sea-surface temperatures (SST) and water color, a measure of marine productivity or sediment concentration. Radar instruments mounted on satellites are active sensors; they emit pulses of microwave radiation and then record the reflected signal to measure surface roughness (an indicator of surface wind speeds and wave heights) as well as ocean-surface elevations, which are used to map bottom topography and surface currents. Techniques to measure salinity and other ocean properties remotely are under development. Such measurements permit studies of ocean surface "weather" (week-to-week variations) as well as ocean "climate" (variability over decades to centuries).

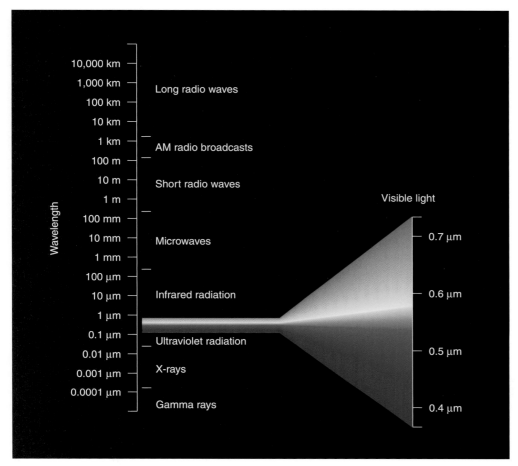

FIGURE 1.12
The electromagnetic spectrum. The various forms of electromagnetic radiation are distinguished by wavelength in micrometers (μm), millimeters (mm), meters (m), and kilometers (km).

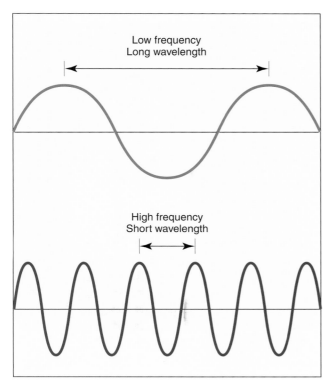

FIGURE 1.13
Wavelength is the distance between two successive crests or, equivalently, the distance between two successive troughs. Wavelength is inversely related to wave frequency.

Satellites that monitor the ocean are in either geostationary or polar orbits. Most of us are familiar with images provided by geostationary satellites, which are launched into relatively high orbits (36,000 km or 22,300 mi) (Figure 1.14). A **geostationary satellite** revolves around Earth at the same rate and in the same direction as the planet rotates so that the satellite always remains over the same point on the equator and its sensors monitor the same portion of Earth's surface. For this reason, these satellites are sometimes described as *geosynchronous*. Each geostationary satellite views about one-third of Earth's surface and five satellites are needed to provide complete and overlapping coverage of the globe between about 60 degrees N and 60 degrees S. Considerable distortion sets in poleward of about 60 degrees latitude.

A **polar-orbiting satellite** is in a relatively low-altitude (800 to 1000 km, 500 to 600 mi) orbit that passes near the north and south poles (Figure 1.15). Earth rotates eastward under the satellite whose orbit remains fixed in space so that sensors view successive strips of Earth. A polar-orbiting satellite that follows the sun (sun-synchronous) passes over the same area twice each 24-hr day. Other polar-orbiting satellites are positioned so that they require several days before passing over the same point on Earth's surface.

The flood of observational data from satellite-based sensors is analyzed and stored by electronic computers. Computer speed doubles about every 18 months so that, ordinary lap-top computers, now widely and cheaply available, far exceed the power of the most powerful, room-sized supercomputers available only a few decades ago. Internet websites now make available details of ocean surface properties that were impossible to obtain only a decade ago.

An example of the value of remotely-sensed data is the determination of the distribution and abundance of chlorophyll (plant pigments). Satellite-derived images of "ocean color" locate much of the food used in marine ecosystems and indicate how its concentration varies with time (Chapter 9). (These same sensors also are used to map the distribution of vegetation on land.) Thus large areas of Earth's marine ecosystems can be routinely studied without risking injury or seasickness onboard research ships. (Refer back to Figure 1.6 for a sample image.)

Another example of remotely sensed data used in ocean studies is sea-surface temperature (SST) patterns obtained by infrared (IR) sensors onboard satellites. The intensity of radiation emitted by an object increases rapidly as the surface temperature of the object rises. By

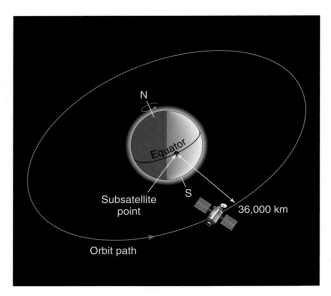

FIGURE 1.14
A satellite in geostationary orbit about the Earth.

calibrating temperature against IR-emission, a satellite sensor measures SST and can distinguish between warm and cold ocean currents. For example, Figure 1.16 is an infrared satellite image of the world ocean SST averaged over three days. SST is color coded so that oranges and reds represent the highest temperatures. In this Northern Hemisphere winter depiction, the highest SST values were in the Southern Hemisphere.

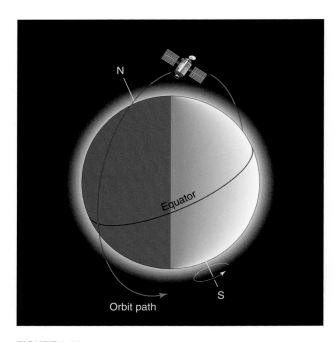

FIGURE 1.15
A satellite in polar orbit about the Earth.

FIGURE 1.16
Satellite-derived sea-surface temperatures (SST) color coded in °C averaged over the period 12-15 January 2008; highest temperatures are shown in orange and red. [NOAA/NESDIS]

Studies of the ocean in the Earth system also require satellite-based communications systems. With communications satellites, scientists working onboard research ships at sea can communicate nearly instantaneously with labs, computers, or colleagues anywhere in the world. They can also work with schools to provide a virtual shipboard experience for students in their classroom. Remotely operated instruments on drifting buoys, or on unmanned autonomous underwater vehicles, can send the data they collect to scientists on shore via communications satellites. These communications capabilities are now routinely combined as one system for observing both the ocean and atmosphere.

Modeling the Ocean

A **model** is an approximate representation or simulation of a real system. It incorporates only the essential features (or variables) of a system while omitting details considered non-essential. Models are widely used to investigate the Earth system and its components, including the ocean. Models are conceptual, graphical, physical, or numerical.

A *conceptual model* is a statement of a fundamental law or relationship. Such a model is used to organize data or describe the interactions among components of a system. For example, conceptual models are used to explore linkages among physical and biological subsystems in the ocean and they enable us to understand why and how ocean water circulates. We use conceptual models throughout this book. A *graphical model* compiles and displays data in a format that readily conveys meaning. For example, ocean scientists make extensive use of bathymetric charts, maps of seafloor elevations and the variations in water depth (Figure 1.17). A *physical model* is a small-scale (miniaturized) representation of a system. For example, before powerful electronic computers were widely available, physical models were used to study the flow of water in harbors and estuaries, such as Puget Sound in Washington. Physical models were used to predict changes in currents that would result from deepening the shipping channels leading into New York Harbor. Although the results of physical modeling were generally useful and easily understood, these models were expensive to build, maintain, and operate.

The physical evolution of some systems (e.g., the orbit of the moon) can be precisely determined by

FIGURE 1.17
A color-coded bathymetric chart. [National Geophysical Data Center, NOAA Satellite and Information Services]

solving a specific mathematical equation. Other systems such as the fluid ocean or atmosphere are too complex to be described by a simple mathematical formula. In these cases, mathematics approximates the behavior of the system on an electronic computer. A *numerical model* consists of mathematical equations that simulate the processes under study. Observational data are used as initial and boundary conditions as well as to guide and verify model predictions. Usually, a numerical model is initialized using current observational data. With the current state of the ocean and/or atmosphere as a starting point, a prediction is made for some subsequent time interval, say 10 minutes hence. Repetition of this process eventually generates a prediction of conditions for the subsequent 12, 24, 36 hrs or longer. Through this iterative process, a numerical model predicts the future state of a complex system.

Today, because powerful electronic computers are readily available, numerical models have essentially replaced physical models in investigating the Earth system. Weather forecasts are probably the most familiar products of numerical models; in fact, numerical models of the Earth-atmosphere system have been used to forecast weather since the 1950s. Very powerful computers are needed to handle the complex mathematics and huge data sets required for ocean, atmosphere, or coupled ocean-atmosphere numerical models. A single set of complex

calculations may require hours to a few days to run. Equations may be altered or new data provided to simulate different situations. For example, a numerical model of New York Harbor is used to predict movements of water and sediment in response to changing wind patterns. For many years, Japanese and American scientists have been developing numerical models that simulate the propagation of a tsunami in the open ocean. Numerical models are powerful tools with which to study the response of Earth's subsystems to long-term environmental change (e.g., global climate change).

As noted, a model is an approximation of a real system and there may be advantages in comparing different models and model runs. Climate change studies, for example, routinely compare the output of multiple numerical models. Interacting atmospheric and oceanic processes are simulated using coupled models of the ocean, atmosphere, and biosphere for predicting responses to global climate change. Numerical models can also be used to simulate currents in ancient ocean basins based on reconstructions of global climate and the shapes of ocean basins at the time. Time scales for these models of ancient oceans can be millions of years.

Humans and the Ocean

Humans impact the ocean and the ocean impacts humans. Humans have altered the Earth system to such an extent that we must now consider human activity to be equal in magnitude to many geological processes. Humans impact the orderly functioning of the ocean (and other components of the Earth system) by altering cycling rates and disrupting the equilibrium of biogeochemical cycles. Agriculture, mining, and electrical power generation are examples of human activities that affect the ocean and other components of the Earth system. Most of the waste byproducts of these activities are widely distributed by winds and/or rivers that discharge into the ocean. The ocean can be responsible for coastal flooding and extensive beach erosion, and supply latent heat for hurricane development. As a preview of topics covered in greater detail later in this book, this section summarizes some of the interactions between society and the ocean.

The ocean influences weather and climate. Ocean waters have a relatively great thermal inertia (resistance to temperature change) so that localities immediately downwind from the ocean have a maritime climate with less summer-to-winter air temperature contrast than inland localities. Among other things, this affects the energy demand for space heating and cooling. The global-scale ocean circulation transports heat energy poleward thereby helping to maintain the air temperature gradient between the equator and poles. As a key player in Earth's climate system, the ocean has a stabilizing effect on climate fluctuations. The ocean is an important factor in both short-term (e.g., El Niño) and long-term (e.g., global warming) climate change.

By burning fossil fuels, deforestation, and other activities, humans are elevating the level of atmospheric carbon dioxide and enhancing Earth's natural greenhouse effect. As a component of the global carbon cycle, the ocean is the principal sink for anthropogenic CO_2 and helps regulate its concentration in the atmosphere. The consequences of global warming include melting glaciers and expanding seawater that raises sea level. Shrinking sea ice cover in the Arctic is likely to exert a positive feedback that will accelerate warming and melting of sea ice and permafrost in the Arctic region. The impact of global warming on marine organisms and ecosystems is likely to be far-reaching and disruptive.

Humans depend on the ocean for fresh water, food, and other resources. Through the global water cycle, seawater eventually falls to Earth's surface as freshwater precipitation that replenishes domestic water supplies. Marine ecosystems are an important source of food, but some human activities threaten that food supply. Overfishing, bycatch, and introduction of exotic species are among the most challenging problems. In addition, runoff of excess nutrients (i.e., nitrogen and phosphorus compounds) from land to sea contributes to harmful algal blooms and the development of dissolved-oxygen-depleted dead zones. In some locations, humans extract seafloor resources including oil and natural gas, sand and gravel, and mineral resources (e.g., certain metals and diamonds). These activities are governed to a large extent by demand, economic conditions, and environmental regulations. To help conserve marine resources (e.g., coral reefs), some areas of the ocean have been set aside as sanctuaries and reserves.

With continued rapid population growth in the coastal zone, humans are becoming more vulnerable to natural hazards including storm surges (generated by tropical cyclones or other coastal storms), tsunamis (most triggered by submarine earthquakes), and seiches (caused by atmospheric conditions or earthquakes). Humans alter the coast for many reasons including control of flooding from storm surges and sea level rise, preservation of recreational beaches, maintenance of harbors and navigation channels, and protection of homes, roads and other structures from wave erosion or slumping of coastal bluffs. (In some cases human activity actually exacerbates the hazard by developing barrier islands or removing protective mangrove swamps.) The traditional approach has been to armor the coast by constructing breakwaters, jetties, groins and seawalls or to artificially nourish storm-eroded beaches with imported sand. These strategies often are ineffective in the long-term prompting other approaches that seek to accommodate rather than confront the forces of nature (e.g., strategic retreat).

Conclusions

The Earth system consists of several subsystems: hydrosphere (including the cryosphere), atmosphere, geosphere, and biosphere. These subsystems adhere to natural laws as they interact globally over time scales ranging from seconds to hundreds of millions of years. Matter and energy cycle through the Earth system via global biogeochemical cycles. Matter cycles in closed systems that obey the law of conservation of matter whereas energy cycles in open systems, as the Earth system continually receives energy from the sun and from Earth's interior while emitting infrared radiation to space.

Application of natural laws combined with monitoring of the Earth system permits subsystem behavior to be understood, modeled, and future conditions to be predicted. Each subsystem is studied using a variety of observation techniques. In situ methods include ships and profilers. Remote sensing by satellite of Earth's subsystems has greatly improved our ability to predict their behavior as a whole and on global scales over long periods of time. The huge quantity of environmental data that is collected via Earth-orbiting satellites is fed into computer models that generate forecasts of the future state of components of the Earth system. In the next chapter, we focus on ocean-geosphere interactions with special emphasis on plate tectonics and its implications for the evolution and characteristics of ocean basins.

Basic Understandings

- A system is an interacting set of components that behaves in an orderly way according to natural laws. The Earth system consists of four major interacting subsystems: hydrosphere (including the cryosphere), atmosphere, geosphere, and biosphere.

- The hydrosphere encompasses water in all three phases (solid, liquid, and vapor) that continually cycles from one reservoir to another in the Earth system. The ocean is the largest reservoir in the hydrosphere, containing 97.2% of all water on the planet and covering 70.8% of Earth's surface. The next largest reservoirs of water in the hydrosphere are the glacial ice sheets that cover much of Antarctica and Greenland.

- In addition to the Antarctic and Greenland ice sheets, the frozen portion of Earth's hydrosphere, called the cryosphere, encompasses mountain glaciers, permafrost, sea ice (frozen seawater), and bergs.

- The ocean features wind-driven surface currents and density-driven deep-ocean currents caused by small differences in temperature and salinity.

- The hydrosphere is dynamic with water flowing at different rates through and between different reservoirs within the Earth system. The time required for water to reach the ocean varies from days to weeks in river channels up to millennia for water locked in ice sheets.

- Earth's atmosphere is a relatively thin envelope of gases and tiny suspended solid and liquid particles (aerosols) surrounding the planet. Based on the average vertical temperature profile, the atmosphere is divided into the troposphere, stratosphere, mesosphere, and thermosphere. The lowest layer, the troposphere, is where most weather occurs and where the atmosphere interfaces with the other subsystems of the Earth system.

- Nitrogen (N_2) and oxygen (O_2), the principal atmospheric gases, are mixed in uniform proportions up to an altitude of about 80 km (50 mi). Not counting water vapor (which has a highly variable concentration), nitrogen occupies 78.08% by volume of the lower atmosphere and oxygen is 20.95% by volume.

- The significance of atmospheric gases and aerosols is not necessarily related to their concentration. Some atmospheric components that are essential for life occur in very low concentrations. Examples are water vapor (needed for the water cycle), carbon dioxide (for photosynthesis), and stratospheric ozone (protection from ultraviolet radiation).

- The atmosphere is dynamic and circulates in response to temperature gradients that arise from different rates of radiational heating and cooling.

- The geosphere is the solid portion of the planet composed of rocks, minerals, and sediments. The rigid uppermost portion of Earth's mantle plus the overlying crust constitutes Earth's lithosphere. Surface geological processes (i.e., weathering and erosion) and internal geological processes (i.e., mountain building, volcanic eruptions) continually modify the lithosphere. Weathering refers to the physical and chemical breakdown of rock into sediments. Agents of erosion (i.e., rivers, glaciers, wind) remove, transport, and subsequently deposit sediments.

- The biosphere encompasses all life on Earth and is dominated on land and in the ocean by bacteria and one-celled plants and animals. Photosynthesis and cellular respiration are processes that are essential for life where sunlight is available and exemplify the interaction of the biosphere with the other subsystems of the Earth system. The biosphere is composed of ecosystems, communities of plants and animals that interact with one another, together with the physical conditions and chemical substances in a specific geographical area. Ecosystems consist of producers (plants), consumers (animals), and decomposers (bacteria, fungi). These organisms occupy trophic levels in food chains.

- Biogeochemical cycles are pathways along which solids, liquids, or gases flow among the various reservoirs within subsystems of the Earth system. Biogeochemical cycles follow the law of conservation of matter, which states that matter can neither be created nor destroyed, but can change chemical or physical form. The time required for a unit mass of some substance to cycle into and out of a reservoir is the residence time of the substance in the reservoir.

- Powered by solar radiation, the ceaseless movement of water among the various reservoirs in the hydrosphere on a planetary scale is known as the global water cycle. The ocean is by far the largest reservoir in the global water cycle.

- Key to the existence of the global water cycle

is the transfer of water between the Earth's surface and atmosphere. Water cycles into the atmosphere from the continents and ocean via evaporation, sublimation, and transpiration. Water cycles from the atmosphere to land and sea via condensation, deposition, and precipitation. To balance the global water budget, the net flow of water is from land to ocean.

- Scientists observe the ocean using both *in situ* and *remote sensing* techniques. With in situ methods, the sensor is immersed in the medium that is being monitored. Remote sensing refers to acquisition of data on the properties of some object without the sensor being in direct physical contact with the object.

- Satellite-based sensors can directly observe only the ocean's surface waters so that other techniques such as acoustic thermometry and instrumented floats, ships, and buoys are used to monitor ocean properties at depth.

- Satellites orbiting the planet are platforms for sensors that monitor the Earth system, measuring the amounts of electromagnetic radiation reflected or emitted by the system. Electromagnetic radiation is both a form of energy and a means of energy transfer. The various forms of radiation are distinguished on the basis of wavelength and frequency.

- Passive and active remote sensing by satellite is a valuable tool for observing the vast expanse of the ocean and other components of the Earth system. A geostationary satellite orbits the planet at a rate that matches Earth's rotation and in the same direction so that it is always positioned above the same spot on Earth's equator. A polar-orbiting satellite travels along relatively low north-south trajectories that take the satellite over polar areas.

- A model is a simulation of a real system and includes only those variables considered essential to the system. Conceptual, graphical, physical, and numerical models have been used to simulate the Earth system and its component subsystems. Numerical models are increasingly important in studying the ocean; they consist of one or more mathematical equations that describe the relationship among variables in a system and are programmed on an electronic computer.

- Humans impact the ocean and the ocean impacts humans. Human activities affect the orderly functioning of the ocean (and other components of the Earth system) by altering cycling rates and disrupting the equilibrium of biogeochemical cycles. The ocean affects humans through its role in weather and climate, natural hazards, and as a source of resources.

Review

1. Identify the second largest reservoir in the hydrosphere and its location.
2. Identify and describe the layer of the atmosphere that interfaces directly with the ocean.
3. Distinguish between weathering and erosion.
4. What is the significance of a food chain?
5. Define *residence time* and compare the residence time of a water molecule in the atmosphere with that of a water molecule in a glacial ice sheet.
6. What role does the ocean play in the global carbon cycle?
7. Identify the various sources of water vapor in the atmosphere. Which one is the principal source?
8. Compare the annual rates of precipitation and evaporation for the ocean versus the continents over the course of a year. What does this imply about the direction of the net horizontal flow of water on Earth's surface and in the atmosphere?
9. Distinguish between geostationary and polar-orbiting satellites.
10. Does remote sensing by sensors onboard Earth-orbiting satellites enable scientists to monitor conditions to great depths in the ocean or only the ocean surface waters?

Critical Thinking

1. Describe how an understanding of the workings of the Earth system relates to our ability to predict how that system might respond to a large-scale disturbance.
2. Provide some examples of how the atmosphere is coupled with the ocean.
3. Identify and describe some of the major interactions between the hydrosphere and geosphere.
4. Speculate on the source of the salt that is dissolved in seawater.
5. About 99% of the water in the atmosphere occurs in the troposphere. Explain why.
6. Satellite-borne sensors that monitor the ocean are either active or passive. Provide examples of each type of sensor.
7. Explain how the ocean stabilizes Earth's climate system.
8. Give an example of how some human activity has altered the rate of biogeochemical cycling within the Earth system.
9. Give some examples of how the various spheres (e.g., hydrosphere, cryosphere) overlap within the Earth system.
10. List several means whereby some human activity affects the orderly operation of the marine environment.

ESSAY: What Killed the Dinosaurs?

Large asteroids striking Earth have repeatedly caused mass extinctions of life, in the ocean and on the continents. Such extinctions have occurred on Earth every few tens of millions to hundreds of millions of years. Some scientists believe the potential for a large asteroid hitting Earth in the centuries ahead is real and could devastate modern society. A well-preserved, small asteroid crater in Arizona is shown in Figure 1.

FIGURE 1
The Barringer Crater, Arizona, formed by a meteorite striking Earth about 49,000 years ago, is more than 1 km (0.6 mi) across. [Courtesy of NASA]

The most recent and best-known large asteroid impact on Earth occurred about 65 million years ago and produced a 180-km (112-mi) wide crater on the floor of the ancient Caribbean Sea (Figure 2). Marine sediments gradually filled the crater and geological forces later elevated a portion of the crater above sea level. Today, what remains of the Chicxulub crater forms part of the Yucatán Peninsula of Mexico. Radar images obtained by the space shuttle Endeavour in 2000 revealed a 5-m (16-ft) deep, 5-km (3-mi) wide trough on the Yucatán Peninsula that may mark the outer rim of the crater. Drilling through the layers of sediment on the floor of the nearby Gulf of Mexico has recovered cores of fractured and melted rock from the impact zone.

FIGURE 2
The Chicxulub Crater, Yucatán Peninsula, Mexico, is about 180 km (112 mi) across. It formed about 65 million years ago when a mountain-size asteroid (10 to 20 km or 6 to 12 mi across) struck Earth's surface. The effects of the impact are thought to be responsible for the extinction of the dinosaurs and about 70% of all species on the planet. [Courtesy NASA, Lunar Planetary Institute, V.L. Sharpton]

Other evidence of the impact consists of bits of glassy rock, which are chilled droplets of molten rock blasted into the atmosphere by the impact. These droplets cooled as they fell through the atmosphere and onto the land or into the ocean. They were recovered from nearby deep-ocean sediments (Chapter 4). Many rocks on land contain mineral grains deformed by the extreme heat and pressure from the impact. Other unusual sediment deposits were produced by enormous waves (tsunamis) generated when the asteroid (about 10 km or 6 mi in diameter) impacted the ocean surface.

The effects of the asteroid impact on life on Earth were catastrophic. Best known is the extinction of the dinosaurs, which had dominated life on Earth for more than 250 million years. Dinosaurs were not the only victims, however. The asteroid impact destroyed more that 70% of the other life forms then existing on the planet. Small mammals evolved rapidly to take the place of the dinosaurs. The impact also caused major extinctions among many groups of marine organisms.

What precisely caused the demise of the dinosaurs? One widely accepted theory is that the asteroid impact vaporized large amounts of sulfur-containing deep-sea sediments. This sulfur was blown in the atmosphere where it generated enormous clouds of tiny sulfate particles. These clouds prevented sunlight from reaching Earth's surface for long periods and most plants died because they could not photosynthesize. Dinosaurs dependent on eating plants starved and the carnivores that fed on them soon met the same fate. Only small animals (like mammals) could survive by eating the dead plants and animals until conditions improved and new food sources became available. Eventually, the sulfate particles settled out of the atmosphere so that photosynthesis could resume and new plants replaced those lost after the impact. Another theory is that red-hot, impact-generated particles rained through the atmosphere making it so hot that most plants and animals were killed directly.

ESSAY: Where Did the Water Come From?

Earth is known as the water planet—ocean waters cover almost 71% of its surface. From a different perspective, Earth is relatively dry in that ocean water accounts for only about 0.02% of the planet's total mass. Yet, in view of how the solar system is believed to have formed, it is surprising that even that much water is present on Earth. Where did the water come from? Scientists do not have a complete explanation but a popular hypothesis attributes water on Earth to the bombardment of the planet by comets and/or *planetesimals*, large meteorites a few kilometers across (Figure 1).

According to astronomers, Earth, the sun, and the entire solar system evolved from an immense rotating cloud of dust, ice and gases, called a *nebula*, more than 4.5 billion years ago. The highest temperatures, density, and pressure were at the center of the nebula, decreasing gradually toward its outer limits. Extreme conditions at the nebula's center vaporized ice and light elements and drove them toward the nebula's outer reaches. Consequently, residual dry rocky masses formed the inner planets (including Earth). Farther out, meteorites and the less-dense giant planets Saturn and Jupiter formed. While meteorites are about 10% ice by mass and the giant planets contain some ice, most of the water in the nebula condensed in comets at distances beyond Saturn and Jupiter. A *comet* is a relatively small mass composed of meteoric dust and ices that moves in a parabolic or highly elliptical orbit around the sun.

Comets are about half ice. During the latter stages of Earth's formation, comets impacted the planet's surface forming a veneer of water. Jupiter's strengthening gravitational attraction may have drawn a multitude of ice-rich comets from the outer to the inner reaches of the solar system on a collision course with Earth. The hypothesis that comets delivered most of Earth's water remained popular until scientists discovered that water on Earth and ice in comets are not chemically equivalent. Spectral analyses of three comets that approached Earth in recent years revealed that comet ice contains about twice as much deuterium as the water on Earth. *Deuterium* is an isotope of hydrogen whose nucleus consists of one proton plus one neutron and is very rare on Earth; a normal hydrogen atom has a single proton. Based on this finding, some scientists suggest that comets accounted for no more than half the water on Earth and perhaps much less. The water in planetesimals, on the other hand, contains less deuterium than comet ice; they may have impacted Earth during the latter stages of the planet's formation. However, the ratio of some other chemical components of planetesimals is not the same as the ratio of those same components on Earth. Yet another possibility is that Earth's water is indigenous; that is, the center of the nebula may have been cooler than previously assumed and some of the materials present in the inner solar system that formed Earth were water-rich.

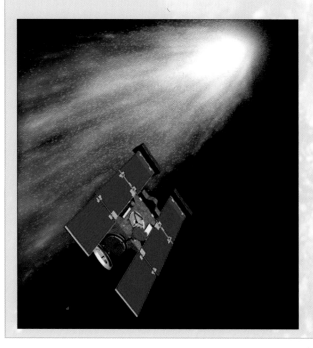

FIGURE 1
An artist's depiction of NASA's Stardust spacecraft encountering Comet Wild 2. Scientists have found a wide range of compositions and structures of ice, dust and gases in Wild 2 particles that were captured and returned to Earth by Stardust. [Courtesy NASA/JPL]

ESSAY: Co-Evolution of the Ocean, Atmosphere, and Life

Whatever the actual source of water on Earth, the ocean likely co-evolved with the atmosphere. At the very beginning, Earth's atmosphere probably was mostly hydrogen (H) and helium (He) plus some hydrogen compounds including methane (CH_4) and ammonia (NH_3). Because these atoms and molecules are relatively light and have high molecular speeds, Earth's weak gravitational field plus high temperatures allowed this earliest atmosphere to escape to space. In time, however, volcanic activity began spewing huge quantities of lava, ash, and gases. By about 4.4 billion years ago, the planet's growing gravitational field was sufficiently strong to retain a thin gaseous envelope of volcanic origin, Earth's primeval atmosphere.

The principal source of Earth's atmosphere was *outgassing*, the release of gases from rock through volcanic eruptions and the impact of meteorites on the planet's rocky surface. Perhaps as much as 85% of all outgassing took place within a million or so years of the planet's formation, but outgassing continues to this day although at a slower pace. Outgassing produced a primeval atmosphere that was mostly carbon dioxide (CO_2), with some nitrogen (N_2) and water vapor (H_2O), along with trace amounts of methane, ammonia, sulfur dioxide (SO_2), and hydrochloric acid (HCl). Radioactive decay of an isotope of potassium in the planet's bedrock added argon (Ar), an inert (chemically non-reactive) gas, to the evolving atmosphere. Dissociation of water vapor into its constituent atoms, hydrogen and oxygen, by high-energy solar ultraviolet radiation contributed a small amount of free oxygen to the primeval atmosphere. (The lighter hydrogen—with its relatively high molecular speeds—escaped to space.) Also, some oxygen combined with other elements in various chemical compounds such as carbon dioxide.

Scientists suggest that between 4.5 and 2.5 billion years ago, the sun was about 30% fainter than it is today. This did not mean a cooler planet, however, because of the abundance of carbon dioxide. Earth's CO_2-rich atmosphere was perhaps 10 to 20 times denser than the present atmosphere. Carbon dioxide slows the escape of Earth's heat to space, contributing to average surface temperatures that may have been as high as 85 °C to 110 °C (185 °F to 230 °F).

By perhaps 4 billion years ago, the planet started to cool and the Earth system underwent major changes. Cooling caused atmospheric water vapor to condense into clouds that produced rain. Precipitation plus runoff from landmasses gave rise to the ocean that eventually may have covered as much as 95% of the planet's surface. The global water cycle (which helped further cool the Earth's surface through evaporation) and its largest reservoir (the ocean) were in place. Rains also helped bring about a substantial decline in the concentration of atmospheric CO_2. Carbon dioxide dissolves in rainwater producing weak carbonic acid that reacts chemically with bedrock. The net effect of this large-scale geochemical process was increasing amounts of carbon chemically locked in rocks and minerals with less and less CO_2 remaining in the atmosphere. The physical and chemical breakdown of rock (*weathering*) plus erosion on land delivered some carbon-containing sediment to the ocean. Also, rains washed dissolved carbon dioxide directly into the sea and some atmospheric CO_2 dissolved in ocean water as sea surface temperatures fell. (Carbon dioxide is more soluble in cold water.)

Although carbon dioxide has been a minor component of the atmosphere for at least 3.5 billion years, its concentration has fluctuated from time to time in the geologic past with important implications for global climate. All other factors being equal, more CO_2 in the atmosphere means higher temperatures at the Earth's surface. For example, geologic evidence points to bursts of volcanic activity on the ocean floor (Chapter 12). Some CO_2 released during that activity eventually found its way to the atmosphere and elevated the global mean temperature by as much as 10 Celsius degrees (18 Fahrenheit degrees). During the Pleistocene Ice Age (1.7 million to 10,500 years ago), atmospheric carbon dioxide levels fluctuated, decreasing during episodes of glacial expansion and increasing during episodes of glacial recession (although it is not clear whether variations in atmospheric CO_2 were the cause or effect of these global-scale climate changes).

Living organisms also played an important role in Earth's evolving atmosphere, primarily through *photosynthesis*, the process whereby green plants use sunlight, water, and carbon dioxide to manufacture their food. A byproduct of photosynthesis is oxygen (O_2). Although vegetation is also a sink for carbon dioxide, photosynthesis probably was not as important as the geochemical processes just described in removing carbon dioxide from the atmosphere. Based on the fossil record, photosynthesis dates to about 2.7 billion years ago with the first appearance of cyanobacteria in the ocean. However, it was not until 2.4 to 2.5 billion years ago that the atmosphere became oxygen-rich. Although oxygen was produced for 200-300 million years, none accumulated in the atmosphere during that period. Why the delay?

Apparently, the ocean and land took up oxygen as fast as it was produced through photosynthesis by cyanobacteria. In the ocean, most oxygen combined with marine sediments while very little entered the atmosphere from the ocean. Eventually, oxidation of marine sediments tapered off and photosynthetic oxygen dissolved in ocean water. According to findings reported in 2007 by researchers L. Kump of Pennsylvania State University and M. Barley of the University of Western Australia, about 2.5 billion years ago, the geologic record indicates a shift from underwater volcanoes to terrestrial volcanoes. This shift was accompanied by a change in the composition of the eruptive gases from those that react with oxygen to those that do not react with oxygen. This shift spurred the build-up of atmospheric oxygen. With the concurrent decline in atmospheric CO_2, within 500 million years, oxygen became the second most abundant atmospheric gas after nitrogen.

During the past 550 million years, the concentration of oxygen in the atmosphere fluctuated significantly. These fluctuations were linked to imbalances in the rates of (1) weathering of organic carbon and pyrite (FeS_2) which decreases atmospheric oxygen, and (2) burial of these materials in sediment which increases atmospheric oxygen. Over the 550 million year period, the percentage of O_2 in the atmosphere is estimated to have varied between about 13% and 31%; at present oxygen is about 21% of the air we breathe. These changes in atmospheric composition affected the evolution of organisms both on land and in the ocean. For example, about 475 million years ago, a time of relatively low atmospheric oxygen, fish apparently evolved a strategy to increase oxygen uptake from seawater. They used their vigorous swimming ability to force greater amounts of water over their gills.

With oxygen emerging as a major component of Earth's atmosphere, the ozone shield formed. Within the *stratosphere*, incoming solar ultraviolet (UV) radiation powers reactions that convert oxygen to ozone (O_3) and ozone to oxygen (Chapter 5). Absorption of UV radiation in these reactions prevents potentially lethal intensities of UV radiation from reaching Earth's surface. By about 440 million years ago, formation of the *stratospheric ozone shield* made it possible for organisms to live and evolve on land. UV radiation does not penetrate ocean water to any great depth so that marine life was able to exist in the ocean depths prior to the formation of the ozone shield. But with the ozone shield, marine life was able to thrive in surface waters.

Nitrogen (N_2), a product of outgassing, became the most abundant atmospheric gas because it is relatively inert chemically and its molecular speeds are too slow for this gas to readily escape Earth's gravitational pull. Furthermore, compared to other atmospheric gases, such as oxygen and carbon dioxide, nitrogen is less soluble in water. All these factors greatly limit the rate at which nitrogen cycles out of the atmosphere. While nitrogen continues to be generated as a minor component of volcanic eruptions, today the principal source of free nitrogen entering the atmosphere is the denitrification process involved in bacterial decay of the remains of plants and animals, both marine and terrestrial. But this input is countered by nitrogen removed from the atmosphere by *biological fixation* (i.e., direct nitrogen uptake by leguminous plants such as clover and soybeans) and *atmospheric fixation* (i.e., the process whereby the high temperatures associated with lightning (Figure 1) causes nitrogen to combine with oxygen to form nitrates that are washed by rains to Earth's surface).

In summary, although scientists are unsure of the ultimate origins of water on Earth, a picture is emerging as to how the Earth system formed. It is evident that Earth's ocean, atmosphere, and biosphere gradually co-evolved through billions of years.

FIGURE 1
High temperatures of lightning causes nitrogen to combine with oxygen to form nitrates that are then washed to the earth's surface. [Photo by C. Clark. Courtesy NOAA OAR/ERL/National Severe Storms Laboratory (NSSL)]

CHAPTER 2

OCEAN BASINS AND PLATE TECTONICS

Case-in-Point
Driving Question
Distribution of the World Ocean
Oceanic Crust and Continental Crust
    Earth Materials
    Rock Cycle
Ocean Bottom Profile
    Continental Margins
    Ocean Basins
Plate Tectonics and Ocean Basin Features
    Evidence for Plate Tectonics
    Divergent Plate Boundaries
    Convergent Plate Boundaries
    Transform Plate Boundaries
    Mantle Convection and Sea Level
    Marine Volcanism
    Hydrothermal Vents
Spreading and Closing Cycles
Conclusions
Basic Understandings/Review/Critical Thinking
ESSAY: Investigating the Ocean Bottom
ESSAY: Hotspot Volcanism and the Hawaiian Islands

Sakura-Jima is one of a chain of stratovolcanoes caused by the subduction of a tectonic plate off the coast of Japan. [Landsat/ USGS]

Case in Point

Tectonic activity (deformation of Earth's lithosphere) plays a central role in the evolution of the basins occupied by the ocean. In addition, through the years volcanic eruptions and earthquakes produced by tectonic activity both at sea and on land have claimed many lives and caused considerable property damage. (Recall, for example, the role of submarine earthquakes in the generation of tsunamis as discussed in the Case-in-Point of Chapter 1.) Study of the Earth system has greatly improved scientific understanding of tectonic processes and the conditions

that contribute to volcanic eruptions, earthquakes, and their after-effects. This basic understanding is enabling scientists to develop techniques to provide the public with advance warning of volcanic eruptions and earthquakes, thereby promising to save many lives.

    The seventh greatest volcanic explosion of the past 10,000 years took place about 3650 years ago on the Greek island of Santorini in the eastern Mediterranean Sea. This violent eruption and the gigantic ocean waves it caused nearly destroyed the island, possibly giving rise to the legend of the "lost city" of Atlantis. About 30 cubic km (7 cubic mi) of ash drifted downwind over the eastern Mediterranean and Turkey. Widespread destruction throughout the region apparently hastened the decline of the Minoan civilization on the nearby island of Crete and the subsequent spread of Greek colonies.

One of the greatest natural disasters of the past few centuries was the eruption of Krakatoa, a volcano on a small island in the Sunda strait between Java and Sumatra in Indonesia. In 1883, after 200 years of inactivity, Krakatoa came to life and was moderately active for several weeks. On 26-27 August, the volcano erupted and violent explosions were heard as far away as Rodriguez Island, 4653 km (2885 mi) across the Indian Ocean, and the atmospheric pressure waves generated were recorded around the world. Two days of gigantic explosions obliterated two-thirds of the volcanic island and triggered enormous tsunami waves which reached estimated heights of 40 m (130 ft). Tsunamis swept inland 16 km (10 mi) on the densely populated islands of Java and Sumatra, killing at least 36,000 people and destroying 165 coastal villages.

Thick clouds of ash carried by winds settled out of the atmosphere producing deep deposits over an area of about 780,000 square km (300,000 square mi), roughly equivalent to the size of Chile. Thinner deposits covered 3.9 million square km (1.5 million square mi), equal to nearly half the area of the United States. Thick beds of ash also accumulated on the surrounding ocean floor. In all, an estimated 21 cubic km (5 cubic mi) of ash and other larger ejecta were blown into the air, with significant amounts of ash rising 50 km (30 mi) into the stratosphere. Ash remained suspended in the upper atmosphere for several years and was transported by winds around the world, causing brilliantly colored sunsets.

In 1815, another Indonesian volcano, Tambora, erupted violently and impacted the climate in many parts of the world. The eruption blasted a considerable amount of sulfur dioxide (SO_2) into the stratosphere where the gas combined with moisture to produce plumes of tiny sulfurous acid droplets and sulfate particles (collectively called *sulfurous aerosols*). Winds transported sulfurous aerosol plumes around the globe. In the stratosphere, sulfurous aerosols reflect some incoming solar radiation back to space and absorb some solar radiation. The net effect was less solar radiation reaching Earth's surface and cooling of the lower troposphere. Cooling was particularly notable during 1816, referred to in New England as the "year without a summer." Late spring snows and midsummer freezes destroyed crops in the northeast United States and across eastern Canada, bringing considerable hardship to many people.

More recently, in June 1991, Mount Pinatubo, located on Luzon Island in the Philippines, erupted violently, ejecting huge amounts of ash and sulfurous aerosols into the stratosphere (Figure 2.1). Among all 20th century volcanic eruptions, Pinatubo ranked second in size to the 1912 eruption of Katmai in Alaska. The eruption of Mount Pinatubo reduced the summit elevation from 1745 m (5725 ft) to approximately 1485 m (4870 ft) above sea level. Sulfurous aerosols in the stratosphere decreased the amount of solar radiation reaching Earth's surface. The consequent cooling temporarily interrupted the post-1970s global warming trend and was likely responsible for the relatively cool summer of 1992 over continental areas of the Northern Hemisphere. The death toll of

FIGURE 2.1
The June 1991 explosive eruption of Mount Pinatubo in the Philippines was rich in sulfur dioxide (SO_2). The resulting sulfurous aerosol veil in the stratosphere caused cooling at the Earth's surface, interrupting the post-1970s global warming trend for a few years. [U.S. Geological Survey photo]

approximately 350 was relatively low in this eruption in large part due to advance warning and better communications and transportation systems.

Several major volcanic eruptions have occurred in North America, but fortunately none since the continent became heavily populated. Even the spectacular eruption of Mount St. Helens in Washington on 18 May 1980 was relatively small compared to the many massive eruptions that shaped Earth and impacted its inhabitants in the past. Processes that take place in Earth's solid interior, discussed in this chapter, are responsible for volcanic eruptions.

Driving Question:

What processes shape the lithosphere and how do these processes affect ocean basins?

Many forces working together shape and reshape Earth's lithosphere, creating and destroying both ocean basins and continents. (Recall from Chapter 1 that the *lithosphere* is the rigid outer part of the planet, consisting of the upper mantle and crust.) Forces arise primarily from movement of tectonic plates and geological processes that occur mostly at plate boundaries. In this chapter we learn about these forces, their origins, and the features they produce on the ocean floor. We compare the properties of oceanic crust with those of continental crust in terms of rock type, density, and thickness. The ocean bottom profile shows the transition from continental crust to oceanic crust and is divided into the continental shelf, slope, and rise. Although the shelf, slope, and rise are submerged, they are part of the continental crust whereas the abyssal plains, trenches, and ridges beyond are portions of the oceanic crust. Once thought to be flat and featureless, modern technology has revealed many features on the ocean bottom that provide clues as to the origin of the ocean basins; features include prominent volcanic mountain ranges and deep trenches. These and other characteristics of the ocean bottom are associated with processes that take place at divergent, convergent, and transform plate boundaries. We begin by examining the geographical distribution of the world ocean.

Distribution of the World Ocean

Ocean basins and continents are unevenly distributed over Earth's surface (Figure 2.2). The ocean covers about 71% of the planet with the remaining 29% land. However, ocean is less dominant in the Northern Hemisphere than in the Southern Hemisphere. The Northern Hemisphere is 39.3% land and 60.7% ocean whereas the Southern Hemisphere is 19.1% land and 80.9% ocean. The world ocean is composed primarily of the separate, but connected oceans called the Pacific, Atlantic, and Indian Oceans as the largest basins, with the smaller Arctic Ocean basin connected to the far north Atlantic. In 2000, an international agreement defined the Southern Ocean as the waters between 60 degrees S and the Antarctic continent. In the Southern Ocean, the Antarctic Circumpolar Current flows eastward around the Antarctic continent virtually unimpeded by landmasses. The only exception is the northward deflection of currents caused by a combination of the relatively narrow Drake Passage (about 650 km or 400 mi across between the southern tip of South America and Antarctica), the wind field, and bottom topography. A comparison of polar areas shows the Arctic as an ocean surrounded by continents whereas the Antarctic is a continent surrounded by the Southern Ocean.

Where no convenient continental boundaries exist, arbitrary lines delineate ocean basins. For example, the 150 degrees E longitude line from Australia to Antarctica separates the Pacific and Indian Ocean basins. North of Australia, the islands of Indonesia divide the Pacific and Indian Ocean basins. Far to the north, the Bering Strait (between Alaska and Siberia) separates the Pacific and the Arctic Ocean. The 70 degrees W longitude line between Cape Horn (the southern tip of South America) and Antarctica is considered the boundary between the Pacific and Atlantic Oceans. Still another north-south meridian (20 degrees E) from the Cape of Good Hope (southern tip of Africa) to Antarctica separates the Atlantic and Indian Oceans. In addition, numerous seas and gulfs occur adjacent to and connected to the main ocean basins.

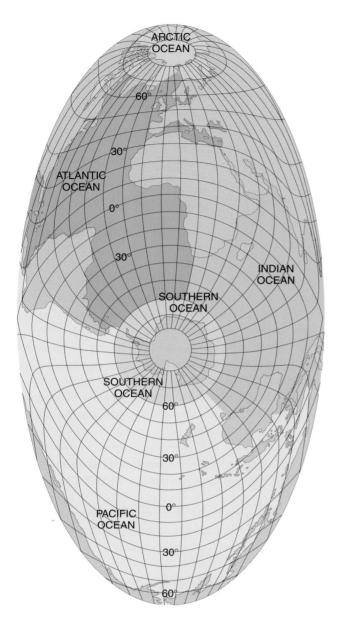

FIGURE 2.2
Ocean basins and continents are unevenly distributed on Earth's surface. Ocean dominates both hemispheres whereas most land is in the Northern Hemisphere.

Oceanic Crust and Continental Crust

Earth's relatively thin solid crust is the portion of the lithosphere that interfaces with the ocean, atmosphere, cryosphere, and biosphere. The crust beneath the ocean differs from the crust of the continents in composition, density, and thickness. In this section, we compare the characteristics of oceanic and continental crust beginning with the basic distinction among rock types.

EARTH MATERIALS

As noted in Chapter 1, internal and surface geological processes continually shape and reshape the lithosphere. These same processes produce a multitude of rock types that compose the crust. Rocks, in turn, are made up of one or more minerals. A *mineral* is a naturally occurring inorganic solid characterized by an orderly internal arrangement of atoms (the basic structural units of all matter) and fixed physical and chemical properties. Some rocks and minerals on land and on the sea floor are economically important resources (Chapter 4).

Rocks composing the crust are classified as igneous, sedimentary, or metamorphic based on the general environmental conditions in which the rock formed. Cooling and crystallization of hot molten *magma* produces **igneous rock**. Magma originates in the lower portion of the lithosphere or upper mantle and migrates upward towards the Earth's surface. Magma may remain within the crust and cool slowly forming coarse-grained igneous rock such as granite or it may spew onto Earth's surface as *lava* through vents or fractures in bedrock and solidify rapidly forming fine-grained igneous rock such as basalt or glassy material such as obsidian.

Sedimentary rock may be composed of any one or a combination of compacted and cemented fragments of rock and mineral grains, partially decomposed remains of dead plants and animals (e.g. shells, skeletons), and minerals precipitated from solution. Sediments form as rocks undergo physical disintegration and chemical decomposition when exposed to rain, atmospheric gases, and fluctuating temperatures at or near Earth's surface. These are weathering processes. Sediments are washed into rivers that transport them to the sea and other standing bodies of water where they settle out of suspension, accumulate on the bottom, and eventually compact into layers of solid sedimentary rock. Sediments are also transported and deposited by wind, glaciers, and icebergs at sea. Most sedimentary rocks have a granular texture; that is, they are composed of individual grains that are compressed or cemented together (e.g., sandstone, shale), although some consist of precipitated minerals and are crystalline (e.g., limestone, rock salt).

Like many sedimentary rocks, **metamorphic rock** is derived from other rocks. A rock is metamorphosed (changed in form) when exposed to high pressure, intense heat, and chemically active fluids—conditions that exist in geologically active mountain belts. Like igneous rocks, metamorphic rocks are crystalline; that is, they are composed of crystals that interlock like the pieces of a jigsaw puzzle. Marble is a common metamorphic rock formed by the metamorphism of limestone ($CaCO_3$) and quartzite is a very durable metamorphic rock formed by metamorphism of sandstone (mostly SiO_2).

Most of the bedrock composing Earth's crust is igneous with some metamorphic rock locally. In many places, thick layers of sedimentary rock and unconsolidated sediments overlie crystalline igneous and metamorphic rocks. Unconsolidated sediments include soil (on land) and clay, silt, sand, or gravel (on land and ocean bottom) and deposits of sediment vary widely in thickness, from a thin veneer to thousands of meters.

Continental crust is mostly granite, a coarse-grained rock rich in minerals containing silica and aluminum. **Oceanic crust**, on the other hand, is mostly basalt, a fine-grained rock rich in minerals containing iron and magnesium. Continental crust is thicker (20 to 90 km or 12 to 56 mi) and less dense than oceanic crust (only 5 to 10 km or 3 to 6 mi thick). As noted in Chapter 1, both continental and oceanic lithosphere includes the crust and the rigid upper portion of the mantle (Figure 1.5). Oceanic lithosphere has a maximum thickness of about 100 km (62 mi) whereas continental lithosphere ranges in thickness from 100 to 150 km (62 to 93 mi). The lithosphere floats on the underlying **asthenosphere**, a deformable portion of the upper mantle. With temperatures at the base of the lithosphere ranging from about 450 °C to 750 °C (840 °F to 1380 °F), the asthenosphere exhibits plastic-like behavior; that is, it readily deforms in response to stress. As we will see later in this chapter, the lithosphere is continually generated in the oceanic ridge system and drawn down into the mantle at subduction zones.

Granite is less dense than basalt so that continental lithosphere floats higher and extends deeper into the mantle than oceanic lithosphere. In fact, most of the continental lithosphere is below sea level. The continents float in the upper mantle similar to icebergs floating in the ocean. (This form of buoyancy is known as *isostacy*.) Figure 2.3 is a comparison between land elevation and ocean depth. Where ocean waters are less than 1000 m (3300 ft) deep, the ocean bottom is usually a submerged portion of the continental crust (the *continental margin*). Where the ocean is deeper than 4000 m (13,000 ft), the bottom is usually oceanic crust. Mountains higher than 6000 m (20,000 ft) are rare on land, as are portions of ocean basins deeper than 6000 m (20,000 ft). These extreme heights and depths occupy less than 1% of Earth's surface.

Traditionally, *mean sea level (msl)* has served as the fixed reference point for specifying topography on land and bathymetry at sea. Topography is a measure of the elevation of the land surface above msl whereas

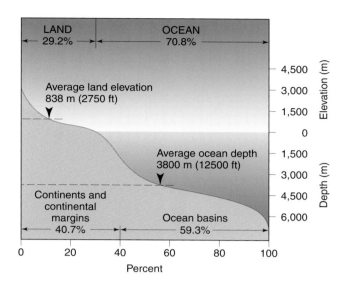

FIGURE 2.3
Hypsographic curve of Earth's surface, showing the relative distribution of ocean and land.

bathymetry is a measure of ocean depth below msl. In coastal areas, a tide gauge is used to determine mean sea level. However, significant real or apparent changes occur in mean sea level due to global climate change, postglacial rebound, tectonic processes, or coastal subsidence. In response, NOAA's National Geodetic Survey has changed the official reference point from mean sea level to the North American Vertical Datum for the U.S., Canada, and Mexico.

A major factor contributing to the elevation of land above sea level is the temperature of continental crust. Like most other solids, the continental crust expands when heated. Heat originating in Earth's interior and from the decay of radioactive elements in the crust causes the continental crust to expand and rise. Researchers D. Hasterok and D.S. Chapman of the University of Utah argue that heating from below accounts for about half of the elevation of the North American continent. In fact, without this heating, the cities of Los Angeles, Denver, and New York would be below sea level. Hasterok and Chapman also point out that in addition to crustal temperature, land elevation varies with differences in the composition, density, and thickness (due to tectonic stresses) of continental crust from one place to another.

ROCK CYCLE

Surface and internal geological processes transform rock from one type to another in the **rock cycle** (Figure 2.4). Through the rock cycle, rocks and

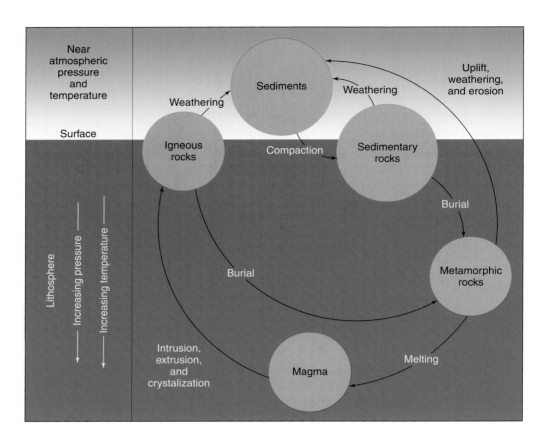

FIGURE 2.4
Through the rock cycle, geological processes (black arrows) convert rock from one type to another.

their component minerals are continually regenerated. Consider an example. Physical and chemical weathering processes fragment an igneous rock mass that is exposed to the atmosphere into sediments which are subsequently transported by running water and deposited in a low-lying basin. In time, the accumulated sediments compact and are cemented together as they gradually convert to sedimentary rock. The mounting weight of the continually accumulating sediments forces the sedimentary rock to greater depths within the crust. (As we will see later in this chapter, subduction also transports crustal material to great depths in the mantle.) Temperature and confining pressure increase with depth so that the rock is eventually metamorphosed, that is, recrystallized into metamorphic rock. At some depth in the subsurface, the temperature is so high that the metamorphic rock melts into magma. The magma may subsequently migrate upward along fractures within the crust, and then cool and crystallize into igneous rock, thereby completing the rock cycle.

Rock transformations involved in the rock cycle are extremely slow; regeneration of rocks and minerals may take many millions of years. Hence, in the time frame of a human lifetime or even of civilization, the rate of regeneration of rock, mineral, and fuel resources (e.g., coal, natural gas) is so slow that for all practical purposes the supply is fixed and finite. For this reason, the resources found in the Earth's crust are essentially *nonrenewable*. We have more to say about resources from the ocean bottom in Chapter 4.

Ocean Bottom Profile

Ocean depth varies markedly from one place to another. Over large areas water depth is less than 200 m (650 ft); in other areas the water is as deep as 11,000 m (36,000 ft). Average ocean depth is about 3800 m (12,500 ft). Here, we examine the vertical cross-sectional profile of the ocean bottom, including the continental margin and ocean basin (Figure 2.5). In places the ocean bottom is nearly flat and essentially featureless whereas in other places the ocean floor exhibits considerable topographic relief. Parts of the ocean bottom are volcanically active with lava interacting chemically with seawater. But over vast areas of the ocean floor, the only significant geological process operating is a very gentle rain of particles that resembles dust settling in a classroom.

CONTINENTAL MARGINS

Based on measurements of water depth, ocean scientists delineate three distinct zones seaward from the coastline. The zone closest to the beach features a very

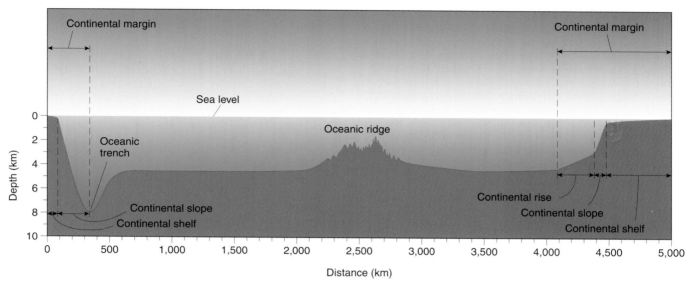

FIGURE 2.5
Cross-sectional profile of the continental margin and ocean bottom with the vertical scale greatly exaggerated.

gentle slope extending out to a water depth that averages about 130 m (430 ft). Seaward from there to a depth of about 3000 m (9800 ft) the water depth increases much more rapidly with distance offshore. Then a relatively narrow zone is transitional from the steep slope of the previous zone to the more-or-less flat ocean basin. The initial, gently sloping zone is the **continental shelf**; the second, more steeply sloping zone is the **continental slope**; and the third transitional region is the **continental rise**. The continental shelf, slope, and rise together comprise the *continental margin*. This is not a misnomer because the bedrock of the continental margin is the same as the continental crust. From a geological perspective, the continents do not end at the beach, but at the continental rise. At its outer edge, the continental margin merges with the deep-sea floor or descends into an oceanic trench (Figure 2.5).

The continental shelf is nearly flat, sloping less than 1 degree seaward. Although water depth generally increases with distance offshore, the rate of increase is quite small—averaging about 2 m per km (10 ft per mi). Shelf width generally ranges from a few tens of meters to 1000 km (620 mi). As a general rule, the shelf is narrowest where the continental margin is tectonically active (e.g., subduction zones) and is widest where the continental margin is passive (i.e., no plate boundary nearby). Hence, the North American shelf is wider along the passive East Coast (as much as several hundred kilometers) than the tectonically active West Coast (a few kilometers). About 7.5% of the total area of the ocean overlies the continental shelves.

The inclination of the continental slope averages about 4 degrees but ranges between 1 and 25 degrees; water depth typically increases by about 50 m per km (265 ft per mi) in a seaward direction, a significantly greater rate of increase than in the shelf zone. In many places such as around the margin of the Atlantic Ocean, the continental slope merges with the more gently sloping continental rise. (The term "rise" here means sloping less steeply to the flat ocean bottom.) In this passive continental margin, sediment spreads over the ocean floor forming vast, flat **abyssal plains** seaward of the continental rise. Along tectonically active continental margins, such as that surrounding nearly the entire Pacific Ocean basin, the slope descends directly into deep ocean trenches. Land-derived sediment flows into trenches and is not available to form either a continental rise or abyssal plains. About 15% of the total area of the ocean is situated over the continental slopes and rises.

Large numbers of deep, steep-sided **submarine canyons** slice into the continental slope and some run up onto the continental shelf; many of these canyons cut into solid rock (Figure 2.6). A variety of mechanisms are responsible for creating submarine canyons including erosion by turbidity currents or ancient rivers. A **turbidity current** is a gravity-driven flow of water heavily laden with suspended sediment (silt, sand, and gravel) making it denser than normal seawater. In many respects, turbidity currents resemble underwater avalanches. Sediment delivered to the ocean by rivers accumulates on the continental shelf. Eventually the pile of sediments builds to an unstable height and suddenly (perhaps triggered

FIGURE 2.6
The darker water in the upper right of this NASA Space Shuttle image is the southern portion of the Tongue of the Ocean in the Bahamas, one of two main branches of the Grand Bahama Canyon. This submarine canyon's nearly vertical walls rise 4285 m (14,000 ft) above the canyon floor. The Grand Bahama Canyon has a length of more than 225 km (140 mi) and a width of 37 km (23 mi) at its deepest point. The lighter blue water covers the shallow Bahama shelf, much of which was above sea level during the last glacial maximum. At the time water draining into the canyon eroded the gullies that are visible at the shelf edge. [Courtesy of NASA]

by an earthquake) slides downhill as a unit, scouring the ocean bottom in the process. These sediments accumulate at the base of the continental rise as a series of overlapping **submarine fans**. Turbidity currents have been clocked at speeds as great as 100 km per hr (60 mph), so it is easy to imagine these flows gouging the ocean bottom and clearing submarine canyons of accumulated sediments.

Many submarine canyons appear to be natural extensions of existing rivers lending support to a turbidity current origin. Some submarine canyons may have originated as valleys cut by rivers during the Pleistocene Ice Age (1.7 million to 10,500 years ago). At times during the Pleistocene, sea level was as much as 130 m (425 ft) lower than today (because so much water was locked up in glaciers) and much of the continental shelf was above sea level. With a steeper gradient, rivers flowed across exposed shelves and eroded deep canyons that were subsequently flooded at the close of the Pleistocene when glaciers melted and sea level rose. For example, the Hudson Canyon off the New York Bight likely formed during the last glacial maximum about 18,000 to 20,000 years ago when sea level was lowest (Figure 2.7). At the time, the Hudson River delivered sediment directly to the head of the canyon and turbidity currents were active. Today, the head of Hudson Canyon is located about 250 km (155 mi) offshore in 90 m (300 ft) of water. Extending about 500 km (310 mi) offshore, the Hudson Canyon is one of the largest canyons on the Atlantic continental shelf. For submarine canyons having no obvious association with existing rivers, sediment sources may be located upstream of longshore currents. As discussed in Chapter 8, longshore currents transport sand and other sediment along the shoreline.

FIGURE 2.7
Bathymetry of the coastal ocean showing New York's Hudson Canyon. This submarine canyon appears to be the natural extension of the Hudson River. [NOAA Ocean Explorer]

OCEAN BASINS

Fringed by continental margins, **ocean basins** encompass the remaining portion of the oceanic area. Ocean basins have a varied topography featuring deep trenches, seamounts, and submarine mountain ranges. Indeed, undersea terrain is just as diverse as terrestrial terrain and exhibits even greater relief. Nevertheless, much of the ocean bottom (about 42%) is comprised of plains and low hills, most rising no more than about 100 m (330 ft) above the plain. Blanketed with sediments that tend to smooth out any irregularities in the bedrock below, abyssal plains and abyssal hills are typical of ocean basin topography—apart from the 23% of the ocean bottom that is covered by ridge systems.

Ocean scientists use many different instruments and techniques to investigate the properties and composition of the ocean bottom. For more on this topic, refer to this chapter's first Essay.

Plate Tectonics and Ocean Basin Features

The most prominent features of the ocean basins, including trenches and mid-ocean ridge systems, are products of tectonic stresses. Earth's lithosphere is divided into many plates that move very slowly over the face of the globe (Figure 2.8). All plates, except the Pacific, include parts of continents as well as ocean basins. Mountain building and most volcanic activity and earthquakes take place at boundaries between plates, many of which occur either within the ocean basins or along their margins.

EVIDENCE FOR PLATE TECTONICS

Plate tectonics is a unifying concept that combines continental drift plus sea floor spreading to describe the generation, movement, and destruction of

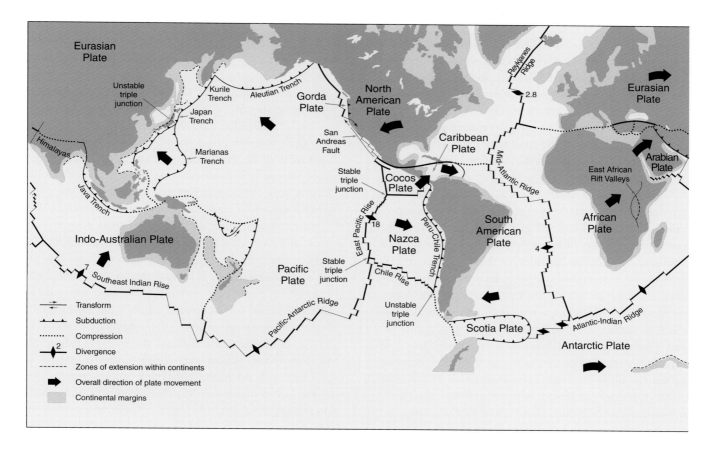

FIGURE 2.8
Divergent, convergent, and transform boundaries of major lithospheric plates. [U.S. Geological Survey]

Earth's lithosphere and the formation of ocean basins. The historical evolution of this concept illustrates a systematic form of inquiry involving observation, interpretation, speculation, and reasoning—all components of critical thinking.

Evidence for the continental drift part of plate tectonics dates back at least to the time of the British Philosopher Francis Bacon (1561-1626) who noticed how the eastward bulge of South America closely fits the configuration of a portion of the west coast of Africa. (Comparing the edge of the continental shelves reveals an even better fit than coastlines.) By the middle of the 19th century scientists and others proposed that the Atlantic Ocean formed when landmasses separated during some catastrophic event. Early in the 20th century, the Austrian geologist Eduard Suess (1831-1914) hypothesized that at one time the individual continents of the Southern Hemisphere were together as one huge continent, which he called Gondwanaland. Around 1910, the German meteorologist Alfred Wegener (1880-1930) and the American geologist Frank B. Taylor (1860-1939) independently proposed **continental drift**, the hypothesis that the continents move over the surface of the planet. Wegener proposed that the supercontinent *Pangaea* split into *Laurasia* (encompassing present day North America and Eurasia) and *Gondwanaland* (encompassing South America, Africa, India, Australia, and Antarctica). He based his idea on the observed close fit between continental margins, similarities in fossil plants and animals, and the continuity of rock formations and mountain ranges between continents on either side of the Atlantic Ocean.

Wegener's hypothesis was ridiculed and mostly ignored by geologists on the grounds that he did not provide a scientifically sound mechanism for driving the continents. At the time, most scientists believed that continents and ocean basins were fixed in place; it was difficult to understand how Wegener's continents could plow through solid rock on the bottom of the ocean. At the time, little was known about the ocean floor or Earth's interior. All this began to change in the 1950s and 1960s when investigations of the deep sea floor revealed prominent mountain ranges and deep trenches. In the early 1960s, these findings inspired Harry Hess (1906-1969) of Princeton University and the geological oceanographer Robert S. Dietz (1914-1995) to resurrect an idea first presented in 1929 by the British geologist Arthur Holmes (1890-1965). Hess and Dietz proposed that convection in the Earth's mantle was the driving force behind continental drift.

According to Hess and Dietz, rock in the lower mantle is heated by the decay of certain radioactive elements. This warmer less dense and buoyant material gradually rises within the mantle and then flows along the base of the cool, rigid lithosphere. Cooling of the mantle material increases its density and it sinks back toward the lower mantle where it is reheated thus completing the convective circulation. Convection currents drag the lithospheric plates, and are responsible for sea-floor spreading, the divergence of adjacent plates on the ocean bottom. They supply heat and magma to the ocean ridges, and cause subduction, the descent of lithospheric plates into the mantle. Today, some scientists argue that two zones of convection operate in the mantle: deep convection (below about 700 km or 435 mi) and shallow convection (above 700 km) that interfaces with the lithosphere.

In subsequent years, evidence accumulated in support of the Hess-Dietz model and sea-floor spreading. Much of this evidence came from deep-sea drilling from specially outfitted ships (discussed in this chapter's first Essay) and includes: (1) the concentration of earthquake activity along plate boundaries, with the deepest earthquakes generally associated with subduction zones (Figure 2.9), (2) enhanced heat flow from Earth's interior along mid-ocean ridges, (3) increasing age of the oceanic crust with increasing distance on either side of the mid-ocean ridges, and (4) increasing thickness of sea-floor sediment with increasing distance from the mid-ocean ridges.

Perhaps the most convincing argument for plate tectonics was the discovery of a distinctive pattern of anomalies in the Earth's ancient magnetic field on the sea floor. We can visualize Earth's magnetic field as emanating from a huge bar magnet centered in the Earth's core with a north and south magnetic pole. Earth's magnetic poles, however, do not coincide with the planet's geographical poles and precise locations vary over time. Currently, the north magnetic pole is located in northwest Canada while the south magnetic pole is in the Southern Ocean. Magnetic lines of force converge toward the two magnetic poles so that the needle on a compass aligns with the magnetic lines of force and points toward the magnetic north.

Oceanic crust contains the mineral magnetite, an iron oxide, which acts like a compass needle in aligning with the planet's magnetic lines of force. This alignment is frozen into the rock when the temperature of cooling lava drops below the *Curie temperature* of 580 °C or 1076 °F, named for its discoverer Pierre Curie (1859-1906). Hence, information on the direction of the planet's magnetic field at the time lava cooled and solidified is locked in the rocks.

FIGURE 2.9
Most earthquakes occur along or near the boundaries of major lithospheric plates. [U.S. Geological Survey]

Studies of the same magnetite-bearing rock on land reveal times in the past when the polarity of the Earth's magnetic field reversed; that is, the north magnetic pole became the south magnetic pole and vice versa. This rock record indicates 170 reversals over the past 76 million years. Beginning in the 1950s, research vessels and aircraft mapped magnetic polarity reversals over much of the ocean floor. Instruments towed behind ships measured the intensity of the magnetic field and revealed ribbon-like patterns of magnetic anomalies (Figure 2.10). Each anomaly strip was a few kilometers to tens of kilometers wide and thousands of kilometers long and oriented roughly parallel to the mid-ocean ridges. Application of the magnetic land-based chronology to the sea floor enabled scientists to date remotely large areas of the sea floor. Most intriguing was the discovery that the magnetic anomaly pattern on one side of an ocean ridge was the mirror image of the pattern on the other side of the ridge. Furthermore, dating indicated that the oceanic crust became progressively older with increasing distance away from a mid-ocean ridge. In 1963, F.J. Vine and D.H. Matthews of Cambridge University interpreted these anomaly patterns as a record of past magnetic reversals indicating that newly formed crust moved away from the mid-ocean ridges. That is, magnetic anomaly patterns confirmed sea-floor spreading and continental drift and the unifying theory of plate tectonics soon became widely accepted.

FIGURE 2.10
This block diagram shows the regular pattern of magnetic anomalies on either side of the mid-ocean ridge system. The age of the ocean crust increases with increasing distance from the ridge axis. Light blue stripes represent normal polarity; other colored stripes indicate reversed polarity.

Boundaries between the rigid lithospheric plates are principal locales of geological activity. Depending on relative movement, plate boundaries are designated divergent, convergent, or transform. Movements along plate boundaries give rise to a variety of geographic and geological features on the ocean floor and on land.

DIVERGENT PLATE BOUNDARIES

When adjacent plates move apart, they create a **divergent plate boundary**. Diverging lithospheric plates produce rifts (fractures) in the crust through which magma wells up from below (Figure 2.11). Magma (called *lava* when it reaches Earth's surface) at a temperature of about 1200 °C (2200 °F) cools and solidifies rapidly when it comes in contact with much colder seawater (at 2 °C to 5 °C or 36 °F to 41 °F). Through this process, new oceanic lithosphere is generated at divergent plate boundaries. In fact, more than 18 cubic km (4 cubic mi) of new lithosphere is produced in this way every year.

On the seafloor, the outer surfaces of lava flows exhibit characteristic tube-like and pillow-shaped structures (Figure 2.12). These volcanic eruptions at spreading centers are generally tranquil events, unlike the violent explosions that characterize volcanoes associated with subduction zones (discussed below). Also, shallow earthquakes (centered a few kilometers to a few tens of kilometers below the ocean floor) are often associated with these volcanic eruptions.

Newly formed oceanic crust stands higher than nearby older oceanic crust because recently formed warm rock is less dense than older and colder rock. As oceanic crust ages and moves away from plate boundaries, it cools and becomes denser. Also, as the crust is slowly loaded with sediments, it sinks deeper into the underlying asthenosphere (not unlike a ship as it is loaded). Consequently,

FIGURE 2.12
The pillow shape exhibited by these basaltic flows on the slope off Hawaii is characteristic of lava that cools rapidly on the seafloor. [OAR/National Undersea Research Program (NURP); NOAA]

the older the crust, the deeper is the water above it (Figure 2.13). At divergent plate boundaries (mid-ocean ridge), the ocean bottom is about 2500 m (8200 ft) deep, but away from the boundary where the crust is 160 million years old, the oceanic crust is about 6000 m (19,500 ft) below sea level. Thus, the ocean floor not only contains information on magnetic reversals and plate movements, but functions as conveyor belts on either side of the mid-ocean ridge system, moving newly formed crust away from divergent plate boundaries.

The mid-ocean ridge is a volcanic mountain range that winds its way from the Arctic Ocean down the middle of the Atlantic Ocean, curves around South Africa and into the Indian Ocean (*Mid-Indian Ridge*), and then into the Pacific

FIGURE 2.11
Divergent plate boundary at a mid-ocean ridge.

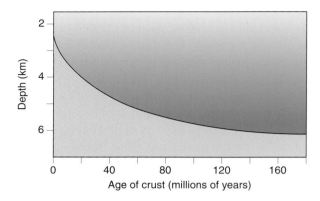

FIGURE 2.13
When formed at a mid-ocean ridge, oceanic crust is about 2.5 km (1.6 mi) below the sea surface. As oceanic crust ages, it cools and becomes denser and moves away from the mid-ocean ridge, accumulating sediment and sinking deeper into the upper mantle. At an age of 160 million years, the oceanic crust is at a depth greater than about 6 km (3.7 mi).

Ocean (*East Pacific Rise*). Its total length is about 55,000 km (34,000 mi), much longer than any mountain range on land. Along the mid-ocean ridge a distinction is made between *fast-spreading* and *slow-spreading* boundaries. At fast-spreading boundaries, plates move apart at 100 to 200 mm per yr. With rapid spreading, hot magma is abundant and lava flows as sheets from a central peak, giving the ridge a narrow tent-like profile. An example is the East Pacific Rise, located in the east Pacific Ocean near South America (Figure 2.8). At slow-spreading boundaries, plates move apart at less than 55 mm per yr. With a slower magma supply, the topography is broader and rougher. Rift valleys, 1 to 2 km (0.6 to 1.2 mi) deep and a few tens of kilometers across, occur along the ridge axis. The Mid-Atlantic Ridge is an example of a slow-spreading boundary.

The Mid-Atlantic Ridge divides the Atlantic Ocean bottom into two (western and eastern) roughly symmetrical halves. Each side can be as much as 1600 km (1000 mi) wide with the rim rising about 2500 m (8200 ft) above the adjacent sea floor (Figure 2.14). The Mid-Atlantic Ridge marks a boundary between oceanic plates that have been diverging for perhaps 200 million years. That divergence split apart the ancient supercontinent *Pangaea*, creating

the Atlantic Ocean basin. Rifting is evident in the gaping fractures that dissect solidified lava flows in Iceland, a volcanic island formed over a localized magma source (called a *hot spot* and described in detail in this chapter's second Essay) along the ridge (Figure 2.15).

Lengthy, nearly straight, parallel fractures are oriented perpendicular to the mid-ocean ridge and off-set segments of the ridge. These *transform faults* allow the spreading motion to adjust to the curvature of the Earth. Rugged sea bottom topography as well as lines of submarine volcanoes or islands mark some fracture zones. The Cape Mendocino Fracture Zone intersects the California coast at Cape Mendocino and extends westward thousands of kilometers on the North Pacific Ocean floor.

Based on spreading rates and geological features, a third category of divergent plate boundary was discovered recently. At *ultraslow-spreading* boundaries, plates move apart at less than 20 mm per yr. Volcanoes occur at more widely spaced intervals and there are no transform faults and few earthquakes. Between volcanoes, the crust fractures and huge slabs of mantle rock rise to the seafloor, providing a glimpse into Earth's interior. Two known sites of ultraslow-spreading are the 1800-km

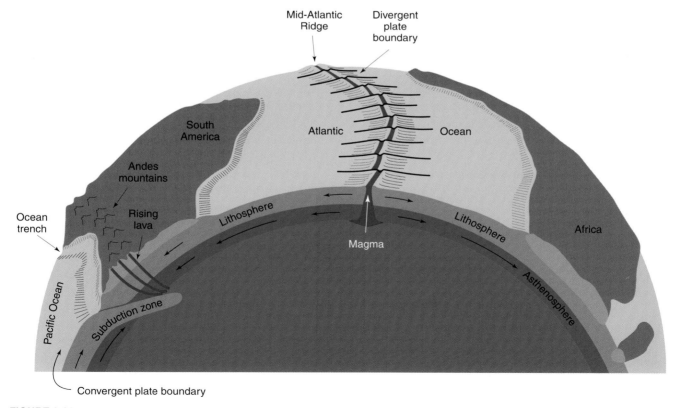

FIGURE 2.14
The Mid-Atlantic ridge occurs where adjacent plates diverge and is part of a lengthy ridge system that winds through the ocean basins.

FIGURE 2.15
Iceland is a volcanic island formed along the Mid-Atlantic ridge. The volcanic rocks exposed in this scene fractured as lava flows cooled, congealed and contracted. [Photo by J.M. Moran]

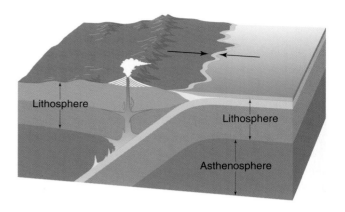

FIGURE 2.16
A convergent plate boundary where an oceanic plate subducts under a continental plate.

(1100-mi) long Gakkel Ridge in 2 km of water under the Arctic ice off the northeast coast of Greenland and the 8800-km (5400-mi) long Southwest India Ridge in the South Atlantic. Some marine geologists estimate that ultraslow-spreading boundaries characterize perhaps one-third of the mid-ocean ridge system.

CONVERGENT PLATE BOUNDARIES

When adjacent plates move toward one another, they create a **convergent plate boundary**. There are three possibilities: (1) two oceanic plates collide (e.g., the Pacific and Philippine plates), (2) an oceanic plate and continental plate collide (e.g., the Nazca and South American plates), and (3) two continental plates collide (e.g., the Indian and Eurasian plates). For locations, refer to the map in Figure 2.8.

A **subduction zone** forms where two oceanic plates converge or where an oceanic plate converges with a continental plate (Figure 2.16). In a subduction zone, the denser oceanic plate slips under the other plate and descends into the mantle. With downward transport of rock and sediment, a deep elongated depression (trench) forms on the ocean floor. Temperature and confining pressure increase with depth within Earth's interior so that a plate is heated and compressed as it descends into the mantle. Also, the friction of plates grinding past one another generates heat and earthquakes. (This is the origin of almost all tsunami-generating earthquakes.) At depths approaching 80 km (50 mi), the subducting plate begins to melt into magma, which migrates upward toward Earth's surface and contributes to mountain building and explosive volcanic eruptions. (The eruptions of Mount St. Helens

and Mount Pinatubo are recent examples.) Whereas new lithosphere forms at divergent plate boundaries, lithosphere is destroyed by being incorporated into the mantle in subduction zones at convergent plate boundaries.

In oceanic-to-oceanic plate collisions, volcanic activity associated with subduction forms **island arcs**, curved chains of volcanic islands. Trenches usually lie on the seaward sides of island arcs with relatively shallow seas near continents. For example, the islands of Japan are part of a volcanic island arc with the Sea of Japan on the continental side and a trench on the Pacific Ocean side. An **ocean trench** is relatively narrow, typically 50 to 100 km (30 to 60 mi) wide, and may be thousands of kilometers long. In cross-section, a trench is slightly asymmetrical with the steeper slope on the continental side. Depths greater than 8000 m (26,250 ft) are not uncommon and some trenches have deep holes called *deeps* that exceed 10,000 m (32,800 ft) in depth. The deepest place on the ocean floor is probably the Challenger Deep, in the Marianas Trench in the Western Pacific, with a maximum depth of 10,923 m (35,838 ft). For all their importance in plate tectonics, trenches make up only 1 to 2% of the ocean basin floor. Trenches surround most of the Pacific Ocean basin but volcanic island arcs are mostly on the western and northern sides of the Pacific. Besides Japan, Alaska's Aleutian Islands/Aleutian Trench is another example of a volcanic island arc/trench system.

At the convergent plate boundary just off the west coast of South America, the Nazca plate subducts under the South American plate, producing the offshore Peru-Chile Trench, which is 5900 km (3660 mi) long, 100 km (62 mi) wide, and more than 8000 m (26,300 ft) deep (Figure 2.17). Associated with subduction of the Nazca plate is the Andes, a prominent mountain range including many volcanoes forming the backbone of South America.

FIGURE 2.17
Color-coded bathymetry/topography of the South Pacific Ocean and adjacent South America. The narrow dark blue band paralleling the coast represents the Peru-Chile Trench produced by subduction of the Nazca plate under the South American plate. [National Geophysical Data Center (NGDC), NOAA Satellite and Information Services]

The only gaps in the circum-Pacific subduction/trench system, also known as the *Pacific Ring of Fire*, are in Antarctica and in western North America. The Pacific Ring of Fire includes the U.S. West Coast, an active continental margin, whereas the East Coast is not a plate boundary and is passive. The action in the Atlantic Ocean is down the middle (along the Mid-Atlantic Ridge) whereas the action in the Pacific is around the rim. This difference is related to the fact that the Atlantic is spreading with little subduction, while the Pacific is shrinking at the subduction zones.

Deep earthquakes (originating at depths greater than 100 km or 60 mi) are usually associated with subduction zones. Earthquakes occur where adjacent crustal blocks move past each other, releasing energy stored in rocks deformed during plate movements when descending into the mantle at subduction zones. This energy travels as waves both along Earth's surface as well as through its interior. The depth to earthquake energy release generally increases with distance inland with the deepest earthquakes originating at depths of about 700 km (430 mi).

Plate movements also cause continents to collide, but such convergence does not form trenches or island arcs. Continents are much thicker and less dense than oceanic crust so they do not subduct into the mantle. A complex continental convergence is taking place in the Mediterranean region, where Africa and Europe are colliding as evidenced by active volcanism in Italy, dormant volcanoes in France, and earthquakes in the eastern Mediterranean. (In this case plate collision combines with some subduction.) The Himalayan Mountains are the result of the continuing collision of the Asian and Indian plates. Over the past 40 million years, the plate containing the Indian subcontinent has moved thousands of kilometers northward through the Indian Ocean and is now colliding with Asia. The Himalayan Mountains occur where the leading edge of the Indian plate thrust under the Asian plate. The Rocky Mountains of North America were formed in a similar manner when the Pacific plate thrust beneath the North American plate. Their present height results from the buoyant, relatively young Pacific plate material lying beneath the North American continental crust.

TRANSFORM PLATE BOUNDARIES

Adjacent plates that slide laterally past one another produce a **transform plate boundary** (Figure 2.18). Although crust is neither created nor destroyed and these boundaries are generally free of volcanic activity, slippage can deform rock and trigger earthquakes. The San Andreas Fault of California, site of frequent earthquakes, occurs along a transform plate boundary where the Pacific plate (carrying a piece of California) slides toward the northwest, past the North American plate (Figure 2.8). The Anatolian fault in Turkey is another transform plate boundary and has been the site of some particularly disastrous earthquakes.

FIGURE 2.18
A transform plate boundary is often the site of shallow earthquakes.

MANTLE CONVECTION AND SEA LEVEL

As noted above, convection in Earth's mantle is responsible for the horizontal movement of tectonic plates leading to sea floor spreading, subduction, and transform faults. In addition, mantle convection causes vertical (up and down) movements of the continents accompanied by apparent changes in sea level. For example, in southern Africa, an expansive plateau about 1600 km (1000 mi) across and almost 1600 m (5200 ft) high has been slowly rising over the past 100 million years. Geologists do not attribute this vertical motion to tectonic activity—the region has been tectonically inactive for 400 million years or so. Rather, a hot mushroom-shaped mass (a *superplume*) several kilometers across ascending within the underlying mantle is pushing the plateau upward. And as the plateau rises, sea level falls.

While hot and buoyant superplumes in Earth's mantle cause upward motion of landmasses, other continental areas are sinking due to mantle convection. In some subduction zones, cold dense slabs of seafloor plunge into the mantle dragging the overlying landmasses downward and accompanied by an apparent rise in sea level. Geologists have found evidence of downward and then upward movement of portions of North America and Australia during the geologic past, far from the possible influence of tectonic plate collisions.

MARINE VOLCANISM

Marine volcanic activity occurs where magma erupts through vents or fissures at Earth's surface, that is, along divergent and convergent plate boundaries and over hot spots. Products of volcanic eruptions include materials that are molten (e.g., lava), solid (e.g., ash, cinders, rock blocks), and gaseous (e.g., water vapor, carbon dioxide). Viscosity (the internal resistance of a substance to flow), gas content, and rate of extrusion of molten material govern volcanic activity and the shape of a volcano built by successive eruptions. Volcanoes range from small cinder cones to massive shield-like accumulations of solidified lava. Whereas about 20 major volcanic eruptions occur annually on the continents, many more eruptions occur on the ocean bottom and almost always are unobserved. Only shallow submarine eruptions and those occurring on islands have been extensively studied, although this is changing because of the development of new underwater observing techniques.

As noted earlier in this chapter, volcanic activity on the ocean floor consists of mostly quiescent lava flows. However, continental volcanoes often erupt violently. This difference in volcanic activity stems from the silica (SiO_2) composition and gas content (volatiles) of the magma that feeds a volcano. Magmas that are silica-rich are relatively viscous and may block volcanic vents. Pressure produced by volatile components (mostly water vapor) beneath the block increases and eventually the volcano explodes. Continental crust is mostly silica-rich granite so that magma formed from melting this crust is also silica-rich and viscous with a relatively high volatile content.

A high volatile content magma develops when water-rich oceanic crust subducts under continental crust and melts at depth. This magma migrates upward carrying volatiles, melting and mixing with continental crust, and forming andesitic to granitic magmas that are 60-70% silica and 3-6% volatiles. Such magmas are responsible for violent eruptions characteristic of volcanoes of the Cascade and Andes mountain ranges. On the other hand, oceanic crust is mostly silica-poor basalt derived from the upper mantle. It is also relatively water-poor with only 1-2% volatile content. Hence, the magma that composes the oceanic crust is volatile-poor, silica-poor, has low viscosity, and flows readily as lava. This explains why mid-ocean spreading centers exhibit quiescent volcanic activity (e.g., Iceland). On the other hand, eruptive behavior is usually violent in volcanic island arcs (e.g., the Aleutian Islands) where one oceanic plate subducts under another oceanic plate. Although the subducting plate is intermediate in silica content, intense heating of the wet oceanic crust causes explosive volcanic activity.

A significant volcanic eruption, usually persisting over a long period of time, builds **seamounts**, underwater volcanic peaks rising more than 1000 m (3300 ft) above the ocean floor. Examples include the Emperor Seamounts in the North Pacific Ocean basin. Massive eruptions may cause the top of the volcano to break the water surface, rising above sea level and forming a volcanic island. The Hawaiian Islands, Iceland, and most other oceanic islands are products of such submarine volcanic activity. With the passage of time and the decline and eventual end of volcanic activity, weathering and erosion rapidly dissect and greatly reduce the elevation of volcanic islands. Meanwhile, the subsurface void produced by the discharge of lava during island formation may start to collapse, causing the island to sink back into the sea. Movement of the oceanic crust away from divergent plate boundaries also transports volcanoes into deeper waters. Such a deep-water seamount featuring a wave-eroded flat top is called a **guyot**.

Another example of an ocean basin feature produced when subsidence follows volcanic activity

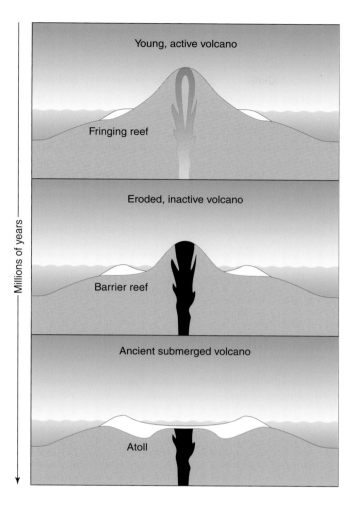

Millions of years

Young, active volcano

Fringing reef

Eroded, inactive volcano

Barrier reef

Ancient submerged volcano

Atoll

FIGURE 2.19
Stages in the development of a coral atoll.

is the coral atoll. A **coral atoll** is a ring-shaped island surrounding a seawater lagoon (Figure 2.19). While serving as a naturalist on the British research ship *HMS Beagle*, Charles Darwin (1809-1882) first proposed that atolls were produced by coral growing upward around the margin of a volcanic island at the same rate that the island gradually sank into the sea. Modern drilling into atolls finds coral remains continuously down to the underlying volcanic rock thus confirming Darwin's hypothesis. Most corals live in warm near-surface waters, so that drilling indicates that the volcanic material was once at the surface, just as Darwin had proposed.

Lithospheric plates are rigid and little volcanic activity takes place away from plate boundaries. An important exception is hotspot volcanism, which is responsible for the Hawaiian Islands, as described in the second Essay of this chapter.

HYDROTHERMAL VENTS

At locations near divergent plate boundaries, superheated water (with temperatures as high as 400 °C or 750 °F) circulates through rock fractures in the seafloor and discharges through spectacular **hydrothermal vents**. A few locations of extremely hot water in the ocean have been known to exist for many years, but it was not until the Woods Hole submersible *Alvin* descended into the Galápagos Rift in 1979 that scientists first observed hydrothermal vents directly. It now appears that hydrothermal vents are more common than previously believed and are associated with all three categories of divergent plate boundaries (*fast-spreading*, *slow-spreading*, and *ultraslow spreading*). Evidence of hydrothermal venting has been reported along most of the mid-ocean ridge system at intervals of less than 200 km (125 mi).

We can think of hydrothermal vents as part of a plumbing system under the mid-ocean ridge. Cold seawater is pulled into the system, superheated, dissolves substances from contacting crustal rock, and is then ejected out of vents on the seafloor. The original assumption was that the high confining pressure forced the seawater into large faults along the flanks of the mid-ocean ridge. Heated by shallow volcanic activity, the water then ascended toward the middle of the ridge and exited into the ocean via a cluster of vents. However, a recent study of a hydrothermal vent system argues for a revision of this model.

The study site is located in 2500 m (8200 ft) of water on the East Pacific Rise about 900 km (565 mi) southwest of Acapulco, Mexico. Scientists placed seismometers around the ridge to record microseisms (small earthquakes). Over a seven month period in 2003 and 2004, the instruments recorded about 7000 shallow microseisms, interpreted to be generated by cold seawater contacting hot rock. Chilling causes the rock to contract and fracture, releasing earthquake energy. By analyzing the microseisms, scientists were able to reconstruct the flow of water in the hydrothermal vent system. In early 2008, participating scientists proposed a new model for the hydrothermal vent system. Cold seawater descends through a 200-m (650-ft) wide chimney atop the ridge. The water then flows through a tunnel-like structure along the ridge axis just above a magma chamber. The superheated water then bubbles up through a series of vents located further along the ridge.

Hydrothermal vent waters are mineral-rich. Substances such as sulfur, iron and other metals precipitate out of solution as the hot oxygen-deprived water mixes with the surrounding cold seawater. Precipitates may appear

FIGURE 2.20
Black smoker emitted at a submarine hydrothermal vent on the Mid-Atlantic ridge. [OAR/National Undersea Research Program (NURP); NOAA]

as dark clouds, called **black smokers**, and accumulate in the form of conical chimneys 10 m (33 ft) or more in height (Figure 2.20). One of the largest hydrothermal chimneys observed to date is near the top of a seamount in the Atlantic Ocean about 2500 km (1550 mi) east of Bermuda; it rises to the height of an 18-story building. Whereas most hydrothermal vents occur along the mid-ocean ridge, this one is located about 15 km (9 mi) from the Mid-Atlantic Ridge.

Hydrothermal activity on the ocean bottom is a source of some dissolved constituents of seawater although the principal source is suspended and dissolved substances delivered to the ocean by rivers and streams (Chapter 4). Seawater circulating through fractures in newly formed oceanic crust (to depths of 600 m or 1950 ft) removes about two-thirds of the heat escaping from recently erupted lavas near ocean ridges with the balance of the heat conducted into the ocean floor. (Fractures form when lava cools, solidifies, and contracts in contact with cold seawater.) The heated seawater dissolves minerals from oceanic crust.

Hydrothermal vents are home to diverse communities of exotic marine organisms, including bacteria, crabs, shrimp, mussels, starfish, and tubeworms. One type of tubeworm found in the Galápagos area of the Pacific Ocean floor may grow to a length of 2.4 m (8 ft). In most marine ecosystems, photosynthesizing organisms form the base of food chains. In the deep water where hydrothermal vents occur, no sunlight is available for photosynthesis, and the base of the food chain (and source of energy) consists of bacteria that practice **chemosynthesis** (Chapters 1 and 9). That is, they oxidize sulfur compounds from hot vent waters and thereby derive energy for themselves and other members of marine food chains. We have more on hydrothermal vent ecosystems in Chapter 10.

Spreading and Closing Cycles

By about 2.5 billion years ago, Earth's lithosphere had much the same make up as it does today, and cycles of ocean basin formation and closing were underway. Since then, the planet probably has undergone three or more cycles of supercontinent formation and break-up (Figure 2.21). That is, during at least three long-term cycles, all the continental pieces were brought together as one huge continent and subsequently split apart into smaller continents. Associated with supercontinents are super-oceans so that when a supercontinent breaks up, one or more new ocean basins form. For example, when the supercontinent Pangaea split into Laurasia (to the north) and Gondwanaland (to the south), *Tethys*, a narrow seaway formed between the two. New ocean basins first expand and later contract as a new supercontinent forms. The entire cycle from start to finish may take 500 to 600 million years. Cycles of ocean basin spreading and closing are called **Wilson cycles** after the Canadian geologist J. Tuzo Wilson (1908-1993) who first recognized and described the stages in the life span of an ocean basin.

We know the most about ocean basin changes over the past 500 to 600 million years, the most recent cycle. During this time, marine animals formed durable shells, which as fossils can be used to date the rocks containing them fairly precisely. Dating older rock devoid of fossils requires analysis of radioactive elements. These techniques have become more accurate and now permit reconstruction of earlier Wilson cycles. Here we describe the stages in the most recent Wilson cycle.

A. Embryonic

Continental plate

Ocean

B. Juvenile

Mid-oceanic ridge

C. Mature

D. Declining

Trench

Subduction zone

E. Terminal

F. Suturing

Ocean basin opening

Ocean basin Closing

FIGURE 2.21

A simplified model of the Wilson cycle, showing the formation and closing of an ocean basin. [Modified from a drawing by Lynn S. Fichter]

A Wilson cycle consists of six stages: embryonic, juvenile, mature, declining, terminal, and suturing. The cycle begins because thick continental crust does not conduct heat as readily as thinner oceanic crust. A supercontinent that remains in one location for hundreds of millions of years acts like a blanket, retarding heat flow from Earth's interior. This causes the mantle beneath the supercontinent to warm. As the underlying mantle warms, it expands, elevating the overlying continent and stretching the continental crust. Convection currents in the mantle also contribute to this stretching and eventually the crust fractures, forming a rift valley. This is Wilson's *embryonic stage* (Figure 2.21A). As noted earlier in this chapter, a *rift valley* is an elongated topographic depression bordered by fractures (faults) in the bedrock. The African continent has been in its present location for about 200 million years and now stands about 400 m (1300 ft) higher than other continents as a consequence of the heating and expansion of the underlying mantle. Fracturing and some spreading of the crust produced the rift valleys of East Africa.

With rifting of the continental crust, the broken sides rise about a kilometer enclosing a valley that often fills with fresh water. In East Africa, long, deep lakes now occupy narrow rift valleys. Rift valleys gradually widen and eventually connect to the ocean and the freshwater lakes become narrow saline gulfs. This is happening now in the Red Sea and Gulf of California and marks the beginning of Wilson's *juvenile stage* (Figure 2.21B). With continued lateral spreading of the rift valley, the divergent plate boundary widens and additional oceanic crust is generated signaling the *mature stage* of the Wilson cycle (Figure 2.21C). Today, the Atlantic is a mature ocean with geologically passive margins.

Subduction becomes more widespread around the border of the ocean basin during the *declining stage* of the Wilson cycle (Figure 2.21D). In time, cooling and the loss of volatiles increase the density of oceanic plates. Under the influence of gravity, these plates slide down and away from the topographic high of the mid-oceanic ridge and sink into the asthenosphere at subduction zones. Today, the Pacific is the best example of a declining ocean with subduction zones forming the Pacific Ring of Fire. This is also now happening on a smaller scale in the South Atlantic (Scotia Arc near Antarctica) and in the West Indies (near Barbados). Typically an ocean basin widens for about 200 million years before subduction begins. As evidence of this, no oceanic crust has been found that is more than 200 million years old. Eventually, the basin begins to close as subduction rates (at trenches) exceed spreading rates (at mid-ocean ridges). For Earth as a whole, spreading must equal subduction—otherwise the planet would be shrinking or expanding. Over the subsequent 200 million years, the ocean basin continues to close and its sediment deposits are deformed and uplifted, creating mountain ranges on the newly assembled supercontinent at the site of the former ocean.

Following the declining stage of the Wilson cycle, the ocean basin closes through subduction as continents from opposite sides of the ocean basin bear down on one another and eventually collide. These events signal the final two stages of the Wilson cycle: the terminal and suturing stages. In the *terminal stage*, the continents are not yet touching but subduction of the intervening oceanic crust causes a narrowing of the sea separating the continents (Figure 2.21E). Volcanic eruptions, earthquakes, uplift, and mountain building accompany subduction of the oceanic crust. An example of this today is the African continent converging with the European continent producing the intervening Mediterranean Sea with nearby volcanism, earthquakes, and young rugged mountains (e.g., the Alps).

During the *suturing stage*, collision of the continents is complete and the intervening sea is gone (Figure 2.21F). The two colliding continental crusts, being less dense than the oceanic crust, do not subduct but rather override one another causing uplift and mountain building. Collision of the continents squeezes out the intervening ocean and causes subduction of oceanic crust. Today, the suturing stage is illustrated by the collision of the Indian and Eurasian plates generating the Himalayan Mountains. The Appalachian Mountains of eastern North America also formed in this way at the end of the previous Wilson cycle, about 450 million years ago.

The Pacific began as a vast super-ocean, known as *Panthalassa*, surrounding the supercontinent Pangaea. When other ocean basins such as the Atlantic started to form, the Pacific Ocean entered the declining stage of the Wilson cycle with concomitant changes in its size and shape. As an ocean basin narrows, subduction accommodates the lithospheric plates that are colliding at or along its margins. Except in a few locations, subduction zones border the Pacific basin. When the Atlantic basin begins closing by expansion of subduction along its margins, subduction in the Pacific basin will diminish or cease.

Wilson cycles also influence sea level relative to the continents over periods of hundreds of millions of years. When supercontinents dominate, continents stand high as the mantle under them warms. When spreading begins, the continental fragments move off the heated mantle and thus stand lower with respect to the sea surface. Furthermore, the newly formed ocean basin floor is relatively shallow reducing the capacity for seawater, and thus low-lying continental areas are flooded.

As the newly formed basin widens and its crust ages, cools, and deepens (under the weight of accumulating sediments), sea level falls. Sea level has apparently varied by as much as 250 m (820 ft) over the past 100 million years. During times of higher sea level, shallow seas, similar to Canada's Hudson Bay, covered large areas of continents. At such times, about 80% of Earth's surface was ocean water. During episodes of lower sea level, shorelines migrated seaward to the continental margins; the ocean then covered about 65% of Earth's surface. Note that sea level also rises and falls in response to changes in Earth's glacial ice cover plus expansion and contraction of seawater as global temperatures fluctuate.

Conclusions

In a geological sense, the present ocean floor is relatively young—the oldest oceanic crust is only about 200 million years old whereas some bedrock on the continents is billions of years old. Oceanic crust is continually generated at divergent plate boundaries (at the mid-ocean ridge system) and incorporated into the mantle as it is drawn down at convergent plate boundaries (subduction zone). Over periods of perhaps 500 million years, ocean basins have opened and closed (the Wilson cycle). In this way, plate tectonics explains the origin of the large-scale features of the deep ocean bottom (e.g., trenches, ocean ridges) and the geological processes (e.g., volcanism, earthquakes) operating mostly at plate boundaries. Furthermore, as we will see in Chapter 12, plate tectonics helps explain some long-term changes in climate.

Processes operating at the interface between the ocean and lithosphere (e.g., hydrothermal vents) affect the composition of seawater. Earth materials dissolve in seawater and influence its salinity. The salinity of seawater coupled with its temperature control its density, which in turn affects its vertical motion (thermohaline circulation). Water is a substance with unique physical and chemical properties that not only influence the salinity of seawater but also the exchange of heat energy and moisture between the ocean and atmosphere. In the next chapter, we examine the uniqueness of water and its implications for the ocean in the Earth system.

Basic Understandings

- Ocean basins and continents are unevenly distributed over Earth's surface with ocean covering about 71% of the Earth and the remaining 29% land. The Northern Hemisphere is 39.3% land and 60.7% ocean whereas the Southern Hemisphere is 19.1% land and 80.9% ocean.

- Earth's relatively thin solid crust is the part of the geosphere that interfaces with the ocean, atmosphere, cryosphere, and biosphere. Rocks composing the crust are classified as igneous, sedimentary, or metamorphic based on the general environmental conditions in which they formed. The rock cycle is the gradual transformation of one rock type to another.

- Earth's crust is composed of mostly igneous rock with some metamorphic rock locally. In most areas, sediments and sedimentary rocks of varying thickness overlie the igneous and metamorphic rock of the crust.

- Oceanic crust is chiefly basaltic (volcanic) rock that is denser and thinner than the mostly granitic rock of continental crust. The lithosphere includes the crust and the rigid upper portion of the mantle and is thicker under the land surface than under the ocean. The lithosphere floats on the underlying asthenosphere, a deformable (plastic-behaving) region of the mantle.

- The continental margin (a submerged part of a continent) consists of a relatively shallow and gently sloping continental shelf, bordered by the continental slope that extends to the deeper continental rise.

- At geologically passive continental margins where plate boundaries are absent (e.g., surrounding the Atlantic basin), sediment spreads over the ocean floor forming flat abyssal plains adjacent to the continental rise. At geologically active continental margins with convergent plate boundaries (e.g., surrounding much of the Pacific basin), the continental slope descends into deep ocean trenches.

- A turbidity current is a gravity-driven downslope flow of water heavily laden with suspended sediments. Fed by river-borne sediment, turbidity currents periodically scour submarine canyons that are cut into the continental shelf.

- The deep ocean basin has a varied topography featuring mountain ranges, trenches, and sea-mounts.
- Plate tectonics is a unifying concept that combines continental drift and sea floor spreading in describing the fragmentation and movement of Earth's lithospheric plates and the formation of ocean basins. Evidence for plate tectonics consists of cross-Atlantic similarities in continental margins, fossils, rock formations, and mountain ranges. Sea-floor spreading, a key aspect of plate tectonics, occurs at divergent plate boundaries and is confirmed by many lines of evidence including the systematic pattern of magnetic anomalies on the sea floor.
- Convection currents in the mantle are proposed as the driving force for plate movement, sea-floor spreading, and subduction.
- New oceanic crust forms at divergent plate boundaries, at the mid-ocean ridge system. This volcanic mountain range winds through the world ocean, forming one of the deep-ocean's most conspicuous features.
- Along the mid-ocean ridge a distinction is made among *fast-spreading*, *slow-spreading*, and *ultraslow-spreading* boundaries. At fast-spreading boundaries, plates move apart at 100 to 200 mm per yr. With rapid spreading, hot magma is abundant and lava flows as sheets from a central peak, giving the ridge a narrow tent-like profile (e.g., the East Pacific Rise). At slow-spreading boundaries, plates move apart at less than 55 mm per yr and the topography is broader, rougher, and features rift valleys (e.g., Mid-Atlantic Ridge). At ultraslow-spreading boundaries, plates move apart at less than 20 mm per yr and great slabs of mantle rock rise to the seafloor.
- Where two oceanic plates converge or where an oceanic plate converges with a continental plate, a subduction zone forms. In a subduction zone, the denser oceanic plate slips under the other plate and descends into the mantle. Hence, lithosphere is incorporated into the mantle in subduction zones. Subduction zones produce trenches on the deep ocean floor and are associated with shallow to deep earthquakes and violent volcanic eruptions.
- A transform plate boundary occurs where adjacent plates slide laterally past one another. They are often the site of earthquake activity but not volcanoes.
- Hot, newly formed oceanic crust is chilled by contact with cold seawater circulating through fractures on the seafloor. This hydrothermal circulation also extracts minerals and salts from rock. Minerals precipitate out of the hot waters and build spectacular vents, tens of meters high, on the mid-ocean ridges.
- The Wilson cycle, with a period of about 500 million years, describes the successive opening and closing of ocean basins through plate tectonics.

Review

1. What percentage of Earth's surface is covered by ocean water? In which hemisphere is most land located?
2. Name the five ocean basins. Which ocean basin is largest?
3. Describe the general origins of igneous, sedimentary, and metamorphic rock. Which type of rock composes most of Earth's crust?
4. Compare and contrast oceanic and continental crust. Which type of crust typically comprises the continental margin?
5. Describe the general relationship between continental shelf width and tectonic activity in the continental margin.
6. Describe the origins of most submarine canyons.
7. Define sea-floor spreading and its significance for oceanic crust.
8. Describe two types of tectonic plate interactions that form a subduction zone.
9. Describe a transform plate boundary and give an example of this type of boundary.
10. What are Wilson cycles? What is the approximate period of each cycle?

Critical Thinking

1. How does the lithosphere of the deep-ocean basins differ from the lithosphere of the continents?
2. What are some of the implications of the relatively slow pace of the geological processes involved in the rock cycle?
3. Compare and contrast the geological characteristics of the continental margins of the west coast versus east coast of North America.
4. Explain why oceanic crust becomes older with increasing distance from the mid-ocean ridge system.
5. What conditions are required for violent volcanic eruptions in the continental margins?
6. Summarize the key evidence in support of the theory of plate tectonics.
7. How does land subsidence influence sea level in coastal areas?
8. How might investigating ultraslow divergent plate boundaries benefit our understanding of Earth history?
9. How do turbidity currents help maintain submarine canyons?
10. Explain why a hydrothermal vent community may have a limited life expectancy (10 to 100 years or so).

ESSAY: Investigating the Ocean Bottom

Ocean scientists employ a variety of techniques to investigate the ocean bottom. Some are relatively simple such as devices that scoop up rock and sediment samples from the ocean floor, whereas others, such as acoustic and gravimetric instruments, are more sophisticated. Some measurements are made *in situ* (where an instrument is immersed in the medium being measured) whereas others depend on remote sensing methods.

Probably the oldest type of measurement involving the ocean bottom is determination of water depth. Classically this was done using a sounding line, a weighted rope marked off in fathoms, where 1.0 *fathom* equals 1.8 m or 6 ft. A line was thrown over the side until the weight reached the ocean bottom. Today, an *echo sounder* (earlier called a *fathometer*) is commonly used to determine water depth. With this instrument, a sound pulse is directed toward the sea floor and its travel time to the bottom and back is recorded. Knowing the speed of sound in seawater, the depth is calculated. Acoustic sounders first came into common use on U.S. Navy ships during World War II, and depth measurements led to the discovery that ocean bottom topography is highly variable.

Depth data are needed for preparation of navigation charts, but acquiring these data by acoustic sounding can be time consuming because ship speeds average only about 30 km per hr (15 knots). An alternative is *laser bathymetry*. A downward directed laser gun is mounted on the underside of an aircraft so that light pulses can be aimed at the ocean bottom while the aircraft is in flight. A computer records the time for a light pulse to reach the bottom and return. An aircraft can travel nearly ten times faster than a ship, so that close to 1000 square km (386 square mi) can be surveyed in a single day. The only limitation to this system is how far the laser light can penetrate into a given water column, limiting the technique to relatively clean and shallow waters. For depths seaward of the continental shelf, ocean scientists depend on acoustic sounding.

Sampling the ocean bottom is straightforward. If a sample of bottom material is desired, a *grab sampler* may be used (Figure 1). This mechanical device operates much as a human hand when it grasps some object. If scientists require a vertical section of the ocean bottom showing sediment layering, a weighted coring tube is lowered to within a few meters of the bottom and then allowed to fall with the weight of the system driving it into the bottom sediments. The sediment core, retrieved when the tube is brought to the surface, is a record over time of local sedimentation, and it is even possible to determine the age of the various layers. Where the ocean bottom is bare rock or covered by thick accumulations of sediment, deep-sea drilling is used to obtain bottom samples much like sediment cores.

FIGURE 1
A Young Modified Van Veen grab sampler ("Young Grab") is being lowered over the side of a ship. When it reaches the ocean bottom, the grab sampler will scoop sediment from a 0.4 square m area. The Young Grab digs down about 10 cm (4 in.) and scoops up the top layers of sediment along with the organisms living in the sediment (infauna). Most benthic infauna live in the top 5 cm (2 in.) of sediment. [NOAA Ocean Explorer]

Our understanding of the deep-sea floor and plate tectonics was greatly advanced by study of sediment and rock cores retrieved by specially outfitted research vessels. The first of these, the *Glomar Challenger*, operated from 1968 until 1983, as part of the *Deep Sea Drilling Program (DSDP)*. The *Glomar Challenger* drilled 1092 holes at 624 deep ocean sites; laid end-to-end, the recovered rock and sediment cores would have a total length of 96 km (60 mi). The success of the DSDP inspired formation of the *Ocean Drilling Program (ODP)*, an international partnership of scientists and research institutions organized to explore the evolution and structure of Earth through study of deep-ocean cores. ODP was sponsored by the National Science Foundation (NSF) and agencies in 20 other nations under the management of *JOIDES (Joint Oceanographic Institutions for Deep Earth Sampling)*.

The 143-m (469-ft) long drill ship *JOIDES* (pronounced *joy-deez*) *Resolution*, was the centerpiece of the Ocean Drilling Program (Figure 2). (It was named after the *HMS Resolution*, commanded by Captain James Cook during exploration of the Pacific Ocean more than 200 years ago.) With this ship, ODP scientists could extract sediment and rock cores in water depths as great as 8235 m (27,018 ft). Built in 1978 in Halifax, Nova Scotia, the ship originally was a conventional oil-exploration vessel. She was converted for scientific research in 1984, equipped with some of the world's finest shipboard laboratories, and went into service for ODP in January 1985. Annually the *JOIDES Resolution* embarked on six scientific expeditions, each lasting about two months. The research ship drilled in all the world's ocean basins, including north of the Arctic Circle (to 85.5 degrees N) and south of the Antarctic Circle in the Weddell Sea (to 70.8 degrees S). As of September 2003, ODP had recovered cores that end-to-end totaled more than 226 km (140 mi) in length.

FIGURE 2
The *JOIDES Resolution* is a drill ship that was the centerpiece of the Ocean Drilling Project (ODP) from 1985 to 2003, extracting sediment and rock cores from the ocean bottom around the world. It is presently performing the same service for the Integrated Ocean Drilling Program (IODP).
[Courtesy of IODP]

After a core is brought to the surface, it is labeled with its original location on the seafloor, coded to distinguish top from bottom, measured, cut into smaller sections, and sliced lengthwise. One half is used for non-destructive analysis before being stored. Scientists seeking to reconstruct a chapter in Earth's history analyze samples extracted from the other half of the core. No aspect of the core is overlooked. Paleontologists examine microfossils in the cores to determine the age of the rock or sediment. Other scientists measure physical properties such as density, strength, and ability to conduct heat. Paleomagnetists use state-of-the-art equipment to read the record of Earth's magnetic field changes, information that helps determine when and where specific rocks were formed. At the end of an expedition, cores are transported to one of four repositories where they are stored and made available for future research. Scientists are able to access these repositories much as the general public uses a library.

In October 2003, the *Integrated Ocean Drilling Program (IODP)* succeeded the ODP. Sponsored initially by the U.S. and Japan, the IODP may eventually involve as many as 20 other nations. The goal of the new drilling program is to use two deep-sea drill ships plus specialized drilling platforms rather than a single general-purpose ship and drill more and deeper holes on the ocean floor. The IODP plan called for an updated *JOIDES Resolution* and a new drill ship capable of investigating a larger portion of the ocean bottom. After about 20 years as a scientific drilling ship, the *JOIDES Resolution* temporarily ceased operations in late 2005. Subsequently, with NSF support, the ship was rebuilt and upgraded with more laboratory space, improved drilling systems, and more sophisticated instrumentation. After work was completed in late 2007, the ship joined the *Chikyu*, a new ship specifically designed for scientific research.

The *Chikyu* (meaning planet Earth in Japanese) was built by Japan and became fully operational in the autumn of 2007. The Japan Agency for Marine-Earth Science and Technology (JAMSTEC) oversees the operation and management of the *Chikyu* (Figure 3). At 210 m (690 ft) in length, the *Chikyu* is much larger than earlier drill ships, technologically more advanced, and equipped with specialized equipment that will minimize environmental hazards (e.g., petroleum blowouts). Lacking such capabilities, DSDP and ODP drilling sites were restricted to the deep-ocean floor far from shore where the chance of encountering oil or natural gas deposits is minimal. *Chikyu* can accommodate up to 10,000 m (32,800 ft) of drill strings (pipes) enabling the ship to drill up to 7000 m (23,000 ft) into the ocean floor in water as deep as 2500 m (8200 ft)—twice as deep as previous drill ships. *Chikyu's* first project will be to investigate earthquake mechanisms by boring into the Nankai Trough subduction zone offshore of Honshu, Japan—a location that was off limits to the *JOIDES Resolution* because of the potential for a petroleum blowout. Another option with IODP is the use of the specialized drilling platforms for areas where drill ships could not safely or efficiently operate, such as in the Arctic multi-year sea ice.

FIGURE 3
The launch of the Japanese drill ship Chikyu (Earth) in Kobe, Japan. [Courtesy of the US Climate Change Science Program]

In addition to deep-sea drilling, other methods are available for study of the ocean bottom. One of these techniques uses a sound source, such as an underwater explosion, coupled with a number of strategically positioned acoustic receiving devices. Knowing that sound travels at different speeds through the same medium, much can be learned about the thickness, extent, and composition of oceanic crust. When combined with gravimetric data (obtained from a gravimeter that measures the acceleration of gravity), information about local crustal mass and composition, can be inferred.

Other ways of directly investigating the ocean bottom include piloted deep-sea research submersibles (e.g., Woods Hole's *Alvin*), sensors tethered to a ship that are dropped overboard, and autonomous underwater vehicles (AUVs). We have more to say about these techniques in Chapter 13.

ESSAY: Hotspot Volcanism and the Hawaiian Islands

Most volcanic activity on Earth takes place along convergent and divergent plate boundaries and is readily explained by plate tectonics theory. However, volcanic activity also occurs on the ocean floor and continental interiors at great distances from plate boundaries. These sites of anomalously high volcanic activity are known as *hot spots*. A prominent product of *hotspot volcanism* is the Hawaiian Islands (Figure 1), a segment of a 6000-km (3700-mi) long chain of volcanoes and seamounts on the Pacific Ocean floor, thousands of kilometers from the nearest plate boundary.

In 1971, only a few years after widespread acceptance of the theory of plate tectonics, Jason Morgan of Princeton University proposed that narrow plumes of hot material originating at the mantle/core boundary and ascending within the mantle delivers copious amounts of melt to the lithosphere where it feeds volcanic eruptions. A hot spot is at the top of a

FIGURE 1
True-color Terra MODIS satellite image of the Hawaiian Islands. View is toward the north with the "Big Island" (Hawaii) to the lower right. From the youngest (the "Big Island") located over the Hawaiian hot spot, progressively older volcanic islands stretch towards the northwest. [Courtesy of NASA]

mantle plume. Morgan and other scientists assumed that plumes, rooted deep in the mantle, anchored hot spots at fixed locations. Over many millions of years, as an oceanic plate moved over a hot spot, submarine volcanic eruptions built massive accumulations of basaltic lava on the ocean floor that eventually emerged above sea level as a volcanic island. Eventually, the plate carried the island beyond its lava source (the hot spot) and volcanic activity died out. With a hot spot stationary and the plate moving, an age-progressive straight-line chain of volcanoes developed.

Today, active volcanism is confined to the "Big Island" at the southeast end of the Hawaiian Chain near 19 degrees N. The "Big Island" is composed of five overlapping volcanoes. Kilauea, the Island's youngest volcano, has been erupting continuously since the early 1980s. The rate of lava emission per unit area at this hot spot is greater than at any other place on the planet. A new, still submerged volcano called Loihi is forming on the Pacific Ocean floor southeast of Hawaii. The other Hawaiian Islands are eroded remnants of now extinct volcanoes. The oldest and most extensively eroded volcanoes, marked by coral atolls, lie at the northwestern end of the Hawaiian chain (i.e., Kauai). This southeast-to-northwest trending chain of progressively older volcanic islands and seamounts was assumed to mark the track of the Pacific plate toward the northwest at about 10 cm per yr passing over a hot spot fixed at 19 degrees N. Beyond the Hawaiian Islands is a chain of deeply submerged seamounts, the Hawaiian-Emperor Seamount Chain, trending to the northwest on the Pacific Ocean

FIGURE 2
The Hawaiian Islands and Emperor Seamount chain stretch more than 6000 km in the Pacific Ocean. [National Geophysical Data Center, NOAA]

floor (Figure 2). The 60° bend (near 170 degrees E) toward a more northerly heading was attributed to a change in direction of the Pacific plate about 47 million years ago. At the northern end of the Emperor Seamount Chain, extinct submarine volcanoes subduct into the Aleutian Trench.

Based on analysis of deep-sea rock cores, evidence is mounting that hot spots are not stationary. In fact, migration of a hot spot rather than movement of the Pacific plate over a fixed hot spot likely explains the origins of the Hawaiian-Emperor Seamount Chain. This conclusion follows from reconstruction of the latitude of volcanic islands at the time of their formation. If a hot spot were stationary, all currently extinct volcanoes and seamounts would have been active when their latitude was 19 degrees N, the same as the now-active "Big Island."

Analysis of rock magnetization enables scientists to reconstruct latitude. As noted elsewhere in this chapter, when magma or lava cools and solidifies, certain minerals (e.g., magnetite) act like tiny bar magnets and align with Earth's magnetic field. Analysis of a volcanic rock sample provides information not only on the direction of Earth's magnetic lines of force at the time of crystallization, but also their inclination, a direct measure of latitude. This technique was applied in 2001 by J.A. Tarduno of the University of Rochester and colleagues to rock samples cored from the Emperor seamounts Detroit, Nintoku, and Koko. Based on the reconstructed latitude at which the volcanic rock formed, Tarduno and colleagues concluded that from 81 to 47 million years ago, the hot spot moved southward at more than 4 cm per yr. Other scientists determined that the 61-million year old Suiko seamount had formed at 27 degrees N.

Some scientists argue that the Hawaiian-Emperor Seamount Chain was the product of the combined southward motion of the Pacific plate and southward movement of the hot spot (now under Kilauea). In addition, evidence is not convincing that the Pacific plate actually changed direction 47 million years ago. Movement of the Hawaiian hot spot relative to the Pacific plate may be a more plausible explanation for the abrupt bend in the trend of the Hawaiian-Emperor Seamount Chain.

What might explain the mobility of a hot spot? One possibility is that the base of a hot spot in the deep mantle may move. Another possibility is that a rising plume may be swayed by convection currents in the mantle. Furthermore, many scientists question whether deep mantle plumes are associated with all hot spots. In 2003, scientists at Princeton University reported on the results of a new technique to investigate Earth's mantle using seismic (earthquake) waves that penetrate Earth's interior. Similar to tomography used to examine the internal organs of humans, this technique enables scientists to search for and locate mantle plumes. They found that plumes originating near the mantle/core boundary feed some hot spots (e.g., Hawaii) but other hot spots (e.g., Iceland, Galápagos) have relatively shallow plumes (originating at depths near 660 km or 410 mi), and some hot spots (e.g., Yellowstone) have no plumes at all.

CHAPTER 3

PROPERTIES OF OCEAN WATER

Case-in-Point
Driving Question
The Water Molecule and Hydrogen Bonding
    Water as Ice, Liquid, and Vapor
    Temperature and Heat
    Changes in Phase of Water
    Specific Heat of Water
    Maritime Influence on Climate
Chemical Properties of Seawater
    Water as a Solvent
    Sea Salts
    Variations in Salinity
    Dissolved Gases
    Seawater pH
    Ocean Acidification
Physical Properties of Seawater
    Water Density and Temperature
    Pressure
    Sea Ice
    Sound Transmission
Conclusions
Basic Understandings/Review/Critical Thinking
ESSAY: Desalination
ESSAY: Sea Ice Terminology

Sea Ice Spring Melt, Tigvariak Island, Alaska. [NOAA]

Case in Point

Since antiquity, people have used sea salt to meet their nutritional needs and, prior to the age of refrigeration, to preserve food for storage and transport. Jericho, an oasis at the northern end of the Dead Sea, was founded almost 10,000 years ago as a salt trading center. The Dead Sea, located on the Israeli-Jordanian border, has long been a source of salt. The lowest spot on Earth's surface at about 400 m (1300 ft) below sea level, the Dead Sea occupies a depression in the transform-fault complex that separates the African and Indian plates (Chapter 2). Massive salt deposits formed when tectonic movements cut off the Mediterranean Sea about 6 million years ago. Some nearby mountains are almost pure salt and persist because of the arid climate.

In the Middle Ages, salted cod was an important commodity for members of the Hanseatic League, a trading group of merchants in northern Germany and the Baltic Sea coast, and later an important food source for American colonists. Salt was so highly valued that it was used as money in Tibet and in many parts of Africa. Today, salt is still used as a seasoning or preservative in meatpacking, fish curing, and food processing. It is also used in curing hides and for control of ice and snow on roads and walkways in winter. In the chemical industry, salt is an ingredient in the manufacture of baking soda, hydrochloric acid, and chlorine and a reagent in metallurgical processes. Salt is also used in water softeners to remove calcium and magnesium compounds.

Most commercial salt used to be evaporated from seawater or natural brines in hot dry climates using the sun. Saltwater is let into shallow ponds where suspended materials such as sand gravitationally settle to the bottom. Water

then flows on to crystallizing pans where water evaporates and salt precipitates. Many different salts precipitate from saltwater in addition to common household table salt (sodium chloride), including, for example, calcium carbonate, calcium sulfate, and magnesium sulfate. As water evaporates, different salts begin to precipitate at different times because each salt has a different solubility in water. Salt is also mined from deposits of rock salt. In some cases, solution mining is used whereby water is pumped into underground salt beds to create brine that is recovered and then evaporated.

Driving Question:
How do the properties of water and dissolved salts affect the physical and chemical properties of seawater?

Although water is a very common component of the Earth system, it has some very uncommon properties compared to other substances of similar molecular size or chemical composition. Water's unusually high freezing and boiling temperatures, coupled with the temperature range at Earth's surface, mean that water exists naturally in the Earth system in all three phases, as solid (ice), liquid, and gas (water vapor). In fact, the three phases of water can coexist in contact with each other such as at the edge of pack ice. Water frequently changes phase and during these transitions, unusually large amounts of heat energy are either absorbed from or released to the environment with no change in the temperature of the water. Furthermore, large quantities of heat are required to change the temperature of water. Water dissolves a wide variety of solids, liquids, and gases and is aptly described as the *universal solvent*. Salinity and temperature affect the density of ocean water, which in turn influences the circulation of the ocean.

In this chapter we examine water's unique properties, the fundamental reasons for those properties, and some of the implications for the functioning of the ocean in the Earth system. We begin by describing the structure of the water molecule and explaining how this structure is the principal reason for water's unique physical and chemical properties. We then explore the chemical properties of seawater, emphasizing the types, sources, and cycling of dissolved salts and gases. The closing discussion of the physical properties of seawater covers the effect of temperature and salinity on water density, pressure exerted by seawater, the formation of sea ice, and the use of sound transmission in the ocean to determine water depth and temperature.

The Water Molecule and Hydrogen Bonding

Compared to other naturally occurring substances, water's thermal properties are unique. For example, based on water's molecular weight as well as the freezing and boiling temperatures of chemically related substances, fresh water should freeze at about –90 °C (–130 °F) and boil at about –70 °C (–94 °F). Actually, fresh water's freezing point is 0 °C (32 °F) and its boiling point is 100 °C (212 °F) at average sea level air pressure. Water's unusual properties arise from the physical structure of the water molecule (H_2O) and the bonding that occurs between water molecules. Without this intermolecular force of attraction, known as **hydrogen bonding**, water would exist only as a gas within the range of surface temperature and pressure on Earth. Furthermore, the planet would have no water cycle, no ocean, no ice caps, and probably no life as we know it.

A water molecule consists of two hydrogen (H) atoms bonded to an oxygen (O) atom (Figure 3.1). Within the water molecule, bonding between hydrogen and oxygen atoms involves sharing of electrons, one from

FIGURE 3.1
The water molecule consists of two hydrogen atoms and one oxygen atom.

each hydrogen atom and two from the oxygen atom. (An *electron* is a negatively charged subatomic particle.) In this bonding, the electrons spend more time near the oxygen so that the oxygen acquires a small negative charge and the hydrogen is left with a small positive charge. This *covalent bonding* is relatively strong so that the water molecule resists dissociation into its constituent hydrogen and oxygen atoms. The 105-degree angle formed by the arrangement of the hydrogen-oxygen-hydrogen atoms produces a charge separation in the water molecule. Molecules having a separation of positive and negative charges are described as *polar*.

Opposite electrical charges attract so that, like tiny magnets, neighboring water molecules link together. The positively charged (hydrogen) pole of one water molecule attracts the negatively charged (oxygen) pole of another water molecule; this attractive force constitutes hydrogen bonding. Each water molecule can form as many as four hydrogen bonds with surrounding water molecules. A hydrogen bond has about 5% to 10% of the strength of a covalent bond between hydrogen and oxygen atoms in individual water molecules. Nonetheless, hydrogen bonding is sufficiently strong to significantly influence the physical and chemical properties of water. Hydrogen bonding inhibits changes in water's internal energy so that it absorbs or releases unusually great quantities of heat energy when changing phase. Because of hydrogen bonding, greater additions or losses of heat are required to change water temperature as compared to other chemically related substances.

WATER AS ICE, LIQUID, AND VAPOR

Matter exists in three basic phases: solid, liquid, and gas. Transformations from one phase to another always involve a large amount of energy to alter the molecular configuration. Water is one of the very few substances that can occur naturally in all three phases within the temperature and pressure ranges found at and near Earth's surface. In this section, we examine how water's molecular structure influences its properties in each phase.

Like all crystalline solids, ice has a regular internal three-dimensional framework consisting of a repeated pattern of molecules. A physical model of the *crystal lattice* of ice is shown in Figure 3.2. Each water molecule is bound tightly to its neighbors but intermolecular bonds are elastic (acting like springs) so that molecules vibrate about fixed locations in the lattice. For this reason, an ice cube retains its shape as long as temperatures are subfreezing. Hydrogen bonding is responsible for the ordered arrangement of water molecules in the crystal lattice and

FIGURE 3.2
A physical model of the crystal lattice of ice. Each water molecule is bound tightly to its neighbors but intermolecular bonds are elastic so that molecules vibrate about fixed locations in the lattice. For this reason, an ice cube retains its shape as long as temperatures remain subfreezing. The ordered arrangement of water molecules in the crystal lattice is responsible for the hexagonal structure of ice crystals. Because the internal framework of ice is an open network of water molecules, the molecules in ice crystals are not as closely packed as a similar number of molecules in liquid water so that ice is less dense than liquid water.

the hexagonal (six-sided) structure of ice crystals. (Many of us are familiar with the six-sided symmetry of snow flakes.) Because ice's internal framework is an open network of water molecules, the molecules in ice crystals are not as closely packed as a similar number of molecules in liquid water. At 0 °C (32 °F), ice has a density of about 0.92 g per cubic cm whereas pure liquid water at the same temperature has a density of nearly 1.0 g per cubic cm. This density difference explains why ice floats on the surface of liquid water. Most common solids would sink if placed in their liquid phase.

Despite the openness of the ice lattice, sea ice (formed when seawater freezes) contains less salt than does seawater. Salt ions are too large to fit into the empty spaces within the crystal lattice of ice and cannot substitute for water molecules. Hence, most impurities (salts and gases) are excluded from ice that forms when seawater freezes.

When ice melts, it becomes liquid water. After observing ice crystals disappearing during melting, we might expect that all hydrogen bonds between water molecules break during the transition from ice to liquid water. This is not the case. Instead, many water molecules remain linked by hydrogen bonding as transient clusters of molecules surrounded by non-bonded (free) water molecules (Figure 3.3). Although molecular clusters persist into the liquid

FIGURE 3.3
When water changes phase from ice to liquid, many water molecules remain linked by hydrogen bonds as transient clusters of molecules surrounded by non-bonded water molecules.

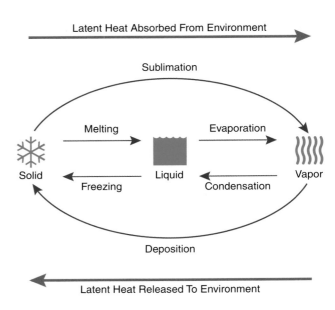

FIGURE 3.4
When water changes phase, heat energy is either absorbed from the environment (melting, evaporation, sublimation) or released to the environment (freezing, condensation, deposition).

phase, water molecules exhibit much greater activity in the liquid than solid phase. In the liquid phase, water molecules undergo vibrational, rotational, and translational (straight-line) motions. This greater freedom of movement explains why liquid water takes the shape of its container.

When liquid water changes to vapor, essentially all hydrogen bonds are broken. Individual molecules move about with even greater freedom than in the liquid phase, diffusing rapidly to fill the entire volume of its container. Gas molecules exhibit vibrational, rotational, and translational motion and exert a force as they bombard a solid or liquid surface. Force per unit area is defined as *pressure*. Heating a closed rigid container of gas accelerates the activity of gas molecules so that they collide more frequently with the inside surfaces of the walls of the container and exert more pressure. Hence, if the volume is held constant, the pressure exerted by a gas increases as the temperature rises. The situation is more complicated for air (a mixture of gases) because the atmosphere is only bounded below (by continents and ocean) and a unit mass of air is free to change volume. When heated, air in the open atmosphere expands and its density and pressure decrease.

Water readily changes phase, contributing to the dynamic nature of the Earth system. In changing phase from ice to liquid to vapor, the energy state (i.e., molecular activity) of water increases. Hence, when water changes phase heat is either absorbed from the environment or released to the environment (Figure 3.4). Melting, evaporation, and sublimation are phase changes that absorb heat. Phase changes that release heat to the surroundings are freezing, condensation, and deposition. Before examining these phase changes of water in detail, we need to review the distinction between temperature and heat.

TEMPERATURE AND HEAT

From everyday experience, we know that temperature and heat are closely related. Heating a pan of soup on the stove raises the temperature of the soup whereas dropping an ice cube into a warm beverage lowers the temperature of the beverage. Although sometimes used interchangeably, temperature and heat are distinctly different concepts.

All matter is composed of atoms or molecules that are in continual vibrational, rotational, and/or translational motion. The energy represented by this motion is referred to as *kinetic molecular energy* or just *kinetic energy*, the energy of motion. In any substance, atoms or molecules actually exhibit a range of kinetic energies. **Temperature** is directly proportional to the average kinetic energy of atoms or molecules composing a substance. At the same temperature, the average kinetic molecular energy of water is the same regardless of the volume of water.

Internal energy encompasses all the energy in a substance, that is, the kinetic energy of atoms and molecules plus the potential energy arising from forces between atoms or molecules. If two objects have different temperatures (different average kinetic molecular energies) and are brought into contact, energy will be transferred between objects; we call this energy in transit, **heat**. Heat transferred from an object reduces the internal energy of that object whereas heat absorbed by an object increases its internal energy. Heat transferred to or from water brings about a change in temperature or a change in phase. An addition or loss of heat can also do work by bringing about a change in volume of a substance. For example, ice expands when heated and contracts when cooled.

Differences in temperature rather than differences in internal energy govern the direction of heat transfer. Heat energy is always transferred from a warmer object to a colder object. Heat is not necessarily transferred from an object having greater internal energy to an object with less internal energy. Consider, for example, a hot marble (at 40 °C) that is dropped into 5 liters of cold water (at 4 °C). The water has much more internal energy than the marble; nonetheless, heat is transferred from the warmer marble to the cooler water.

The following illustration makes clearer the distinction between temperature and heat. A cup of water at 60 °C (140 °F) is much hotter than bathtub water at 30 °C (86 °F); that is, the average kinetic molecular energy of water molecules is greater at 60 °C than at 30 °C. Although lower in temperature, the greater volume of water in the bathtub means that it contains more total kinetic molecular energy than does the cup of water. If in both cases the water is warmer than its environment, heat is transferred from water to its surroundings. However, much more heat energy must be removed from the bathtub water than from the cup of water for both to cool to the same temperature.

Through the years, scientists have devised various scales that express the temperature of an object by a number representing the degree of warmth. Temperature scales were originally derived in the eighteenth century using water. Pure water's fixed points of an ice-water mixture and its boiling point at sea level air pressure, are unique. In this book we use the Celsius temperature scale primarily with the Fahrenheit equivalent in parentheses. The Celsius scale, devised by the Swedish astronomer Anders Celsius in 1742, has the numerical convenience of a 100-degree increment between the freezing point

TABLE 3.1 Temperature Conversion Formulas
F = 9/5 C +32
C = 5/9 (F −32)

(0 °C) and boiling point (100 °C) of fresh water at average sea level air pressure. The United States is one of only a few nations still using the Fahrenheit temperature scale, introduced by the German physicist Gabriel Daniel Fahrenheit in 1714. The Fahrenheit temperature scale features a 180-degree increment between the freezing point (32 °F) and boiling point (212 °F) of fresh water at average sea level air pressure. Formulas for converting between the Celsius and Fahrenheit temperature scales are presented in Table 3.1.

A convenient unit of heat energy is the *calorie*, defined as the amount of heat needed to raise the temperature of one gram of water by one Celsius degree (technically, from 14.5 °C to 15.5 °C). (The Calorie used to measure the energy content of food is actually 1000 heat calories or 1 kilocalorie.) Although the preferred unit of energy in any form, including heat, is the *joule (J)*, we generally use the calorie in this book because of its numerical convenience. Furthermore, thermal characteristics of water were used to define the calorie. For conversion purposes, one calorie equals 4.1868 J and one joule equals 0.239 calorie.

CHANGES IN PHASE OF WATER

A mixture of fresh water and ice has an equilibrium temperature of 0 °C (32 °F). Adding heat to the mixture causes ice to melt, whereas removing heat causes water to freeze. For that reason, 0 °C is called the freezing point of fresh water. Substances dissolved in water suppress the equilibrium temperature of a mixture of ice and water to temperatures below the freezing point of fresh water. The temperature at which seawater begins freezing varies with *salinity*, a measure of the mass (grams) of salts dissolved in a kilogram of seawater. We have more on the effect of salinity on the freezing point of seawater later in this chapter.

When water freezes, **latent heat** is released to the environment and for ice to melt an equivalent amount of latent heat is absorbed from the environment. The word *latent* means "hidden" and refers to the fact that this heat energy is used only to change the phase of water and not the temperature of the water. If heat is added to a mixture of ice and water at 0 °C (32 °F), the temperature of the ice-water mixture remains constant until all the ice melts.

All available heat is used to bring about the phase change by breaking some of the hydrogen bonds that maintain water in the solid (crystalline) phase. Whether freezing or melting is taking place, the latent heat involved is commonly called the **latent heat of fusion**.

At the interface between liquid water and air (e.g., the sea surface), water molecules continually change phase: some crossing the interface from water to air and others from air to water. If more water molecules enter the atmosphere as vapor than return as liquid, a net loss occurs in liquid water mass. This process is known as **evaporation**. Evaporation explains the disappearance of puddles following a rain shower. On the other hand, if more water molecules return to the water surface as a liquid than escape as vapor, net gain of liquid water mass results. This process is called **condensation**. Invisible water vapor condenses on the cold surface of an aluminum beverage can (as tiny visible droplets) on a humid summer day. Heat absorbed from the environment during evaporation and heat released to the environment during condensation are known as the **latent heat of vaporization** and the **latent heat of condensation** respectively.

All of us have experienced **evaporative cooling**. We are chilled upon stepping out of a shower or swimming pool. Water droplets evaporating from the skin absorb heat, lowering the skin's temperature. On a global scale, evaporative cooling is the most important process whereby heat is transferred from the ocean to the atmosphere (Chapter 5). When water evaporates at Earth's surface, water vapor moves into the atmosphere where it may subsequently condense into clouds. Heat absorbed as water evaporates at the surface is later released to the atmosphere during condensation. This latent heat transfer mechanism is also important in powering storms, especially thunderstorms and tropical cyclones (e.g., hurricanes).

Water's latent heat of fusion is 80 calories per g at 0 °C. Considerably greater amounts of heat are required for water to vaporize because essentially all hydrogen bonds are broken during the phase change. (Recall that not all bonds are broken as ice melts; that is, clusters of bonded water molecules persist into the liquid phase.) In fact, the magnitude of water's latent heat of vaporization is about seven times that of its latent heat of fusion and the highest of all common substances. The latent heat of vaporization varies with temperature from 597 calories per g at 0 °C (32 °F) to 540 calories per g at 100 °C (212 °F). More energy is needed to break the tighter and more numerous hydrogen bonds at lower temperatures.

At the interface between ice and air (e.g., the surface of a snow cover), water molecules are also continually changing phase: directly from ice to vapor and from vapor to ice. If more water molecules enter the atmosphere as vapor than become ice, a net loss of ice mass occurs. **Sublimation** is the process whereby ice or snow becomes vapor without first becoming a liquid. Sublimation explains the gradual disappearance of a snow cover even while the air temperature remains well below freezing. On the other hand, if more atmospheric water molecules become ice than move from ice to vapor, a net gain of ice mass results. **Deposition** is the process whereby water vapor becomes ice without first becoming a liquid. During a cold winter night, the formation of frost on automobile windows is an example of deposition.

Heat is absorbed from the environment during sublimation and heat is released to the environment during deposition. Latent heat involved in sublimation or deposition must equal the total amount of heat absorbed or released during the combined solid-liquid plus liquid-vapor phase changes. Sublimation requires the latent heats of fusion plus vaporization, known as the **latent heat of sublimation**. Deposition releases to the environment an equivalent amount of latent heat, that is, the **latent heat of deposition**. The magnitudes of the latent heats of sublimation and deposition are remarkably uniform, varying only from 677 calories per g at 0 °C to 678 calories per g at –30 °C.

SPECIFIC HEAT OF WATER

The temperature change associated with an input (or output) of a specified quantity of heat varies from one substance to another. The amount of heat that is needed to raise the temperature of 1 gram of a substance by 1 Celsius degree is defined as the **specific heat** of that substance. Joseph Black (1728-1799), a Scottish chemist, first proposed the concept of specific heat in 1760. The specific heat of all substances is measured relative to that of liquid water, which is defined as 1 calorie per g per Celsius degree (at 15 °C). The specific heat of ice is about 0.5 calorie per g per Celsius degree (near 0 °C). Specific heats of other familiar substances are listed in Table 3.2. The variation in specific heat from one substance to another implies that different materials have different capacities for storing internal energy.

Suppose that the same quantity of heat energy is supplied to two different substances having different specific heats. The substance with the higher specific heat undergoes a smaller rise in temperature (warms less) than the substance having the lower specific heat.

TABLE 3.2
Specific Heatᵃ of Some Familiar Substances

Water	1.000
Wet mud	0.600
Ice (at 0 °C)	0.478
Wood	0.420
Aluminum	0.214
Brick	0.200
Granite	0.192
Sand	0.188
Dry airᵇ	0.171
Copper	0.093
Silver	0.056
Gold	0.031

ᵃCalories per gram per Celsius degree
ᵇAt constant volume

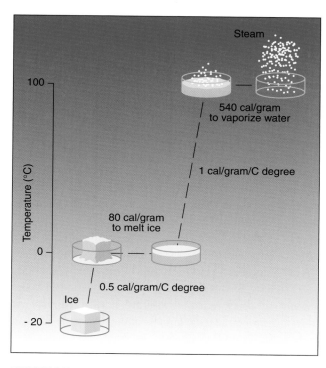

FIGURE 3.5
Heating a 1-gram ice cube causes a rise in temperature plus phase changes, initially to liquid and then to vapor.

Because of hydrogen bonding, water has an unusually high specific heat, in fact the highest specific heat of any naturally occurring liquid or solid. From Table 3.2, water's specific heat is about 5 times that of dry sand. Whereas one calorie of heat will raise the temperature of one gram of water by 1 Celsius degree, the same quantity of heat will raise the temperature of one gram of dry sand by slightly more than 5 Celsius degrees. This contrast in specific heat helps explain why at the beach in summer the sand feels considerably hotter to bare feet than does the water. This also largely explains why wet sand feels cooler than dry sand.

A simple experiment conducted at sea level summarizes water's unusually high latent heats and specific heat (Figure 3.5). A one-gram ice cube initially at –20 °C (–4 °F) is heated to 0 °C (32 °F). Every one Celsius-degree (1.8 Fahrenheit-degree) rise in ice cube temperature requires an addition of 0.5 calorie of heat energy (the *specific heat* of ice). A total of 10 calories of heat (20 C° × 0.5 cal per C°) is required to warm the one-gram ice cube to 0 °C (32 °F). The temperature then remains constant while 80 calories of heat (*latent heat of fusion*) are added to melt the one-gram ice cube. Liquid water is then heated to 100 °C (212 °F). Every one-Celsius degree rise in temperature of the one gram of liquid water requires an addition of one calorie of heat energy (*specific heat* of water). If none of the water evaporates, a total of 100 calories of heat (100 C° × 1 calorie per C°) are required to warm the 1 gram of liquid water to 100 °C. At 100 °C, the water vaporizes requiring an input of 540 calories of heat (*latent heat of vaporization*).

MARITIME INFLUENCE ON CLIMATE

Water's exceptional capacity to store heat has important implications for weather and climate. A large body of water (such as the ocean or Great Lakes) can significantly influence the climate of downwind localities. The most persistent influence is on air temperature. Compared to an adjacent landmass, a body of water does not warm as much during the day (or in summer) and does not cool as much at night (or in winter). In other words, a large body of water exhibits a greater resistance to temperature change, called **thermal inertia**, than does a landmass. Whereas the higher specific heat of water versus land is the major reason for the contrast in thermal inertia, differences in heat transport also contribute. Sunlight penetrates water to some depth and is absorbed (converted to heat) through a significant volume of water. But sunlight cannot penetrate the opaque land surface and is therefore absorbed only at the surface. Furthermore, ocean and lake-waters circulate and transport heat through great volumes of water, whereas heat is conducted only very slowly into the soil. The input (or output) of equal amounts of heat energy causes a land surface to warm (or cool) more than the equivalent surface area of a body of water.

Air temperature is regulated to a considerable extent by the temperature of the surface over which air resides or travels. Air over a large body of water tends to take on similar temperature characteristics as the surface water. Consequently, places immediately downwind of the ocean experience much less contrast between average winter and summer temperatures. Such locales have a **maritime climate**. Places at the same latitude but well inland experience a much greater temperature contrast between winter and summer. Such locales have a **continental climate**. However, in winter the climatic influence of ice-covered bodies of water (e.g., the Bering and Greenland Seas) is more like a landmass than an ocean.

Consider an example of the contrast in maritime versus continental climates. The latitude of San Francisco, CA (37.8 degrees N) is almost the same as that of St. Louis, MO (38.8 degrees N) so that the seasonal variation in the amount of solar radiation striking Earth's atmosphere (due to astronomical factors) is about the same at both places. St. Louis is situated far from the moderating influence of the ocean and its climate is continental. St. Louis' average summer (June, July, August) temperature is 25.6 °C (78.0 °F) and its average winter (December, January, February) temperature is 0.6 °C (33.0 °F), giving an average summer-to-winter seasonal temperature contrast of 25 Celsius degrees (45 Fahrenheit degrees). San Francisco, on the other hand, is located on the West Coast, immediately downwind of the Pacific Ocean; its climate is maritime. The average summer temperature at San Francisco is 17 °C (62.6 °F) and the average winter temperature is 10.2 °C (50.4 °F), giving an average seasonal temperature contrast of only 6.8 Celsius degrees (12.2 Fahrenheit degrees).

The moderating influence of the ocean is also evident in the contrast in climate between Western Europe and Eastern North America. At middle latitudes, prevailing winds blow from west to east so that the maritime influence of the North Atlantic Ocean is much more apparent in Western Europe than Eastern North America. In the same latitude belt, winters are considerably milder in Western Europe than in Eastern North America. Consider, for example, the contrast in average January temperatures for Montreal, Quebec (45.5 degrees N) versus London, England (51.5 degrees N). In January, the average daily high temperature is –6.1 °C (21 °F) at Montreal and 6.7 °C (44 °F) in London. The January average daily low temperature is –14.4 °C (6 °F) at Montreal and 1.7 °C (35 °F) in London. Although London is considerably farther north than Montreal, its January temperatures are significantly milder.

Chemical Properties of Seawater

Pure water is unknown in the Earth system; that is, water free of all dissolved and suspended material does not occur naturally. This is because water is an excellent solvent for a wide range of materials—in fact, that is why water is sometimes referred to as the *universal solvent*. Water dissolves solids, liquids, and gases to varying extents. The ocean, by far the largest reservoir of water in the Earth system, contains so much salt in solution that it cannot be used for most domestic, agricultural or industrial purposes. In this chapter's first Essay, we describe desalination techniques that are designed to remove salts from seawater and augment the supply of fresh water. In this section, we consider water as a solvent and then describe the types and sources of dissolved salts and gases in seawater.

WATER AS A SOLVENT

The polar nature of the water molecule favors the solution (i.e., dissolving) of both ionic and non-ionic substances. Many inorganic materials (primarily salts) are bonded ionically, whereas many organic chemicals have non-ionic bonds. River water, groundwater, and ocean water dissolve some of the rock or sediment (both organic and inorganic) that water contacts and some Earth materials dissolve in water more readily than other Earth materials. In Chapter 4, we consider the types and sources of sediments that dissolve or are suspended in ocean water.

Consider what happens when a pinch of common household table salt is added to water. Table salt is sodium chloride (NaCl), the mineral known as *halite*. In salt's cubic crystalline form, ionic bonds hold the positively charged sodium ions (Na^{+1}) and the negatively charged chloride (Cl^{-1}) ions together (Figure 3.6A). (An *ion* is an electrically charged atom.) Once salt enters the water, however, the hydrogen-bonded complexes of water molecules greatly reduce the force of attraction between oppositely charged sodium and chloride ions. That is, the strength of ionic bonds between sodium and chloride diminishes so that the compound readily dissociates into sodium ions and chloride ions (Figure 3.6B). Sodium ions are attracted to the negatively charged pole of the water molecule while chloride ions are attracted to the positively charged pole of the water molecule. In this way, salt dissolves in water.

SEA SALTS

Seawater is a salt solution of nearly uniform composition; only the relative amount of water in the solution varies. **Salinity** is a measure of the amount of salt dis-

A

B

Water molecules

Hydrated
chlorine ion

Hydrated
sodium ion

FIGURE 3.6
Common household table salt, sodium chloride (NaCl), dissolves
in water. (A) In its cubic crystalline form, ionic bonds hold together
the positively charged sodium ions (Na^+) and the negatively
charged chloride (Cl^-) ions. (B) Once salt enters the water,
however, hydrogen-bonded complexes of water molecules greatly
reduce the force of attraction between oppositely charged sodium
and chloride ions. The compound readily dissociates into sodium
and chloride ions with the sodium ions attracted to the negatively
charged pole of the water molecule and chloride ions attracted to
the positively charged pole of the water molecule.

and locations in the ocean during the worldwide voyage of
HMS Challenger (from December 1872 to May 1876). He
found that although the total amount of dissolved solids
varied among water samples, the ratio of the concentrations
of the major constituents of seawater was the same in all
samples. That is, the major constituents of seawater occur
in the same relative concentrations throughout the ocean,
a characteristic of seawater described as the **principle of
constant proportions**.

The concentrations of the major dissolved
constituents of ocean water, such as chloride (Cl^{-1}) and
sodium (Na^{+1}) ions, are *conservative properties* of
seawater; that is, these ions occur in constant proportions
and change concentration very slowly by mixing or
diffusion. They have no sources or sinks within the ocean.
Seawater constituents that participate in biogeochemical
or seasonal cycles have variable concentrations and are
described as *non-conservative properties*. Recall from
Chapter 1 that the ocean is a reservoir in all biogeochemical
cycles operating in the Earth system. Examples of non-
conservative properties of seawater are concentrations of
silica and calcium compounds, nitrates, phosphates, and
aluminum.

The principle of constant proportions implies
that measurement of the concentration of one of the major
conservative constituents of seawater is all that is needed
to determine the concentrations of any other conservative
constituent (as well as the sum of all other conservative
constituents). This principle made it possible for ocean
scientists to define and measure salinity. Prior to World
War II, salinity was defined as the total amount of solid
materials in grams dissolved in one kilogram of seawater.
The standard method for measuring salinity was chemical
titration to determine the concentration of the chloride
ion (Cl^{-1}), which was then substituted into a formula to
calculate salinity. Salinity was expressed as grams of
dissolved material per kilogram of seawater or parts per
thousand (ppt). The accuracy of this method was about
± 0.02 ppt.

After World War II, scientists discovered that
salinity could be determined from measurements of
the electrical conductivity of seawater with ten times
the accuracy of the old titration method. In 1978 the
international oceanographic community accepted a new
definition of salinity based on conductivity measurements;
that is, the salinity of a water sample is defined as the
ratio of the conductivity of the sample to the conductivity
of *standard seawater*. Samples of standard seawater,
prepared by Ocean Scientific International in southern
England, are supplied to laboratories around the world

solved in seawater. On average, seawater is 96.5% water
and 3.5% dissolved salts. If all ocean water evaporated
and the precipitated salts were spread evenly over the
surface of the Earth, the salts would form a layer about
45.5 m (150 ft) thick—about the height of a fifteen-story
building.

In the 19th century, chemists began examining the
composition of seawater in some detail, and one of them,
William Dittmar, verified an important observation made
by earlier scientists. In 1884, Dittmar began analyzing the
constituents of 77 water samples obtained at various depths

for use in calibrating salinity-measuring instruments. As a ratio, salinity has no units and may be written as a pure number, but for convenience some ocean scientists prefer to express salinity in *practical salinity units (psu)*. In this book, we present salinity values as a number without units. The conductivity-based definition of salinity was designed to retain the validity of measurements made the old way; that is, a salinity of 35 is essentially the same as 35.0 parts per thousand, or 3.5%. A seawater sample having a salinity of 34.82 contains about 34.82 grams of dissolved materials per kilogram.

Although more than 70 chemical elements are dissolved in seawater, six make up more than 99% of all sea salts: chloride (Cl^{-1}), sodium (Na^{+1}), sulfate (SO_4^{-2}), magnesium (Mg^{+2}), calcium (Ca^{+2}), and potassium (K^{+1}) (Figure 3.7). Common table salt (NaCl) alone accounts for nearly 86% of the total. Numerous trace components include aluminum, chromium, gold, lead, nickel, and zinc.

What is the origin of the salts dissolved in seawater? The principal source is weathering and erosion of rock and sediment on land and transport by rivers and streams to the ocean (Chapter 4). As the largest reservoir in the global water cycle, the ocean receives most of its water from rivers. Although seawater is considerably more saline than river water, we might expect the ratios of the different chemical constituents to be essentially the same in river and ocean waters. But this is not the case (Table 3.3).

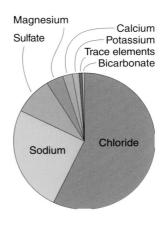

FIGURE 3.7
Although more than 70 different ions are dissolved in seawater, six make up more than 99% of all sea salts: chloride (Cl^{-1}), sodium (Na^{+2}), sulfate (SO_4^{-2}), magnesium (Mg^{+2}), calcium (Ca^{+2}), and potassium (K^{+1}).

Whereas sodium and chloride account for 86% of solids dissolved in seawater, they typically constitute less than 16% of dissolved solids in river water. Calcium (Ca^{+2}) and bicarbonate (HCO_3^{-1}) ions are minor ingredients of seawater (less than 2% of dissolved solids) but major components of river water (almost 50% of dissolved solids). On average, silica (SiO_2) accounts for about 14.5% of the dissolved components of river water but is a minor component of seawater.

TABLE 3.3
Comparison of Composition of Ocean Water with River Water[a]

	Percentage of Total Salt Content	
Chemical Constituent	*Ocean Water*	*River Water*
Silica (SiO_2)	-	14.51
Iron (Fe)	-	0.74
Calcium (Ca)	1.19	16.62
Magnesium (Mg)	3.72	4.54
Sodium (Na)	30.53	6.98
Potassium (K)	1.11	2.55
Bicarbonate (HCO_3)	0.42	31.90
Sulfate (SO_4)	7.67	12.41
Chloride (Cl)	55.16	8.64
Nitrate (NO_3)	-	1.11
Bromide (Br)	0.20	-
Total	100.00	100.00

[a]Source: U.S. Geological Survey

What explains the difference in the chemical makeup of dissolved solids in river water versus seawater? For one, marine organisms extract calcium and silica from seawater to build their shells and skeletons. Also some forms of marine life concentrate, secrete, or excrete certain chemical elements. Differences in solubility and rates of physical-chemical reactions among ions also play a role by limiting the concentration of certain substances in seawater (e.g., calcium) or causing some chemicals to precipitate from solution (e.g., manganese). Furthermore, there are other sources of salts dissolved in seawater besides rivers.

Hydrothermal vents and chemical reactions between seawater and recently formed oceanic crust contribute to the salinity of ocean water (Chapter 2). The entire volume of the world ocean cycles through fractures in new oceanic crust about every 10 million years. Suspended particles settle out of or are washed from the atmosphere by rain or snow. For example, gases emitted during volcanic eruptions dissolve in rainwater and enter the ocean contributing chloride and sulfate ions.

The proportionality of the principal sea salts has remained nearly constant for about the past 1.5 billion years. This is evident from the composition of salt strata (sedimentary rock) formed from the evaporation of seawater in the geologic past, which has changed little over that period of time. This implies that the rate of addition of new salts to the ocean balances the rate of removal. Processes that remove salt ions from the ocean include sea spray that is blown ashore and isolation of arms of the sea from the ocean followed by evaporation to produce salt deposits. For example, about 6 million years ago, northward movement of the African tectonic plate cut off the Mediterranean Sea from the Atlantic Ocean at Gibraltar. In roughly 1000 years, the Mediterranean almost completely dried up precipitating thick layers of salt in the process.

Other processes that remove salt ions from seawater are the following: Certain ions chemically react with one another to form insoluble precipitates and some ions adsorb onto suspended sediments. In both cases, ions settle to the seafloor and mix with other sediments. Compounds used by marine organisms to build shells or skeletons, such as calcium and silica, are removed from seawater and upon death of the organism cycle to the ocean floor as shells, bones, or teeth (Chapter 4). Also, chemical reactions between seawater and newly formed oceanic crust remove some constituents of seawater such as magnesium ions (Mg^{+2}). Residence times of salts in seawater range from hundreds of years (e.g., aluminum, iron) to millions of years (e.g., sodium, potassium).

VARIATIONS IN SALINITY

Processes operating at the atmosphere/ocean interface add or remove water molecules from seawater and largely explain spatial variations in sea-surface salinity. Most dissolved substances are left behind when seawater evaporates or freezes, increasing the surface salinity locally. On the other hand, precipitation, runoff from rivers, and melting ice add fresh water and decrease the local surface salinity. On an average annual basis, freezing of water and melting of ice have a negligible net effect on sea-surface salinity because the increase in salinity produced by ice formation in winter is offset by the decrease in salinity produced by melting ice during summer. Where large rivers enter the ocean, salinity is reduced as fresh water and seawater mix; salinity is also reduced where rainfall is heavy. Runoff is only important in coastal regions, so evaporation and precipitation are the principal processes governing surface salinity over most of the ocean.

Seawater salinity tends to be more variable in coastal areas than the open ocean. The salinity of surface waters of the open ocean averages about 35 and rarely falls below 33 or rises above 38. The surface salinity of the open ocean peaks near the center of each ocean basin, that is, in the subtropics (between 20 and 30 degrees N and between 15 and 25 degrees S) where the annual evaporation rate exceeds precipitation (Figure 3.8). Average sea-surface salinity is generally lowest near the equator and in polar areas where annual precipitation is greater than the rate of evaporation. Salinity peaks at 40 in the Red Sea and Persian Gulf because of high rates of evaporation brought on by high air temperatures. On the other hand, the discharge of freshwater rivers and streams is responsible for the relatively low salinities of the Baltic Sea (5 to 15), Black Sea (less than 20), and Puget Sound, WA (21 to 27).

DISSOLVED GASES

We are well aware from personal experience that solids such as salt and sugar dissolve in water. What may be less obvious is that gases also dissolve in water. For example, carbon dioxide (CO_2) dissolves under pressure in a carbonated beverage. If you open a can of cola, tiny CO_2 bubbles escape, giving the drink its fizz. Dissolved gases are also present in ocean water; these include carbon dioxide, nitrogen (N_2), and oxygen (O_2). (Note that dissolved oxygen is not the O in the H_2O.)

Gases are exchanged between the atmosphere and ocean at the ocean surface. The saturation (maximum) concentration of a gas in water depends primarily on temperature in freshwater bodies such as lakes and rivers

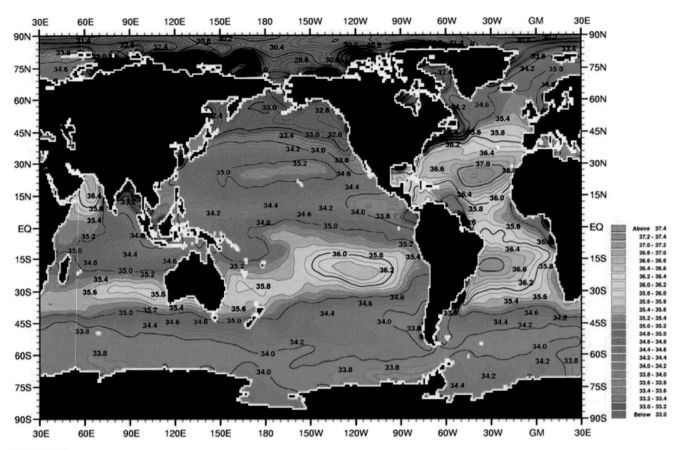

FIGURE 3.8
Global pattern of average annual sea-surface salinity shows the highest values in the subtropics of the Northern and Southern Hemispheres. Salinity values are in parts per thousand. [NOAA, National Oceanographic Data Center]

and a combination of temperature and salinity in seawater. Almost all gases are more soluble in cold water than in warm water (Figure 3.9). For example, all other factors being equal, we would expect less dissolved oxygen in lakes in summer than in the cooler seasons. As the temperature or salinity of seawater increases, water holds less gas at saturation; of the two factors, temperature is much more important. If seawater is not saturated with a specific gas, the gas is transferred from air to ocean. If seawater is supersaturated with the gas (containing levels of gas above the normal saturation concentration), the gas transfer is in the opposite direction. When water is saturated with a gas, the rate at which the gas dissolves in water equals the rate at which the gas escapes to the atmosphere.

Waves on the ocean surface facilitate the transfer of gases between the atmosphere and ocean. Waves roughen the surface and increase the surface area of ocean water exposed to the atmosphere for gas exchange. Another important mechanism in the transfer of gases at

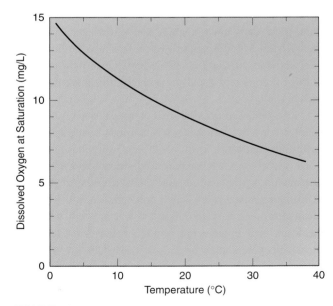

FIGURE 3.9
The saturation value of dissolved oxygen in fresh water decreases with rising temperature.

the air/sea interface is **bubble injection** whereby breaking waves introduce a foam composed of small bubbles below the surface greatly enhancing exchange rates. On the other hand, in cold climates, sea-ice cover is a barrier to gas transfer at the ocean surface.

Below the ocean-atmosphere interface, biochemical processes play important roles in controlling the proportions of certain dissolved gases. Within the **photic zone**, the sunlit upper layer of the ocean where photosynthesis takes place, dissolved oxygen is enhanced relative to carbon dioxide. As noted in Chapter 1, *photosynthesis* is the process whereby green plants (e.g., phytoplankton) use sunlight, water, and carbon dioxide to manufacture their food and generate oxygen as a byproduct. In surface ocean waters, the principal dissolved gases are nitrogen (48%), oxygen (36%), and carbon dioxide (15%). At ocean depths greater than the photic zone, photosynthesis is absent and decomposer activity and cellular respiration are the most important biochemical processes. Recall from Chapter 1 that *cellular respiration* is the process whereby organisms break down food and release energy in a usable form. Through cellular respiration, marine organisms use dissolved oxygen and release carbon dioxide as a byproduct. For the ocean as a whole, CO_2 is the most abundant dissolved gas, accounting for 83% of the total.

Carbon dioxide is much more abundant in the ocean than the atmosphere. As noted in Chapter 1, CO_2 is only 0.038% by volume of the gases composing the atmosphere below an altitude of 80 km (50 mi). About fifty-one times as much CO_2 is sequestered in the ocean. Carbon dioxide is highly soluble in water because it reacts with water to produce carbonate (CO_3^{-2}) and bicarbonate (HCO_3^{-1}) ions that readily dissolve in water. At a temperature of 0 °C (32 °F) and sea level air pressure, one liter of water that is saturated with carbon dioxide has dissolved about 1.7 liters of CO_2. The flux of atmospheric carbon dioxide into the ocean has important implications for global climate change (Chapter 12) and ocean acidification (discussed later in this chapter).

If a dissolved gas does not participate in any biochemical process such as photosynthesis or cellular respiration, its concentration in a parcel of seawater remains unchanged except by the relatively slow movements of gas molecules (*diffusion*) through the water or the mixing of water masses containing different amounts of dissolved gas. Generally, nitrogen and inert (chemically non-reactive) gases such as argon and neon behave in this way and their concentrations are described as *conservative properties*. As noted above, biochemical processes influence the concentration of some gases dissolved in seawater,

primarily oxygen and carbon dioxide; the concentrations of these dissolved gases are examples of *non-conservative properties*.

SEAWATER pH

Water in the various reservoirs of the Earth system can vary in acidity and alkalinity. An acid is a hydrogen-containing compound that releases hydrogen ions (H^{+1}) when dissolved in water. Strong acids more readily release hydrogen ions than weak acids. An alkaline substance releases hydroxyl ions (OH^{-1}) when dissolved in water and may be weak or strong. Pure water has properties of both acids and alkaline materials as water molecules continually break up (into hydrogen and hydroxyl ions) and form. That is,

$$H_2O \leftrightarrows H^{+1} + OH^{-1}$$

The acidity of water (or any other substance) is expressed as **pH**, a measure of the hydrogen ion concentration. On the **pH scale**, the pH increases from 0 to 14 as the hydrogen ion concentration decreases (Figure 3.10). Pure water has a pH of 7, which is considered neutral; a pH above 7 is increasingly alkaline whereas a pH below 7 is increasingly acidic. The pH scale is logarithmic; that is, each unit increment corresponds to a tenfold change in acidity or alkalinity. Hence, a two-unit drop in pH (e.g., from 5.6 to 3.6) represents a hundredfold (10×10) increase in acidity.

The pH of pristine seawater ranges between 8.0 and 8.3; that is, seawater is slightly alkaline. The relatively narrow variation in the pH of seawater is very important for marine organisms whose shells and skeletons are composed of calcium carbonate ($CaCO_3$). If ocean water were even slightly acidic, calcium carbonate would dissolve and would be unavailable for these organisms.

Carbon dioxide plays a key role in controlling the pH of seawater. A substance that stabilizes a chemical system in this way is known as a **buffer**. Atmospheric CO_2 dissolves in ocean water producing carbonic acid (H_2CO_3) that dissociates into hydrogen (H^{+1}), carbonate (CO_3^{-2}), and bicarbonate (HCO_3^{-1}) ions. A chemical equilibrium develops in which carbon dioxide, carbonic acid, hydrogen ions, carbonate ions, and bicarbonate ions co-exist. Adding acid to the ocean shifts the equilibrium so that there are fewer carbonate ions, which in turn reduces the hydrogen ion concentration and raises the pH. Adding alkaline materials to ocean water raises the pH but the equilibrium shifts in such a way as to return the pH to the normal range.

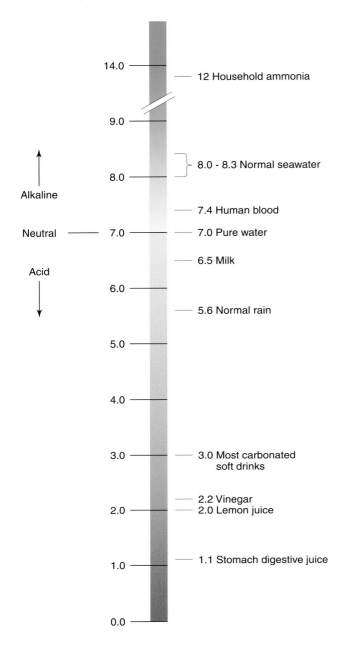

Alkaline

Neutral

Acid

- 14.0 — 12 Household ammonia
- 9.0
- 8.0 — 8.0 - 8.3 Normal seawater
- — 7.4 Human blood
- 7.0 — 7.0 Pure water
- — 6.5 Milk
- 6.0
- — 5.6 Normal rain
- 5.0
- 4.0
- 3.0 — 3.0 Most carbonated soft drinks
- — 2.2 Vinegar
- 2.0 — 2.0 Lemon juice
- 1.0 — 1.1 Stomach digestive juice
- 0.0

FIGURE 3.10
The acidity of water is expressed as pH, a measure of the hydrogen ion concentration. On this scale, pH increases from 0 to 14 as the hydrogen ion concentration decreases. Pure water has a pH of 7, which is considered neutral; a pH above 7 is increasingly alkaline and a pH below 7 is increasingly acidic.

Lake waters generally are not as well buffered as seawater and can exhibit greater variations in pH in response to influxes of acid precipitation or runoff. Rain and snow are normally slightly acidic as a result of dissolving atmospheric CO_2. Where air also contains oxides of sulfur (e.g., from coal burning) or oxides of nitrogen (e.g., byproducts of high-temperature industrial processes), precipitation can become much more acidic than normal. Rainwater that is saturated with CO_2 has a pH of 5.6 and any rain or snow having a pH below this value is designated **acid rain** (or *acid snow*). Lakes whose basins consist of carbonate rocks (i.e., limestone or dolostone) usually have sufficient carbonates to neutralize acid rain whereas lakes with non-carbonate basins (e.g., granite) cannot buffer the acid rain, snow, and runoff they receive. Lowering the pH of lake waters is known to endanger aquatic life.

OCEAN ACIDIFICATION

With the continuing upward trend in the concentration of atmospheric carbon dioxide, ocean scientists and others are concerned about the potential effects on the ocean's buffering ability and the viability of certain marine organisms. CO_2 that is absorbed by the ocean participates in chemical reactions that increase the acidity (lowers the pH) of ocean waters. This so-called **ocean acidification** is potentially harmful to marine organisms that use carbonate ions (CO_3^{-2}) to build calcium carbonate ($CaCO_3$) shells or skeletons.

The atmospheric carbon dioxide concentration has been rising since the beginning of the Industrial Revolution (currently about 1% per year) principally because of the burning of fossil fuels. About half of all CO_2 released to the atmosphere from fossil fuel combustion during that time period has been taken up by ocean waters. At present, the atmospheric CO_2 concentration is about 30% higher than it was 200 years ago and is increasing at a rate that could see at least a doubling of the concentration by the close of this century. Today, about 40% of CO_2 from fossil fuel combustion stays in the atmosphere, 30% is taken up by terrestrial vegetation via photosynthesis, and 30% is absorbed by the ocean.

Dissolved in the ocean, CO_2 combines with water to produce carbonic acid (H_2CO_3) that mostly dissociates into acidifying hydrogen ions (H^{+1}) and bicarbonate ions (HCO_3^{-1}). Some bicarbonate ions, in turn, dissociate into carbonate ions (CO_3^{-2}) plus hydrogen ions. Carbonate ions combine with hydrogen ions to form bicarbonate ions. The net effect of these chemical reactions is a decline in the pH of ocean waters and a reduction in the concentration of carbonate ions needed by certain marine organisms to build their shells and other hard parts. According to some studies, the current trend in the flux of CO_2 into the ocean will result in a 50% reduction in the ocean's carbonate concentration by the end of the century. Over the past 200 years, the pH of surface ocean waters has decreased by about 0.1 unit. An additional drop in pH by 0.3 unit could occur by 2100, a level not duplicated in the ocean for many millions of years.

Marine organisms that are particularly vulnerable to ocean acidification are coccolithophorids, foraminifera (phytoplanktonic organisms), and pteropods (small marine snails). These organisms are an important food source in marine food webs. Also vulnerable are corals which filter plankton from ocean water and secrete calcium carbonate. A reduction in carbonate ion concentration impairs the ability of reef-building coral to generate their calcium carbonate skeletons thereby adversely affecting coral growth. Complicating matters is the fact that calcium carbonate shells occur in three different mineral forms that differ in solubility. Aragonite and magnesium calcite are more soluble than calcite. Corals and pteropods produce aragonite shells that more readily dissolve in acidic waters. On the other hand, the shells of high latitude calcareous phytoplankton and zooplankton are composed of calcite and are less soluble. We have more to say about the implications of ocean acidification in Chapter 4.

Physical Properties of Seawater

Some properties of water vary with salinity. Adding salts to water changes its temperature of initial freezing and the temperature at which it reaches maximum density. Because salt ions can not fit into the crystal lattice of ice, dissolved salts inhibit the formation of hexagonal ice crystals and this depresses the initial freezing point to temperatures below 0 °C. Seawater of average salinity (about 35) has an initial freezing temperature of −1.9 °C. Furthermore, seawater does not remain at the same temperature while freezing as does fresh water. Since salts are excluded from the ice structure as seawater freezes, the remaining unfrozen water becomes saltier and therefore freezes at still lower temperatures. This process is known as **brine rejection**. Unless cooled to very low temperatures, some concentrated liquid brine remains trapped in cells of sea ice, although the brine does migrate downward over time toward the warmer water under the ice.

WATER DENSITY AND TEMPERATURE

Density is defined as mass per unit volume, which may be expressed as grams per cubic cm. When placed in water an object that is less dense than water

will float to the surface whereas an object that is denser than water will sink. Freshwater density varies primarily with temperature whereas seawater density varies chiefly with temperature and salinity. Water is only slightly compressible (1-2%) so that pressure arising from the weight of overlying water does not significantly impact its density except in the deep ocean.

Most substances contract when cooled and expand when heated; their density increases with falling temperature and decreases with rising temperature. As the average kinetic molecular energy decreases (i.e., as the temperature falls), the same number of molecules occupies a progressively smaller volume. However, for fresh water, it is not quite that simple (Figure 3.11). As the temperature of fresh water falls steadily from say 25 °C (77 °F), the water contracts and its density increases. The density of fresh water reaches a maximum at about 4 °C (39.2 °F), but with additional cooling (below 4 °C), the water expands and its density decreases.

Ice-like molecular clusters continually form and break-up in liquid water and are responsible for the anomalous behavior of fresh water density at temperatures below 4 °C. As the temperature drops, the water molecules have less kinetic energy and move closer together so that the number of hydrogen bonds increases resulting in more ice-like clusters. These clusters occupy more volume than the unorganized water molecules in the liquid phase. Recall that ice crystals are open hexagonal (six-sided) structures with widely spaced water molecules (Figure 3.2). As

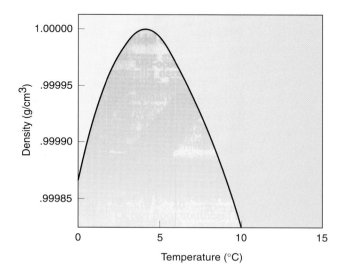

FIGURE 3.11
The density of fresh water reaches a maximum at about 4 °C (39.2 °F) and, with additional cooling (below 4 °C), liquid water expands until it freezes at 0 °C.

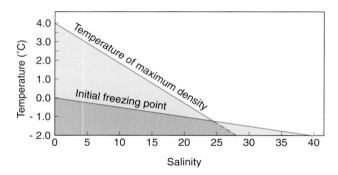

FIGURE 3.12
Water's temperature of maximum density and initial freezing point temperature decrease at different rates as the salinity increases. At a salinity of 24.7, the temperature of maximum density is the same as the freezing temperature (–1.33 °C).

the water temperature drops below 4 °C, the decrease in water density caused by increasing numbers of ice-like molecular clusters more than compensates for the increase in water density that would accompany a decline in kinetic molecular activity. Whereas most liquids contract when they solidify, as water freezes, its molecules bond into an open hexagonal structure so that the density of ice is about 92% of liquid water.

The unique temperature-density behavior of fresh water explains why the less dense ice floats in more dense water and lakes freeze from the top down rather than the bottom up. If ice were denser than liquid water, ice that forms at the air-water interface would sink and in winter lakes in cold climates would freeze solid from the bottom up, destroying all aquatic life. In autumn, lakes begin cooling at the air-water interface when the temperature of the overlying air falls below that of the lake surface. With the continued decline in air temperatures in fall, lake-surface waters cool, contract, become denser and sink to the bottom. This process of cooling and sinking of surface waters is repeated until the entire lake develops a uniform temperature of 4 °C (and the same density). Then, with additional cooling of surface waters below 4 °C, water density decreases and the coldest water remains at the surface. At 0 °C an ice cover begins to form. Once formed, ice contracts (becomes denser) as its temperature falls. But no matter how cold, ice remains less dense than liquid water.

The situation changes when salt is added to water. At constant temperature, the density of seawater increases with increasing salinity because the atomic mass of dissolved salts is greater than that of water molecules. Hence, less dense fresh water floats on more dense seawater. The salinity of seawater also affects the temperature of maximum density and the freezing temperature for the same

reason: adding dissolved materials such as salt apparently interferes with the formation of ice-like clusters. As shown in Figure 3.12, the temperature of maximum density decreases linearly with increasing salinity. At any salinity less than 24.7, the maximum density of water occurs at a temperature above the freezing point (which also decreases linearly with increasing salinity). At a salinity of 24.7, the temperature of maximum density is the same as the freezing temperature (–1.33 °C). For salinities greater than 24.7, the temperature of maximum density is lower than the freezing point so that the water freezes before reaching maximum density. The density of seawater of average salinity (about 35) varies inversely with temperature; that is, seawater density always increases with falling temperature and decreases with rising temperature. Hence, seawater becomes denser with cooling and sinks. Except in a few important high latitude locations in the North Atlantic Ocean and the Southern Ocean around Antarctica (Chapter 6), relatively dense seawater usually does not sink to the deep ocean bottom but descends to a level where the density of the surrounding water is the same.

Figure 3.13 shows the relative effects of temperature and salinity on seawater density. At a constant temperature of 15 °C, increasing the salinity from 33.7 to 34.9 raises the density from 1.025 g per cubic cm to about 1.026 g per cubic cm. Density changes an equivalent amount by cooling water with a constant salinity of 34.6 from 18 °C to 14 °C, a change of 4 Celsius degrees. Such variations in temperature are common at the ocean surface. As we will see in Chapter 6, differences in seawater density, caused by variations in temperature and

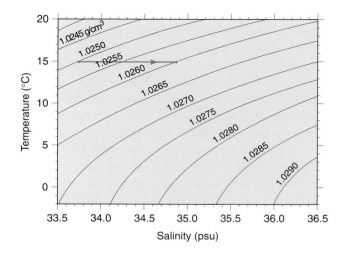

FIGURE 3.13
The density of seawater varies with temperature and salinity.

salinity, are important controls of the vertical circulation of ocean water. (Note that ocean scientists usually write density in a shorthand notation. Because the density of seawater almost always starts with 1.0, they subtract 1 and then multiply by 1000. In this way, a seawater density of 1.02178 g per cubic cm becomes 21.78 with no units.)

PRESSURE

Ocean water exerts **pressure** (i.e., force per unit area). It is useful to compare water pressure to air pressure. Atmospheric pressure can be thought of as the weight of a column of air acting over a unit area at the base of the column. By convention, *standard atmospheric pressure* is the average air pressure at sea level at 45 degrees latitude and an air temperature of 15 °C (59 °F). This pressure is equivalent to the weight exerted by a mass of 1.03 kg on a square cm (14.7 lbs per square in.) or 1013.25 millibars (mb). (A millibar is a unit of pressure where 1000 mb equals one bar.) Water is much denser than air so that a column of equivalent height produces much greater pressure.

A column of fresh water with a height of 10.33 m (33.9 ft) exerts a pressure at its base that approximately equals one standard atmosphere. Hence, the pressure at the deepest known place in the ocean, the Challenger Deep in the Marianas Trench in the Western Pacific where the ocean depth is 10,923 m (35,838 ft), is more than 1000 times greater than standard atmospheric pressure. At that depth, the water pressure is 1097 kg per square cm (7.8 tons per square in.). When determining pressure, water can be approximated as an incompressible fluid; that is, water density does not vary significantly with increasing pressure. To a good first approximation, the pressure at any point in a water column is directly related to depth and the relationship is linear; that is, doubling the depth doubles the pressure. At a depth of 10.33 m, the water pressure is 1.03 kg per square cm. At ten times this depth, 103.3 m (339 ft), the water pressure is ten times as great, that is, 10.3 kg per square cm. The tremendous pressures encountered in deep ocean waters prevent direct exploration except by special submersible vehicles designed to withstand potentially crushing stresses.

Pressure has long been used as a measure of depth in the ocean because pressure is far easier to measure in situ than depth and to a good approximation (error of less than 2%) pressure is equivalent to depth. Ocean scientists, like their counterparts in atmospheric science, commonly use the bar and its derivatives as a standard unit of pressure. The water pressure expressed in *decibars* (0.1 bar) is numerically equivalent to the water depth expressed in meters. The interchangeability of the two measures (i.e.,

water pressure in decibars and water depth in meters) greatly simplifies data analysis. For example, the water pressure at 100 m (330 ft) depth is about 100 decibars.

SEA ICE

Each winter, seawater freezes at high latitudes and even in some coastal areas of middle latitudes. When seawater is chilled below its freezing point, microscopic ice crystals form, later growing into hexagonal needles 1 to 2 cm (0.4 to 0.8 in.) long. At this stage, the sea surface takes on a dull appearance. As freezing continues, individual ice crystals freeze together and cover the surface like a blanket of wet snow. Eventually ice crystals begin to grow downward and form a thin, flexible, plastic-like ice layer, honeycombed with small cells that fill with seawater. Ice crystals themselves contain no salt, but the brines trapped in the small cells can be saltier than seawater. Typically 1 kg of newly formed sea ice consists of about 800 g of ice (salinity 0) and 200 g of seawater (salinity 35). Thus, the average salinity of newly formed sea ice is about 7. As temperatures fall, more ice forms beneath the initial ice layer. The brines in the cells also partially freeze, making the remaining brines saltier. If temperatures continue to fall, the salt in the brine eventually crystallizes as the last bit of water freezes.

The salt content of newly formed sea ice depends on temperature. At temperatures near freezing, sea ice forms slowly, which allows brines to flow out leaving little seawater in the cells. Such ice therefore contains little salt. At lower temperatures, ice forms more rapidly and traps seawater; this sea ice contains more salt but is less salty than the seawater from which it formed. Ice forms in the upper colder region of a brine cell while ice melts in the lower warmer region of the brine cell, causing the brine cell to migrate toward higher temperatures.

An ice layer up to 1 m (3 ft) or so thick can form in one winter; this is called *first-year ice* (Figure 3.14). First-year ice dominates the Southern Ocean around Antarctica. But in the Arctic pack ice of the central basin, sea ice melts little during summer and *multi-year ice* dominates. Over several seasons, the maximum thickness of multi-year ice is usually 2 to 3.5 m (about 7 to 11 ft). Winds, however, can pile up floes of ice, forming pressure ridges offshore and ice-shove ridges along the coast. Pressure ridges extend many meters above and below the ice pack and are hazardous to submarines navigating under the Arctic ice and impede icebreakers traveling through the ice pack. Many different terms are used to describe the various forms of sea ice. For more on sea ice terminology, see this chapter's second Essay.

median ice edge

FIGURE 3.14
Sea ice extent in December 2007, based on satellite passive microwave data for (A) the Arctic where it was winter and (B) the Southern Ocean/Antarctica where it was summer. Total sea ice extent was 12.4 million square km in the Arctic and 12.6 million square km in the Antarctic. [Courtesy of F. Fetterer, K. Knowles, W. Meier, and M. Savole, NOAA's National Snow and Ice Data Center, Boulder, CO.]

SOUND TRANSMISSION

Seawater is essentially transparent to sound just as the clear atmosphere is nearly transparent to sunlight. Whales use sound to communicate across ocean basins and to attract mates. Ocean scientists have developed techniques that take advantage of the sound propagating ability of seawater to determine ocean depth, locate underwater objects such as submarines and schools of fish, and to determine small changes in water temperature over great distances.

Sound propagates through some medium (e.g., air or water) as compression (push-pull) waves with the speed of propagation dependent on the properties of the medium. The speed of sound in ocean water (about 1500 m per sec or 5000 ft per sec) is more than four times the average speed of sound in air because water is less compressible than air. Knowing the speed of sound in seawater is the principle behind an *echo sounder* used by most seagoing vessels to determine the depth of water beneath the ship. This instrument sends a narrow beam of sound vertically to the seafloor where it is reflected back to the ship. The time interval between emission and return of the sound signal (the *echo*) is calibrated in terms of water depth. *Fish finders* are echo sounders that send and receive sound waves that are reflected by schools of fish.

SONAR (SOund NAvigation and Ranging) is similar to an echo sounder except that the operator of the instrument can alter the direction of the sound signal. Pulses of sound are sent out to locate targets such as submarines and the return echoes are displayed electronically on a monitor. Complicating the use of SONAR for target location are changes in the speed of sound in water that can cause the sound wave to bend (refract). Sound waves bend toward regions where sound waves travel more slowly and away from regions where sound waves travel faster. The speed of sound in seawater is influenced by temperature, pressure, and salinity.

Variation of the speed of sound due to temperature/salinity differences in the ocean gives rise to the **SOFAR channel**, a zone centered at an ocean depth of about 1000 m (3300 ft) where the speed of sound is at a minimum value (Figure 3.15). (*SOFAR* is the acronym for *SOund Fixing And Ranging*). Sound waves are vertically trapped in the SOFAR channel and can travel thousands of kilometers horizontally with little loss of energy. Why does the speed of sound reach a minimum and produce the SOFAR channel? The speed of sound in seawater increases with increasing temperature, salinity, and depth (i.e., pressure). From the sea surface down to a depth of about 1000 m, temperature usually decreases

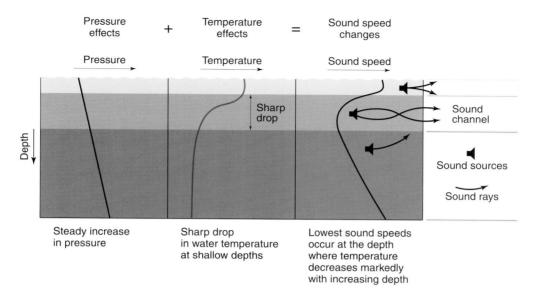

FIGURE 3.15
Refraction of sound waves as they travel through ocean waters gives rise to the SOFAR channel, a zone centered at a depth of about 1000 m (3300 ft) where the speed of sound is at a minimum value.

and is the primary control of sound speed. Hence, sound speed decreases with depth to 1000 m. At greater depths, the water temperature tends to be uniformly low and variations in sound speed depend chiefly on pressure change with depth. With increasing depth and pressure, sound speed increases. As shown in Figure 3.15, sound waves are refracted upward (from below the SOFAR) or downward (from above the SOFAR) toward the region of minimum sound velocity within the SOFAR channel.

During the 1990s, with increased interest in global climate change, scientists at the Massachusetts Institute of Technology and Scripps Institution of Oceanography developed and tested a method of monitoring temperature changes within the SOFAR channel. The approach, known as **acoustic thermometry**, is based on the dependency of the speed of sound on ocean water temperature and can measure very small temperature changes—to a few thousandths of a degree—over great distances in the ocean. An increase in sound speed between sound transmitters and receivers over a period of time would indicate warming of the ocean. Indeed, such warming has been observed in the Arctic basin using acoustic thermometry.

Conclusions

Water has unusual physical and chemical properties resulting from the water molecule's unique polar structure that gives rise to hydrogen bonding. Water is a powerful solvent, dissolving both salts and gases, and is an effective heat-storage and transporting medium. Consequently, the ocean plays a major role in Earth's weather and climate. Temperature, salinity, and pressure affect most physical properties of seawater such as density and sound velocity. The density of seawater, in turn, influences ocean currents. In the next chapter, we continue our examination of ocean properties by focusing on the types and sources of marine sediments.

Basic Understandings

- The unusual physical and chemical properties of water (H_2O) arise from the unique structure of the water molecule, consisting of two hydrogen (H) atoms bonded to an oxygen (O) atom. The bonding angle of 105° allows a slight positive charge to reside on each of the hydrogen atoms and a slight negative charge to reside on the oxygen atom. This makes the water molecule a polar molecule. The positively charged (hydrogen) poles of a water molecule attract the negatively charged (oxygen) poles of other water molecules; this attractive force is known as hydrogen bonding and is the reason for the unique properties of water.
- Water is one of the few substances occurring naturally in all three phases within the usual range of temperatures and pressures at or near

Earth's surface. Ice has a three-dimensional internal framework consisting of a hexagonal ring of molecules that vibrate about fixed locations. Liquid water consists of non-bonded and transient clusters of hydrogen bonded molecules. When liquid water changes to vapor, all hydrogen bonds are broken and individual molecules rapidly diffuse to fill the entire volume of its container.

- Temperature is directly proportional to the average kinetic energy of the atoms or molecules composing a substance. Heat is the name given to the energy transferred between objects at different temperatures and is always transferred from the warmer object to the colder object.

- When water changes phase heat is either absorbed from the environment to break hydrogen bonds (melting, evaporation, sublimation) or released to the environment when hydrogen bonds form (freezing, condensation, deposition). Heat energy that is involved in the phase change of water is known as latent heat.

- The thermal response of a unit mass of a substance to a given input of heat, known as the specific heat of the substance, differs for various materials and is highest for water. Water's high specific heat has consequences for climate. Compared to the surface of an adjacent landmass, the surface of a body of water does not warm as much during the day (or in summer) and does not cool as much at night (or in winter). Places immediately downwind of the ocean have a maritime climate in which the average temperature contrast between summer and winter is less than it is at the same latitude but well inland.

- Water is an excellent solvent, readily dissolving solids, liquids, and gases. The polar nature of the water molecule favors the solution of both ionic and non-ionic substances. Seawater is a solution of nearly constant salt composition with an average concentration of about 3.5%.

- Salinity is based on measurements of the electrical conductivity of seawater and is determined as the ratio of the conductivity of the seawater sample to the conductivity of standard seawater. As a ratio, salinity has no units but numerically is essentially equivalent to grams of salt per kilogram of seawater (parts per thousand).

- Salts dissolved in seawater are derived from weathering and erosion of rock and sediment on land, chemical reactions between cold seawater and newly formed oceanic crust, and volcanic eruptions. Rivers and streams deliver the products of terrestrial weathering and erosion to the ocean; this is the principal source of salt in the sea.

- Gases are exchanged between the atmosphere and ocean at the ocean surface. If seawater is not saturated with a specific gas, the gas is transferred from air to ocean. If seawater is supersaturated with the gas, the transfer is in the opposite direction. When water is saturated with a gas, the rate at which the gas dissolves in water equals the rate at which the gas escapes to the atmosphere.

- The saturation concentration of a gas in water depends primarily on temperature in fresh water bodies such as lakes and rivers and a combination of temperature and salinity in seawater. In general, cold water can hold more dissolved gases than warm water. Also, solubility of a gas in water depends on the gas species so that, for example, oxygen and carbon dioxide are more soluble than nitrogen.

- Below the ocean-atmosphere interface, biochemical processes control the proportions of certain dissolved gases. Within the photic zone, the sunlit upper portion of the ocean where photosynthesis takes place, dissolved oxygen is enhanced relative to carbon dioxide. Beneath the photic zone, decomposer activity and cellular respiration are the most important biochemical processes. For the ocean as a whole, CO_2 is the most abundant dissolved gas, accounting for 83% of the total.

- The pH of pristine seawater ranges between 8.0 and 8.3; that is, seawater is slightly alkaline. The relatively narrow range in the pH of seawater is very important for marine organisms whose shells and skeletons are composed of calcium carbonate ($CaCO_3$).

- The density of fresh water reaches a maximum at a temperature of 4 °C (39.2 °F) and freshwater ice is less dense than fresh water. This explains why ice floats and why lakes freeze from the top down. At constant temperature, seawater density increases with increasing salinity so that less dense fresh water floats on more dense seawater. As salinity increases, the freezing temperature and temperature of maximum density decrease.

- Temperature and salinity are the principal controls of seawater density. Lower temperature and increasing salinity cause density to increase. In the surface waters of the open ocean, temperature dominates density in warmer waters whereas salinity dominates density in colder waters. Changes in salinity are important near shorelines (due to freshwater runoff), in polar areas (due to cold water and sea ice formation and melting), and in regions of high precipitation or evaporation.

- Pressure is the force exerted by a column of water per unit area at the base of the column. Water is only slightly compressible so that water pressure increases linearly with depth. Water pressure expressed in units of decibars is numerically equivalent to depth when expressed in meters.

- Sea ice forms in polar regions and at some middle latitude coastal areas. As seawater freezes, salts are excluded from the sea ice and the resulting brines increase the salinity of surrounding waters. First-year ice dominates the Southern Ocean around Antarctica whereas multi-year ice dominates in the Arctic Ocean.

- Ocean scientists have developed techniques that take advantage of the sound propagating ability of seawater to determine ocean depth, locate underwater objects such as submarines and schools of fish, and to determine small changes in average water temperature.

- Variations in the speed-of-sound due to temperature/salinity differences in the ocean waters give rise to the SOFAR channel, a zone centered at an ocean depth of about 1000 m (3300 ft) where the speed of sound is at a minimum value. Sound waves are vertically trapped in the SOFAR channel and can travel thousands of kilometers horizontally with little loss of energy.

Review

1. Describe how hydrogen bonds form between neighboring water molecules. During which phase change of water are all hydrogen bonds broken?
2. Distinguish between temperature and heat.
3. Identify and describe three phase changes of water during which latent heat is released to the environment.
4. Define specific heat. When the same quantity of heat is added per unit mass, does a substance having a lower specific heat warm more or less than a substance having a higher specific heat?
5. Distinguish between a maritime climate and a continental climate in terms of annual temperature range and name some U.S. or Canadian cities having these climates.
6. Compare the salinity of surface ocean waters in regions where the precipitation is low and evaporation rates are high to the global annual average sea-surface salinity.
7. For the ocean as a whole, what is the most abundant gas dissolved in seawater? Explain the role of this gas in photosynthesis and cellular respiration.
8. What is the pH of pure water? Is the average pH of ocean water slightly acidic or alkaline?
9. At constant temperature, how does the density of seawater change with increasing salinity? With constant salinity, how does the density of seawater change with falling temperature?
10. What is the significance of the SOFAR channel?

Critical Thinking

1. Suppose that ice were denser than liquid water. Speculate on some of the consequences.
2. Describe the seasonal change in temperature of the ocean surface first in subtropical and then in polar latitudes. Explain the differences.
3. Describe how changes in the phase of water bring about a transfer of heat energy within the Earth system.
4. The ocean is a major player in Earth's climate system. Explain why.
5. River water ultimately empties into the ocean and yet the average salinity of river water is much less than the average salinity of seawater. Explain the difference.
6. How do biological processes influence the type and amount of gases dissolved in seawater?
7. What is the significance of a seawater salinity of 24.7?
8. What factors govern surface water salinity in the open ocean?
9. Explain how surface water salinity can act as a rain gauge over large areas of the ocean.
10. Identify two conservative properties of seawater. Explain why these are considered conservative.

ESSAY: Desalination

The Red Sea port of Jeddah, Saudi Arabia is a growing city of more than 3.4 million people. Rapid population growth is taking place in spite of an arid climate in which the average annual rainfall is only about 6.1 cm (2.4 in.) and no significant freshwater sources exist nearby. There are no rivers or lakes and very little groundwater. For their freshwater supply, residents of Jeddah depend mostly on saline water piped in from the Red Sea and desalinated. Jeddah's five desalination plants produce more than 380 million liters (100 million gal) of fresh water per day.

Desalination is a process whereby dissolved solids (principally salts) are removed from saline water to make the water potable, that is, suitable for domestic and agricultural uses. According to the World Health Organization (WHO), water is considered potable when it contains less than 500 milligrams per liter (mg/L) of dissolved solids. (Most people report a disagreeable taste when dissolved salts approach 1000 mg/L and an insipid taste when the salt content is too low.) On average, seawater contains about 35,000 mg/L of dissolved solids—almost all salts. Most desalination worldwide utilizes one of two basic technologies: distillation or reverse osmosis. The combination of multistage flash distillation and reverse osmosis accounts for about 88% of worldwide capacity.

With *distillation*, water is purified through phase changes (usually from liquid to vapor and back to liquid). The simplest (and least expensive) distillation device is a plastic transparent dome placed over a reservoir of seawater. Solar radiation penetrates the dome, is absorbed (converted to heat), and is the source of latent heat for evaporating the water. Water vapor then condenses as freshwater drops on the inside surface of the dome and the drops drip into a collection trough. This so-called *solar still* works best in sunny tropical climates where solar radiation is intense year-round.

For much more rapid distillation of large quantities of salty water, desalination utilizes *multistage flash distillation (MFD)*. With MFD, the intake water is superheated, that is, under pressure the water temperature rises above its normal boiling point but remains liquid. The water then pours into another vessel where the pressure is somewhat lower and the water flashes into steam. Water vapor rises and condenses into collection devices. This same process is repeated many times as the remaining intake water flows into vessels at progressively lower pressure. The output is fresh water and concentrated brine. In most cases, MFD facilities utilize the waste heat from nearby fossil-fuel electric power plants as the energy source for desalination.

With *reverse osmosis*, pressure applied to saltwater forces water molecules through a thin semi-permeable membrane. Up to 97% of the substances dissolved in seawater including salts, other dissolved solids, and nonvolatile organics cannot pass through the membrane and are left behind. Pretreatment of the intake water with substances such as chlorine, hydrogen peroxide, or sulfuric acid may be necessary to prevent biological fouling or calcium carbonate scaling of the membrane surface.

Reverse osmosis is used at desalination facilities on the Outer Banks of North Carolina where fresh water is in limited supply. At the Kill Devil Hills facility, operating since 1989, brackish (somewhat saline) water is pumped from 10 wells at a rate of up to 1900 liters (500 gal) per well per minute and then filtered and pretreated with sulfuric acid. Water is pumped under pressure to three reverse osmosis units, each of which produces about 3.8 million liters (1 million gal) of water per day. Chlorine, fluoride, and a corrosion inhibitor are then added to the desalinated water. More recently, the new reverse osmosis desalination facility operated by Florida's Tampa Bay Water came up to full production supplying 95 million liters (25 million gal) per day, about 10% of the Tampa Bay region's drinking water supply.

One of the drawbacks of desalination is the discharge of concentrated brine into the ocean. For example, about 25% of the intake water at the Kill Devil Hills facility becomes a highly saline waste stream that empties into the Atlantic Ocean. The salinity of this wastewater stream typically is about twice that of ordinary seawater. Conservationists are concerned that this dense brine will sink to the ocean bottom and adversely impact marine ecosystems. Also, some marine organisms may be killed by the seawater intake system. Desalinated water used for irrigation may require pre-treatment because of elevated levels of boron (B) that is toxic to many crop species and deficiencies in nutrients required for plant growth (e.g., calcium, magnesium). A major limitation to desalination of large quantities of water is the relatively high cost of energy-intensive technologies (distillation more so than reverse osmosis). For example, California's desalinated water costs more than twice that of water from watershed transfers or groundwater pumping. But the economics is becoming more favorable with the development of more efficient desalination technologies and the rising cost of fresh water from conventional sources.

Desalination (via both distillation and reverse osmosis) is most common in the Middle East where energy is abundant and inexpensive. In that arid region of the world where freshwater resources are in short supply, 1700 desalination plants convert a total of 20.9 billion liters (5.5 billion gal) of seawater to fresh water each day—estimated by Global Water Intelligence to be about 72% of the world's capacity. The world's largest reverse osmosis desalination facility, located in Ashkelon, Israel on the southern Mediterranean coast, has been operating since December 2005. The 100 million cubic m per year production is used for both human consumption and irrigation.

With increasing demand for potable water by the rapidly growing human population in the coastal zone (especially where groundwater supplies are insufficient) plus the pressing need for more irrigation water, desalination of seawater is becoming more popular. (In some coastal areas, freshwater supply is the limiting factor for community growth and 69% of the world freshwater supply is used for irrigation.) From 1994 to 2004, the worldwide desalination capacity more than doubled, from 17.3 to 35.6 million cubic m per day. As of 2007, desalination of seawater supplies approximately 1% of the world's drinking water.

ESSAY: Sea Ice Terminology

Over the years, a complex terminology has evolved concerning sea ice, its development and various forms. The World Meteorological Organization (WMO) standardized definitions for many of these terms more than three decades ago. The purpose of this Essay is to define some terms that you may encounter while exploring sea ice.

Sea ice refers to any form of ice floating in ocean waters that originated from the freezing of seawater. As noted elsewhere in this chapter, the salt dissolved in seawater lowers slightly the freezing point of water. For example, seawater having a salinity of 34 (about 3.4% salt) begins to freeze when its temperature drops to about –1.9 °C (28.6 °F) whereas the freezing point of fresh water is 0 °C (32 °F). Note that icebergs are not sea ice; they are massive chunks of ice that break away from the snout of a glacier advancing from land to sea (or a large lake) or calve off the edge of an ice shelf. Icebergs consist of frozen fresh water and may be floating or grounded.

Sea ice is broadly classified based on age (and thickness) as *new ice* (less than 10 cm thick), *young ice* (10 to 30 cm thick), *first-year ice* (30 cm to as much as 120 cm thick), or *old ice* (second-year or multi-year ice). First-year ice is the product of no more than one winter's growth of sea ice. *Second-year ice* has survived one melt season (summer) whereas *multi-year ice* has persisted through at least two summers' melt. The latter is typically around 3 m (10 ft) thick and is more common in the Arctic Ocean than the Southern Ocean. Sea ice near Antarctica varies seasonally with summer ice cover usually ranging up to 150 km (93 mi) from shore whereas winter ice can extend from 450 km (280 mi) to more than 1700 km (1050 mi) from shore. Maximum sea-ice coverage occurs in the Weddell Sea and accounts for about 80% of the multi-year ice in the Antarctic.

During the initial stage of sea ice formation, frazil ice develops in the upper few centimeters of seawater. *Frazil ice* consists of millimeter-size platelets or discs that give the sea surface an oily appearance. Wave action can stir frazil ice to a depth of several meters. With continued freezing, frazil ice crystals coagulate to form a soupy mix that reflects little light and gives the surface a matte appearance, sometimes referred to as *grease ice*. Frazil ice and grease ice are forms of new ice but do not form distinctive ice floes. An *ice floe* is any contiguous piece of ice that can vary greatly in size from a few meters to more than 10 km across. Other types of new ice include frozen slush (an accumulation of water-saturated snow on an ice surface or floating in water) and *nilas* (a thin crust of elastic gray-colored ice on a calm sea that readily bends into interlocking fingers).

Grease ice aggregates into small chunks of ice, which then become pancake-shaped ice floes. *Pancake ice* consists of nearly circular pieces of ice from 30 cm to 3.0 m (1 to 10 ft) in diameter and having a thickness of up to 10 cm (4 in.). Collisions with other ice floes are responsible for the upturned rim that is characteristic of pancake ice (Figure 1). With

FIGURE 1
Pancake ice consists of pieces of ice 0.3 to 3.0 m across, up to 10 cm thick, with upturned rims caused by collisions with other pieces of ice. [Courtesy of Environment Canada]

falling temperature, the ice cover thickens. Winds, waves, and currents cause ice floes to override one another (known as *rafting*) further thickening the ice cover generally to 40-60 cm (15-24 in.). However, in some fierce winter storms in the Bering Sea, scientists have reported 3-m (10-ft) thick ice floes rafting onto other ice floes and building the ice to a thickness of 6 m (20 ft), of which about 90% is below sea level. Rafting also produces a rough surface on the ice floe.

Fast ice forms along the coast and is attached to the shore or shallow sea bottoms so that it cannot move laterally. This happens, for example, off the coast of northern Alaska. It may extend from a few meters to several hundred kilometers offshore and may be more than one year old. *Pack ice* is any area of sea ice that is not anchored to land and moves with the wind and ocean currents. Pack ice is described as very open (1/10 to 3/10 ice cover), open (4/10 to 6/10 ice cover), close (7/10 to 8/10 ice cover), very close (9/10 to less than 10/10), and compact (10/10 ice cover with no water visible). If ice floes are frozen together, the compact pack ice is described as consolidated. The *extent of sea ice* is defined as the area in which ice covers at least 15% of the ocean surface.

A significant portion of Antarctic sea ice thickens through a process whereby seawater floods the snow that has accumulated on top of the ice turning it to slush; at low temperatures the slush then freezes into snow ice. If the snow cover is sufficiently massive, the ice/snow interface is suppressed below sea level allowing seawater to intrude and turn the snow to slush. Alternately, water may migrate upward through brine channels within the sea ice and enter the snow.

Stresses produce fractures in sea ice that vary from a few meters to many kilometers in length. Where fast ice is attached to the shore, tide-induced vertical motions of the ice may produce *tide cracks*. These fractures are important for some forms of marine life; for example, they allow penguins and seals access to the ocean. A fracture that is wide enough to be navigable by surface vessels is known as a *lead* and may occur between the shore and the pack ice or between fast ice and pack ice or simply between large ice floes or in the ice pack at sea. At sea, leads provide breathing holes for whales. Leads also permit exchange of heat and moisture between the ocean and atmosphere. In addition, converging ice floes (perhaps wind- or current-driven) may be forced upward into a wall of fractured ice, known as a *pressure ridge*. Pressure ridges can extend several meters above the surrounding sea ice and ocean surface. The fractured ice that is forced downward meters below the ridge is known as an *ice keel*.

A non-linear shaped kilometer-scale opening in the sea ice cover that persists or reoccurs regularly (often annually), is called a *polynya*. These holes in the ice would not normally exist because of sub-freezing temperatures were it not for some mechanism that keeps them open. In some cases, persistent gravity-driven cold winds (*katabatic winds*) blow ice away from land (e.g., Antarctica), islands, and grounded ice leaving surface waters ice-free. In a second mechanism, warm water welling up from below melts the ice cover. Also, polynyas are common at the mouths of large rivers. Major polynyas in the Northern Hemisphere include the St. Lawrence polynya in the Bering Sea and polynyas off the northeast and northwest coasts of Greenland. These are called North East Water and North Water respectively.

CHAPTER 4

MARINE SEDIMENTS

Case-in-Point
Driving Question
Classification of Marine Sediments by Size
　　Size and Sorting
　　Terminal Velocity
Classification of Marine Sediments by Source
　　Lithogenous Sediment
　　Biogenous Sediment
　　Hydrogenous Sediment
　　Cosmogenous Sediment
Marine Sedimentary Deposits
　　Continental-Margin Deposits
　　Deep-Ocean Deposits
Marine Sedimentary Rock
Resources of the Seafloor
　　Oil and Natural Gas
　　Mineral Resources
　　Exclusive Economic Zone
Conclusions
Basic Understandings/Review/Critical Thinking
ESSAY: Heinrich Events
ESSAY: Burgess Shale: A Glimpse into Ancient Marine Life

Steeply sloping muddy sediments cut by narrow canyons characterize the terrain of the ocean floor just north of Cape Hatteras known as "The Point". Notice the "marine snow" that falls in the foreground. This "snow" is composed of fine-grained sediments and organic matter. [Courtesy NOAA Ocean Explorer]

Case in Point

Wastewater enters rivers and streams via overland flow (e.g., agricultural runoff), groundwater, or direct input from drainage pipes (e.g., storm sewer systems). The net flow of water from land to sea in the global water cycle implies that all water-borne wastes eventually enter the ocean, either dissolved or suspended in water. Also as part of the global water cycle, rain and snow wash suspended particles from the atmosphere into the ocean. Furthermore, in some cases, industries located along the coast discharge wastes directly into the ocean or barge them out to sea for dumping.

Some wastes discharged at sea rapidly decompose physically, chemically, or biologically; others resist decomposition. These persistent chemicals enter food chains and move from one trophic level to the next higher trophic level increasing in concentration along the way. Problems caused by persistent chemicals are especially serious when they are toxic or hazardous to living organisms. In such cases, remediation requires either removal of the contaminants by dredging or capping them with layers of uncontaminated sediments to prevent their reentry into the ecosystem.

Perhaps the most infamous example of a toxic discharge to the sea that had serious consequences for human health took place in the small coastal village of

Minamata, Japan. For many years, the Chisso Chemical Plant discharged industrial waste containing mercury into Minamata Bay. Because elemental mercury is insoluble in water, it was expected to sink to the bottom sediments and remain inert, causing no harm to the ecosystem or humans. Such was not the case.

Fish and shellfish taken from local waters were part of the staple diet of Minamata residents. But, in the early 1950s, they began noticing bizarre behavior in their cats, including twitching and stumbling, which we now recognize as signs of brain damage caused by mercury poisoning. In 1956, a five-year-old girl lapsed into a convulsive delirium and was diagnosed with neurological damage. A few weeks later, numerous people reported a variety of debilitating symptoms including numbness, headaches, loss of muscle control, and slurred speech. In some individuals, symptoms worsened and they developed violent trembling and paralysis. Children were born with physical deformities as well as severe mental retardation. Some victims died.

Upon investigation, fish and shellfish taken from Minamata Bay were found to contain high levels of methyl mercury in their tissues, a soluble and highly toxic form of mercury. Methyl mercury that enters the body attacks the central nervous system. In 1959, scientists demonstrated that bacteria in bottom sediments taken from Minamata Bay converted mercury to methyl mercury. Methyl mercury was subsequently taken up by aquatic organisms, readily moved up the food chain, and was consumed by people. In eating fish and shellfish from Minamata Bay, people were exposed to dangerous levels of a highly toxic material. More than 3500 people were seriously affected and about 50 died from methyl mercury poisoning—now referred to as Minamata disease. After many years of litigation, the Chisso Company finally accepted some responsibility for the Minamata tragedy and was required to make reparations to victims.

Discharge of mercury into Minamata Bay ceased in the late 1960s and the cleanup began. This involved dredging and removal of mercury-contaminated sediment deposits. These sediments were placed in reclamation areas where they were surrounded by dikes with impervious fabric liners and covered by clean sands to prevent run-off and further contamination of bay waters. By July 1997, the waters of Minamata Bay and its marine organisms were found to meet Japan's environmental standards. Minamata Bay was declared safe and reopened for human use including fishing and recreational activities but monitoring of mercury levels in the water, sediments, and marine life continues.

Driving Question:
What are the types and sources of sediment that enters the ocean?

Particles (sediments) blanket much of the ocean floor. Most of these particles are generated at the interfaces among Earth's various subsystems and are transported by rivers, wind, ice, and gravity to the ocean. Some particles originate in the sea (e.g., the excretions and secretions of marine organisms). Marine sediment deposits consist of rock fragments, soil particles, and the shells, bones and teeth of marine organisms, and some material from outer space. Locked in the layers of ocean bottom sediments and marine sedimentary rock is a chronology of the history of Earth's subsystems over the past 200 million years, that is, since formation of the present ocean basins (Chapter 2). Analysis of sediments enables scientists to reconstruct past variations in parameters such as sea-surface temperature, salinity, carbon dioxide concentration, sea level, nutrient supply, and productivity. The main goal of geological oceanographers is to decipher the history of the ocean basins including past climate changes (Figure 4.1). We cannot begin to understand possible future climate change without understanding what has happened in the past and why.

The primary focus of this chapter is the types, sources, distribution, and environmental significance of marine sediments. We first describe how sediments are classified by size and the factors governing their rate of accumulation on the ocean floor. We then focus on the classification of marine sediments based on mode of origin, which largely determines their composition. There follows a description of the sedimentary deposits of the continental margin and the deep ocean floor and how geological processes modify these deposits. This provides the background for a brief overview of seafloor resources including oil, natural gas, and minerals.

FIGURE 4.1
Scientists retrieve a box core used to gather samples of the ocean bottom sediments and fauna from the Canada Basin in the Arctic Ocean. This four-week international expedition, conducted during summer 2002, was designed to help reconstruct the history of climate. [NOAA Ocean Explorer; photo courtesy of Mike Vecchione, NOAA/Smithsonian Institution]

Classification of Marine Sediments by Size

Particles that accumulate on the sea floor are known as **sediment**. Marine sediments differ in source, composition, size, and the rate at which they accumulate on the sea floor. Of the many ways of classifying marine sediments, the two most popular are by particle size and source. In this section we describe the size range of sediments and the factors governing the settling rate of particles in ocean water.

SIZE AND SORTING

Marine sediments are classified by size into three broad categories: mud, sand, and gravel. As shown in Table 4.1, these categories are further subdivided by size using common descriptive terms. The smallest particle of mud (clay) has a diameter less than 0.0039 mm, too small to be seen without a microscope. At the other end of the scale, a boulder is more than 256 mm (10 in.) in diameter.

TABLE 4.1
Wentworth Classification of Sediments by Size[a]

Sediment	Type	Diameter (mm)
Gravel	Boulder	>256
	Cobble	64-256
	Pebble	4-64
	Granule	2-4
Sand	Very coarse	1-2
	Coarse	0.50-1.0
	Medium	0.25-0.5
	Fine	0.125-0.25
	Very fine	0.0625-0.125
Mud	Silt	0.0039-0.0625
	Clay	<0.0039

[a]Adapted from C.K. Wentworth, *Journal of Geology* 30 (1922):377-392.

Accumulations of sediment (*sediment deposits*) on the seafloor also vary in the range of grain size, known as **sorting** (Figure 4.2). A well-sorted sediment deposit has a narrow range of grain sizes whereas a poorly sorted deposit has a broad range of grain sizes. In general, the greater the distance that sediment is transported by running water, ocean currents, or wind, the better sorted it becomes. For example, marine sediments that originated on land tend to be larger and more poorly sorted in the continental margin than on the deep ocean floor. Grain size along with sorting can be used to infer the current direction and speed, the overall energy of the environment, and the transport mechanism (e.g., river, glacier, or wind).

Well-sorted sand   Poorly-sorted sand

FIGURE 4.2
Well-sorted sediment deposit has a relatively narrow range of grain size whereas a poorly-sorted sediment deposit has a broad range of grain size.

Deposits of marine sediment are thickest on the continental margins (and near islands) where accumulation rates are relatively high. Most of these sediments are transported to the sea in suspension by rivers. As rivers flow downhill under the influence of gravity, some of the *kinetic energy* of moving water is used to erode the channel and transport sediment in suspension. Rivers also transport dissolved materials in solution and strong currents can push or roll larger sediment along the channel bottom. A river slows and diverges as it enters the ocean; dissipation of its kinetic energy reduces the river's ability to transport particles in suspension. More energy is required to transport larger particles than smaller ones. Hence, with diminishing kinetic energy, larger particles settle out of suspension almost immediately whereas finer particles are carried farther away from the coast before settling to the sea bottom.

Near the mouths of large sediment-transporting rivers, sediment accumulation rates can be enormous—perhaps as much as 8000 m (26,000 ft) per 1000 years. Waves and currents transport this material along the coast or offshore. Typical accumulation rates on the continental shelf and slope, on the other hand, range from 10 to 40 cm (4 to 16 in.) per 1000 years. The rain of sediment in the deep-ocean has been likened to the barely perceptible fall of dust in a classroom. Accumulation rates generally average from 0.5 to 1.0 cm (0.2 to 0.4 in.) per 1000 years. The thickness of deposits depends on the supply of particles and the length of time that sediments have been settling onto the ocean floor. As noted in Chapter 2, ocean floor sediments generally are thickest where the ocean crust is oldest so that deposits become thicker with increasing distance from the mid-ocean ridges (divergent or spreading plate boundaries). We would expect very little sediment on top of undersea mountains at a spreading center, but on the order of 1000 to 2000 m (3000 to 6000 ft) of sediment at distances farthest away from the spreading center at the edge of the ocean basins where the underlying oceanic crust approaches 200 million years old.

The length of time it takes for a particle to sink to the ocean bottom primarily depends on particle size. For example, a sand-sized particle may take a few days to sink to the bottom of the ocean whereas a clay-sized particle may take more than a century to cover the same distance. The longer it takes a particle to reach the ocean bottom, the greater the horizontal displacement of the particle by deep ocean currents and the more likely it is for soluble particles to dissolve in seawater. An important concept in understanding the ability of a fluid to transport a particle in suspension and the rate at which particles accumulate on the seafloor is terminal velocity.

TERMINAL VELOCITY

Terminal velocity is the constant speed attained by a particle falling through a motionless fluid such as water or air (Figure 4.3). The speed of a falling particle in calm water or air is regulated by (1) *gravity*, the force that accelerates the particle directly downward towards Earth's surface, and (2) the *fluid resistance* offered by the medium through which the particle is falling. A downward accelerating particle meets increasing fluid resistance while gravity remains essentially constant. The magnitude of the upward resisting force eventually equals gravity; that is, the two opposing forces come into balance. When forces are balanced, the downward moving particle attains a constant speed. According to **Newton's first law of motion**, an object in constant straight-line motion or at rest remains that way unless acted upon by an unbalanced force. In this case, the fluid resistance (directed upward) balances gravity (acting downward) and the particle continues moving downward at constant speed. That speed is the particle's terminal velocity.

For a given medium, the terminal velocity increases with increasing particle size (assuming that the density and shape of particles vary little). This is the reason why sand-size particles settle to the ocean bottom faster than clay-size particles. Furthermore, the terminal velocity of a given particle varies with the medium. Water is more viscous (offers more frictional resistance) than air. Hence, a particle of a given size has a greater terminal velocity in air than in water. For a particle to remain in suspension, turbulent motions in the medium must counter the terminal velocity. A fast-flowing river can be quite turbulent and can transport relatively large particles in suspension. The wind, on the other hand, ordinarily can transport only sand-size particles within a meter or so of the Earth's surface but can carry clay and silt-size sediment to altitudes of tens of thousands of meters and over horizontal distances of thousands of kilometers. Hence, as the wind or running water slows and becomes less turbulent, suspended particles settle out of suspension in an orderly sequence from larger to smaller particles.

FIGURE 4.3
Terminal velocity is the constant downward-directed speed of a particle within a motionless fluid due to a balance between gravity (acting downward) and fluid resistance (directed upward).

Because of differences in terminal velocity, we would expect a deep ocean current to transport small slowly sinking particles a greater horizontal distance than a large rapidly sinking particle. For example, for a slow current of 1 km (0.6 mi) per day, the sand-size particle mentioned above which takes a few days to sink to the bottom of the ocean will be displaced horizontally only a few kilometers, whereas the clay-size particle which may take more than a century to reach the bottom can be displaced thousands of kilometers. For this reason, we might expect fine sediments on the seafloor to be quite different from the particles directly above them in the surface waters. Frequently, however, this is not the case because in seawater small particles tend to aggregate and form larger particles that rapidly settle to the sea bottom. The attractive force between particles having opposite electrical charges may be a reason why particles aggregate. Also, biological particles (e.g., fecal pellets) may stick together to form larger particles.

Classification of Marine Sediments by Source

Ocean scientists classify marine sediments based on their source as *lithogenous* (from rock), *biogenous* (from living organisms or their remains), *hydrogenous* (precipitated from seawater), and *cosmogenous* (from outer space). Cosmogenous sediments are much less common than the other three. In this section, we describe each of these sediment types and the processes that form them.

LITHOGENOUS SEDIMENT

Lithogenous sediment accounts for about three-quarters of all marine sediments and owes its origin mostly to weathering and erosion of pre-existing rock. As noted in Chapter 2, **weathering** refers to the physical disintegration and chemical decomposition of rocks that are exposed to the atmosphere. **Erosion** is the transport of the products of weathering by running water, wind, glaciers, and gravity. Bruce Wilkinson of the University of Michigan estimates that about 86% of natural erosion takes place at land elevations greater than 4000 m (13,125 ft) above sea level, representing only 2% of Earth's surface. In this steep terrain, rapidly flowing rivers and streams are powerful agents of erosion. The annual discharge of South American rivers to the ocean is about twice that of Asian rivers and yet the South American rivers deliver less than half the volume of sediments to the ocean. The difference can be attributed to the fact that Asia is a larger continent with more land at higher elevations.

As the velocity of a current of water flowing over a sediment deposit increases, eventually the sediment grains are set in motion in a down-current direction. That is, the running water begins to erode the sediment deposit. Based upon experimental work, the Hjulström diagram relates the velocity of a current of water needed to move (mobilize) a particle to the size (diameter) of the particle (Figure 4.4). The particle is assumed to be on a plane bed at a water depth of 1.0 m. Current velocity is plotted on the vertical axis, increasing upward, while grain size is plotted on the horizontal axis increasing from left to right.

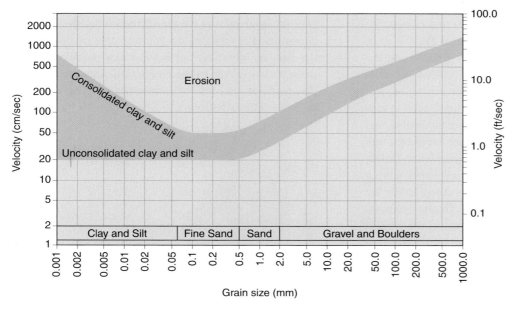

FIGURE 4.4
The Hjulström diagram relates the velocity of a current of water needed to move a particle in a down-current direction to the size (diameter) of the particle. [From Sundborg, A., 1956, *Geografiska Annaler*, Ser. A, v. 38, Fig. 16, p. 197.]

The shaded area on the diagram represents the *critical current velocity*; above this area particles are in motion (undergoing erosion) and below this area particles are not in motion.

According to the Hjulström diagram, for particles having a diameter greater than 0.5 mm, the critical current velocity steadily increases with increasing grain size, from sand to gravel to boulders. For finer grain sediment (less than 0.05 mm in diameter), the relationship between sediment size and critical current velocity is more complicated and depends on how well the particles are consolidated. For consolidated silt and clay, the critical velocity increases with decreasing sediment size and may be the same for consolidated silt and clay as for boulders. One of the principal reasons why fine particles become consolidated (adhere to one another) is the attraction between particles arising from opposite electrochemical charges, especially for clay and other soil particles. A similar effect is achieved when mucous webs produced by certain marine organisms coat marine sediments making them sticky so that they adhere to one another.

Agents of erosion deliver particles to the ocean where they are further dispersed by waves and currents. Where highlands form the coastline, waves undercut cliffs and under the influence of gravity rock debris slides or slumps into the sea. Explosive volcanic eruptions also contribute lithogenous fragments of various sizes, shapes and composition that fall through the air and accumulate in the ocean; these particles collectively are known as **tephra**.

The composition of lithogenous sediments produced through weathering depends on their source rock. The most abundant elements in the Earth's crust are oxygen (O) accounting for 46.6% by weight and silicon (Si) accounting for 27.7% by weight (Table 4.2). The most common rocks in the Earth's crust are igneous and are made up of mostly silicate minerals. The primary chemical building block of silicate minerals is the silicon-oxygen tetrahedron, consisting of one silicon atom bonded to four oxygen atoms (Figure 4.5). In the three-dimensional crystal lattice of a silicate mineral, silicon-oxygen tetrahedra link together through a sharing of oxygen atoms. Hence, the actual ratio of silicon atoms to oxygen atoms varies among silicate minerals. Quartz, one of the most common silicate minerals, has the chemical formula SiO_2. Quartz makes up about 12% of Earth's crust and is the principal component of most beach sand.

The silicon-oxygen tetrahedron is combined chemically with ions such as calcium, magnesium, and aluminum. *Ferromagnesian silicate minerals*

TABLE 4.2	
The Most Common Elements in the Earth's Crust	
Element	*Weight Percent*
Oxygen (O)	46.6
Silicon (Si)	27.7
Aluminum (Al)	8.1
Iron (Fe)	5.0
Calcium (Ca)	3.6
Sodium (Na)	2.8
Potassium (K)	2.6
Magnesium (Mg)	2.1
All others	1.5

contain iron and magnesium ions and are dark in color and relatively dense. An igneous rock that is rich in ferromagnesian minerals is also dark and dense; basalt, the chief constituent of oceanic crust, is an example. *Non-ferromagnesian silicate minerals* contain aluminum, calcium, sodium, or potassium ions and are relatively light in both appearance and density. An igneous rock that is rich in non-ferromagnesian silicate minerals is similarly light in color and comparatively less dense; granite, the chief constituent of continental crust, is an example.

As a general rule, igneous rocks that are rich in ferromagnesian silicate minerals weather more rapidly than those that are composed of mostly non-ferromagnesian silicate minerals. But given sufficient time, all rocks and minerals eventually break down chemically and physically. Differences in rates of weathering determine the dominant composition of lithogenous sediments that are delivered to the sea—mainly quartz grains and clay particles. Quartz is the most resistant of the common silicate minerals and clay particles are common weathering products of silicate minerals such as feldspars.

Oxygen

Silicon

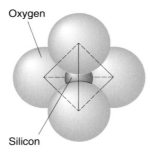

FIGURE 4.5
The silicon-oxygen tetrahedron is the building block of silicate minerals, the most common rock-forming minerals in the Earth's crust.

Warm, temperate regions account for about two-thirds of river-borne marine sediments at least in part because of the greater rate of chemical weathering in such climates. As noted earlier in this chapter, rivers transport the products of weathering in suspension, solution, or as part of the bed load. When a river reaches the coast, the denser and larger particles settle out first and are deposited in deltas, estuaries, or shallow bays. Currents flowing nearly parallel to the shoreline supply sediment to beaches while the finer sediment can be carried to the continental shelf and beyond (Chapter 8).

Almost every part of the ocean receives wind-borne dust. In fact, this is the primary mechanism whereby lithogenous particles reach the far-from-land deep ocean. Such fine particles compose much of the deep-sea red and brown clays located near the centers of major ocean basins, especially around 30 degrees N and 30 degrees S. Because of the planetary-scale atmospheric circulation regime (Chapter 5), these latitudes are characterized by arid and semi-arid climates, resulting in large subtropical deserts such as the Sahara. Furthermore, these regions of the ocean are nutrient-poor and have low biological productivity. Hence the supply of biogenous sediments that would cover the clays on the bottom is very limited. High mountains and dry-lake beds also are sources of wind-blown dust because their barren surfaces are particularly susceptibly to erosion during frequent episodes of strong winds. Volcanic ash is another source of windblown particles that settle into the ocean.

Satellite images confirm wind transport of dust from the deserts of North Africa to the Atlantic basin (Figure 4.6). Strong winds associated with weather systems that track across North Africa pick up dust particles from the dry topsoil and carry them to altitudes of 3000 m (10,000 ft) or so. Trade winds, blowing from the northeast toward the southwest, transport plumes of the smallest dust particles over the Atlantic and Caribbean and into Central America and the southeastern United States. This transoceanic journey takes about 1 to 2 weeks and occurs mostly from June to October, peaking in July.

Scientists have identified possible links between North African dust and red tides in the Gulf of Mexico and threatened coral reefs in the Caribbean. In the summer of 2001, scientists reported that iron in North African wind-borne dust particles fertilized the Gulf of Mexico waters, increasing the frequency of toxic algal blooms, commonly known as **red tides**. Red tides have been implicated in the die-off of great numbers of fish, marine mammals, and birds as well as causing respiratory problems and skin irritations in humans. Enhanced levels of iron enable special-

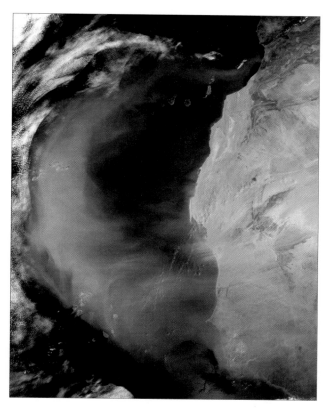

FIGURE 4.6
Saharan Air Layer outbreak moving off of Africa into the North Atlantic on March 2, 2003, where vast amounts of Saharan dust can be seen as captured by the MODIS instrument aboard NASA's Terra satellite. [Courtesy of NASA]

ized bacteria to convert nitrogen gas dissolved in seawater to a form that can be used by marine organisms, triggering an explosive growth in populations of microscopic marine algae, including toxin-producing species that form red tides. North African dust may be harming coral reefs in the Caribbean through nutrient enhancement, spurring the growth of populations of algae and phytoplankton that colonize the same environment as coral and interfere with its growth. Furthermore, North African dust may also harbor a soil fungus that attacks coral reefs.

Glaciers erode bedrock and transport rock fragments of varying size and shape to the ocean. Sediments carried by glaciers are usually angular and can range in size from a fine powder to blocks of rock the size of an automobile or even larger. As a glacier flows into the ocean it floats on the denser seawater, giving rise to stresses that fracture the ice into floating bergs. The process whereby the leading edge of a glacier breaks up into icebergs upon entering the ocean (or large lake) is known as **calving**. Transported by ocean currents and wind, icebergs eventually melt in warmer environments, releasing a poorly sorted mix of sand and boulders, which quickly sinks to the bottom. Such ice-rafted glaciomarine sediments occur on about 20% of the sea floor; they cover the Antarctic continental shelf and are common in the Arctic Ocean and on the nearby deep-ocean bottom. Layers of such glacial debris, alternating with non-glacial sediments, have also been identified in cores extracted from deep-ocean sediments of the North Atlantic. These deep-sea sediment layers record sudden releases of icebergs during the last Ice Age, known as Heinrich Events. For more on this, see the first Essay at the end of this chapter.

BIOGENOUS SEDIMENT

Biogenous sediment includes the excretions, secretions, and remains of organisms. Examples include shells, fragments of coral, and skeletal parts. The chemical composition of most biogenous sediments is either calcium carbonate ($CaCO_3$) or silica (SiO_2)—substances secreted by organisms to form their shells. Organic carbon in these particles is largely consumed by organisms or decomposed by bacteria while sinking to the bottom or after deposition while the particle is exposed on the sea floor. Biogenous sediments dominate 30% to 70% of the ocean's mid-depths and skeletal remains alone account for 25% to 50% of all particles suspended in seawater.

Calcareous sediments are the most abundant of all biogenous sediment on the sea floor (Figure 4.7). They consist of calcium carbonate *tests* of *foraminifera* (single celled organisms), shells of *pteropods* (small, floating snails), and *coccoliths* (platelets secreted by tiny, one-celled algae known as *coccolithophorids)*. Figure 4.8A is a scanning electron microscope photograph of a common species of coccolithophorids with platelets that resemble tiny hubcaps. Robust shells such as characterize many foraminifera make it to the deep-ocean bottom without entering into solution (Figure 4.8B). If later covered over by sediment, they are preserved. This is the origin of the calcareous mud that covers nearly half the deep-ocean bottom and is most abundant where ocean depths are shallower than about 4500 m (15,000 ft). They accumulate at rates of between 1 and 4 cm (0.4 and 1.6 in.) per 1000 years.

Many of the larger biogenous particles are **fecal pellets**, undigested organic matter that is concentrated and excreted by animals feeding in near-surface waters. Because of their large size, fecal pellets have relatively high terminal velocities and can sink hundreds of meters per day, reaching the ocean bottom perhaps within a few days. In this way, fecal pellets transport organic matter from surface waters and serve as a food source for bottom-dwelling

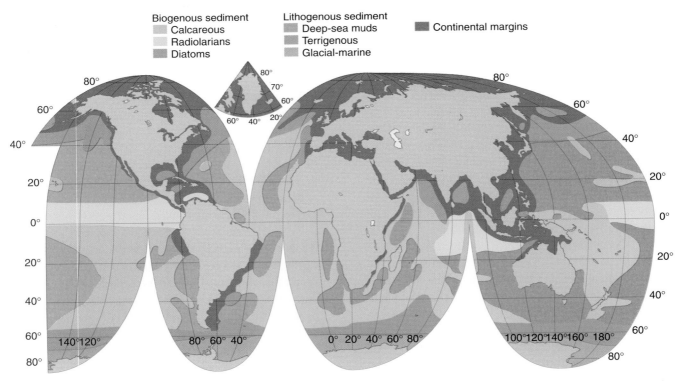

FIGURE 4.7
Distribution of lithogenous and biogenous sediments on the floor of the world ocean.

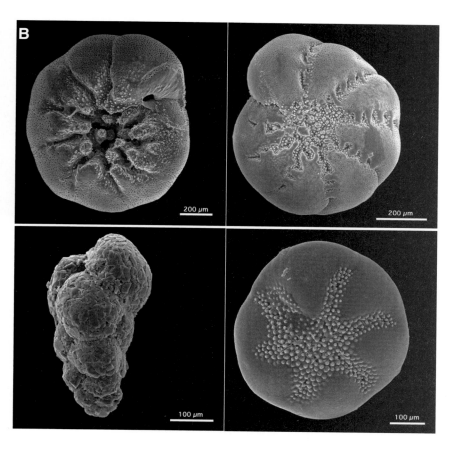

FIGURE 4.8
Examples of sources of calcareous biogenous sediment. (A) Scanning electron microscope photograph of *Emiliania huxleyi*, a common species of coccolithophorids. Each plate is a separate coccolith which settles to the ocean bottom after the organism dies. [Courtesy of Jeremy R. Young, The Natural History Museum, London] (B) Photographs of foraminifera. The remains of foraminifera preserved in marine sediments provide a record of changes in Earth's past climate and environmental conditions that can be studied in cores extracted from the sea floor. [U.S. Geological Survey]

organisms in the deep ocean. Smaller particles that are not ingested directly at the surface are often trapped by shredded pieces of large mucous webs produced by certain marine animals. These mucous fragments cause particles to clump together, making them larger so that they descend more rapidly to the sea floor (somewhat like fecal pellets although probably not as fast). The continual fall to the deep ocean floor of the remains of organisms from the upper, sunlit layer of the ocean, along with their fecal pellets and various forms of non-living matter, is sometimes called *marine snow*.

In the deep ocean, the smaller and more soluble particles slowly sink and may dissolve prior to reaching the bottom, thereby altering the chemical composition of deep-ocean waters. In addition to organic matter, dissolving particles transport nutrients (nitrogen, phosphate, and silicate compounds), essential for photosynthetic organisms living in sunlit surface waters, to the deep-ocean waters. The most soluble particles dissolve rapidly and hence accumulate only on shallow ocean bottoms below regions where shell-forming organisms occur in abundance. For example, some organisms such as pteropods are abundant in near-surface waters, but their fragile shells are made of a particularly soluble form of calcium carbonate and readily

dissolve in the more acidic deeper seawater. Consequently, pteropod shells are present only in sediment deposits on the tops of shallow seamounts; at greater depths, pteropod shells are not preserved.

Siliceous sediments are second in abundance to calcareous sediments on the ocean floor. These sediments consist of "shells" that are secreted by *diatoms*, single-celled algae (Figure 4.9A), and *radiolaria*, single-celled organisms (Figure 4.9B). Siliceous particles dissolve at all ocean depths (slightly more in shallow warm water) so their presence on the seafloor indicates areas where source organisms are particularly abundant. Siliceous mud is most common in the Pacific; diatom-rich mud nearly surrounds the Antarctic continent and occurs in the northernmost Pacific. Radiolaria are abundant in warm waters so that radiolarian-rich sediments dominate the ocean floor in equatorial latitudes.

Phosphatic sediments (rich in phosphate) are rare in marine sediment deposits. Such deposits, primarily consisting of fish bones, teeth, and scales, occur mostly on shallow, isolated banks or near coastal areas where rates of biological productivity are especially high. Such near-shore phosphatic deposits may someday be exploited for their phosphate, which is used in manufacturing fertilizers.

A

B

FIGURE 4.9
Examples of sources of siliceous biogenous sediment.(A) Diatoms as viewed through a microscope; they have silica exoskeletons. [Courtesy of NOAA and Dr. Neil Sullivan, University of Southern California] (B) These radiolaria have diameters of 0.5 to 1.5 mm. [Courtesy of National Park Service, U.S. Department of the Interior]

HYDROGENOUS SEDIMENT

Hydrogenous sediment encompasses particles that are chemically precipitated from seawater, in some cases forming coatings on other seafloor sediment. In addition, some hydrogenous sediment is the product of chemical reactions taking place in hot seawater discharged by hydrothermal vents on the sea floor (Chapter 2). Examples of hydrogenous sediment include some carbonates, halite (NaCl), gypsum (CaSO$_4$ ·2H$_2$O), and manganese nodules. A rise in the temperature of shallow water may cause dissolved carbonate to precipitate as tiny pellets known as *ooliths*, perhaps 0.5 to 1.0 mm (0.02 to 0.04 in.) in diameter. Where evaporation rates are high and rainfall is low, salts precipitate from seawater in the sequence: carbonate salts, sulfate salts, and halite.

FIGURE 4.10
A box core from the floor of the tropical Pacific showing a relatively high density of manganese nodules. Box cores preserve the character of the undisturbed ocean bottom. [Courtesy of NOAA]

Most conspicuous of all hydrogenous sediments are **manganese nodules**, irregularly shaped, sooty black or brown nodules on the sea floor (Figure 4.10). Manganese nodules on average contain about 18% manganese by weight, 17% iron, and more importantly, small amounts (generally less than 1%) of copper, cobalt, and nickel. They range in size from tiny grains to large slabs weighing hundreds of kilograms; most, however, are the size of potatoes. Manganese nodules occur on the floor of all ocean basins except the Arctic and in a variety of marine environments from abyssal plains to mid-ocean ridges. They are most abundant in an east-west belt about 5000 km (3000 mi) long on the floor of the tropical Pacific Ocean southeast of Hawaii and north of 10 degrees N.

Manganese nodules begin as coatings on hard objects (e.g., rock fragments, whale ear bones, shark teeth) that are exposed on the ocean bottom for lengthy periods of times. Burrowing organisms turn the nodules over, exposing all sides to seawater so that a coating forms on all sides of the object. Manganese nodules grow extremely slowly, ranging from about 1 to 10 mm (0.004 to 0.04 in.) per million years. With such slow growth rates, manganese nodules must remain unburied on the ocean bottom. Otherwise, sediments would cover the nodules, isolating them from contact with seawater and greatly inhibiting growth. In areas of the ocean receiving an abundant influx of sediment, only small (pea-sized or smaller) micronodules develop because they are buried before they can grow into larger nodules. Accordingly, rich manganese nodule deposits are found only in regions of the ocean far from shore, where input of lithogenous sediments is small and in unproductive areas where the rate of accumulation of biogenous particles is also low.

COSMOGENOUS SEDIMENT

Cosmogenous sediment comes from outer space, for example, as meteorite fragments. Perhaps 90% of the extraterrestrial solid particles entering Earth's atmosphere burns up prior to reaching the surface due to frictional heating. Most particles that survive the journey through the atmosphere and enter the ocean are so small that they dissolve before reaching the bottom. Nonetheless, cosmogenous particles are found mixed with other ocean bottom sediments. In addition, some cosmogenous particles that fall on the Greenland and Antarctic ice sheets enter the ocean via melting snow and ice.

Some cosmogenous sediments are remnants of the formation of planets in the solar system. These iron-rich particles likely have a chemical composition similar to Earth's core and mantle and their unique composition make them readily recognizable in deep ocean sediment deposits. Other particles, formed from silicate rocks blasted off other planets or the moon by meteorite impacts, are more difficult to identify as cosmogenous because they resemble lithogenous sediment.

A special type of sediment that is indirectly cosmogenous in origin consists of solidified droplets of rocks melted when huge meteorites struck the Earth. These small black fragments of silica-rich glass are known as **tektites**. Tektites are typically 2.5 to 5 cm (1 to 2 in.) across and have a teardrop or dumbbell shape indicating that they were once fluid. They formed when droplets of molten rock produced by a meteorite impact were blasted into Earth's atmosphere and rapidly cooled and solidified. For example, the meteorite impact about 65 million years ago that is hypothesized to have killed off the dinosaurs generated great numbers of tektites that accumulated in and around the impact site, that is, Mexico's Yucatán Peninsula (Chapter 1). Tektites also have been identified in ocean bottom sediments off southern Australia and in the Indian Ocean.

Marine Sedimentary Deposits

The different types of marine sediments (i.e., lithogenous, biogenous, hydrogenous, and cosmogenous) occur in varying proportions and thicknesses on the ocean bottom as marine sedimentary deposits. In this section, we describe marine sediment deposits of the continental margin and the deep ocean basins.

CONTINENTAL-MARGIN DEPOSITS

Most marine sediment deposits in the continental margin, called **neritic deposits**, are lithogenous and occur in a wide range of sediment sizes. Most river-borne lithogenous sediments that reach the coast do not travel very far seaward of the shoreline. About 95% of the largest sediments transported to the ocean by rivers are trapped and deposited in bays, wetlands, estuaries, beaches or deltas. Only about 5% of river-borne sediment brought to the shoreline reaches the continental shelf or slope and very little sediment of terrestrial origin is transported beyond the continental margin into the deep-ocean basins. A notable exception is seaward of the mouths of major sediment-transporting rivers such as the Mississippi (United States), Ganges (Bangladesh), and Yangtse (China). Massive submarine avalanches and turbidity currents can transport sediments hundreds or thousands of kilometers out onto the continental rise and to the sea floor beyond.

Where a river enters the ocean, the water slows so that sediments begin settling out of suspension. As long as currents do not carry off sediments as fast as they are deposited, sediments accumulate at the mouth of the river as a **delta**, so-called because this deposit resembles a triangle or the Greek letter *delta* (Δ) when viewed from above. Water flows in a branching series of channels, known as *distributaries*, spreading sediment over the surface of the delta. Unless artificially stabilized, the main current of the river may abruptly shift from one distributary to another.

Many factors govern the shape of a delta including river discharge, sediment load and compaction, subsidence of the sea (or lake) bottom, tides, and waves. Depending on which factor prevails, deltas are classified as *river-dominated* (e.g., Mississippi), *wave-dominated* (e.g., Niger), or *tide-dominated* (e.g., Ganges). In a river-dominated delta, the rate of input of sediments (from rivers or streams) exceeds the rate of removal of sediments (by waves and currents) and the delta develops the classic triangular shape (as viewed from above). In a wave-dominated delta, strong wave action and currents produce only a slight bulging of an overall straight coastline. In a tide-dominated delta, tidal currents rework river-supplied sediments into long, narrow islands and submarine ridges.

The scene in Figure 4.11 looking toward the northwest shows the Nile River Delta, photographed from a NASA Space Shuttle. The delta stretches about 160 km (100 mi) north and south and 240 km (150 mi) west and east. Beginning at Cairo, Egypt, the delta disperses the

FIGURE 4.11
The Nile River Delta. Photograph taken from NASA Space Shuttle in May 1996. [Courtesy of NASA]

flow of the Nile through a fan-shaped network of channels into the Mediterranean Sea. At the edge of the delta, the Nile splits into two branches, the Rosetta to the west and the Damietta to the east, each about 240 km (150 mi) long, that cross the delta and empty into the Mediterranean Sea. For thousands of years, suspended sediment delivered and deposited by the Nile and its branches provided the Nile Delta with the most fertile soils on the African continent.

Wetlands are low-lying flat areas that are covered by water or have soils that are saturated with water for at least part of the year. They are common on deltas and coastal plains of the mid-Atlantic U.S. and Gulf of Mexico and in many other areas of passive continental margins worldwide. Wetlands such as salt marshes accumulate large amounts of brown or black organic matter and support numerous and diverse populations of marine plants, animals and birds. Wetlands help control coastal flooding by acting as a sponge taking up water during high water episodes.

As noted in Chapter 2, near the mouths of many major sediment-transporting rivers that empty into the ocean, intermittent avalanches of dense, mud-rich waters, called **turbidity currents**, flow down submarine canyons, carrying sediment onto the ocean floor (Figure 4.12A). Such flows are rarely directly observed in the ocean but are well known in lakes and reservoirs behind dams. Turbidity currents are sufficiently powerful to break submarine

cables, especially near the mouths of major rivers, such as the Congo (Zaire) and Ganges. Sedimentary deposits produced by turbidity currents are known as **turbidites** (Figure 4.12B).

Although occurring infrequently, turbidity currents transport and deposit large amounts of sediment that form thick beds over broad areas of the deep ocean floor. For example, in 1929 an earthquake triggered a submarine avalanche that produced a turbidity current off the Grand Banks, south of Newfoundland. Sediments were deposited on the nearby deep-ocean floor over an area that measured 100 km (60 mi) by 300 km (190 mi). Based on the time elapsed between the earthquake and submarine-cable breaks, scientists calculated the speed of the turbidity current at about 20 km per hr (12 mph), about the speed of a slow freight train. Submarine avalanches not only cause turbidity currents but also may trigger dangerous tsunamis (Chapter 7).

Turbidity currents are much denser than seawater because of the added suspended sediment load. Hence, they flow along the ocean bottom, often eroding channels just as rivers do on land. Such flow behavior explains why turbidites have unusual textures and contain abundant shells and other remains of shallow-water dwelling organisms.

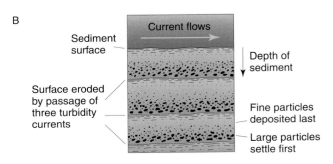

FIGURE 4.12
Turbidity currents can transport lithogenous sediment into the deep-ocean bottom. (A) Vertical profile of a turbidity current flowing on the continental slope and rise. (B) Vertical cross-section of turbidites deposited by three successive turbidity currents.

Submarine canyons near the mouths of major sediment-transporting rivers would soon fill with sediments unless periodically scoured by turbidity currents.

Obstructions on the ocean bottom deflect turbidity currents and can prevent their flow onto the deep-ocean floor. This is particularly the case in the Pacific Ocean basin, where submarine ridges associated with volcanic island arcs and trenches block near-bottom waters flowing toward the adjacent deep-ocean bottom. In the Atlantic, northern Indian, and Arctic Oceans, thick sediment deposits form the conspicuous continental rise (Chapter 2). The tops of seamounts and submarine ridges typically are unaffected by turbidity currents and are free of turbidites.

In coastal areas, especially near large rivers or in deltas, marine sediment accumulates rapidly, typically at rates of several meters per thousand years. Sediments are buried too quickly to react fully with seawater or the oxygen dissolved in the water. Furthermore, bottom-dwelling organisms cannot consume all of the food sources. These sediments exhibit a wide variety of colors, including greens and blues, due to the various oxidation states of iron on the particles.

Human activity plays an important role in the delivery of sediment to the ocean. In 2005, an international research team reported that through soil erosion, human activity (e.g., agriculture, deforestation) has increased the amount of sediment transported by global rivers by 2.3 ± 0.6 billion metric tons per year. In fact, human activity is responsible for mobilizing about 15 times as much sediment as natural processes. At the same time, retention of sediments in reservoirs (e.g., behind dams) reduced the flux of sediment reaching the coast by 1.4 ± 0.3 billion metric tons per year. More than 100 billion metric tons of sediment is now sequestered in reservoirs most of which were constructed in the past 50 years or so. On the positive side, retention of river-borne sediment in reservoirs behind dams may reduce the need for dredging of harbors and offshore coral reefs may benefit from less turbid waters and more sunlight. On the negative side, deltas are deprived of sediments and undergo subsidence, wave erosion, and loss of productivity.

Since the 1970 completion of the Aswan High Dam on the Nile River, the Nile delta's natural evolution has been disrupted. Prior to the Aswan High Dam, perhaps 90% of the sediment transported by the Nile reached the delta; today, almost all the sediment is trapped in Lake Nasser, the huge reservoir behind the dam. With much less sediment input coupled with continued compaction and subsidence of the delta, erosive forces (e.g., waves) are dominating and the delta's coastline is retreating—at the mouth of the Nile by about 10 m (33 ft) per year. Saline water from the Mediterranean is also seeping into parts of the delta. And nutrient-rich sediments formerly transported downstream to the Mediterranean have been reduced, thereby depleting the populations of some fish species in the Nile and the eastern Mediterranean. For example, the sardine catch at the mouth of the Nile has plunged 95% since completion of the Aswan Dam.

DEEP-OCEAN DEPOSITS

Fine-grained sediments that gradually accumulate particle-by-particle on the deep-ocean floor form **pelagic deposits**. Most of these sediments are biogenous and their accumulation rates are considerably slower than neritic (near shore) sediments. On average, a 1 mm-thick layer forms in about 1000 years. (A 1-inch thick layer forms in about 25,000 to 250,000 years.) In spite of these very low accumulation rates, sufficient time has passed since formation of the ocean basins that the average thickness of pelagic deposits is 500 to 600 m (1600 to 2000 ft).

Very small particles have relatively low terminal velocities and sink slowly through the ocean depths. Many of these particles are eaten by filter feeders or trapped in mucus nets secreted by marine organisms. Their relatively long suspension times in the water mean that they are widely dispersed by currents. There is also ample time for chemical reactions to occur. For example, iron minerals in suspended clay particles react chemically with dissolved oxygen in seawater, forming a rusty (iron oxide) coating. The abundance of such red- or brown-stained particles in deep-sea mud is responsible for the colors and common names of these deposits, that is, *red clay* and *brown mud*. Colors of deep-sea clays range from brick red (derived from the Saharan Desert) in the Atlantic Ocean to chocolate brown in the Pacific Ocean.

Pelagic deposits that are more than 30% biogenous by weight are called either calcareous ooze or siliceous ooze depending on composition. **Calcareous ooze**—made up of the tests (protective shells) of coccolithophorids, pteropods, and foraminifera—are the most abundant of pelagic oozes. Calcareous oozes generally are confined to ocean waters shallower than the **carbonate compensation depth (CCD)**, the depth of the ocean below which calcium carbonate ($CaCO_3$) shells and skeletons dissolve and do not accumulate (Figure 4.13). (The CCD is also called the *saturation horizon*.) The rate at which calcium carbonate dissolves in seawater increases with falling temperature;

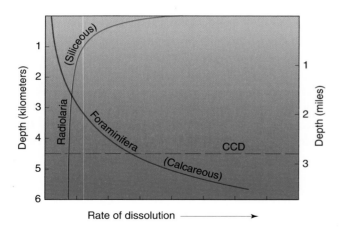

FIGURE 4.13
The rate at which radiolaria (siliceous) and foraminifera (calcareous) shells dissolve with increasing ocean depth in terms of percent weight loss. Siliceous shells more readily dissolve in surface waters whereas calcareous shells more readily dissolve at depth. The carbonate compensation depth (CCD) is defined as the depth at which the amount of calcareous particles declines to less than 20% of the mass of all particles present.

that is, cold water can hold more carbon dioxide which dissociates to form carbonic acid that dissolves $CaCO_3$. Ocean temperature usually drops with increasing depth below surface waters so that more and more calcareous particles dissolve with increasing water depth. Above the CCD, waters are relatively warm and saturated with respect to the carbonate minerals calcite and aragonite. At the CCD, the rate of production of calcareous tests equals the rate of calcite dissolution. Below the CCD, waters are under saturated with respect to carbonate minerals, colder, and sufficiently acidic to dissolve carbonate shells and skeletons.

Worldwide, the carbonate compensation depth averages about 4500 m (14,800 ft). Calcareous oozes accumulate on ocean bottom features having depths shallower than 4500 m, such as the crest and slopes of the mid-ocean ridges. If the ocean basins were to suddenly dry up, the tops of volcanic peaks that had been above the CCD would appear light in color due to the accumulation of carbonate-rich sediments. Hence, the CCD is somewhat analogous to the snow line on terrestrial mountain ranges.

As discussed in Chapter 3, the increasing flux of atmospheric CO_2 into the ocean is lowering the pH of seawater. (Recall that ocean waters are slightly alkaline.) In response to this *ocean acidification*, the CCD has shifted upward an estimated 50 to 200 m (165 to 660 ft) since the beginnings of the Industrial Revolution and humankind's increasing reliance on fossil fuels. The expected continued increase in atmospheric CO_2 concentration is likely to be accompanied by a further thinning of the portion of the ocean that is friendly to organisms having calcareous shells and skeletons.

Siliceous ooze is composed of tests of diatoms and radiolaria (described earlier in this chapter). Ocean water is under-saturated with silica so that these tests dissolve at all ocean depths (Figure 4.13). They occur on the sea floor below surface waters only where source organisms are particularly abundant. Siliceous and calcareous oozes consist of clay size particles and dominate the deep-ocean bottom sediment (Figure 4.7). Sand-size particles make up less than 10% of the deep-ocean sediments and the coarsest deep-ocean sediment deposits are the products of explosive volcanic eruptions and ice rafting.

As noted above, in the deep ocean, accumulations of seafloor sediments on average are hundreds of meters thick. However, in 2005, ocean scientists discovered an area in the South Pacific Ocean about 4000 km (2500 mi) east of New Zealand where pelagic sediments form an unusually thin veneer over basaltic oceanic crust—in some places sediments have a thickness of only 50 cm (20 in.). Approximately the size of the Mediterranean Sea, this so-called *South Pacific Bare Zone* owes its relative dearth of sediments to a number of factors. Surface waters are nutrient-poor limiting the populations of plankton and other organisms so that there are little organic remains to contribute to the rain of biogenous particles. The deepest water is relatively low in carbonate and silica so that the remains of organisms with carbonate or silica hard parts dissolve before reaching the seafloor. The region's great distance from a landmass means a limited supply of windblown dust. Little or no hydrothermal activity limits the amount of dissolved minerals that could precipitate as hydrogenous particles. Furthermore, surface currents that steer Antarctic ice bergs and their load of lithogenous sediment bypass the region.

Another recent discovery by ocean scientists calls for a revised description of the deep ocean abyss as a serene place where small particles gently rain down and settle on the ocean floor as pelagic deposits. Instruments lowered to the sea floor to measure currents and the resulting mobilization of bottom sediments detected a much more active environment than expected. Scientists found that occasionally bottom currents and **abyssal storms** scour the ocean floor, generating moving clouds of suspended sediment. Although called an abyssal storm, the water motion pales by comparison to the wind speeds in atmospheric storms.

Abyssal currents and storms apparently derive their energy from surface ocean currents. Wind-driven surface ocean currents flow about the margins of the ocean basins as huge gyres centered near 30 degrees latitude (Chapter 6). Viewed from above, these *subtropical gyres* rotate clockwise in the Northern Hemisphere and counterclockwise in the Southern Hemisphere. For reasons given in Chapter 6, surface currents flow faster, are narrower, and extend to greater depths on the western side of the gyres. They are known as *western boundary currents* and include, for example, the Gulf Stream of the North Atlantic Ocean basin. Abyssal currents are likewise most vigorous on the western side of the ocean basins, flowing along the base of the continental rise, which is on the order of several kilometers deep.

Abyssal storms may be caused by eddies (called *rings*) that occasionally break off from the main current of the Gulf Stream and other western boundary currents. During an abyssal storm, the eddy or ring may extend to the ocean bottom causing the typical velocity of a bottom current to increase 10-fold to about 1.5 km per hr (1 mph). While unimpressive as a wind speed, water is much denser than air so that its erosive ability and sediment-transport capacity is significant even at only 1.5 km per hr. At this higher speed, the suspended sediment load in the bottom current increases by a factor of ten. Abyssal storms scour the sea floor leaving behind long furrows in the pelagic deposits. After a few days to a few weeks, the current weakens or the eddy (ring) is reabsorbed into the main surface ocean circulation and the suspended load settles to the ocean floor. In this way, abyssal storms can transport tons of sediment great distances, thereby disrupting the orderly depositional sequence of layers of deep-sea sediments. Scientists must take this disruption into account when interpreting deep-sea sediment cores for their record of past environmental conditions (Chapter 12).

Marine Sedimentary Rock

As noted in Chapter 1, sediment is generated at the interfaces between the lithosphere, atmosphere, hydrosphere, cryosphere, and biosphere. Physical and chemical weathering processes break down exposed bedrock forming rock fragments (sediments) that are transported by rivers, glaciers, wind, and gravity to the ocean. Weathering also releases soluble constituents, such as calcium and sodium that dissolve in water and are transported in solution to the ocean.

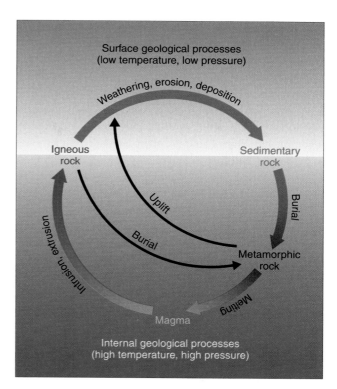

FIGURE 4.14
As shown in this schematic diagram, the conversion of marine sediments to sedimentary rock is part of the rock cycle.

As part of the *rock cycle* (Figure 4.14), over the millions of years that constitute geologic time, sediment that is deposited on the ocean floor is gradually converted to solid marine sedimentary rock through lithification. **Lithification** usually involves both compaction and cementing of sediments at relatively low temperatures (under 200 °C or 390 °F). Sediments are compacted by the increasing weight of sediments accumulating above that squeeze deeper sediments closer together. Siliceous and calcareous fluids migrating through the tiny openings between individual sediment grains precipitate minerals that fill the pore spaces, cementing grains to one another. The product of lithification is sedimentary rock such as shale, sandstone, or limestone depending on the composition and particle size of the constituent sediments. With deeper burial and further increases in temperature, pressure, and access to chemically active fluids, sedimentary rock may be converted to metamorphic rock such as slate, schist or gneiss.

Most sediment and sedimentary rock deposited on the ocean floor is transported with the underlying moving lithospheric plate, eventually entering a subduction zone, where they slide down into the mantle and are metamorphosed or melted into magma. Magma produced in subduction zones is differentiated into lighter magma that is ejected by andesitic/rhyolitic volcanoes landward of the subduction zones. Some of the heavier magma might be extruded in backarc spreading areas but most enters the asthenosphere. While much of the marine sedimentary strata on the continents originated in extensive shallow seas, some marine sedimentary deposits were scraped off subducting oceanic plates and physically attached to a continental plate. This plus other tectonic activity such as mountain building explains why marine sedimentary rocks are found high in continental mountains. For an example of this, see this chapter's second Essay.

Resources of the Seafloor

Resources extracted from the seafloor include oil, natural gas, sand, gravel, and minerals. While oil and natural gas account for more than 95% of the total monetary value of resources extracted from the seafloor, sand and gravel are the seafloor resources most commonly mined worldwide. Approximately 25% of the oil and 20% of the natural gas consumed in the U.S. each year comes from offshore sources including the Gulf of Mexico, Persian Gulf, and North Sea.

Global economics plays a central role in governing the amount of ocean floor mining and is the principal reason why few resources are mined from the sea (other than oil, natural gas, sand, and gravel). Production costs are usually much lower for onshore mining versus offshore mining. In the future, however, shifts in the international minerals markets and increased demand for strategically important minerals may make it feasible to begin mining more seabed resources.

OIL AND NATURAL GAS

Petroleum and natural gas are derived from the remains of marine plants and animals and occur in the pore spaces of marine sedimentary rock. Both oil and natural gas consist of hydrocarbons, compounds whose molecules contain only hydrogen and carbon atoms. Oil is a mixture of thousands of different hydrocarbons. By volume, natural gas is up to 99% methane (CH_4), plus small quantities of ethane (C_2H_6), propane (C_3H_8), and butane (C_4H_{10}).

Today's major deposits of oil and natural gas developed under very restricted and unusual biological and geological conditions millions of years ago. Petroleum formation requires that substantial amounts of organic matter must accumulate at the bottom of a shallow quiet sea. Decomposer organisms reduce the dissolved oxygen

to levels that can be tolerated by only anaerobic bacteria. (*Anaerobic* organisms can live and grow without free oxygen.) Products of anaerobic decomposition include methane and other light hydrocarbons. With continued accumulation of organic and other sediment on the sea floor, the deeper organic-rich sediments were subject to increasing temperature and pressure that spurred their lithification and the conversion of organic matter to oil and natural gas.

Conditions favorable to oil and natural gas production occurred primarily during the geologic periods known as the Ordovician (505-438 million years ago), Permian (286-245 million years ago), Jurassic (208-144 million years ago) and Cretaceous (144-65 million years ago). At those times, sea level was unusually high and ocean waters spread over low-lying portions of the continents producing large shallow seas. Enhanced biological productivity in those seas provided the raw material for the eventual formation of oil and natural gas deposits.

Oil and natural gas migrated upward from their source rock into more porous layers of sandstone or limestone, displacing the water that occupied the pore space in these strata. An overlying layer of less permeable rock trapped the petroleum in the so-called *reservoir rock*. Extraction wells must penetrate this reservoir rock to tap the oil or natural gas. Oil formed when sediments were buried to depths of at least 2 km (1.2 mi) and generally does not occur at depths greater than 3 km (1.9 mi). Natural gas is usually found in marine sedimentary rocks at depths of less than 7 km (4.3 mi).

MINERAL RESOURCES

Great quantities of sand, gravel, and shells are mined from the near-shore, shallow ocean bottom, especially near coastal cities. These resources are used primarily in road construction and the production of cement and concrete. Also, sand dredged from the shallow ocean bottom is used to replenish and restore nearby beaches eroded by storm waves (Chapter 8).

In some locales, valuable metallic and non-metallic minerals such as iron, tin, platinum, gold, and diamonds occur mixed with coastal sands. Most of these resources are products of weathering and erosion of continental rock and sediment and are transported to the sea in suspension by rivers along with other lithogenous particles. Ocean waves and currents sort and concentrate metals and gemstones in coastal or submarine deposits, known as **placer deposits**. Placer minerals typically are relatively dense and resistant and were left behind as a *lag concentrate* as waves and currents removed the less dense sand grains. Although hundreds of such deposits are known from around the world, very few are actually being exploited. Today, dredging of placer deposits usually takes place in shallow waters just offshore and yields tin (Thailand and Indonesia), gold (Alaska, New Zealand, and the Philippines), and diamonds (Namibia and South Africa). Rivers also deliver minerals in solution to the sea including phosphorite (a deposit rich in phosphate that precipitates from seawater and accumulates on the seafloor under upwelling or other biologically productive areas), and manganese (which forms manganese nodules via biogeochemical cycling).

As noted earlier in this chapter, manganese nodules on the deep ocean floor have been studied extensively as potential sources of copper, nickel, and cobalt. Cobalt-rich manganese crusts occur at intermediate depths (2 to 3 km, or 1 to 2 mi) on the slopes of extinct volcanoes that form many Pacific islands. But after decades of exploration and development of deep-ocean mining techniques, there is still insufficient economic incentive for commercial production from the deep-ocean floor. Furthermore, environmental safeguards and financial obligations imposed by the United Nations Convention on the Law of the Sea, ratified in 1994, have greatly reduced interest in mining manganese nodules.

Development of the plate tectonics theory spurred interest in another source of marine mineral deposits: geological processes taking place at submarine plate boundaries (Chapter 2). Ocean basins include sites where mineral deposits form in place (a process called *mineralization*) rather than being delivered to the sea by rivers. Seawater, magma, and new oceanic crust interact at plate boundaries (including spreading centers and subduction zones), exchanging heat and chemicals and producing *hydrothermal mineral deposits.* Magma from Earth's interior heats the seawater that circulates through fractures and vents in the oceanic crust. Hot seawater dissolves metals from the magma and crust, and those metals react with sulfur to precipitate as sulfide minerals on the ocean floor. These hydrothermal deposits are potential sources of copper, zinc, silver, gold, and other metals.

As is the case with seabed placer deposits, development of hydrothermal mineral deposits depends on favorable economic conditions as well as consideration of potential environmental impacts. In any event, sulfide metals associated with subduction zones (e.g., in the western Pacific) or hydrothermal vents are economically more promising for several reasons: a greater percentage

of precious metals, occurrence at shallower ocean depths (1000 to 2000 m or 3300 to 6600 ft), and location within the 370-km (200-nautical mi) jurisdiction of coastal or island nations. Worldwide, about 250 sites of massive sulfide deposits have been identified on the sea-floor.

The first sea-floor exploration activity for massive sulfide deposits was completed successfully in 2007. Interest focused on an active hydrothermal vent system in the waters within the Exclusive Economic Zone (EEZ) of Papua New Guinea. This hydrothermal deposit features higher concentrations of gold, copper, zinc, and silver than the yield of terrestrial mines and developers are encouraged by the availability of appropriate mining technology and rising metal prices. Because the proposed mine site is located within an EEZ, developers are not subject to the environmental restrictions of the U.N. Convention on the Law of the Sea. Within EEZs (discussed below), it is up to the individual nation to issue mining permits and impose environmental regulations. For economic reasons, Papua New Guinea is expected to be relatively lenient in this regard and mining is scheduled to begin in 2009.

Conservationists are concerned that although mining of sulfide deposits will be restricted to small areas of the ocean bottom (each about 1.0 square km), mining activities would create benthic disturbances and produce sediment plumes that could smother or contaminate hydrothermal vent communities. Meanwhile, developers argue that the planned deep-sea mining will be less environmentally disruptive than similar mining conducted on land. For one, mining will focus on deposits associated with extinct vents thereby avoiding contact with lava and superheated water. Furthermore, developers point out that deep-sea mining of sulfide ores produces far less waste material than terrestrial mining. (Typically, a targeted metal represents only a tiny fraction of a huge rock mass.)

EXCLUSIVE ECONOMIC ZONE

Since 1958, the United Nations has worked to formulate international policies concerning exploitation of seabed resources, including fuels and minerals. But progress has been slow because of conflicts among the more than 150 nations involved in negotiations. A fundamental philosophical division exists between less-developed and more-developed nations. Many less-developed nations view ocean resources as the common heritage of all people, but they fear that the world's richest and most technologically advanced nations will reap the bulk of the harvest. While the U.S. and many other more-developed nations adhere to the common heritage concept, they fear that too much power would be vested in the governments of less-developed nations if they were granted significant say in shaping ocean resource policy.

The 1982 U.N. Convention on the Law of the Sea granted jurisdiction over an **exclusive economic zone (EEZ)** to each of 151 coastal nations. In March 1983, the U.S. (later joined by fifty other nations) defined its jurisdiction over ocean resources (including minerals, fuels, and fisheries) to extend 370 km (200 nautical mi) offshore, encompassing an area that is 1.7 times that of the total land area of the U.S. and its territories. Within the EEZ, the federal government regulates all economic activity beyond the limits of the individual state's jurisdiction. For the U.S., the National Oceanic and Atmospheric Administration (NOAA) and the Interior Department share responsibility for managing seabed mineral resources.

The 370-km exclusive economic zone may or may not encompass the entire continental shelf associated with the landmass of a specific coastal nation (Figure 4.15). Hence, a provision of the 1994 U.N. Convention on the Law of the Sea allows a nation to expand its EEZ to the edge of the continental shelf, if it can establish that the new territory is a "natural prolongation" of its landmass. (Recall from Chapter 2 that the continental shelf is a submerged extension of a continent.) The challenge is to establish scientifically the outer boundary of the continental shelf, that is, where the continental shelf ends and the slope begins. Nations have until 2009 to prove their case. By one estimate, the U.S. stands to gain an additional 750,000 square km (290,000 square mi) of the Atlantic, Pacific and Arctic Oceans as the EEZ includes the shelf surrounding every one of the nation's islands and possessions, no matter how small or remote.

Conclusions

Sediments are produced by processes operating at the interfaces between the lithosphere, atmosphere, hydrosphere, cryosphere, and biosphere. Rivers, winds, glaciers, and gravity transport sediment from land to sea while some sediment originates in the ocean. Sediment deposits on the ocean floor record changes in the various subsystems of the Earth system over millions of years, that is, since formation of the present ocean basins. In later chapters, we revisit deep-sea sediments as we seek to understand how the various subsystems have changed through Earth history and what is revealed about past variations in Earth's climate.

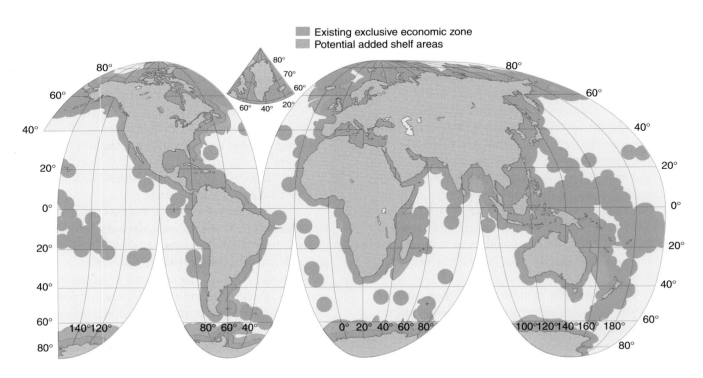

FIGURE 4.15
Current exclusive economic zones (brown) in the near future could be extended to the limits of the continental shelf (orange).

Sedimentary processes (e.g., weathering, erosion, lithification) are key players in the functioning of the Earth system. For example, sequestering of carbon in sediments and sedimentary rocks is responsible for Earth's fossil fuel resources and accounts for the relatively small amount of carbon dioxide in Earth's modern atmosphere. Atmospheric carbon dioxide is one of many gases that contribute to the planet's greenhouse effect. We learn more about Earth's climate system in the next chapter where we consider the flux of heat energy and water between the ocean and atmosphere.

Basic Understandings

- Particles that accumulate on the sea floor are known as marine sediments. They differ in source, composition, size, and the rate at which they accumulate on the sea floor.
- Sediments are classified by size into three broad categories as mud, sand, or gravel. Accumulations of sediment on the seafloor also vary in the range of grain size, known as sorting. A well-sorted sediment deposit has a narrow range of grain sizes whereas a poorly sorted one has a broad range of grain sizes. Sediment size, sorting, and composition provide information on past environmental conditions.
- Terminal velocity is the constant speed attained by a particle as it falls through a motionless fluid such as water or air. The speed of a falling particle in calm water or air is regulated by gravity and the resistance offered by the medium through which the particle falls. The magnitude of the resisting force eventually equals gravity; that is, the two forces come into balance. When forces are balanced, then according to Newton's first law of motion, the downward moving particle attains a constant speed (the terminal velocity). Within a given fluid, the terminal velocity generally increases with increasing particle size.
- Ocean scientists classify marine sediments based on their source as lithogenous (from rock), biogenous (from organisms or their remains), hydrogenous (precipitated from seawater), and cosmogenous (from outer space).
- Lithogenous particles (most of which originate from weathering of rock on land) are transported to the ocean by rivers, winds, glaciers, and gravity. Some lithogenous sediments are of volcanic origin.
- The largest lithogenous particles are deposited close to where they enter the ocean; smaller particles are transported further out to sea. Fine windblown sediment (i.e., clay and silt particles) can travel thousands of kilometers from its source.
- According to the Hjulström diagram, the critical current velocity required to mobilize particles having a diameter greater than 0.5 mm increases with increasing grain size (from sand to gravel to boulders). For finer grain sediment (less than 0.05 mm in diameter), the relationship between sediment size and critical current velocity depends on how well the particles are consolidated. For consolidated silt and clay, the critical velocity increases with decreasing sediment size.
- Biogenous sediment includes the excretions, secretions, and remains of organisms living in the ocean, usually in the sun-lit, near-surface waters. The chemical composition of most biogenous sediments is either calcium carbonate ($CaCO_3$) or silica (SiO_2).
- Hydrogenous sediments are precipitated from seawater, in some cases forming coatings on other seafloor sediment. In addition, some hydrogenous sediment is the product of chemical reactions in seawater circulating in hydrothermal vent systems.
- Most marine sediment deposits on the continental margin, called neritic deposits, are lithogenous and occur in a wide range of sizes. About 95% of the largest sediments transported to the ocean by rivers are trapped and deposited in bays, wetlands, estuaries, beaches or deltas. Only about 5% of river-borne sediment brought to the shoreline reaches the continental shelf or slope.
- Fine-grained sediments that slowly accumulate on the deep-ocean floor form pelagic deposits. Most of these sediments are biogenous and their accumulation rate is considerably slower than neritic (near shore) sediments.
- Occasional bottom currents and abyssal storms scour the pelagic deposits on the ocean bottom, generating moving clouds of

suspended sediment which disrupts the orderly accumulation of sediments.

- Calcareous ooze—made up of the tests (protective shells) of coccolithophorids, pteropods, and foraminifera—are the most abundant of pelagic oozes. They occur where the deep ocean is shallower than the carbonate compensation depth (CCD).

- Siliceous ooze is composed of tests of diatoms and radiolaria. Ocean water is under-saturated with silica so that these tests dissolve at all ocean depths. Hence, they occur on the sea floor only in those portions of the ocean where source organisms in the surface waters are abundant and deposition outpaces dissolution.

- Over the millions of years that constitute geologic time, sediment that is deposited on the ocean floor is gradually converted to solid marine sedimentary rock through lithification, which usually involves both compaction and cementing of sediments at relatively low temperatures (under 200 ºC or 390 ºF).

- Oil and natural gas are derived from the remains of marine organisms and occur in the pore spaces of marine sedimentary rock.

- Great quantities of sand, gravel, and shells are mined from the near-shore, shallow ocean bottom, especially near coastal cities, primarily for road construction and production of cement and concrete. In some locales, valuable metallic (e.g., tin) and non-metallic (e.g., diamonds) minerals occur mixed with coastal sands as lag concentrates.

- Since 1958, the United Nations has been working on international policies concerning the exploitation of seabed resources, including fuels and minerals. But progress has been slow because of long-standing conflicts among the more than 150 nations involved in negotiations. At present, the exclusive economic zone (EEZ) extends to 370 km (200 nautical mi) offshore with the possible extension to the edge of the continental shelf by the year 2009.

Review

1. What is the relationship between the degree of sorting of a sediment deposit and the range in size exhibited by the sediments? Are sediments better sorted in the continental margins or on the deep-ocean floor? Explain your answer.
2. Define terminal velocity and describe the relationship between terminal velocity and particle size in a specified medium such as water or air.
3. What are the four major groups of marine sediments? Briefly describe the source of each sediment type.
4. What are the two most common types of biogenous sediment on the ocean floor?
5. A deep-ocean manganese nodule is an example of what type of marine sediment? Describe the ocean environment in which the largest nodules are found.
6. Compare the locations and accumulation rates of neritic and pelagic marine sediment deposits on the ocean bottom.
7. What are the two types of pelagic deposits that are more than 30% biogenous by weight? Which type is unlikely to occur on the ocean bottom at depths greater than about 4500 m (14,800 ft) below sea level?
8. Define lithification and describe the processes involved in lithification.
9. How are economically important deposits of methane (natural gas) generated?
10. Compare the area of the U.S. exclusive economic zone (EEZ) to the nation's total land area (including its territories).

Critical Thinking

1. What sequence of events could account for the presence of relatively coarse sediment on the deep-ocean floor?
2. Why are quartz grains and clay particles the most common lithogenous sediments transported to the ocean by rivers and streams?
3. How might a lowering of the pH of seawater affect the abundance of calcareous sediment that accumulates on the sea floor?
4. Only a small fraction of the particles entering Earth's atmosphere from outer space ends up on the ocean floor as cosmogenous sediment. Explain why.
5. What is the significance of the carbonate compensation depth (CCD)? How might ocean acidification affect the CCD?
6. What would explain the near absence of sediment on some portions of the deep-ocean floor?
7. How might abyssal storms affect our interpretation of the record of past climatic episodes obtained from analysis of deep-sea sediment cores?
8. Is the composition of biogenous sediment on the ocean floor always an indicator of the type of marine organisms living in the surface waters directly above? Explain your response.
9. List the advantages and disadvantages of mining in an EEZ versus the open-ocean beyond the EEZ.
10. Explain why the bulk of lithogenous sediment originates at relatively high land elevations.

ESSAY: Heinrich Events

Cores extracted from sediment deposits on the deep ocean floor of the North Atlantic Ocean contain layers of pebbles and other coarse rock fragments, called *Heinrich layers*, named for the German researcher Hartmut Heinrich who first described them in 1988. The size of these sediments is in marked contrast to the typically fine-grained pelagic sediments that blanket the deep-ocean floor. Heinrich sediments apparently were released by unusually large numbers of melting icebergs in the North Atlantic Ocean and settled to the seafloor (Figure 1). Heinrich layers were associated with massive discharges of icebergs from northeastern Canada (Hudson Bay and the St. Lawrence River) during the last Ice Age. From analysis of North Atlantic sediment cores, Heinrich identified six layers dating from the past 100,000 years. The layers were deposited during episodes of exceptionally low sea surface temperatures.

FIGURE 1
During Heinrich Events, ice rafting delivered relatively coarse sediment to the deep ocean floor. [From John T. Andrews and Thomas G. Andrews, NOAA Paleoclimatology Program and INSTAAR, University of Colorado, Boulder, CO]

During the last Ice Age, Earth's mean surface temperature may have fluctuated as much as 2 to 5 Celsius degrees (5 to 10 Fahrenheit degrees) with a regular periodicity, with deposition of Heinrich layers coinciding with the close of a cold episode. In addition to producing Heinrich layers, the massive influx of icebergs chilled the surface waters and the addition of large quantities of fresh water from the melting ice may have altered the ocean's deep current system that exerts a major influence on the climate of northern Europe (Chapter 6). Another effect of injections of melting icebergs was a rapid rise in sea level that drowned Caribbean coral reefs.

The cause of Heinrich events is still disputed but Doug MacAyeal of the University of Chicago has proposed an intriguing explanation. Scientists have known for several decades that major fluctuations in the planet's glacial ice cover arise from regular variations in Earth's orbital parameters that control the seasonal and latitudinal distribution of incoming solar radiation (Chapter 12). During episodes when Earth's orbital parameters favored warmer winters and cooler summers in central and northern Canada, some of the winter snows persisted year-round. In time, these climatic conditions gave rise to the Laurentide ice sheet that thickened and eventually spread over much of what is now Canada and the northern tier of the U.S. According to MacAyeal, over Hudson Bay the ice sheet initially was frozen to the bedrock but things changed as the ice sheet thickened. The growing ice sheet acted as an insulating blanket over Earth's surface and trapped enough geothermal heat conducted from Earth's interior that the bottom layer of the ice sheet thawed. Loaded with rock debris, this lubricated ice flowed rapidly into the North Atlantic releasing a massive surge of icebergs responsible for the Heinrich layers, changes in ocean circulation, and sea level rise. The now thinner ice sheet then re-froze to the bedrock and the cycle began anew as the ice sheet again thickened.

Smaller, shorter, and more frequent iceberg discharges into the North Atlantic Ocean are called *Dansgaard-Oeschger events* (named for the paleoclimatologists Willi Dansgaard and Hans Oeschger) or "flickers" because of their relatively short period. The Greenland ice core record contains indications of some 23 Dansgaard-Oeschger events during the period from 110,000 to 15,000 years ago. There is more on the Dansgaard-Oeschger events and their climatic implications in the first Essay of Chapter 12.

ESSAY: Burgess Shale: A Glimpse into Ancient Marine Life

The earliest known fossil record of life on Earth dates back to the Precambrian Era around 3.5 billion years ago, about a billion years after Earth formed, and about half billion years after ocean waters first covered portions of the planet. Over the next 2 billion years or so, life on Earth consisted of simple soft-bodied unicellular marine organisms. The earliest hard-shelled animals appeared in the ocean about 650 million years ago, near the close of the Precambrian. Then, in an evolutionary big-bang known as the *Cambrian explosion*, a broad spectrum of complex animal forms appeared in the ocean in just 10 to 30 million years—a mere blink of an eye in the perspective of geological time. While these organisms were still primarily invertebrates, this event represented a huge expansion of marine biodiversity and included the ancestors of modern shellfish, corals, crustaceans, and other inhabitants of the sea. The Cambrian explosion also brought creatures that would eventually disappear. What caused the Cambrian explosion is still debated, although it is known that the transition between the Precambrian and Paleozoic Eras was a time of extreme fluctuations in climate.

A lack of fossils has hindered detailed study of the Cambrian explosion. Two conditions favor the preservation of the remains of organisms as fossils: Rapid burial and possession of hard parts (e.g., shells). Rapid burial slows or prevents the decay of soft body parts and prevents scavenging of both soft and hard body parts. Almost none of the early unicellular life forms from the Precambrian appear in the fossil record. In fact, in spite of nearly continuous sedimentation and burial in the ocean, even fossils from the diverse community of animals from the Cambrian explosion are almost nonexistent—except in a very few unique rock outcrops. One of these outcrops is that of the *Burgess Shale*, consisting of layers of shale and mudstone located high in the Canadian Rockies near the little town of Field in eastern British Columbia. The Burgess Shale contains an abundance of fossils of soft-bodied animals from the Cambrian Period (570 to 505 million years ago).

The Burgess Shale provides us with a rare window on marine life some 40 million years after the Cambrian explosion. So far, the Burgess Shale has yielded tens of thousands of unique specimens representing 170 species, the majority of which are benthic (sea-floor dwelling) organisms, many of which do not exist today. The most remarkable feature of the Burgess Shale fossils is the excellent preservation of soft-bodied organisms; 60-80% of the fossils found are preserved soft bodies. How were they preserved?

During the Cambrian Period, the paleo-North American continent was located in the tropics astride the equator. Life was restricted to the ocean while the land was barren and uninhabited. The continental margin of this paleo-continental coast was a warm, shallow tropical sea and offshore, a great reef had formed creating a steep underwater cliff or escarpment. This algal reef and cliff, now known as the Cathedral Escarpment, fell away hundreds of meters deeper into the ocean. Between the reef and the cliff, sediment accumulated forming submarine mud banks. A rich and diverse community of marine organisms lived in and on the mud banks around the productive reef. This community consisted of mostly large, soft-bodied benthic invertebrates including coelenterates, echinoderms, mollusks, worms, and sponges. Among them were polychaete annelids, bristly scavenging worms (Figure 1) and more exotic spiny velvet worm creatures (Figure 2).

Periodically the accumulated mud became unstable and flowed down the escarpment as turbidity currents (described elsewhere in this chapter). Turbidity currents transported the animals in a slurry down slope to the base of the reef escarpment where most were buried fast and deep enough that they were preserved as fossils, sealed off from scavengers and decomposing bacteria. This process was repeated many times over a period of about 360 million years, building a 10,000-m (33,000-ft) sequence of fine-grained fossil-rich layers of sediment. In time, sediments were lithified into shale and mudstone.

Beginning about 175 million years ago (during the Jurassic Period), stresses associated with mountain building elevated and transported (via thrust faulting) the fossil beds from their ocean burial ground many kilometers eastward to their current position high on a mountain ridge in Canada's Yoho National Park. Fortunately, thrust faulting carried the shale beds above and out in front of the region where tectonic forces were forming the Rocky Mountains. Otherwise, the shale would have been metamorphosed and the fossils destroyed. The Burgess Shale is located at the eastern edge of the Canadian Rockies just west of the Alberta plains. Following their close escape from tectonic metamorphism, these ancient shale and mudstones with their fabulous treasure of fossils have been gradually exposed by erosive forces including glaciers, wind, running water, landslides, avalanches, and people.

FIGURE 1
Burgess shale fossil of a Canadia spinosa (a polychaete annelid). [Reproduced with permission from the Smithsonian Institution, Museum of Natural History, Department of Paleobiology]

FIGURE 2
Burgess shale fossil of a Hallucigenia sparsa (an onychophoran). [Reproduced with permission from the Smithsonian Institution, Museum of Natural History, Department of Paleobiology]

In 1886, R.G. McConnell of the Geological Survey of Canada was the first geologist to visit the area. He described one of the fossils he found as an "odd shrimp." It was almost 100 years later that scientists figured out that in fact the "odd shrimp" was the molted claw of a giant predator. Charles D. Walcott (1850-1927) heard reports about "stone bugs" (trilobites) and first visited the site in 1909. He served as director of the U.S. Geological Survey (1894-1907) and director of the Smithsonian Institution (1907-1927). Walcott is credited with discovering the Burgess Shale (named after nearby Mt. Burgess in the Canadian Rockies), and found fossils unlike any he had ever seen before. He collected many specimens for the Smithsonian and attempted to classify them, eventually identifying100 of the 170 recognized species. At present more than 65,000 specimens are housed at the Smithsonian Institution's National Museum of Natural History in Washington, DC.

In the late 1960s, paleontologist Harry Whittington of Cambridge, England, along with his graduate students Derek Briggs and Simon Conway Morris, began a thorough study of the Burgess Shale fossils (including those in storage). They were unable to classify all the fossil animals using the modern classification system and described those they didn't know as "unknown phyla." The implication was that there had been a greater diversity of basic animal forms half a billion years ago than today. The American paleontologist Stephen J. Gould (1941-2002), in his book *Wonderful Life: The Burgess Shale and the Nature of History* (1989), based on Whittington's work, concluded that "more than half the major animal groups are extinct." This was one of five major extinctions during Earth history.

Continuing work on the Burgess Shale fossils resulted in classification of some of the previously unclassified fossil species. However, just as many new unclassifiable forms have been found. The biodiversity represented by the Cambrian explosion is still greater than exists in the modern ocean. The fossil record reveals odd feeding devices and body configurations and proportions, some of which are so odd and enigmatic that they do not belong to any known phyla and would have been unknown if not for the Burgess Shale. None of the body plans discovered seem to be any more viable than any other and perhaps luck resulted in survival of certain species to become ancestors of living floral and fauna. Debate, research, and further exploration continue to surround the possible implications of the Burgess Shale fossils for evolutionary processes.

While the fossils of the Burgess Shale are very rare, similar fossils have been found in Cambrian shale deposits near the town of Chengjiang in China's Yunnan Province. This mud/shale is about 15 million years older than Burgess Shale. Over 100,000 specimens have been found there, with some similar species found in both places so we know that the Cambrian explosion was not geographically limited but rather ocean wide.

The Burgess Shale is an exceptional site of fossil preservation and records a diversity of rare animals. Its beautifully preserved fossils constitute a valuable snapshot of Cambrian life, far more complete than deposits containing fossils with only hard parts. In 1981, the Burgess Shale was declared a UNESCO World Heritage Site.

CHAPTER 5

THE ATMOSPHERE AND OCEAN

Case-in-Point
Driving Question
Weather and Climate
Heating and Cooling Earth's Surface
    Solar Radiation
    Solar Radiation Budget
    Solar Radiation and the Ocean
    Infrared Radiation and the Greenhouse Effect
Heating Imbalances: Earth's Surface versus Atmosphere
    Latent Heating
    Sensible Heating
Heating Imbalances: Tropics versus High Latitudes
    Heat Transport by Air Mass Exchange
    Heat Transport by Storms
    Heat Transport by Ocean Circulation
Circulation of the Atmosphere: The Forces
    Pressure Gradient Force
    Coriolis Effect
Circulation of the Atmosphere: Patterns of Motion
    Planetary-Scale Circulation
    Synoptic-Scale Weather Systems
Conclusions
Basic Understandings/Review/Critical Thinking
ESSAY: Location at Sea, A Historical Perspective
ESSAY: The Stratospheric Ozone Shield and Marine Life

Clouds developing over the open ocean. [NOAA/NCEP/OPC]

Case in Point

At middle latitudes, prevailing winds blow from west to east so that the moderating influence of the North Atlantic Ocean on climate is much more evident over Western Europe than Eastern North America. It is interesting to speculate on what would happen to the climate of Western Europe if this moderating influence were to weaken as it has at times in the past.

In Western Europe, the air temperature contrast between summer and winter is less than it is over most of North America. For reasons discussed in Chapter 3, sea surface temperatures (SST) change relatively little through the course of a year and this stable SST regime dampens the summer-to-winter temperature contrast of air flowing over the ocean to downwind Western Europe. Whereas summer average air temperatures are somewhat lower, winter average air temperatures are milder in Western Europe compared to upwind North America. The northward-moving warm Gulf Stream parallels the U.S. coastline from Florida to the Mid-Atlantic States and then the current turns east and northeastward across the North Atlantic. In winter, the relatively warm ocean surface moderates cold air masses as they surge from polar areas southeastward toward the British Isles and Western Europe.

Compare, for example, January and July temperatures at Cork, Ireland (51 degrees, 54 minutes N) and Saskatoon, Saskatchewan, Canada (52 degrees, 8 minutes N). At both places on average, January and July are the coldest and warmest months of the year respectively. Although located at about the same latitude, the two cities have markedly different climates. The average temperature contrast between July and January is about 36.5 Celsius degrees (65.7 Fahrenheit degrees) at continental Saskatoon but only about 11 Celsius degrees (20 Fahrenheit degrees) at maritime Cork. The reduced seasonal contrast at Cork is mostly due to much higher winter temperatures. January average temperature is 4.5 °C (40.1 °F) at Cork but −18.5 °C (−1.3 °F) at Saskatoon. July average temperatures are not much different at the two locations with 18 °C (64.4 °F) at Saskatoon and 15.5 °C (59.9 °F) at Cork.

Historical records indicate that during periods in the past, winters were much colder in the British Isles and other parts of Western Europe. The *Little Ice Age*, lasting from about CE 1400 to 1850, was one such period when relatively cold winters were more frequent than today. Sea ice cover expanded over the North Atlantic, mountain glaciers advanced, and growing seasons shortened over Western Europe bringing erratic harvests and much hardship for many people. Evidence of other cold episodes in the North Atlantic comes from climate signals unlocked from deep-sea sediment cores and annual ice layers in the Greenland ice sheet (Chapter 12). The past 10,000-year epoch (since the close of the last Ice Age) was punctuated by multi-century cold episodes that began abruptly (within decades) and occurred about every 1500 years. Across Northern and Western Europe, average winter temperatures during cold episodes were as much as 7 Celsius degrees (13 Fahrenheit degrees) lower than today.

A possible cause of the Little Ice Age and prior cold episodes in Western Europe is periodic weakening of the North Atlantic circulation. The Gulf Stream is part of a planetary-scale thermohaline circulation that transports enormous amounts of heat throughout the world ocean (Chapter 6). The flow in the Gulf Stream is at least 500 times that of the Amazon River. Researchers at Lamont-Doherty Earth Observatory of Columbia University propose that runoff of unusually great amounts of fresh water into the North Atlantic alters the salinity (and density) of surface ocean waters, produces less dense deep water, and weakens the thermohaline circulation. A weaker circulation would cause winter average temperatures in Western Europe to plunge abruptly by perhaps 5 Celsius degrees (9 Fahrenheit degrees). For Cork, this would mean winters more like those experienced at Spitsbergen, some 1000 km (600 mi) north of the Arctic Circle.

Driving Question:
What role does the ocean play in the long-term average state of the atmosphere?

To this point in our investigation of the ocean in the Earth system we have emphasized primarily the physical properties of ocean water and the ocean basin. In this chapter, our principal focus shifts to the flow of energy into and out of the Earth system especially as it involves its fluid subsystems and those processes operating at the interface between the ocean and atmosphere. In doing so, it quickly becomes apparent that the ocean plays a key role in the global radiation budget, the transport of heat between Earth's surface and atmosphere, the flow of heat from the tropics to higher latitudes, and the development of storm systems. For these reasons, the ocean is a major player in the state of the atmosphere (weather) and the climate system.

In this chapter, we examine radiational heating and cooling of the **Earth-atmosphere system** (Earth's surface plus overlying atmosphere), the interaction of incoming solar radiation with the atmosphere, ocean, and continents, the flow of infrared radiation to space, and the greenhouse effect. In response to heating imbalances within the Earth-atmosphere system, temperature gradients develop and heat is transferred via phase changes of water, conduction and convection, exchange of air masses, and ocean currents. Atmospheric and oceanic circulation operating at various spatial and temporal scales transports heat from where it is warmer to where it is colder. We begin our discussion by distinguishing between weather and climate.

Weather and Climate

Weather and climate are closely related concepts. We can think of **weather** as the state of the atmosphere at some place and time described in terms of such variables as temperature, precipitation, cloud cover, and wind speed. A place and time must be specified when describing weather because the atmosphere is dynamic; that is, its state is always changing from one place to another and with time. At the same hour the weather may be cold and snowy in Philadelphia, sunny and warm in Dallas, and cool and rainy in Seattle. *If you don't like the weather, wait a minute* is an old saying that is not far from the truth in many places. From personal experience, we know that tomorrow's weather may differ considerably from today's weather.

Climate is popularly defined as weather at a particular place averaged over a specific interval of time. By international convention, average values of weather elements such as temperature or precipitation are computed over a 30-year period beginning with the first year of a decade. At the close of a decade the averaging period is shifted forward ten years. As of this writing, the official averaging period is 1971-2000. Thirty-year average monthly and annual temperatures and precipitation totals are commonly used to describe climate. Other useful climatic parameters include average seasonal snowfall, length of growing season, and frequency of thunderstorms. Ultimately, climate governs the supply of fresh water, the geographical distribution of plants and animals, and the type of crops that can be cultivated.

Climate encompasses extremes in weather in addition to average values of weather elements. Tabulation of extreme values usually covers the entire period of record (or at least for the period when the weather station was at the same location). Specifying the frequency of weather extremes provides information on the variability of climate at a particular place and gives a more complete and useful description of climate. Climate scientists study not only trends in average temperature and precipitation, but also changes in the frequency of extreme events such as excess heat, cold, drought, or rainfall.

Heating and Cooling Earth's Surface

As Earth orbits the sun, its atmosphere and surface are absorbing energy radiated by the sun. Absorption of solar radiation heats the Earth-atmosphere system. At the same time the entire planet is emitting infrared radiation to space, which has a cooling effect on the Earth-atmosphere system. Over the long term, radiational cooling of the planet essentially balances radiational heating of the planet so that Earth remains in radiative equilibrium with surrounding space.

The sun emits a band of electromagnetic radiation having wavelengths mostly between 0.25 and 2.5 micrometers. (One micrometer is a millionth of a meter or about one-tenth the thickness of a human hair.) Solar radiation is most intense at a wavelength of about 0.5 micrometer, in the green of the visible portion of the electromagnetic spectrum (Figure 1.12). The Earth-atmosphere system, on the other hand, emits to space a broad band of electromagnetic radiation having wavelengths mostly between 4 and 24 micrometers, in the infrared portion of the electromagnetic spectrum. The peak intensity of infrared radiation emitted by Earth's surface is at a wavelength of about 10 micrometers. In this section, we take a closer look at radiational heating and cooling of the Earth system.

SOLAR RADIATION

Earth's motions in space govern daily and seasonal variations in the amount of solar radiation striking Earth's surface. Once every 24-hrs, Earth completes one rotation on its axis. At any instant, half the planet is illuminated by solar radiation (day) while the other half is in darkness (night). The tilt of Earth's spin axis is responsible for the seasons. Earth's spin axis is tilted 23 degrees 27 minutes from the perpendicular to the plane defined by the planet's annual orbit about the sun (Figure 5.1). During Earth's annual revolution about the sun, its spin axis remains in the same alignment with respect to the background stars (the North Pole always pointing toward *Polaris*, the North Star) while its orientation to the sun changes continually. Simply put, the Northern Hemisphere tilts away from the sun in fall and winter and toward the sun in spring and summer. In the Northern Hemisphere, astronomical winter begins on the winter solstice, on or about 21 December, and ends on the first day of spring (the vernal or spring equinox), on or about 21 March. Summer begins on the summer solstice, about 21 June, and continues until the first day of autumn (the autumnal equinox), on or about 23 September. Precise dates of solstices and equinoxes vary

FIGURE 5.1
The seasons change because Earth's equatorial plane is inclined (at 23 degrees, 27 minutes) to the orbital plane. Seasons are given for the Northern Hemisphere. Note that the eccentricity of Earth's orbit is greatly exaggerated.

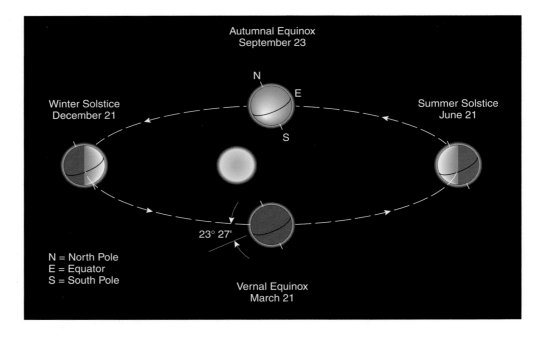

because Earth completes one orbit of the sun in 365.24 days, necessitating the leap year adjustment.

Regular changes in solar altitude and length of daylight accompany the annual periodic changes in the planet's orientation to the sun. These changes, in turn, affect the amount of solar radiation that strikes Earth's surface at a point. **Solar altitude** is the angle of the sun above the horizon and varies from 0 degrees (at sunrise or sunset) to as much as 90 degrees (where and when the sun is directly overhead), and *length of daylight* is the number of hours and minutes between sunrise and sunset. At middle and high latitudes, the altitude of the noon sun is higher, daylight is longer, and solar radiation is more intense in summer than in winter.

With clear skies, the intensity of solar radiation striking Earth's surface at a point varies directly with solar altitude. With increasing solar altitude, more solar energy strikes a unit area of Earth's surface in a unit of time (Figure 5.2). Earth is so far from the sun (a mean distance of 150 million km or 93 million mi) that solar radiation reaches the planet as nearly parallel beams of essentially uniform intensity. But the almost spherical Earth presents a curved surface to incoming solar radiation so that the noon solar altitude is higher in the tropics than at higher latitudes. Greater solar altitudes in the tropics translate into more intense radiation and higher temperatures at Earth's surface.

The daily path of the sun through the sky on the solstices and equinoxes is shown schematically in Figure 5.3 for the equator, a middle-latitude Northern

FIGURE 5.2
The intensity of solar radiation striking Earth's surface per unit area varies with the solar altitude. Consider this analogous situation: (A) A flashlight beam shines on a horizontal surface most intensely when the flashlight shines from directly overhead (analogous to a solar altitude of 90 degrees). (B) At an angle decreasing from 90 degrees, the flashlight beam spreads over an increasing area of the horizontal surface so that the light is less concentrated (less radiational energy received per unit area).

Hemisphere location, and the North Pole. At the middle-latitude location and North Pole, the altitude of the noon sun is greatest on the summer solstice but at the equator the noon solar altitude is maximum on the equinoxes (when the sun is directly overhead). The only places on Earth where the solar altitude ever reaches 90 degrees during the course of a year are within the latitude belt bounded by the Tropic of Cancer (23.5 degrees N) and the Tropic of Capricorn (23.5 degrees S).

Daylight is shortest on the winter solstice and longest on the summer solstice. On the equinoxes, the length of daylight and night are about the same (12 hrs) everywhere on the planet except at the poles. Daylight is longer than night during spring and summer, and daylight is shorter than night during autumn and winter. The difference in length of daylight between the summer

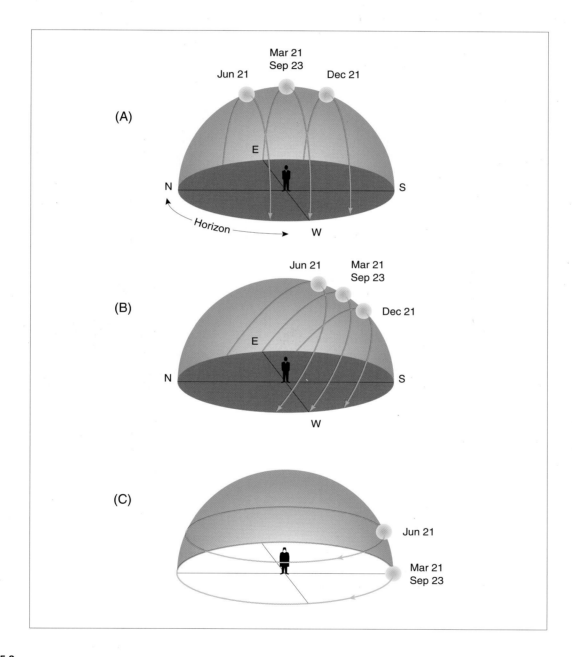

FIGURE 5.3
Path of the sun through the sky on the solstices and equinoxes at (A) the equator, (B) a middle latitude location in the Northern Hemisphere, and (C) the North Pole.

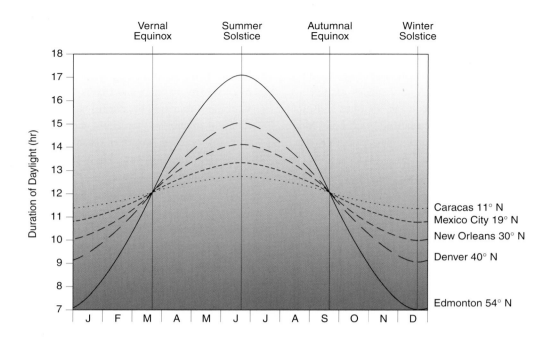

FIGURE 5.4
Variation in the number of hours and minutes of daylight through the year increases with increasing latitude.

and winter solstices increases from zero at the equator to a maximum (24 hrs) at the Arctic and Antarctic Circles (Figure 5.4). Regular variations in maximum solar altitude and length of daylight through the year are ultimately responsible for changes in the receipt of solar radiation and monthly average temperatures (Figure 5.5). Little annual variation in maximum solar altitude and length of daylight in the tropics translates into relatively uniform monthly mean temperatures through the year. In the tropics, the temperature difference between day and night often is

greater than the summer-to-winter temperature contrast. At middle and high latitudes, however, maximum solar altitudes and length of daylight vary considerably through the year and are responsible for marked contrasts between average summer and winter temperatures.

For reasons presented in Chapter 3, a large body of water such as the ocean influences the climate of downwind localities. Places downwind of the ocean experience a smaller contrast between average winter and summer temperatures and have a *maritime climate*. Places at the same latitude but well inland experience a greater temperature contrast between winter and summer and have a *continental climate*. Proximity to large bodies of water also affects the timing of the average warmest and coldest time of the year. Outside of the tropics, the annual temperature cycles lags (*follows in time*) the annual solar radiation cycle; that is, the warmest period of the year on average occurs after the summer solstice while the coldest period of the year occurs after the winter solstice. The Earth-atmosphere system takes time to adjust to seasonal changes in solar energy input. In the interior United States, the air temperature cycle lags the solar radiation cycle by an average of 27 days. But in coastal localities having a strong maritime influence (e.g., coastal California, Florida), the average lag time is up to 36 days.

Before modern navigational aids, mariners used

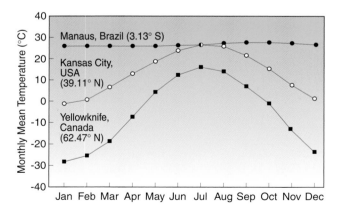

FIGURE 5.5
The seasonal contrast in monthly mean temperature generally increases with increasing latitude.

the regular changes in the location of the sun and other celestial bodies in the sky to locate themselves at sea. For an historical perspective on the challenges of navigating at sea, refer to this chapter's first Essay.

SOLAR RADIATION BUDGET

Solar radiation intercepted by Earth travels through the atmosphere and interacts with its component gases and aerosols. These interactions consist of scattering, reflection, and absorption. Solar radiation that is not absorbed or scattered or reflected back to space reaches Earth's surface where additional interactions occur.

With **scattering**, a particle disperses radiation in all directions: up, down, and sideways. Within the atmosphere, both gas molecules and aerosols (including the tiny water droplets and ice crystals that compose clouds) scatter solar radiation. Scattering explains the blue color of the clear daytime sky. Visible sunlight is made up of all colors (from violet at the short wavelength end of the solar spectrum to red at the long wavelength end). Air molecules preferentially scatter short wavelength visible light (blue-violet), causing it to enter the observer's eyes from many directions.

Reflection is a special case of scattering in which a large surface area redirects radiation in a backward direction. The fraction of incident radiation that is reflected by a surface is known as the **albedo** of that surface, that is,

albedo = [(reflected radiation)/(incident radiation)] × 100%.

Surfaces having a high albedo reflect a relatively large fraction of incident solar radiation and appear light in color. Surfaces having a low albedo reflect relatively little incident solar radiation and appear dark in color.

Within the atmosphere, the tops of clouds are the most important reflectors of incoming visible sunlight. Cloud top albedo depends primarily on cloud thickness and varies from under 40% for thin clouds to 80% or more for thick clouds. The average albedo for all cloud types and thicknesses is about 55%, and at any point in time, clouds cover about 60% of the planet. All other factors being constant, solar radiation striking the Earth's surface is more intense and surface air temperatures are higher when the daytime sky is clear rather than cloudy.

Scattering and reflection within the atmosphere alter the direction of solar radiation without its conversion to heat. **Absorption**, however, is a process whereby some of the radiation that strikes an object is converted to heat energy. Oxygen, ozone, water vapor, and various aerosols (including cloud particles) absorb solar radiation. Absorp-

tion by atmospheric gases varies with wavelength; that is, each gas absorbs strongly in some wavelengths and weakly or not at all in other wavelengths. Essential for life on Earth is the strong absorption of ultraviolet (UV) radiation by oxygen and ozone (O_3) in the stratosphere, which shields organisms from exposure to potentially lethal intensities of UV. These absorption processes create the so-called *stratospheric ozone shield.* For more on the stratospheric ozone shield and marine life, see this chapter's second Essay.

Solar radiation not scattered or reflected to space or absorbed by atmospheric gases or aerosols reaches Earth's surface where it is either reflected or absorbed. The portion that is not reflected is absorbed (i.e., converted to heat). High-albedo surfaces, such as snow-covered ground or pack ice, reflect a considerable amount of incident solar radiation whereas low-albedo surfaces, such as an asphalt road or a conifer forest, reflect much less incident solar radiation. The albedo of some common surfaces is listed in Table 5.1.

In the visible satellite image in Figure 5.6, the

TABLE 5.1

Average Albedo (Reflectivity) of some Common Surface Types for Visible Solar Radiation

Surface	Albedo (% reflected)
Deciduous forest	15-18
Coniferous forest	9-15
Tropical rainforest	7-15
Tundra	15-35
Grasslands	18-25
Desert	25-30
Sand	30-35
Soil	5-30
Green crops	15-25
Sea ice	30-40
Fresh snow	75-95
Old snow	40-60
Glacial ice	20-40
Water body (high solar altitude)	3-10
Water body (low solar altitude)	10-100
Asphalt road	5-10
Urban area	14-18
Cumulonimbus cloud	90
Stratocumulus cloud	60
Cirrus cloud	40-50

FIGURE 5.6
In this visible satellite image, the ocean surface appears dark because of its low albedo for visible solar radiation. White areas are clouds.

ocean surface appears dark because of its strong absorption of solar radiation, that is, its low albedo. The albedo of the ocean surface varies with the angle of the sun above the horizon (solar altitude). Under clear skies, the albedo of a flat, tranquil water surface decreases with increasing solar altitude (Figure 5.7). The albedo is almost a mirror-like 100% near sunrise and sunset (when the solar altitude

FIGURE 5.7
Under clear skies, the albedo of a flat and undisturbed water surface changes with solar altitude. A wave-covered water surface has a slightly higher albedo at high solar altitudes and a slightly lower albedo at low solar altitudes.

is near 0 degrees) but declines sharply as the solar altitude approaches 20 degrees. When the sun is low in the sky (small solar altitude), light rays reflect off the water surface with little penetration. However, when the sun is high in the sky, light rays penetrate the water to some depth and most of the sunlight is scattered below the surface with little scattered back to the atmosphere or space. With cloud-covered skies, only diffuse solar radiation strikes the water surface and the albedo varies little with solar altitude and is uniformly less than 10%. The roughness of a wave-covered water surface decreases its albedo. On a global basis, the albedo of the ocean surface averages only about 8%; that is, the ocean absorbs 92% of incident solar radiation. Considering that the ocean covers about 71% of the surface of the planet, the ocean is the principal sink (absorber) for solar radiation striking Earth's surface.

Measurements by sensors onboard Earth-orbiting satellites indicate that the Earth-atmosphere system reflects or scatters back to space on average about 31% of the solar radiation intercepted by the planet. This is Earth's **planetary albedo**. The atmosphere (i.e., gases, aerosols, clouds) absorbs only about 20% of the total solar radiation intercepted by the Earth-atmosphere system. In other words, the atmosphere is relatively transparent to solar radiation. The remaining 49% of solar radiation is absorbed by Earth's surface—mostly the ocean.

Earth's surface is the principal recipient of solar heating, and heat is transferred from Earth's surface to the atmosphere, which eventually radiates this energy to space. Hence, Earth's surface is the main source of heat for the atmosphere; that is, the atmosphere is heated from below. This is evident from the average vertical temperature profile of the troposphere (Figure 1.4). Normally, air is warmest close to the Earth's surface, and the temperature drops with increasing altitude, that is, away from the main source of heat.

SOLAR RADIATION AND THE OCEAN

Whereas the atmosphere is relatively transparent to (and absorbs little) solar radiation, the ocean absorbs most solar radiation within relatively shallow depths. As shown in Figure 5.8, the ocean's absorption of the visible portion of solar radiation is selective by wavelength. Water absorbs the longer wavelengths (i.e., reds and yellows) of visible light more efficiently than the shorter wavelengths (i.e., greens and blues) so that green and blue penetrate to greater depths. Within clear, clean water, red light is completely absorbed within about 15 m (50 ft) of the surface, whereas green and blue-violet light may penetrate to depths approaching 250 m (800 ft). More

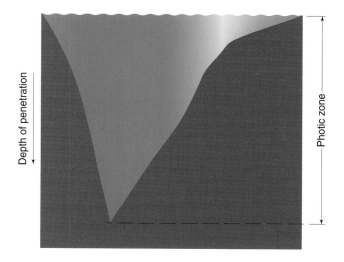

FIGURE 5.8
Visible solar radiation is selectively absorbed by wavelength as it penetrates the surface waters of the open ocean.

green and blue light is scattered to our eyes, explaining the blue/green color of the open ocean. Suspended particles significantly boost absorption so that sunlight often is completely absorbed at shallower depths. In fact, some near-shore waters are so turbid (cloudy) that little if any sunlight reaches much below 10 m (35 ft). Suspended particles preferentially scatter yellow and green light, giving these waters their characteristic color.

The **photic zone** is the sunlit surface layer of the ocean, down to the depth where light is just sufficient for photosynthesis. The base of the photic zone is generally where the light is just 1% of the radiation incident on the surface. In clear ocean waters, this depth is usually from 100 to 200 m (330 to 650 ft) but is much shallower in highly productive or turbid waters. Although a small amount of light penetrates below the photic zone (into the so-called *twilight zone*), light is insufficient for plants to survive.

As the concentration of particles and dissolved organic matter in seawater increases, the color of light that penetrates deepest into the water shifts to yellow-green in coastal areas and to red in the most turbid estuarine waters. Hence, as light becomes dimmer with increasing depth, its color also changes. This color change affects plant production because each plant pigment is most efficient with a specific color of light. The combination of pigments in any type of phytoplankton determines its optimal depth distribution.

With some notable exceptions, marine life depends directly or indirectly on sunlight and organic productivity in the ocean's photic zone (Chapters 9 and 10). Even the diverse community of animals living at great depths on the ocean floor depends on organic particles produced within the photic zone that settle to the sea floor (Chapter 4); exceptions are organisms living near hydrothermal vents who depend upon *chemosynthesis* (Chapter 9).

INFRARED RADIATION AND THE GREENHOUSE EFFECT

If solar radiation were continually absorbed by the Earth-atmosphere system without any compensating flow of heat out of the system, Earth's surface temperature would rise steadily. Eventually, life would be extinguished and the ocean would boil away. Actually, global air temperature changes very little from one year to the next. **Global radiative equilibrium** keeps the planet's temperature in check to some extent; that is, emission of heat to space in the form of infrared radiation balances solar radiational heating of the Earth-atmosphere system. Although solar radiation is supplied only to the illuminated half of the planet, infrared radiation is emitted to space ceaselessly, day and night, by the entire Earth-atmosphere system. This explains why nights are usually colder than days and why air temperatures typically drop throughout the night.

While the clear atmosphere is relatively transparent to solar radiation, certain gases in the atmosphere impede the escape of infrared radiation to space thereby elevating the temperature of the lower atmosphere. This important climate control, the so-called **greenhouse effect**, refers to the heating of Earth's surface and lower atmosphere caused by strong absorption and emission of infrared radiation (IR) by certain gaseous components of the atmosphere, known as **greenhouse gases**. Solar radiation and terrestrial infrared radiation peak in different portions of the electromagnetic spectrum, their properties differ, and they interact differently with the atmosphere. As noted earlier, the atmosphere absorbs only about 20% of the solar radiation intercepted by the planet. The atmosphere absorbs a greater percentage of the infrared radiation emitted by Earth's surface, and the atmosphere, in turn, radiates some IR to space and some to Earth's surface. Hence, Earth's surface is heated by absorption of both solar radiation and atmosphere-emitted infrared radiation.

The similarity in radiational properties between infrared-absorbing atmospheric gases and the glass or plastic glazing of a greenhouse is the origin of the term greenhouse effect. Greenhouse glazing, like the atmosphere, is relatively transparent to visible solar radiation but strongly absorbs infrared radiation. A greenhouse (where plants are grown) takes advantage of the radiational properties of glazing. Sunlight readily penetrates greenhouse glazing and much of it is absorbed (converted to heat) within the greenhouse. Objects in the greenhouse emit infrared radiation that is strongly absorbed by the glazing. The glazing, in turn, emits IR to both the atmosphere and to the greenhouse interior, thereby raising the temperature within the greenhouse. The analogy between the atmosphere and a greenhouse is not strictly correct, however. A greenhouse also functions as a shelter from the wind and this is the principal reason for the elevated temperature observed within most greenhouses. Nonetheless, *greenhouse effect* is such a commonly used term (especially by the media) that we use it in this book.

The greenhouse effect is responsible for considerable warming of Earth's surface and lower atmosphere. Viewed from space, the planet (Earth-atmosphere system) radiates at about −18 °C (0 °F) whereas the average temperature at Earth's surface is about 15 °C (59 °F). The temperature difference is due to the greenhouse effect and amounts to:

$$[15\ °C - (-18\ °C)] = 33\ \text{Celsius degrees}$$
$$\text{or}$$
$$[59\ °F - (0\ °F)] = 59\ \text{Fahrenheit degrees.}$$

Without the greenhouse effect, Earth would be too cold to support most forms of plant and animal life. Water vapor is the principal greenhouse gas. Other greenhouse gases include carbon dioxide, ozone, methane (CH_4), nitrous oxide (N_2O), and halocarbons (once widely used as refrigerants and aerosol spray propellants). As shown in Figure 5.9, the percentage of infrared radiation absorbed by these gases varies with wavelength. An **atmospheric window** is a range of wavelengths over which little or no radiation is absorbed. A *visible window* extends from about 0.3 to 0.9 micrometers and the major *infrared window* is from about 8 to 13 micrometers. Significantly, this latter window includes the wavelength of the planet's peak infrared emission (about 10 micrometers). Through this window, most heat from the Earth-atmosphere system escapes to space as infrared radiation. IR sensors on Earth-orbiting satellites monitor this upwelling radiation which is calibrated in terms of the surface temperature of the radiating object: the higher the temperature, the more intense is the emission of IR radiation (Chapter 1).

Warming caused by atmospheric water vapor is evident even at the local or regional scale. Consider an example. Locations in the Desert Southwest and along the

FIGURE 5.9
Absorption of radiation by selected gaseous components of the atmosphere as a function of wavelength. *Absorptivity* is the fraction of radiation absorbed and ranges from 0 to 1 (0% to 100% absorption). Absorptivity is very low or near zero in the *atmospheric windows*. Note the infrared (IR) windows near 8 and 10 micrometers.

Gulf Coast are at about the same latitude and on a clear day receive essentially the same input of solar radiation. In both places, summer afternoon high temperatures commonly top 32 °C (90 °F). At night, however, air temperatures often differ markedly. Air is relatively dry (low humidity) in the Southwest so that infrared radiation readily escapes to space and air temperatures near Earth's surface may drop well under 15 °C (59 °F) by dawn. People who camp in the desert are well aware of the dramatic fluctuations in temperature between day and night. Infrared radiation does not escape to space as readily through the Gulf Coast atmosphere where the air is more humid. Water vapor strongly absorbs outgoing IR and emits IR back towards Earth's surface so that early morning low temperatures may dip no lower than the 20s Celsius (70s Fahrenheit). The smaller day-to-night temperature contrast along the Gulf Coast is due to more water vapor and a stronger greenhouse effect.

Clouds are composed of IR-absorbing water droplets and/or ice crystals, and also contribute to the greenhouse effect. All other factors being equal, nights usually are warmer when the sky is cloud-covered than when the sky is clear. Even high thin cirrus clouds through which the moon is visible can reduce the nighttime temperature drop at Earth's surface by several Celsius degrees.

Natural biogeochemical cycles continually transport greenhouse gases into and out of the atmosphere and ocean. In Chapter 3, for example, we saw how carbon dioxide cycles out of the atmosphere and into the ocean. Human activities alter the rate of biogeochemical cycling so that, for example, the atmospheric concentration of certain greenhouse gases is increasing. The consequent enhancement of the natural greenhouse effect is causing global-scale warming that has implications for all sectors of society. Since the beginning of the Industrial Revolution, combustion of fossil fuels (i.e., coal at first, oil and natural gas later) and clearing of forests and other vegetation have altered the global carbon cycle so that the atmospheric concentration of CO_2 is now about 35% higher than it was some 200 years ago in the pre-industrial era and continues to increase because of human activities.

The **Callendar effect** is the theory that global climate change can be brought about by enhancement of the natural greenhouse effect by increased levels of atmospheric CO_2 from anthropogenic sources, principally the burning of fossil fuels. The theory is named for the British engineer Guy Stewart Callendar (1898-1964) who investigated the link between global warming and fossil fuel combustion beginning in the late 1930s. We have more to say on the Callendar effect and its impacts on the Earth system in Chapter 12.

Heating Imbalances: Earth's Surface versus Atmosphere

Sensors onboard Earth-orbiting satellites detect imbalances in rates of radiational heating and radiational cooling. One important aspect of this heating imbalance involves Earth's surface versus the atmosphere.

Figure 5.10 shows how solar radiation intercepted by planet Earth interacts with the atmosphere and Earth's surface. Numbers are global and annual averages. For every 100 units of solar radiation that enters the upper atmosphere, the Earth-atmosphere system reflects or scatters 31 units (31%), the atmosphere absorbs 20 units (20%) and Earth's surface (principally the ocean) absorbs 49 units (49%). In response to radiational heating, Earth's surface emits 114 units of infrared radiation. Atmospheric gases and clouds absorb 105 units of infrared radiation and emit 95 units to Earth's surface (*greenhouse effect*). A total of 69 units of IR radiation are emitted out the top of the atmosphere to space, equal to the amount of solar radiation absorbed by the Earth-atmosphere system.

The global average annual distribution of incoming solar radiation and outgoing infrared radiation implies net warming of Earth's surface and net cooling

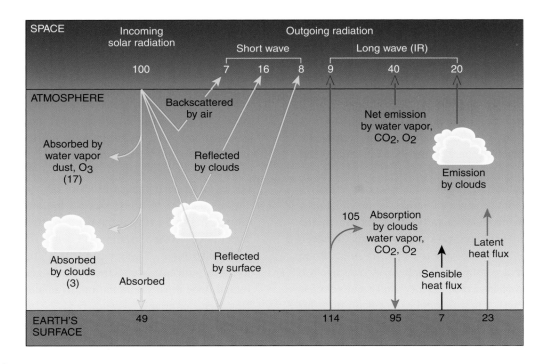

FIGURE 5.10
Globally and annually averaged distribution of 100 units of solar radiation entering the top of the atmosphere. Depicted from left to right are fluxes of solar radiation (yellow), infrared radiation (red), sensible heat (black), and latent heat (green).

TABLE 5.2
Global Radiation Balance

Solar radiation intercepted by Earth	100 units
Solar radiation budget	
Scattered and reflected to space (7 + 16 + 8)	31
Absorbed by the atmosphere (17 + 3)	20
Absorbed at the Earth's surface	49
Total	100 units
Radiation budget at the Earth's surface	
Infrared cooling (95 − 114)	−19
Solar heating	+49
Net heating	+30 units
Radiation budget of the atmosphere	
Infrared cooling (− 40 − 20 + 105 − 95)	−50
Solar heating	+20
Net cooling	−30 units
Non-radiative heat transfer: Earth's surface to atmosphere	
Sensible heating (conduction plus convection)	7
Latent heating (phase changes of water)	23
Net transfer	30 units

of the atmosphere (Table 5.2). At Earth's surface, absorption of solar radiation is greater than emission of infrared radiation. In the atmosphere, on the other hand, emission of infrared radiation to space is greater than absorption of solar radiation. That is, on a global average annual basis, Earth's surface undergoes net radiational heating and the atmosphere undergoes net radiational cooling.

The atmosphere is not actually cooling relative to Earth's surface because radiation is not the only heat transfer mechanism at work. In response to the radiationally induced temperature gradient between Earth's surface and atmosphere, heat is transferred from Earth's surface to the atmosphere. A combination of latent heating (phase changes of water) and sensible heating (conduction and convection) is responsible for this transfer of heat. As shown in Figure 5.10, on a global annual average basis, 30 units of heat energy are transferred from Earth's surface to the atmosphere: 23 units (about 77% of the total) by latent heating and 7 units (about 23%) by sensible heating.

LATENT HEATING

Latent heating refers to the transfer of heat energy from one place to another as a consequence of phase changes of water. As discussed in Chapter 3, when water changes phase, heat energy is either absorbed from the environment (i.e., melting, evaporation, sublimation) or released to the environment (i.e., freezing, condensation, deposition). As part of the global water cycle, latent heat that is used to vaporize water at the Earth's surface is transferred to the atmosphere when clouds form. Significantly for Earth's climate, ocean water covers a large portion of Earth's surface and is the principal source of water vapor that eventually returns to Earth's surface as precipitation. In general, only well inland does most precipitation originate as evaporation from the continents (Figure 5.11). Also, the ocean is a major source of salt crystals that spur condensation and cloud development in the atmosphere. These *cloud condensation nuclei* have a special chemical affinity for water molecules and readily promote cloud formation. When sea waves break, drops of salt water enter the

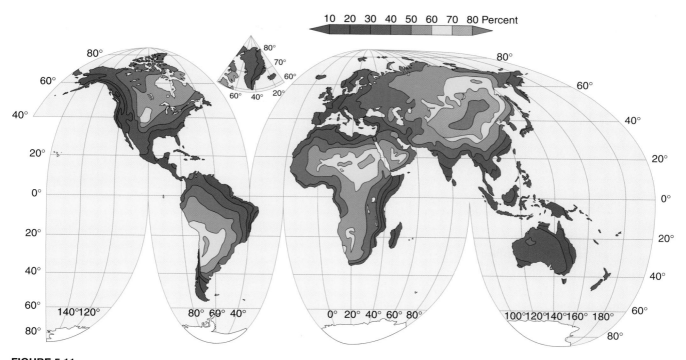

FIGURE 5.11
Percentage of precipitation over land that originated as evaporation on the continents, annually averaged over 15 years. In many land areas, the principal source of water for precipitation is evaporation from the ocean. [World Climate Research Programme, Global Energy and Water Cycle Experiment]

atmosphere and evaporate leaving behind sea-salt crystals that function as nuclei.

As Earth's surface absorbs radiation (both solar and infrared), some of the heat energy is used to vaporize water from the ocean, glaciers, lakes, rivers, soil, and vegetation (*transpiration*). The latent heat required for vaporization (evaporation or sublimation) is supplied at the Earth's surface, and heat is subsequently released to the atmosphere during cloud development. Within the

troposphere, clouds form as some of the water vapor condenses into liquid water droplets or deposits as ice crystals. During cloud formation, water changes phase and latent heat is released to the atmosphere. Through latent heating, then, heat is transferred from Earth's surface to the troposphere. In fact, latent heat transfer is more important than either radiational cooling or sensible heat transfer in the cooling of Earth's surface (Figure 5.12).

A.	B.	C.
Latent Heating	Net IR Radiation	Sensible Heating
23 Units	19 Units	7 Units
(46.9%)	(38.8%)	(14.3%)

FIGURE 5.12
Earth's surface is cooled through (A) vaporization of water, (B) net emission of infrared radiation to the sky, and (C) conduction plus convection. Numbers are global annual averages based on 100 units of solar radiation entering the top of the atmosphere.

SENSIBLE HEATING

Heat transfer via conduction and convection can be monitored (sensed) by temperature changes; hence, **sensible heating** encompasses both of these processes. Heat is conducted from the relatively warm surface of the Earth to the cooler overlying air. Heating reduces the density of that air, which is forced to rise by cooler denser air replacing it at the surface (Figure 5.13). In this way, convection transports heat from Earth's surface into the troposphere. Because air is a relatively poor conductor of heat, heat convection is much more important than conduction as a transfer mechanism within the troposphere.

Often sensible heating combines with latent heating to channel heat from Earth's surface into the troposphere. This happens during thunderstorm development. Updrafts (ascending branches) of vapor-laden air in convection currents often produce *cumulus clouds*, which resemble puffs of cotton floating in the sky (Figure 5.14A). These clouds are sometimes referred to as *fair-weather cumulus* because they seldom produce rain or snow. On the other hand, if atmospheric conditions are favorable, convective currents can surge to great altitudes, and cumulus clouds merge and billow upward to form towering *cumulonimbus clouds*, also known as thunderstorm clouds (Figure 5.14B).

A

B

FIGURE 5.14
Latent heating and sensible heating are combined in the formation of (A) cumulus clouds and (B) cumulonimbus (thunderstorm) clouds.

In retrospect, two important heat transfer processes (a combination of latent heating and sensible heating) took place last summer when that thunderstorm sent you scurrying for shelter at the beach.

At some times and places, heat transfer is directed from the troposphere to Earth's surface, the reverse of the global average annual situation. This reversal in direction of heat transport occurs, for example, when mild winds blow over cold, snow-covered ground or when warm air moves over a relatively cool ocean surface. Heat transport from the atmosphere to Earth's surface is the usual situation at night (especially when skies are clear) when radiational cooling causes Earth's land surface to become colder than the overlying air.

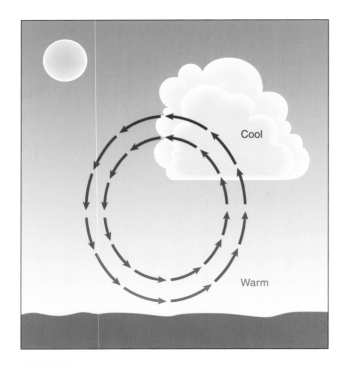

FIGURE 5.13
Convection currents transport heat from Earth's surface into the troposphere.

The **Bowen ratio** describes how the heat energy received at Earth's surface (by absorption of solar and infrared radiation) is partitioned between sensible heating and latent heating. That is,

Bowen ratio = [(sensible heating)/(latent heating)]

At the global scale,

Bowen ratio = [(7 units)/(23 units)] = 0.3.

The average Bowen ratio varies from one place to another depending on the amount of surface moisture. The wetter the surface, the less important is sensible heating and the more important is latent heating. The Bowen ratio ranges from about 0.1 (one-tenth as much sensible as latent heating) for the ocean to about 5.0 (five times as much sensible as latent heating) in deserts. Ocean waters cover much of Earth's surface so it is not surprising that the global Bowen ratio is a relatively low 0.3.

Heating Imbalances: Tropics versus High Latitudes

On a global scale, imbalances in radiational heating and cooling occur between not only Earth's surface and atmosphere but also the tropics and higher latitudes. Because the planet is nearly a sphere, parallel beams of incoming solar radiation strike the tropics more directly than higher latitudes. (That is, solar altitudes are higher in the tropics and lower at higher latitudes.) At higher latitudes, solar radiation spreads over a greater area and is less intense per unit horizontal surface area than in the tropics.

Emission of infrared radiation by the Earth-atmosphere system also varies with latitude but less than solar radiation. Because air temperatures are generally lower at higher latitudes, IR emission also declines with increasing latitude. (Recall from earlier in this chapter that radiation emission is temperature dependent.) Consequently, over the period of a year at higher latitudes, the rate of infrared cooling to space exceeds the rate of warming caused by absorption of solar radiation. At lower latitudes the reverse is true; that is, over the course of a year, the rate of solar radiational heating is greater than the rate of infrared radiational cooling (Figure 5.15). Averaged over the globe, incoming energy (absorbed solar radiation) must equal outgoing energy (IR emitted to space). That is, the areas under the two curves in Figure 5.15 are equal. The balance between energy entering and

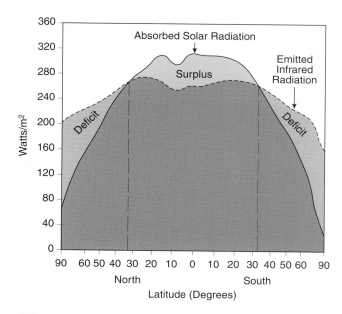

FIGURE 5.15
Variation by latitude of absorbed solar radiation and outgoing infrared radiation derived from satellite sensor measurements. [From NOAA/NESDIS]

leaving the Earth-atmosphere system (*global radiative equilibrium*) is the prevailing condition on Earth.

Measurements by sensors onboard Earth-orbiting satellites indicate that the division between regions of net radiational cooling and regions of net radiational warming is close to the 35-degree latitude circle in both hemispheres. By implication, latitudes poleward of about 35 degrees N and 35 degrees S should experience net cooling over the course of a year, while tropical latitudes are sites of net warming. In fact, lower latitudes do not become progressively warmer nor do higher latitudes become colder because heat is transported poleward from the tropics into middle and high latitudes. **Poleward heat transport** is brought about by (1) air mass exchange, (2) storm systems, and (3) ocean circulation. The atmosphere and ocean share equally in the poleward transport of heat.

HEAT TRANSPORT BY AIR MASS EXCHANGE
North-south exchange of air masses transports sensible heat from the tropics into middle and high latitudes. An **air mass** is a huge volume of air covering thousands of square kilometers that is relatively uniform horizontally in temperature and humidity. The properties of an air mass largely depend on the characteristics of the surface over which the air mass forms (its *source region*) or travels (Figure 5.16). Air masses that form at high

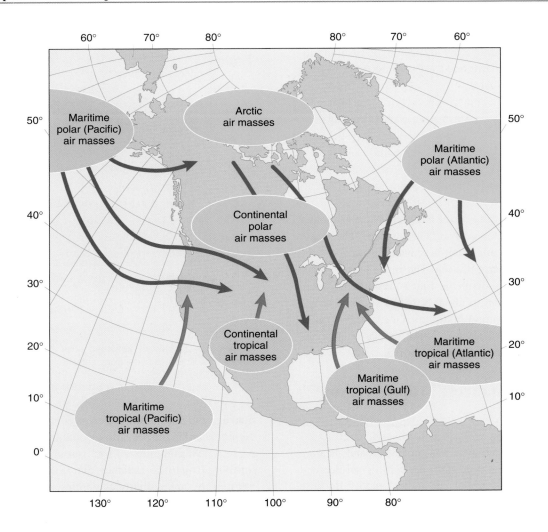

FIGURE 5.16
Source regions of air masses that regularly move over North America.

latitudes over cold, often snow- or ice-covered surfaces are relatively cold. Those air masses that form at low latitudes are relatively warm. Air masses that develop over the ocean are humid and those that form over land are relatively dry. Hence, there are four basic types of air masses: cold and humid, cold and dry, warm and humid, and warm and dry.

As shown in Figure 5.16, warm air masses that form in lower latitudes flow toward the pole while cold air masses flow toward the equator from source regions at high latitudes. Air masses modify (become cooler, warmer, drier, more humid) to some extent as they move away from their source region, gaining or losing heat energy and/or moisture in the process. In this north-south exchange of air masses, a net transport of heat energy takes place directed from lower to higher latitudes.

HEAT TRANSPORT BY STORMS

Acquisition and subsequent release of latent heat in storm systems (*cyclones* or *lows*) plays an important role in the poleward transport of heat. At low latitudes, water that evaporates from the warm ocean surface may be drawn into the circulation of a developing storm system. As the storm travels into higher latitudes, some of that water vapor condenses into clouds, thereby releasing latent heat to the troposphere. Latent heat of vaporization acquired at low latitudes is thereby delivered to middle and high latitudes. Because they entrain much more water vapor and latent heat, tropical storms and hurricanes are greater contributors to poleward heat transport than ordinary middle latitude (*extratropical*) storms. We discuss middle latitude and tropical cyclones in greater depth in Chapter 8.

HEAT TRANSPORT BY OCEAN CIRCULATION

The ocean contributes to poleward heat transport via wind-driven surface currents and the deeper thermohaline circulation. Surface water that is warmer than the overlying air is a *heat source* for the atmosphere; that is, heat is conducted from sea to air. Surface water that is cooler than the overlying air is a *heat sink* for the atmosphere; that is, heat is conducted from air to sea. Warm surface currents, such as the Gulf Stream, flow from the tropics into middle latitudes, supplying heat to the cooler middle latitude troposphere. At the same time, cold surface currents, such as the California Current, flow from high to low latitudes, absorbing heat from the relatively warm troposphere and greater solar radiation in the tropics. There is much more on wind-driven ocean currents in Chapter 6.

The ocean's **thermohaline circulation** is the density-driven movement of water masses, traversing the lengths of the ocean basins. As noted in Chapter 3, the density of seawater increases with decreasing temperature and increasing salinity. More dense water tends to sink while less dense water rises. The thermohaline circulation transports heat energy, salt, and dissolved gases (e.g., the greenhouse gas carbon dioxide) over great distances and to great depths in the world ocean and plays an important role in Earth's climate system. In the North Atlantic, for example, a warm surface ocean current flows north and eastward from the Florida Strait. At high latitudes, the surface waters cool, sinks, and flows southward as cold bottom water. This heat transporting circulation is also known as the **meridional overturning circulation (MOC)**.

In recent years, based on the output of coupled global climate models, some scientists predicted that global warming could cause the MOC to gradually weaken with implications for the climate of northern latitudes, particularly Europe. To test this hypothesis, a team of U.S. and British scientists from the *Rapid Climate Change Program* (begun in 2001) strung an array of moored instruments along the 26.5 degree N latitude circle across the North Atlantic Ocean. They reported their findings in *Science* in August 2007. Based on measurements made over a one-year period, scientists discovered considerable intra-annual variability in the MOC. The MOC varied by a factor of 8, from a low of 4.0 Sv to a high of 34.9 Sv with an average of 18.7 ± 5.6 Sv. (1.0 Sv = 1.0 Sverdrup = 1.0 million cubic m per sec.) The challenge is to separate out any long-term trend from the substantial natural variability of the MOC but this would require a much more lengthy observational record. For now, there is no indication that the MOC is weakening. We have more to say about the ocean's thermohaline circulation in Chapter 6.

Circulation of the Atmosphere: The Forces

As discussed earlier, the atmosphere circulates in response to temperature gradients that develop within the Earth-atmosphere system. These temperature gradients are due to differences in rates of radiational heating and radiational cooling between (1) Earth surface and atmosphere, and (2) the tropics and high latitudes. Circulation of the atmosphere and ocean transports heat from warmer locations to colder locations. In this section, we describe the principal forces operating in large-scale atmospheric circulation: the pressure gradient force and the Coriolis Effect. Other forces that influence atmospheric circulation are friction (important within about 1000 m or 3300 ft of Earth's surface), and gravity.

PRESSURE GRADIENT FORCE

Air exerts a force on the surfaces of all objects that it contacts. (A *force* is a push or pull on an object and is computed as mass times acceleration. A force is a vector quantity; that is, it has both magnitude and direction.) As noted in Chapter 3, we can think of **air pressure** at a given location on the Earth's surface as the weight per unit area of the column of air above that location. Unlike ocean water, air is highly compressible. The pull of gravity compresses the atmosphere so that the maximum air density and pressure are at the Earth's surface, and air density and pressure decrease rapidly with increasing altitude. The average air pressure at sea level is about 1013.25 millibars (mb). At an altitude of only 5500 m (18,000 ft), air pressure is about half of its average value at sea level. The rapid drop in air pressure with altitude means that significant changes in air pressure accompany relatively minor changes in elevation. For example, the average air pressure at Denver, the mile-high city, is about 83% of the average air pressure at sea level.

Air pressure varies with both space and time and this drives the circulation of the atmosphere. Variations in air pressure are not always due to variations in elevation. In fact, atmospheric scientists are most interested in air pressure variations that arise from factors other than elevation. Hence, weather observers determine an equivalent sea-level air pressure value; that is, for weather stations located above sea level, they adjust air pressure readings to approximately what the pressure would be if the station were actually located at sea level. When this adjustment to sea level is carried out everywhere, air pressure is observed to vary from one place to another and fluctuate from day to day and even from one hour to the next. Spatial and temporal changes in air pressure at Earth's surface arise from variations in air temperature (principally), humidity (concentration of water vapor in air), and atmospheric circulation.

In the free atmosphere, air density varies inversely with both temperature and humidity. That is, air density increases with falling temperature and decreasing humidity. Cold, dry air masses are denser and usually produce higher surface pressures than warm, humid air masses. Warm, dry air masses, in turn, often exert higher surface pressures than equally warm, but more humid air masses. As one air mass replaces another at a specific location, the air pressure at that location may change. Falling air pressure often signals a turn to stormy weather whereas rising air pressure indicates clearing skies or continued fair weather.

On a weather map, a *HIGH* or *H* symbol designates places where sea-level air pressure is relatively high compared to the air pressure in surrounding areas. A high is also known as an *anticyclone* and is usually a fair weather system. A *LOW* or *L* symbol signifies regions where sea-level air pressure is relatively low compared to the air pressure in surrounding areas. A low is also known as a *cyclone* and often brings stormy weather.

A change in air pressure from one place to another is known as an **air pressure gradient**. Air pressure gradients occur both vertically and horizontally within the atmosphere. A vertical air pressure gradient is a permanent feature of the atmosphere because air pressure always decreases with increasing altitude (at a rate dependent on the density of the air column). A horizontal air pressure gradient refers to pressure changes along a surface of constant altitude (e.g., mean sea level). Horizontal air pressure gradients can be determined on weather maps from patterns of *isobars*, lines joining points having the same air pressure (adjusted to sea level). Usually isobars are drawn on weather maps at 4-millibar intervals.

In response to a horizontal air pressure gradient, the wind blows from where the pressure is relatively high toward where the pressure is relatively low. The force that causes air to move as the consequence of an air pressure gradient is known as the **pressure gradient force** and is always directed across isobars and toward low pressure. The magnitude of the pressure gradient force is inversely related to the spacing of isobars. The wind is relatively strong where the pressure gradient is steep (closely spaced isobars), and light or calm where the pressure gradient is weak (widely spaced isobars).

CORIOLIS EFFECT

If Earth did not rotate, surface winds would blow directly from the cold poles (where surface air pressure is relatively high) to the hot equator (where surface air pressure is relatively low). And these winds would push ocean surface currents directly toward the equator. But because Earth rotates, anything moving freely over the planet's surface, including air and water, is deflected to the right in the Northern Hemisphere and to the left in the Southern Hemisphere (Figure 5.17). This deflection is known as the **Coriolis Effect**, named for Gaspard-Gustave de Coriolis (1792-1843), the French mathematician who first described the phenomenon quantitatively in 1835.

According to **Newton's first law of motion**, an object in constant, straight-line motion remains that way unless acted upon by an unbalanced force. Winds in the atmosphere (and water moving in the ocean) exhibit this behavior. But these motions occur on a rotating Earth so that as air moves in a straight line, Earth everywhere except at its equator, exhibits a sense of rotation beneath the moving air. Even with no net force operating, the wind everywhere except at the equator, is displaced from

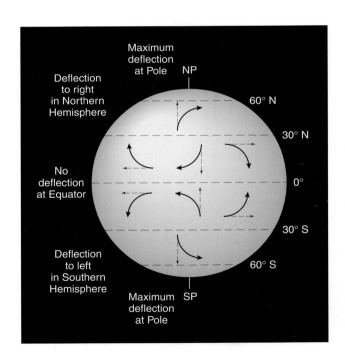

FIGURE 5.17
The Coriolis Effect arises from the rotation of Earth on its axis and causes deflection of winds (and ocean currents) to the right in the Northern Hemisphere and to the left in the Southern Hemisphere.

a straight-line path when its motion is measured with respect to the rotating Earth. This inconsistency can be incorporated in Newton's first law of motion by explaining the deflection to be the result of an apparent force, the Coriolis Effect.

Reversal in the direction of the Coriolis Effect between the Northern and Southern Hemispheres is related to the difference in an observer's sense of Earth's rotation. To an observer looking down from high above the North Pole, the planet rotates counterclockwise, whereas to an observer looking down from high above the South Pole, the planet rotates clockwise. For an Earth-bound observer, this reversal in the sense of Earth's rotation between the two hemispheres translates into a reversal in Coriolis Effect. That is, moving air (and water) is deflected to the right in the Northern Hemisphere and to the left in the Southern Hemisphere.

Although the Coriolis Effect influences the wind regardless of direction, the amount of deflection varies significantly with latitude; that is, the magnitude of the Coriolis Effect varies from zero at the equator to a maximum value at the poles. This variation with latitude can be understood by visualizing the daily rotation of a tower about its vertical axis when located at different latitudes. In a 24-hr day, Earth completes one rotation, as would a tower if located at the North or South Pole. In the same period, a tower at the equator would not rotate at all around its vertical axis because of its orientation perpendicular to Earth's axis of rotation. At any latitude in between, some rotation of a tower occurs but not as much as at the poles.

The magnitude of the Coriolis Effect also varies with wind speed and spatial scale of atmospheric circulation. The Coriolis Effect increases as the wind strengthens because, in the same period of time, faster moving air parcels cover greater distances than slower moving air parcels. The longer the trajectory, the greater is the underlying rotation of the Earth. For practical purposes, the Coriolis Effect significantly influences the wind only in large-scale weather systems, that is, systems larger than ordinary thunderstorms. Large-scale weather systems also have longer life expectancies than small-scale systems so that air parcels cover greater distances over longer periods of time.

Circulation of the Atmosphere: Patterns of Motion

Air pressure gradients, the Coriolis Effect, and the physical properties of Earth's surface shape the circulation of the atmosphere. For convenience of study, atmospheric scientists subdivide atmospheric circulation into discrete weather systems operating at various spatial and temporal scales (Table 5.3). The large-scale wind belts encircling the planet (e.g., westerlies of middle latitudes, trade winds in the tropics) are **planetary-scale systems**. **Synoptic-scale systems** are continental or oceanic in scale; migrating cyclones are examples. **Mesoscale systems** include, for example, thunderstorms and sea breezes— circulation systems that are so small and short-lived that they may influence the weather in only a portion of a large city (Figure 5.18). A weather system covering only a very small area (e.g., a weak tornado) represents the smallest spatial subdivision of atmospheric circulation, **microscale systems**. This section focuses primarily on atmospheric circulation patterns operating at the planetary and synoptic scales.

PLANETARY-SCALE CIRCULATION

As shown in Figure 5.19, three broad wind belts encircle both the Northern and Southern Hemispheres. In the Northern Hemisphere, prevailing surface winds blow from the northeast (*trade winds*) between the equator and about 30 degrees N, from the southwest (*westerlies*) between about 30 and 60 degrees N, and from the northeast (*polar easterlies*) between about 60 degrees N and the North Pole. In the Southern Hemisphere, prevailing surface winds are southeasterly (*trade winds*) between the equator and about 30 degrees S, northwesterly (*westerlies*) between about 30 and 60 degrees S, and southeasterly (*polar easterlies*) between about 60 degrees S and the South Pole.

TABLE 5.3
Scales of Atmospheric Circulation

Circulation	Space scale	Time scale	Example
Planetary scale	10,000 to 40,000 km	weeks to months	Westerlies
Synoptic scale	100 to 10,000 km	days	High, Low
Mesoscale	1 to 100 km	hours	Thunderstorm
Microscale	1 m to 1 km	seconds to minutes	Tornado

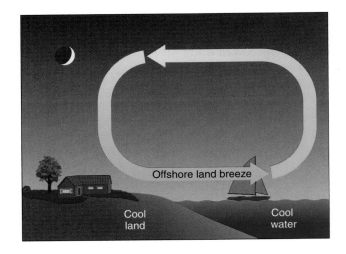

FIGURE 5.18

A sea breeze is a relatively cool mesoscale surface wind that develops during daylight hours and blows inland from the ocean in response to differential heating of land and sea. During the day, the land surface warms more than the sea surface inducing a horizontal air pressure gradient with high pressure over the ocean surface and low pressure over the land surface. At night, land becomes relatively colder than the sea surface. The circulation reverses and a land breeze blows offshore.

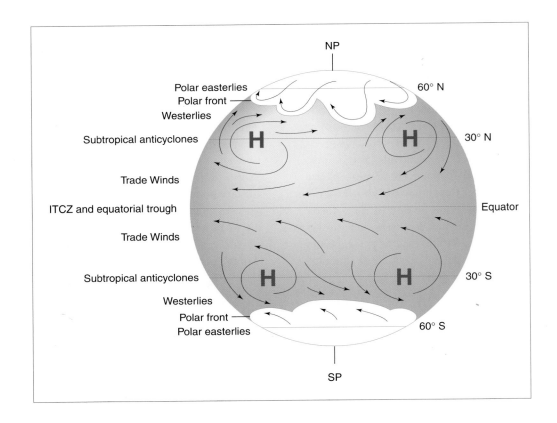

FIGURE 5.19

Schematic representation of the planetary-scale surface circulation of the atmosphere.

The planetary-scale atmospheric circulation plays an important role in the horizontal transport of water vapor between ocean basins (as part of the global water cycle). For example, the trade winds transport water evaporated from the tropical Atlantic Ocean basin across Central America to the tropical Pacific Ocean where it condenses into clouds that produce rain. This transport of water increases the salinity of Atlantic surface waters and freshens the Pacific surface waters.

In both hemispheres, trade winds blow out of the equatorward flank of the subtropical anticyclones and the westerlies blow out of the poleward flank of the subtropical anticyclones. A **subtropical anticyclone** (or high) is a massive semi-permanent high pressure system. Centered over the ocean basins near 30 degrees N and S, they are imposing features of the planetary-scale circulation that undergo seasonal changes in both location and strength. Viewed from above in the Northern Hemisphere, surface winds blow clockwise and outward about the center of a subtropical high. Viewed from above in the Southern Hemisphere, surface winds blow counterclockwise and outward about the center of a subtropical high. In both hemispheres, climates are relatively dry on the eastern flank of the subtropical highs and moist on the western flank. Broad areas of ocean basins under the subtropical highs experience persistent episodes of warm dry weather. Low precipitation coupled with high temperatures cause high rates of evaporation and therefore relatively high salinity of surface waters (refer back to Figure 3.8).

Over a broad region surrounding the center of a subtropical high, the horizontal pressure gradient is weak so that surface winds are very light or the air is calm over extensive areas of the subtropical ocean. This situation played havoc with early sailing ships, which were becalmed for days or even weeks at a time. Ships setting sail from Spain to the New World were often caught in this predicament and crews were forced to jettison their cargo of horses when supplies of water and food ran low. For this reason, early mariners referred to this region as the **horse latitudes**, a name now applied to all latitudes between about 30 and 35 degrees N and S under subtropical highs.

On the poleward side of the subtropical highs, surface westerlies flow into regions of low pressure. In the Northern Hemisphere, there are two separate subpolar lows: the *Aleutian low* over the North Pacific Ocean and the *Icelandic low* over the North Atlantic Ocean. These pressure systems mark the convergence of the middle latitude westerlies with the polar easterlies. By contrast, in the Southern Hemisphere, the middle latitude westerlies

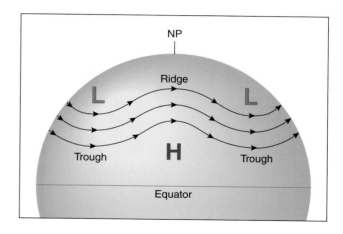

FIGURE 5.20
In the middle and upper troposphere, the Northern Hemisphere westerlies blow from west to east in a wave-like pattern of ridges (clockwise turns) and troughs (counterclockwise turns).

and the polar easterlies converge along a nearly continuous belt of low pressure surrounding the Antarctic continent.

At middle and high latitudes of the Northern Hemisphere, prevailing winds at altitudes from about 5500 to 12,000 m (18,000 to 40,000 ft) blow generally from west to east in a wave-like pattern of ridges (clockwise turns) and troughs (counterclockwise turns) as illustrated in Figure 5.20. The temperature gradient between the relatively warm tropics and relatively cold polar areas induces a northward flow of air aloft that is deflected to the right (to the east) by Earth's rotation (the Coriolis Effect). A similar situation occurs in the Southern Hemisphere where the Coriolis Effect deflects a southward-directed flow of air aloft to the left, resulting in a west wind in that hemisphere. The belts of westerlies encircle the planet and steer air masses, storms, and fair-weather systems generally from west to east.

Also part of the weaving westerlies are narrow corridors of exceptionally strong winds in the upper troposphere known as *jet streams*. In the Northern Hemisphere, the middle-latitude jet stream is situated over a boundary (called the *polar front*) between colder air to the north and warmer air to the south and contributes to the development of storm systems.

SYNOPTIC-SCALE WEATHER SYSTEMS

The most important synoptic-scale weather systems are *highs* (or anticyclones) and *lows* (or cyclones). As noted earlier, highs usually are accompanied by fair weather whereas lows often bring clouds and precipitation. Whereas subtropical highs and subpolar lows are nearly stationary, synoptic-scale highs and lows move with the prevailing winds blowing at altitudes of several kilometers above Earth's surface, generally eastward across North America. Highs follow lows and lows follow highs. As a general rule, highs track toward the east and southeast whereas lows track toward the east and northeast. Important exceptions are tropical cyclones (e.g., hurricanes) that are imbedded in the trade wind flow and generally track from east to west over the tropical Atlantic and Pacific. Eventually these systems come under the influence of the middle-latitude westerlies and turn toward the north and northeast.

Highs originating over northwestern Canada bring cold, dry weather in winter and cool, dry weather in summer. Highs that develop farther south bring hot weather in summer and mild, dry weather in winter. Viewed from above in the Northern Hemisphere, surface winds in a high-pressure system blow in a clockwise and outward spiral as shown in Figure 5.21. Reversal of the Coriolis Effect in the Southern Hemisphere means that surface winds in a high blow in a counterclockwise and outward spiral south of the equator. Surface winds spiraling outward induce descending dry air near the center of a high—hence, fair weather.

Viewed from above in the Northern Hemisphere, surface winds in a low blow in a counterclockwise and inward spiral as shown in Figure 5.22A. Because the Coriolis Effect reverses direction in the Southern Hemisphere, surface winds in a low blow in a clockwise and inward spiral south of the equator. For middle and high latitude lows, surface winds spiraling inward bring together contrasting air masses and induce ascending air

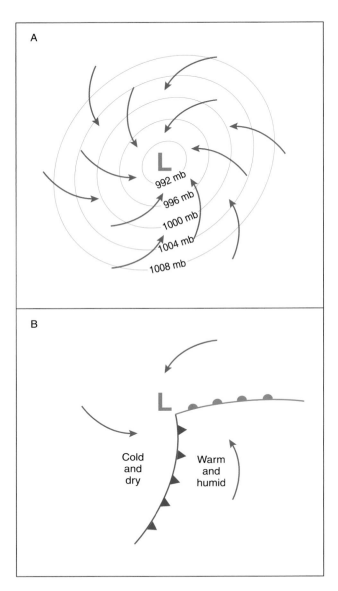

FIGURE 5.22
Viewed from above in the Northern Hemisphere, (A) surface winds blow counterclockwise and inward in a low (cyclone), (B) bringing together contrasting air masses to form fronts. Contour lines are isobars drawn at 4-millibar intervals. The curved blue line with spikes is the leading edge of relatively cold and dry air (a cold front) while the curved red line with half circles is the leading edge of relatively warm and humid air (a warm front).

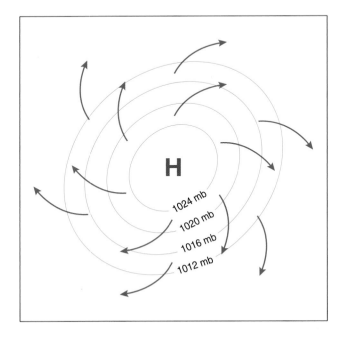

FIGURE 5.21
Viewed from above in the Northern Hemisphere, surface winds blow clockwise and outward in a high (anticyclone). Contour lines are isobars drawn at 4-millibar intervals.

along fronts (Figure 5.22B). A *front* is a narrow zone of transition between air masses that contrast in temperature and/or humidity. Air expands and cools as it ascends along a front causing water vapor to condense into clouds—hence, stormy weather.

Lows that track across the northern United States or southern Canada are more distant from sources of moisture and usually produce less rain- or snowfall than lows that track farther south (such as lows that move along the Gulf Coast or up the Eastern Seaboard). Weather to the left side (west and north) of a storm's track (path) tends to be relatively cold, whereas weather to the right (east and south) of a storm's track tends to be relatively warm. For this reason, winter snows are most likely to the west and north of the path of a low-pressure system. We have more to say about storms and their impact on the coastal zone in Chapter 8.

Conclusions

In this chapter we have seen how the ocean plays a key role in the global radiation balance. The ocean, covering about 71% of Earth's surface, has a very low average albedo for incident solar radiation and is the principal sink for incoming solar radiation. The ocean also is the chief source of water vapor and latent heat for the atmosphere. Latent heat is absorbed when water evaporates from the ocean surface and is released to the atmosphere when water vapor condenses during cloud formation. This latent heat transfer is the principal means whereby heat is channeled from the Earth's surface to the atmosphere. Furthermore, ocean currents contribute to heat transport from the tropics to higher latitudes and breaking ocean waves are an important source of cloud condensation nuclei.

The atmosphere is frictionally coupled to the ocean surface and winds supply the kinetic energy that drives surface ocean currents and generates ocean waves. Large-scale surface ocean currents mirror the prevailing planetary-scale atmospheric circulation. In the next chapter, we begin our examination of motion in the ocean with a look at wind-driven surface currents and the deeper thermohaline circulation.

Basic Understandings

- Weather is the state of the atmosphere at some time and place. Climate is popularly defined as weather at a particular location averaged over a specified interval of time (30 years, by international convention). Climate also encompasses extremes in weather.

- As Earth orbits the sun, its atmosphere and surface absorb a tiny fraction of the total radiation continually emitted by the sun. Absorption of solar radiation heats the Earth-atmosphere system. At the same time the planet continually emits infrared radiation to space, which cools the Earth-atmosphere system, the balance resulting in a nearly constant planetary average temperature.

- As Earth orbits the sun, regular changes occur in the solar altitude and length of daylight, that affect the intensity of solar radiation striking Earth's surface at a point. Solar altitude is the angle of the sun above the horizon and varies from zero to a maximum of 90 degrees. The amount of solar energy striking a unit area of Earth surface in a unit of time increases with increasing solar altitude. The difference in length of daylight over the year between the summer and winter solstices increases from zero at the equator to a maximum within the Arctic and Antarctic Circles. Variation of incoming solar radiation through the course of a year is reflected in the march of average monthly temperatures.

- The moderating influence of ocean water reduces the average temperature contrast between summer and winter. Locations immediately downwind of the ocean experience a maritime climate whereas locations well inland from the ocean have continental climates. Proximity to large bodies of water also affects the timing of the average warmest and coldest periods of the year. In the United States, the air temperature cycle lags the solar radiation cycle by an average 27 days. But in coastal localities having a strong maritime influence, the average lag time is up to 36 days.

- Solar radiation intercepted by Earth interacts with the atmosphere's component gases and aerosols. Interactions involve scattering, reflection, and absorption. Scattering and reflection alter only the direction of the radiation, but with absorption radiation is converted to heat energy.

- Surfaces having a high albedo reflect a relatively large fraction of incident solar radiation and appear light in color. Surfaces having a low albedo reflect a relatively small fraction of incident solar radiation and appear dark in color. Within the atmosphere, cloud tops are the most

- important reflectors of solar radiation.
- Solar radiation that is not scattered or reflected to space or absorbed in the atmosphere strikes Earth's surface. There, some radiation is absorbed and some is reflected depending on the albedo of the surface. On a global basis, the average albedo of ocean water is only about 8% so that the ocean, covering about 71% of Earth's surface, is the principal sink for solar radiation.
- On a global average annual basis, Earth's planetary albedo is about 31%. The atmosphere absorbs only about 20% of the total solar radiation intercepted by the planet, and Earth's surface (mostly ocean) absorbs 49%. Hence, the atmosphere is relatively transparent to solar radiation.
- Ocean waters absorb most incident solar radiation within relatively shallow depths. Water absorbs the longer wavelengths (i.e., reds and yellows) of visible light more efficiently than the shorter wavelengths (i.e., greens and blues) so that green and blue penetrate to greater depths. The upper portion of the ocean in which solar radiation is detectable is known as the photic zone.
- The greenhouse effect refers to the heating of Earth's surface and lower atmosphere caused by strong absorption and emission of infrared radiation by certain gaseous components of the atmosphere. The principal greenhouse gas is water vapor. Without the greenhouse effect, Earth would be much too cold to support most forms of plant and animal life.
- The Callendar effect is the theory that global climate change can be brought about by enhancement of the natural greenhouse effect by increased levels of atmospheric CO_2 from anthropogenic sources, principally the burning of fossil fuels.
- The global distribution of incoming solar radiation and outgoing infrared radiation implies net radiational warming of Earth's surface and net radiational cooling of Earth's atmosphere. In response to the resulting temperature gradient, heat is transferred from Earth's surface to the atmosphere via latent heating and sensible heating. Latent heating refers to the transport of heat from one place to another as a consequence of phase changes of water. Sensible heating involves heat transport via conduction and convection.

- The Bowen ratio describes how heat available at Earth's surface is partitioned between sensible heating and latent heating. The Bowen ratio is lowest for wet surfaces and highest for dry surfaces, varying between 0.1 for oceans and 5.0 for deserts. The global average Bowen ratio is 0.3.
- On a global average annual basis, radiational heating exceeds radiational cooling between about 35 degrees N and S latitude. Radiational cooling exceeds radiational heating poleward of about 35 degrees N and 35 degrees S. Imbalances in radiational heating and cooling imply net heating in the tropics and subtropics and net cooling at middle and high latitudes. But lower latitudes are not warming relative to higher latitudes because heat is transferred from the tropics toward the poles (poleward heat transport).
- Poleward heat transport is brought about by north-south exchange of air masses and latent heat in storm systems. The ocean contributes to poleward heat transport via wind-driven surface currents and deeper thermohaline circulation that traverses the lengths of ocean basins.
- When air pressure readings are adjusted to sea level everywhere (to remove the influence of elevation), air pressure varies from one place to another and fluctuates from day to day and even from one hour to the next. Spatial and temporal changes in air pressure at Earth's surface arise from variations in air temperature (principally), humidity (water vapor concentration in air), and atmospheric circulation.
- On a weather map, a HIGH or H symbol designates places where sea-level air pressure is relatively high compared to the air pressure in surrounding areas. A high is also known as an anticyclone and is usually a fair weather system. A LOW or L symbol signifies regions where sea-level air pressure is relatively low compared to the air pressure in surrounding areas. A low is also known as a cyclone and often brings stormy weather.
- In response to an air pressure gradient, the wind blows from where the pressure is relatively high toward where the pressure is relatively low. The pressure gradient force is always directed across isobars and toward low pressure. The magnitude of the pressure gradient force is inversely related to the spacing of isobars.

- Because Earth rotates, anything moving freely over Earth's surface, including air and water, is deflected to the right in the Northern Hemisphere and to the left in the Southern Hemisphere. This deflection is known as the Coriolis Effect. The magnitude of the Coriolis Effect increases from zero at the equator to a maximum at the poles.

- Viewed from above in the Northern Hemisphere, surface winds blow clockwise and outward in a high, and counterclockwise and inward in a low. Viewed from above in the Southern Hemisphere, surface winds blow counterclockwise and outward in a high, and clockwise and inward in a low.

- At the planetary scale, three broad wind belts encircle both the Northern and Southern Hemispheres. Trade winds characterize the tropics, the westerlies encircle middle latitudes, and the polar easterlies prevail at high latitudes. The trade winds and westerlies are linked to the subtropical highs, massive semi-permanent systems that are centered over the ocean basins near 30 degrees N and S.

- Whereas subtropical highs and subpolar lows are nearly stationary, synoptic-scale highs and lows move with the prevailing winds blowing several kilometers above the surface. Highs follow lows and lows follow highs, shaping day-to-day weather.

Review

1. Distinguish between weather and climate.
2. Compare the length of daylight at a middle latitude location on the winter solstice with that on the summer solstice. Also compare the solar altitude at noon local time on these two days.
3. Outside of the tropics, what is the relationship between the annual solar radiation cycle and the annual temperature cycle? How is this relationship influenced by proximity to large bodies of water?
4. For incoming solar radiation, compare the average albedo of the ocean surface to the average albedo of cloud tops. What is the albedo of the Earth-atmosphere system (i.e., the planetary albedo)?
5. Define the photic zone and describe how its depth is affected by the concentration of suspended particles and dissolved organic matter in seawater.
6. What is the cause and significance of Earth's greenhouse effect?
7. Define latent heating and sensible heating and compare the importance of the two processes in transferring heat energy from Earth's surface to atmosphere on a global average annual basis.
8. Describe the processes involved in poleward heat transport within the Earth-atmosphere system.
9. How does the Coriolis Effect deflect large-scale winds and ocean currents in the Northern and Southern Hemispheres? Why is there no Coriolis Effect at the equator?
10. Describe the surface horizontal winds in high and low pressure systems as viewed from above in the Northern Hemisphere.

Critical Thinking

1. Why does the ocean have a moderating influence on the climate of downwind coastal areas?
2. The average albedo of the ocean is only 8%. What is the significance of this relatively low albedo for Earth's climate system?
3. Speculate on how higher sea surface temperatures (SST) might impact Earth's greenhouse effect.
4. Describe the ocean's role in poleward heat transport.
5. How do the subtropical anticyclones influence the salinity of surface ocean waters?
6. How does an enhanced greenhouse effect influence Earth's global radiative equilibrium?
7. How does less ice cover in the Arctic Ocean affect the flux of water vapor from the ocean to the atmosphere?
8. How does less ice cover in the Arctic Ocean affect heat transport from the ocean to the atmosphere?
9. Why are hurricanes and other tropical cyclones important contributors to poleward heat transport?
10. Why is it challenging for scientists to determine whether the MOC is strengthening, weakening, or stable?

ESSAY: Location at Sea, A Historical Perspective

When humans first left their caves they faced the challenge of determining their location, how to get to where they wanted to go, and how to get back to where they started from. On land and inland waters, while not easy, the task was manageable. Using prominent landmarks such as shorelines or rock pinnacles as signposts, travelers developed a sense of direction and distance. Eventually common routes of travel for discovery, trade, and communication produced well-worn paths. Upon leaving land for the open ocean, the problem of location became much more difficult. Once out of sight of the shore, with water in all directions as far as the eye could see, ancient mariners depended mostly on luck to return them to port. It is not surprising that early seafaring was mostly a coastal affair.

Eventually humans developed a rudimentary understanding of winds and ocean currents and became familiar with the local geography of coastlines and the seas they regularly plied. Knowledge of the true shape of Earth allowed sailors to understand the relationship between their north-south position (latitude) and the location of the stars and sun in the sky. By day, mariners determined their latitude by measuring the altitude of the sun at its highest point in the sky (zenith) and knowing the calendar date. But they never knew with any certainty where their vessel was located in terms of the east-west direction. And when clouds obscured the sky or storm-tossed seas prevented an estimate of sun or star angle, even the north–south position was in doubt. The inability to determine longitude with any certainty led to many shipwrecks, thousands of lives lost, and huge financial losses.

About CE 150, the Egyptian astronomer and geographer Ptolemy (ca. CE 85-165) proposed the concept of latitude and longitude as imaginary reference lines on the globe by which location could be specified. His zero degree parallel (latitude) was set at the equator because he knew that the sun, moon and planets pass almost directly over that location. His zero-degree longitude line (the *prime meridian*) was set in the Canary Islands. Perhaps for political reasons, others drew the prime meridian through Paris, Philadelphia, Moscow, and at least a half dozen other places. Since 1884, by international convention the prime meridian runs through Greenwich, England, a bit to the east of Ptolemy's mark. Longitude is measured in degrees to the east and west of that line to the common 180-degree meridian, essentially the *International Date Line* (the imaginary line on Earth that separates two consecutive calendar days).

The search for a connection between longitude and the regular motions of celestial bodies would challenge navigators and astronomers for more than 1000 years. By the early 18th century, governments of various maritime nations offered substantial prize money for the person who could solve the "longitude problem," that is, develop a reliable method for determining longitude at sea. With the Longitude Act of 1714, the British Parliament offered the highest prize—several million dollars in today's money. A Board of Longitude was appointed consisting of a blue-ribbon panel charged with conducting trials of proposals and awarding prize money. The Board disbanded in 1828.

A promising approach to solving the longitude problem was to develop a way to determine precisely the time of the day. Earth is roughly a sphere that rotates through 360 degrees once every 24 hrs, that is, 15 degrees per hour. If one knew the current time at the prime meridian (from a clock) and the current time at one's location at sea (based on the sun's position in the sky), it would be easy to calculate the number of degrees represented by the difference between the two times to yield the longitude. For example, at local noon on a ship, if the clock read 3 p.m., the longitude of the ship was 3 hours or 45 degrees west of the prime meridian.

The search for a solution to the longitude problem also involved considerable work on possible astronomical techniques (analogous to the way latitude was determined). The Board of Longitude favored astronomical solutions because they were considered more scientific than reliance on clocks. Nonetheless, the most successful efforts to solve the longitude problem focused on the design and construction of a very accurate clock that could keep time over a lengthy sea voyage and withstand the harsh conditions at sea without suffering mechanical failure.

The first in his series of five accurate and durable nautical chronometers was invented by the English clockmaker John Harrison (1693-1776) (Figure 1) in 1733. Forty years later, he was awarded the 20,000 Pounds Sterling prize offered by Great Britain for a clock that could be used to determine longitude to within one-half a degree (30 nautical miles at the equator) on a voyage from England to any port in the West Indies. It would be another 50 or so years for this technology to find its way onto virtually every ship. Meanwhile, most sea captains continued to rely on dead reckoning to determine their location. The clock-method for determining longitude was used for more than two centuries until supplanted by satellite-based techniques including the *Global Positioning System (GPS)*, described in the first Essay in Chapter 6.

For more details on the longitude problem and how it was solved, refer to the delightful book *Longitude* by Dava Sobel (Penguin Books, 1995).

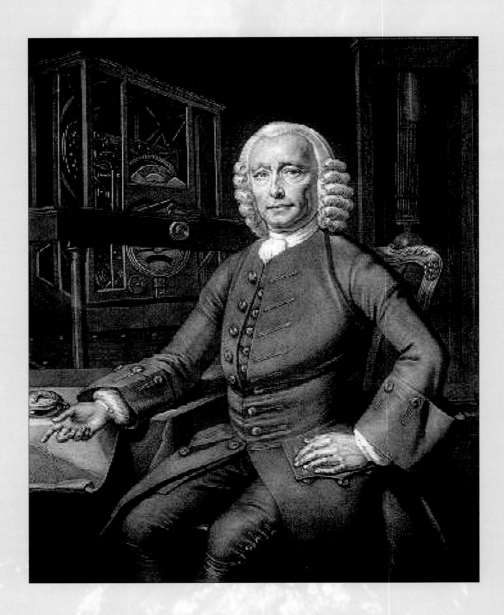

FIGURE 1
The English clockmaker John Harrison (1693-1776) was credited with solving the longitude problem by developing an accurate sea-worthy clock. Harrison's clock passed the test by determining the longitude to within 0.5 degree on a voyage from England to a port in the West Indies.

ESSAY: The Stratospheric Ozone Shield and Marine Life

Ozone (O_3) is a relatively unstable molecule made up of three atoms of oxygen, but has certain physical and chemical properties that distinguish it from free oxygen (O_2). The greatest concentration of ozone occurs naturally in the stratosphere at altitudes near 40 km (25 mi). Stratospheric ozone shields marine and terrestrial organisms from exposure to potentially lethal intensities of solar ultraviolet (UV) radiation. Without this so-called *stratospheric ozone shield*, life as we know it could not exist on Earth. It was not until about 1 billion years ago that the atmosphere contained sufficient oxygen (from which ozone is generated), that an effective ozone shield was present. From that point on, for example, marine organisms could thrive in surface waters. Another 560 million years would pass until there was sufficient ozone to allow life to leave the protection of the seas. However, in the latter portion of the 20th century, scientists became aware of a serious threat to the stratospheric ozone shield that poses a hazard for all forms of life including marine organisms.

Within the stratosphere, two sets of competing chemical reactions, both powered by solar ultraviolet radiation, continually generate and destroy ozone (Figure 1). During ozone production, UV strikes an oxygen molecule (O_2) causing it to split into two free oxygen atoms (O). Free oxygen atoms then collide with molecules of oxygen to form ozone molecules (O_3). At the same time ozone is destroyed. Ozone absorbs ultraviolet radiation, splitting the molecule into one free oxygen atom (O) and one molecule of oxygen (O_2). The free oxygen atom then collides with an ozone molecule to form two molecules of oxygen. The net effect of these opposing sets of chemical reactions is a minute reservoir of ozone that peaks at only about 10 parts per million (ppm) in the middle stratosphere. Ultraviolet radiation (at different wavelengths) powers both sets of chemical reactions so that much but not all UV radiation is prevented from reaching Earth's surface.

The most dangerous portion of UV radiation that strikes Earth's surface is designated *UVB* and spans the wavelength band from 0.29 to 0.32 micrometer. Prolonged exposure to UVB or an increase in the intensity of UVB reaching Earth's surface threatens the health and wellbeing of living organisms. As a general rule, every 1% decline in stratospheric ozone concentration translates into a 2% increase in the intensity of UV that passes through the ozone shield. The increase in UVB that actually reaches Earth's surface depends on cloudiness and the dustiness of the atmosphere.

The effects on human health of exposure to too much UVB are well known and include increased incidence of skin cancer, premature aging of the skin, cataracts of the eye, and suppressed immune system. Perhaps less well known is the impact on marine ecosystems. Too much UV penetrating ocean surface waters can disrupt the orderly functioning of marine food webs, adversely affecting predator-prey relationships, competition, species diversity, and the dynamics of trophic (feeding) levels. Particularly important is the potential impact of elevated levels of solar ultraviolet radiation on autotrophs that form the base of marine food webs. Too much UV adversely affects the growth and reproduction of autotrophs thereby reducing the food (energy) supply for organisms occupying higher trophic levels (Chapter 9). Some phytoplankton can move out of harms way, but exposure to UVB impairs their orientation mechanisms and motility making even those species more susceptible to radiation damage. In addition, too much UV impairs larval development, harms young fish, shrimp, crabs, and amphibians, and threatens macro-algae and sea grasses.

More than three decades ago, scientists discovered that a group of chemicals, known as CFCs (for *chlorofluorocarbons*), poses a serious threat to the stratospheric ozone shield. First synthesized in 1928, CFCs were widely used as chilling (heat-transfer) agents in refrigerators and air conditioners, for cleaning electronic circuit boards, and in the manufacture of foams used for insulation. F.S. Rowland and M.J. Molina of the University of California at Irvine first warned of the threat of CFCs to the stratospheric ozone shield in 1974. Five years later, use of CFCs as propellants in common household aerosol sprays such as deodorants and hairsprays was banned in the United States, Canada, Norway, and Sweden. For their pioneering work on the depletion of stratospheric ozone, Rowland, Molina (now at the Massachusetts Institute of Technology), and P.J. Crutzen (of the Max Planck Institute for Chemistry, Germany) were awarded the 1995 Nobel Prize in chemistry.

Increasing worldwide acceptance of the threat of CFCs and other chemicals to the stratospheric ozone shield prompted the United Nations Environmental Program in 1987 to draw up the *Montreal Protocol on Substances that Deplete the Ozone Layer*. The original goal of the Montreal Protocol was to cut CFC production in half by 1992 (compared to 1986 levels). However, the seriousness of the problem led to amendments expanding the list of regulated substances (e.g., to include bromine-containing halons) and requiring the worldwide phase out of the manufacture and use of CFCs in January 1996.

OZONE PRODUCTION	OZONE DESTRUCTION
High energy ultraviolet radiation strikes an oxygen molecule...	Ozone absorbs a range of ultraviolet radiation...
...and causes it to split into two free oxygen atoms.	...splitting the molecule into one free oxygen atom and one molecule of ordinary oxygen.
The free oxygen atoms collide with molecules of oxygen...	The free oxygen atom then can collide with an ozone molecule...
To form ozone molecules.	To form two molecules of oxygen.

FIGURE 1
Production and destruction of stratospheric ozone.

Certain CFCs are inert (chemically non-reactive) in the troposphere, where they accumulated for decades. Atmospheric circulation transports CFCs into the stratosphere where, at altitudes above about 25 km (15.5 mi), intense UV radiation breaks down CFCs, releasing chlorine (Cl), a gas that readily reacts with and destroys ozone. Products of this reaction are chlorine monoxide (ClO) and molecular oxygen (O_2). Chlorine (Cl) is a catalyst in chemical reactions that convert ozone to oxygen. In this way, each chlorine atom can destroy perhaps tens of thousands of ozone molecules.

First signs of a thinner stratospheric ozone shield came from Antarctica. For about six weeks during the Southern Hemisphere spring (mainly in September and October), the ozone layer in the Antarctic stratosphere (mostly at altitudes from 11 to 23 km, or 7 to 14 mi) thins drastically and then recovers during November. This so-called *Antarctic ozone hole* is defined as the thinning of the ozone layer over the continent to levels significantly below what it was in 1979. Research conducted during the National Ozone Expeditions to the U.S. McMurdo Station in 1986-87 plus NASA aircraft flights into the Antarctic stratosphere in 1987 led to the discovery of relatively high concentrations of chlorine monoxide (ClO) in the Antarctic stratosphere. This discovery established a convincing link between ozone depletion and CFCs.

The 2000 ozone hole, the largest on record, covered an area larger than Antarctica and exposed southern portions of Argentina and Chile to elevated levels of UV. The Antarctic ozone hole covered a maximum area of 28 million square km in 2006 and 24.7 million square km in 2007. For some perspective on these numbers, the area of North America is 24.25 million square km.

What causes the Antarctic ozone hole and why does it fill in by November? During the long, dark Antarctic winter, extreme radiational cooling causes stratospheric temperatures to plunge below –88 °C (–126 °F). At such frigid temperatures, *polar stratospheric clouds (PSCs)* form. These clouds (composed of tiny particles of water ice, nitric acid, and sulfuric acid) promote ozone depletion by providing surfaces on which chlorine and bromine compounds that are inert toward ozone are converted to active forms that destroy ozone. Once the sun reappears in spring, solar radiation supplies the energy that causes active forms of chlorine and bromine to begin destroying ozone.

Ozone depletion takes place while the Antarctic atmosphere is essentially cut off from the rest of the planetary-scale atmospheric circulation by the *circumpolar vortex*, a belt of strong winds that encircles the outer margin of the Antarctic continent. A month or so into spring, however, the circumpolar vortex begins to weaken, allowing warmer ozone-rich air from lower latitudes to invade the Antarctic stratosphere. Polar stratospheric clouds vaporize and the stratospheric ozone concentration returns to normal levels; that is, the Antarctic ozone hole fills in.

Scientists investigating stratospheric chemistry in the Arctic in early 1989 discovered ozone-destroying chlorine compounds and a slight thinning of ozone. An Arctic ozone hole comparable in magnitude to the Antarctic ozone hole is unlikely for two reasons. For one, in winter the Arctic stratosphere averages about 10 Celsius degrees (18 Fahrenheit degrees) warmer than the Antarctic stratosphere, making formation of polar stratospheric clouds unlikely. Secondly, the circumpolar vortex that surrounds the Arctic weakens earlier than its Antarctic counterpart. However, an exceptionally cold Arctic winter coupled with an unusually persistent circumpolar vortex could translate into significant ozone depletion in the Arctic.

Phase out of CFCs and other ozone-destroying chemicals slowed the release of chlorine into the atmosphere. However, CFCs have a long residence time in the atmosphere (up to 100 years or longer) so that the concentration of chlorine in the stratosphere is not expected to begin to decline until about 2010 and complete recovery of the Antarctic ozone layer is not likely to occur until at least 2050. Meanwhile, scientists continue to monitor stratospheric ozone levels worldwide.

CHAPTER 6

OCEAN CURRENTS

Case-in-Point
Driving Question
Ocean's Vertical Structure
Ocean in Motion: The Forces
    Wind-Driven Currents and Ekman Transport
    Geostrophic Flow
Wind-Driven Surface Currents
    Subtropical and Sub-polar Gyres
    Equatorial Currents
    Boundary Currents
    Ocean Rings
    Upwelling and Downwelling
Monitoring the Ocean Depths
Thermohaline Circulation
    Formation of Deep Water
    Water Masses
    Implications for Climate
Conclusions
Basic Understandings/Review/Critical Thinking
ESSAY: Global Positioning System
ESSAY: Profiling the Ocean Depths
ESSAY: Bottles and Rubber Duckies, Tracking
    Currents with Flotsam and Jetsam

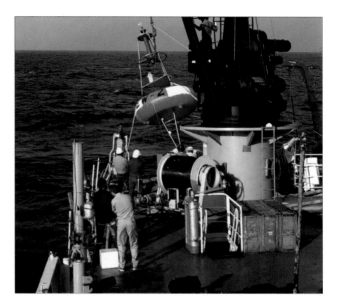

Deploying a deep-ocean moored buoy. Current meter, water-temperature sensor, and meteorological instruments on buoy. [NOAA]

Case in Point

For much of human history, knowledge of the ocean and its currents was not recorded for many reasons. For one, most sailors could not write so their basic understandings of the sea were passed on orally. Even after the European nations (Portugal, Spain, Netherlands, England, France, and Russia) began systematic ocean exploration, their discoveries were closely guarded secrets, far too valuable to be made public. Hence, we know little of what sailors understood about ocean currents during the period of great ocean exploration from the 15th to 18th centuries.

Existence of the Gulf Stream, a major surface ocean current, was known as early as 1519. Bishop Resen of Copenhagen drew the first map of the Gulf Stream in 1605 based on records from trans-Atlantic voyages of the English explorer Martin Frobisher (1535-1594) and a crude sketch attributed to Icelanders. Subsequent charts showing the Gulf Stream were published in 1678 (by the Jesuit Athanasius Kircher) and 1685 (by a German named Happelius).

More widely known is Benjamin Franklin's study of the Gulf Stream. Franklin (1706-1790) served as colonial deputy postmaster general from 1753 to 1774. He found that British merchant ships arriving in the colonies from England took many days to weeks longer to make the voyage across the Atlantic than American

FIGURE 6.1
The location of the Gulf Stream (A) plotted on the 1769 Franklin-Folger map, and (B) on a much more recent infrared satellite depiction of sea-surface temperatures. Shades of red indicate the highest sea-surface temperatures. [Source: NOAA; University of Miami, Rosenstiel School of Marine & Atmospheric Science]

vessels. British postal authorities asked Franklin for an explanation. Franklin consulted with his cousin, Timothy Folger, a Nantucket, MA whaling ship captain, who told him about the Gulf Stream, the strongest surface current in the North Atlantic (often 10 to 12 km per hr or 6 to 7 mph—roughly the speed of a modern sailing ship). On eastbound voyages, American captains sailed with the current but on the return voyage they would avoid it, cutting up to weeks off the journey. At the time, British captains were unaware of the Gulf Stream.

Franklin published his cousin's chart showing the location of the Gulf Stream and presented it to the British. Interestingly, the location of the Gulf Stream plotted on the 1769 Franklin-Folger map shown in Figure 6.1A is remarkably similar to the location of the Gulf Stream as revealed by satellite-derived sea surface temperature (SST) patterns shown in Figure 6.1B. British authorities refused to take advantage of or even acknowledge the Franklin-Folger map. Franklin took measurements of sea surface temperatures during his many crossings of the Atlantic Ocean, thereby developing a navigational technique based on the location of the relatively warm Gulf Stream waters.

In the mid 19th century, the American naval officer Matthew Fontaine Maury (1806-1873) conducted the first systematic study of the ocean's surface currents and winds (Figure 6.2). Maury compiled information on currents and winds from the logbooks of sailors' observations stored

FIGURE 6.2
The American naval officer Matthew Fontaine Maury (1806-1873) compiled wind and ocean current data from thousands of ships' logs and produced the first reliable wind and current charts of the ocean. [Source: U.S. Navy]

at the U.S. Navy's Depot of Charts and Instruments and published the first charts of the North Atlantic in 1847. He estimated current direction and speed by analyzing deflections in a ship's course caused by surface ocean currents. Failure to correct a ship's course for current-induced deflections meant that the ship's final position at the end of a run would differ from its intended destination. Combining thousands of such observations, Maury constructed a map of average surface currents over much of the ocean. A skilled navigator having knowledge of currents can correct a ship's course to compensate for current-induced deflections.

Studies of ocean currents continue today for many reasons, ranging from military operations to predicting oil spill trajectories at sea. Through the years, instruments used to monitor currents have become more sophisticated. Satellite observations and data from in situ instruments have largely replaced analysis of ships' logs. Global Positioning Systems (GPS) now measure a ship's location to within 5 to 10 m (16 to 33 ft) so that the deflection caused by ocean currents can be determined accurately and instantaneously. For more on GPS, see this chapter's first Essay.

Driving Question:

What causes ocean waters to circulate and what are the prevailing patterns of ocean currents?

Energy and matter (e.g., heat, water) are continually exchanged between the ocean and atmosphere, and these processes drive the ocean circulation. Evaporation, precipitation, runoff from the continents plus heating and cooling bring about changes in the temperature and salinity of surface waters. Density changes that accompany variations in temperature and salinity can cause water to sink or rise in the ocean. *Kinetic energy* (energy of motion) is transferred from near-surface winds to the ocean's surface layer, driving the currents that dominate the motion of the ocean's upper hundred meters or so. Winds are responsible for not only horizontal currents but also vertical water motions within the surface layer.

Most seawater (90%) is in the deep ocean, isolated from the atmosphere and its winds. Deep-ocean waters are cold and dark and come to the surface primarily at high latitudes where they interact with the atmosphere. Differences in water density drive the sluggish circulation of deep water. Typically these waters flow at speeds of less than 1 cm per sec or 1 km per day—about 240 times slower than the Gulf Stream. Because of its volume and isolation from the atmosphere, the deep ocean is both a storehouse for heat (acting as a buffer for global-scale temperature change) and a reservoir for dissolved gases such as carbon dioxide that are sequestered for centuries to millennia.

The ocean features wind-driven surface currents and the deep ocean's slower density-driven thermohaline circulation. In this chapter, we examine the characteristics of these two circulation regimes, and the governing forces. We begin by describing the vertical structure of the ocean.

Ocean's Vertical Structure

Most of the ocean is divided into three horizontal depth zones based on density: the mixed layer, pycnocline, and deep layer (Figure 6.3). At high latitudes, a weak pycnocline may rise to the surface.

Wind-driven surface currents are restricted to the ocean's uppermost 100 m (300 ft.) or less. The strongest currents occur in the ocean's surface layer, although some surface currents such as western boundary currents like the Gulf Stream (discussed later) can be relatively strong to depths of several hundred meters. Surface currents are changeable, continually responding to variations in the wind, precipitation, and heating or cooling. Stirring of surface waters by the wind produces a well-mixed layer of uniform or nearly uniform density. For this reason, the surface ocean is known as the **mixed layer**. We are most familiar with the properties of the mixed layer because sensors onboard ships, aircraft, and Earth-orbiting satellites can readily monitor it.

The **pycnocline**, situated between the mixed layer and the deep layer, is where water density increases rapidly with depth because of changes in temperature and/or salinity. Recall that cold water is denser than warm water and seawater is denser than fresh water. Where declining temperature is responsible for the increase in density with depth, the pycnocline is also a **thermocline**; this is the case for most of the world ocean. On the other hand, if an increase in salinity is responsible for the increase in density with depth, the pycnocline is also a **halocline**.

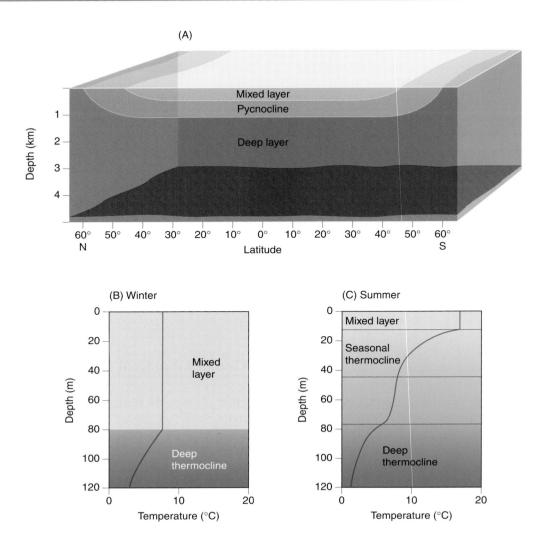

FIGURE 6.3
A model of density stratification in the ocean. (A) Except at high latitudes, a shallow mixed layer of relatively warm low-density water overlies the pycnocline characterized by a rapid increase in density with depth. The pycnocline, in turn, overlies the dark and cold deep layer accounting for 90% of the ocean's mass. In temperate latitudes, seasonal variations in the temperature profile are evident in (B) winter versus (C) summer. In these two seasonal cases, the pycnocline is equivalent to a thermocline and in summer a shallow thermocline develops above the main thermocline (pycnocline) in response to intense solar radiation.

Typically, the pycnocline extends to a depth of 500 to 1000 m (1600 to 3300 ft), but in middle latitudes seasonal pycnoclines may develop within the mixed layer (Figure 6.3B). The dark, cold deep layer below the pycnocline accounts for most of the ocean's mass. Within the **deep layer**, density increases gradually with depth and water moves slowly; in only a few locations (usually near the ocean bottom) are water movements fast enough to be considered currents.

The ocean's three-layer structure is an example of how gravity stratifies a fluid into layers such that the density of each layer is less than the density of the layer below it. More dense fluids sink and less dense fluids rise.

The ocean's pycnocline is very stable thus suppressing mixing between the mixed layer and deep layer; that is, the pycnocline acts as a barrier to vertical motion within the ocean. The concept of stability is useful in understanding this property of the pycnocline.

Stability affects the vertical motion of ocean water. A system is described as stable if it tends to persist in its original state without changing. Following a disturbance (i.e., vertical motion), a **stable system** returns to its initial state or condition. As noted above, the usual stable state of the ocean features a layer of water that is warmest near its interface with the atmosphere (the mixed layer) and the mixed layer overlies water that becomes denser with increasing depth (the pycnocline). Strong storm winds may temporarily disturb this stable stratification bringing colder than usual water to the surface. Once the wind slackens, however, the original layered structure is soon restored.

To demonstrate the effects of differences in water density on the circulation of ocean water, you can conduct a simple experiment. You will need two glasses or glass beakers, food coloring, salt, and a medicine dropper. Fill one glass with fresh water and the other with salt water. Add several drops of food coloring to the salt water and mix thoroughly. Let the glasses of water stand for a few minutes. Use the medicine dropper to put a drop of colored salt water into the glass of fresh water. Observe that the denser salt water sinks to the bottom of the fresh water. Now empty and wash the two glasses. Again fill one glass with fresh water and the other glass with salt water. Add several drops of food coloring to the freshwater sample and mix thoroughly. Again, let the glasses of water stand for a few minutes. Use the medicine dropper to put a drop of the colored fresh water into the glass of salt water. You will observe that the fresh water remains at the surface because it is less dense than the salt water. Carefully add more fresh water with the dropper to form a two-layered system.

Suppose we add a drop of slightly salty water of intermediate density (using a different food coloring) to our two-layered system. The drop will come to rest at the boundary between the two layers due to the differences in density between the water layers and the drop. The density distribution is stable when the denser water (in this case the saltiest) is at the bottom and the less dense water is on top. Immediately after adding a drop of more dense salt water, we created an unstable density distribution. Because the drop is denser than the surrounding water, it sinks. However, if a drop of slightly salty water is carefully injected into the very salty water, it rises; this is an example of an unstable density distribution because the water drop is less dense than the surrounding waters and is buoyed upward. Hence, an **unstable system** shifts spontaneously towards a more stable density stratification.

Mixing the system so that water density is uniform throughout produces a neutrally stable density distribution. In fact, if the original two-layered system stands long enough, salt that is dissolved in water diffuses such that water density eventually becomes uniform throughout the container. Following a disturbance, a **neutrally stable system** neither departs from its new state nor returns to its previous state.

Ocean in Motion: The Forces

Once the wind sets surface waters in motion as a current, the Coriolis Effect, Ekman transport, and the configuration of the ocean basin modify the speed and direction of the current. In this section, we consider the forces involved in the coupling of wind and ocean surface waters.

WIND-DRIVEN CURRENTS AND EKMAN TRANSPORT

Wind blowing over the ocean exerts a frictional drag that moves surface waters. Ripples or waves provide the surface roughness necessary for the wind to couple with surface waters (Chapter 7). A wind blowing steadily over deep water for 12 hrs at an average speed of about 100 cm per sec (2.2 mph) would produce a 2 cm per sec current (about 2% of the wind speed).

If Earth did not rotate, frictional coupling between moving air and the ocean surface would push a thin layer of water in the same direction as the wind. This surface layer in turn would drag the layer beneath it, putting it into motion. This interaction would propagate downward through successive ocean layers, like cards in a deck, each moving forward at a slower speed than the layer above. However, because Earth rotates, the shallow layer of surface water set in motion by the wind is deflected to the right of the wind direction in the Northern Hemisphere and to the left of the wind direction in the Southern Hemisphere. We discussed the reason for the *Coriolis Effect* in Chapter 5. Except at the equator, where the Coriolis Effect is zero, each layer of water put into motion by the layer above shifts direction because of Earth's rotation.

Using vectors to represent the direction and speed of layers of water at successive depths, we can show a highly simplified model of the current pattern caused by a steady horizontal surface wind (Figure 6.4A). (A *vector* is an arrow representing a physical quantity such that length is directly proportional to magnitude and orientation represents direction.) This model is known as the **Ekman spiral**, named for the Swedish physicist V. Walfrid Ekman (1874-1954) who first described it mathematically in 1905.

Ekman based his model on observations made by the Norwegian explorer Fridtjof Nansen (1861-1930). Nansen was interested in learning about the currents of polar seas. In 1893, he allowed his 39-m (128-ft) wooden ship, the *Fram*, to freeze into the Arctic pack ice about 1100 km (685 mi) south of the North Pole. His goal was to drift with the ice and cross the North Pole thereby determining how ocean currents affect the movement of

A

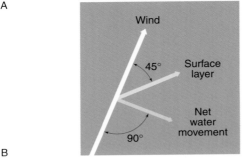

B

FIGURE 6.4
The Ekman spiral describes how the horizontal wind sets surface waters into motion. (A) As represented by horizontal vectors, the speed and direction of water motion change with increasing depth. (B) Viewed from above in the Northern Hemisphere, the surface layer of water moves at 45 degrees to the right of the wind. The net transport of water through the entire wind-driven column (Ekman transport) is 90 degrees to the right of the wind.

pack ice. The *Fram* remained locked in pack ice for 35 months but came no closer than about 394 km (245 mi) to the North Pole. As the *Fram* slowly drifted with the ice, Nansen noticed that the direction of ice and ship movement was consistently 20 to 40 degrees to the right of the prevailing wind direction.

The Ekman spiral indicates that the direction of water movement changes with increasing depth. In an ideal case, a steady wind blowing across an ocean of unlimited depth and extent causes surface waters to move at an angle of 45 degrees to the right of the wind in the Northern Hemisphere (45 degrees to the left of the wind in the Southern Hemisphere). Each successively lower layer moves more toward the right and at a slower speed. At a depth of about 100 to 150 m (330 to 500 ft), the Ekman spiral has gone through less than half a turn. Yet water

moves so slowly (about 4% of the surface current) that this depth is considered to be the lower limit of the wind's influence on the movement of ocean waters.

In the Northern Hemisphere, the Ekman spiral predicts net water movement through a depth of about 100 to 150 m (330 to 500 ft) at 90 degrees to the right of the wind direction (Figure 6.4B). That is, if one adds up all the vectors in Figure 6.4A, the resulting flow is at 90 degrees to the right of the surface wind direction. In the Southern Hemisphere, the net water movement is 90 degrees to the left of the surface wind direction. This net transport of water due to the coupling between the surface wind and waters is known as **Ekman transport** and is an important type of flow in the ocean's mixed layer.

The real ocean departs from the idealized conditions represented by the Ekman spiral; that is, wind-induced water movements often differ appreciably from theoretical predictions. To arrive at 45 degrees as the angle between the directions of the surface waters and surface winds, Ekman made many simplifying assumptions. In the real ocean however the angle is closer to 15 to 20 degrees at the most, regardless of the depth of the water. The stable pycnocline inhibits the transfer of kinetic energy to deeper waters, restricting wind-driven currents to the mixed layer; that is, the pycnocline acts as a floor for Ekman transport. More fundamentally, because momentum is efficiently mixed within the mixed layer, what actually happens instead of an Ekman spiral is more like an Ekman slab.

Ekman transport piles up surface waters in some areas of the ocean and removes surface waters from other areas, producing variations in the height of the sea surface, causing it to slope gradually. One consequence of a sloping ocean surface is the generation of horizontal differences (gradients) in water pressure. These pressure gradients, in turn, give rise to geostrophic flow.

GEOSTROPHIC FLOW

The horizontal movement of surface water arising from a balance between the pressure gradient force and the Coriolis Effect is known as **geostrophic flow**. Geostrophic flow characterizes **gyres**, large-scale roughly circular surface current systems in the ocean basins. Depending on location, gyres are either subtropical or sub-polar and are the dominant type of flow within the ocean's pycnocline layer.

To a large extent, horizontal movement of ocean surface waters mirrors the long-term average planetary-scale circulation of the atmosphere. As shown in Figure 5.19, three prevailing surface wind belts encircle each hemisphere: trade winds (equator to 30 degrees latitude), westerlies (30 to 60 degrees), and polar easterlies (60 to 90 degrees). The trade winds, on the equatorward flank of a subtropical high pressure system, and the westerlies, on the poleward flank of a subtropical high pressure system, drive the **subtropical gyres**. The subtropical gyres are centered near 30 degrees latitude in the North and South Atlantic, the North and South Pacific, and the Indian Ocean. Subtropical gyres in the Northern and Southern Hemispheres are similar except that they rotate in opposite directions because the Coriolis Effect reverses direction in the two hemispheres. Viewed from above, subtropical gyres rotate in a clockwise direction in the Northern Hemisphere but in a counterclockwise direction in the Southern Hemisphere.

Driven by the long-term average (prevailing) winds in the semi-permanent subtropical high pressure systems, Ekman transport causes waters to converge from all sides toward the central region of a subtropical gyre. This transport produces a broad mound of water as high as 1 m (3 ft) above mean sea level near the center of the gyre (Figure 6.5). As more water is transported toward the center of the gyre, the surface slope of the mound becomes steeper. At the same time, the horizontal water pressure gradient produced under the sloping sea surface increases. In response to the horizontal gradient in water pressure, water parcels move from where the pressure is higher toward where the pressure is lower, that is, downhill from the center of the gyre. Simultaneously, the Coriolis Effect shifts the direction of the parcels to the right in the Northern Hemisphere (to the left in the Southern Hemisphere). The outward-directed *pressure gradient force* balances the Coriolis Effect and the water parcels flow

around the gyre and parallel to contours of elevation of sea level as geostrophic flow.

In the central regions of the ocean basins are broad expanses of generally light winds or calm air associated with the semi-permanent subtropical anticyclones centered near 30 degrees latitude (Chapter 5). These massive fair-weather systems are semi-permanent in that they persist throughout the year but undergo seasonal shifts in relative strength and location. Following the sun, the subtropical highs shift a few degrees northward in spring and a few degrees southward in fall. Persistent fair weather and high temperatures enhance the rate of evaporation in these regions of the subtropical ocean resulting in surface waters with salinities significantly higher than the global average (Figure 3.8). An example is the vast *Sargasso Sea* which lies under the Bermuda-Azores subtropical high of the North Atlantic and features an average surface water salinity of 36.5 to 37.0 (Chapter 10).

Sub-polar gyres, smaller than their subtropical counterparts, occur at high latitudes of the Northern Hemisphere; they are the Alaska gyre in the far North Pacific and the gyre south of Greenland in the far North Atlantic. The counterclockwise surface winds in the Aleutian and Icelandic sub-polar low pressure systems drive the sub-polar gyres. (The *Aleutian low* and *Icelandic low* are persistent features of the atmosphere's planetary-scale circulation.) Hence, viewed from above, the rotation in the sub-polar gyres is opposite that of the Northern Hemisphere subtropical gyres. Ekman transport causes surface waters to diverge away from the central region of the sub-polar gyres. The thinner surface layer permits more nutrient-rich waters from deeper in the ocean to move upward into the photic zone, thereby increasing biological productivity in these regions (Chapter 9).

Wind-Driven Surface Currents

The long-term average pattern of ocean surface currents is plotted in Figure 6.6. Some currents are relatively warm whereas others are cold. Some (i.e., western boundary currents) are faster moving than others. Winds associated with passing storm systems disturb the ocean surface and can cause the actual flow of ocean currents locally to deviate temporarily from the long-term average pattern.

Most wind-driven surface currents transport water within a specific ocean basin. One of the few areas of the world ocean where inter-basin transport takes place is the so-called *Indonesian Through-flow*. The islands of Indonesia

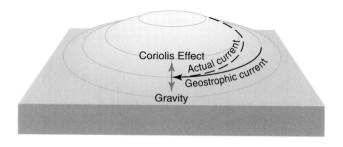

FIGURE 6.5
Ekman transport causes surface waters to converge toward the central region of a subtropical gyre from all sides, producing a broad mound of water. A balance develops between the Coriolis Effect and the force arising from the horizontal water pressure gradient such that surface currents flow parallel to the contours of elevation of sea level. This current is known as geostrophic flow.

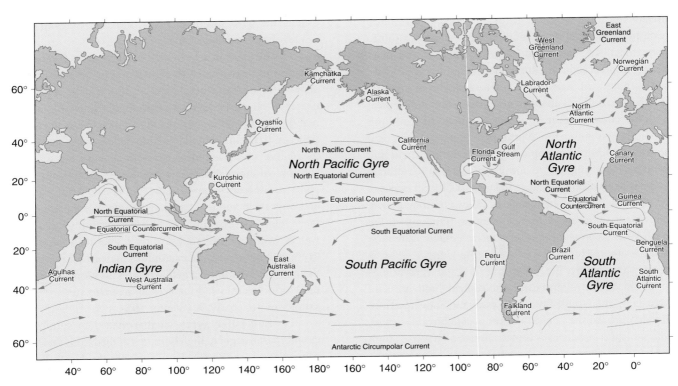

FIGURE 6.6
The long-term average pattern of wind-driven ocean-surface currents.

mark the boundary between the Indian and Pacific Oceans but only partially block the flow between the two ocean basins. Although details are still lacking, it is clear that warm, low-salinity waters from the Pacific are transported into the Indian Ocean via the many passages between the thousands of Indonesian islands. These waters replenish the large amounts of water removed by evaporation from the northern Indian Ocean. The summer Asian monsoon winds transport this water vapor from sea to land over India and Southeast Asia where it falls as torrential rains. After flowing westward across the Indian Ocean, waters enter the South Atlantic via the Agulhas Current flowing around southern Africa. In addition, partial blocking by the Indonesian Islands also causes warm surface waters to accumulate in the western equatorial Pacific Ocean, an important aspect of El Niño/La Niña (Chapter 11).

In this section, we examine the basic characteristics of wind-driven surface-ocean currents, components of the gyres that dominate the ocean basins. Western boundary currents are the strongest segments of the subtropical gyres and often spawn warm-and cold-core eddies known as rings. In coastal and equatorial regions, coupling of wind and surface waters can cause upwelling and downwelling.

SUBTROPICAL AND SUB-POLAR GYRES

Surface currents within subtropical gyres vary considerably in strength, width, and depth. The northeastward flowing Gulf Stream of the northwestern Atlantic and the Kuroshio Current of the northwestern Pacific are the swiftest surface currents with velocities averaging 3 to 4 km per hr (1.8 to 2.5 mph). Those currents are also relatively deep and narrow, usually measuring no more than 50 to 75 km (30 to 47 mi) across. On the eastern arms of these gyres, the southward flowing Canary and California Currents, respectively, are hundreds of kilometers wide and rarely flow at more than 1 km per hr (0.6 mph).

The westward flowing South Equatorial Current links the two subtropical gyres of the Atlantic Ocean. The eastward projection of Brazil splits the South Equatorial Current into two segments. The segment flowing southward forms the western arm of the South Atlantic gyre, the Brazil Current. The segment flowing northward merges with the North Equatorial Current, which then splits into two currents that rejoin as they exit the Gulf of Mexico between Florida and Cuba to become the Florida Current. This current then becomes the Gulf Stream that flows northeastward and passes Cape Hatteras, NC. In that region, the current speed may be as great as 9 km per hr (5.5 mph). Near Chesapeake Bay, the amount of water transported in the Gulf Stream exceeds 90 million cubic m per sec (90 Sv); the volume of water transported falls to about 40 Sv by the time the current reaches southern Newfoundland. (For comparison purposes, 90 Sv is about 4500 times the discharge of the Mississippi River—enough to fill the Lake Superior basin in about 1.5 days.) In the North Atlantic at about 40 degrees N and 45 degrees W, the Gulf Stream becomes the North Atlantic Current and flows toward the east. The Canary Current flows southward along the west coast of Spain, Portugal, and North Africa and then merges with the North Atlantic Equatorial Current, thus completing the North Atlantic subtropical gyre.

Like their Northern Hemisphere counterparts, currents in the South Pacific Ocean and South Atlantic Ocean are narrowest and flow most rapidly along their western margins but are broad and slow-moving along their eastern margins. The Indian Ocean subtropical gyre varies more than the others because of seasonal reversals in the monsoon winds. During the high-sun season, surface winds blow from sea to land and during the low-sun season, surface winds blow from land to sea.

In addition to the South Pacific and South Atlantic Ocean subtropical gyres, prevailing winds generate the Antarctic Circumpolar Current. At about 60 degrees S, this current also makes up, at least in part, the southern segments of the subtropical gyres of the Atlantic, Pacific, and Indian Oceans. This easterly-flowing current encircles the Antarctic continent rather than rotating as a basin-centered gyre and features the ocean's greatest water flow. Such a globe-circling current is possible only in the Southern Ocean; elsewhere, continents interrupt east-west currents. The Drake Passage, the relatively narrow strait between Cape Horn (the southern tip of South America) and the Antarctic Peninsula, deflects a portion of the Antarctic Circumpolar Current.

As part of the sub-polar gyre of the far North Atlantic, the cold Labrador Current flows southeastward between Canada and Greenland while the East Greenland Current flows southwestward between Greenland and Iceland. Farther east, the North Atlantic Current splits into the Norwegian Current which flows northeasterly between Iceland and Europe along the coast of Norway. In the sub-polar gyre of the far North Pacific, the Kamchatka current flows southwestward on the west side of the Bering Sea while the Alaska Current flows northwest off the south coast of Alaska.

EQUATORIAL CURRENTS

The tropical ocean encompasses broad areas of the Atlantic, Pacific, and Indian Ocean basins and is closely linked to the tropical atmosphere. The prevailing surface winds over the tropical ocean are the trade winds that blow from the northeast (toward the southwest) in the Northern Hemisphere and from the southeast (toward the northwest) in the Southern Hemisphere. The name for these winds was coined by sea captains who sailed for trading companies and took advantage of the persistent speed and direction of the trade winds when crossing the ocean. Trade winds drive both North and South Equatorial Currents westward, thus transporting warm ocean-surface waters in that direction. Equatorial Counter Currents and Equatorial Under Currents return some warm waters eastward. Counter Currents flow along the surface whereas Under Currents flow at greater depths below the surface.

The trade winds of the two hemispheres converge along a narrow east-west belt located near the equator known as the *intertropical convergence zone (ITCZ)*. The ITCZ is an important component of the planetary-scale atmospheric circulation that is particularly well defined over the tropical ocean. Warm and humid air ascends in the ITCZ giving rise to clusters of showers and thunderstorms that produce locally heavy rainfall (Figure 6.7). For mariners this region of the tropical ocean is known as the **doldrums,** feared by the captains of sailing ships because of light and variable winds. Seasonally, the ITCZ moves with the sun, shifting northward during the Northern Hemisphere spring and southward during the Northern Hemisphere autumn but

FIGURE 6.7
Vertical cross-section of the prevailing atmospheric circulation in the tropics showing the location of the Hadley cells and intertropical convergence zone (ITCZ). The ITCZ is marked by clusters of showers and thunderstorms and shifts north and south with the seasons.

generally remaining north of the equator, especially over the Atlantic Ocean. Consequently, the eastward-flowing Equatorial Counter Current, separating the surface current systems of the two hemispheres, also lies mostly just north of the equator.

The South Equatorial Current crosses the equator in the Atlantic and to a lesser extent in the Pacific. In this way, it transports surface waters and heat into the Northern Hemisphere. The return flow is through subsurface currents. The cape at the easternmost point of South America diverts part of the flow of the South Equatorial Current into the southward flowing Brazil Current. The remainder continues northwestward along South America's northeast coast into the Caribbean Sea.

BOUNDARY CURRENTS

In each of the subtropical ocean gyres, the circulation is asymmetrical in the east-west direction; that is, the gyre circulation appears to be shoved toward the western side of the ocean basin (Figure 6.8). On the western sides of the basin close to the east coasts of continents, currents are relatively fast, narrow, and deep. These are the **western boundary currents** and include, for example, the Gulf Stream, Kuroshio Current, and Brazil Current. Flows in the major western boundary currents transport 50 to 100 times the total water discharged by all the world's rivers. Conversely, on the eastern sides of the ocean basins, the currents are slower, much wider, shallower, and not as close to the coast. These **eastern boundary currents** include, for example, the Canary, California, and Peru Currents.

To explain why the western boundary currents are stronger than the eastern boundary currents and why the subtropical gyres are not centered in the ocean basin but shifted westward, we must invoke the principle of the **conservation of angular momentum**. This same principle applies to a figure skater performing a spin. The skater slows down when he/she extends the arms and spins faster when he/she pulls the arms closer to the body. The conservation of angular momentum in an ocean gyre involves three factors that must balance for the current to flow in a curved path. These factors are surface winds, the Coriolis Effect, and frictional drag of the coast, that is, the continental slope.

The large-scale surface winds in the North Atlantic subtropical high rotate the subtropical gyre in a clockwise direction (viewed from above) over much of the ocean basin. Near the equator, little horizontal spinning or rotation of the ocean water occurs because the Coriolis Effect is almost zero (Chapter 5). Along the western side of the ocean basin (U.S. Eastern Seaboard), the Gulf Stream transports this non-rotating ocean water northward. In traveling northward, the Coriolis Effect increases, shifting motion to the right in the Northern Hemisphere. Hence, the water that exhibited no spin at the equator picks up clockwise spin or rotation as it travels northward.

Once this ocean water reaches the northwest quadrant of the North Atlantic, it then flows eastward across the North Atlantic as part of the North Atlantic Current in balance with its acquired Coriolis Effect (clockwise spin). Upon entering the northeast quadrant of the North Atlantic, the ocean water turns again, but this time toward

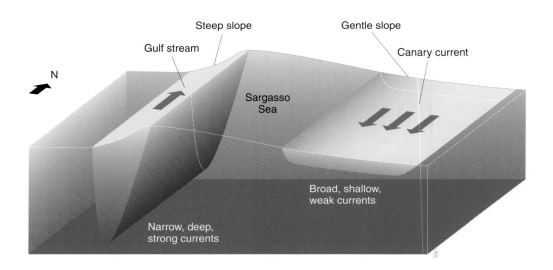

FIGURE 6.8
Surface ocean currents are faster, narrower, and deeper on the western side of an ocean basin. These are known as western boundary currents. Note that the vertical scale is greatly exaggerated.

the south on the east side of the ocean basin. Now the Canary Current is transporting water with clockwise spin from high latitudes toward the equator where the water began its journey and the Coriolis Effect is weak. That is, in the transit from north to south, the water must lose the clockwise spin it gained at northern latitudes and stay in balance with the nearly zero Coriolis Effect near the equator (equivalently, the southward moving water must gain counterclockwise spin).

On the eastern side of ocean basins, surface winds add clockwise spin while movement southward subtracts clockwise spin to create an approximate balance. However, on the west side of the subtropical gyres, both wind and northward movement (increasing Coriolis Effect) add clockwise spin so that there is too much clockwise spin and hence an imbalance. The question then is how does the west side of the subtropical gyre gain counterclockwise spin to balance the excessive clockwise spin and not break into rotational eddies all over the North Atlantic?

The answer is that the western boundary current gains counterclockwise spin by accelerating, deepening, and pushing up against the coast thereby increasing frictional drag. *Shoving its shoulder* against the coast contributes a counterclockwise turning. The Gulf Stream (and the other western boundary currents) accelerates and produces enough friction against the coast to generate sufficient counterclockwise turning to balance the clockwise spin. To generate sufficient spin, however, the current becomes faster, deeper, and flows closer to the Eastern Seaboard. Conversely, on the eastern side of the ocean basin, the subtropical gyre does not need to generate much clockwise spin to balance angular momentum and so does not push against the coast, but rather remains relatively wide, slow, shallow, and away from the coast.

In our discussion of the ocean boundary currents, we have used a Northern Hemisphere example, but the same interactions occur in the Southern Hemisphere except that the spin is in the opposite direction because of the reversal of the Coriolis Effect. In the Southern Hemisphere, the circulation of subtropical gyres and winds are in the opposite direction but then so is the Coriolis Effect. Hence, the strongest boundary currents also occur on the west side of the subtropical gyre and flow poleward.

OCEAN RINGS

Sensors on Earth-orbiting satellites reveal that the ocean surface is much more dynamic than indicated by maps and charts that portray ocean conditions averaged over decades. Satellite images show that cur-rents change in response to variations in oceanic and atmospheric conditions. For example, relatively swift western boundary currents occasionally spawn large turbulent rotating warm-core and cold-core eddies, also known as **rings**. A ring forms when a meander in a boundary current (or the Antarctic Circumpolar Current) becomes a loop that pinches off (separates) from the main current and moves independently as an eddy. Currents bordering a ring can rotate at more than 1.0 knot (1.0 nautical mi per hr or 1.86 km per hr or 1.15 mph), essentially isolating waters and organisms in rings from the surrounding waters. Rings extend to some depth in the ocean and should be thought of as cylindrical pools of water rather than simply surface features.

Rings form on either side of the Gulf Stream. On the north side, rings are typically 100 to 200 km (60 to 120 mi) across. These rings enclose warm waters from the Sargasso Sea located to the south and east of the Gulf Stream; hence, they are called **warm-core rings**. Viewed from above, these warm-core rings rotate in a clockwise direction. Because of the strong contrast in sea-surface temperatures, they are readily detected on infrared satellite images. Warm-core rings are also readily distinguished from the surrounding surface waters by their relatively low levels of biological production (Figure 6.9). The pool of water in a warm-core ring can extend to a depth of 1500 m (4900 ft) so that they cannot move onto continental shelves, which are shallow— typically 200 m (650 ft) deep or less. However, rings can come close enough to the shelf edge to modify coastal currents and transport unusual organisms onto the shelf. Occasionally boaters and fishers in normally cool coastal waters encounter organisms (e.g., sea turtles, tropical fish) that live in much warmer water having been transported in a warm core ring that spun off the Gulf Stream.

Rings that spin off the south side of the Gulf Stream entrain relatively cold and productive coastal waters and are called **cold-core rings**. These rings have diameters of about 300 km (185 mi) and, viewed from above, rotate in a counterclockwise direction. Cold-core rings are more difficult for satellites to track because their originally cool surface waters are warmed by absorption of solar radiation making them almost indistinguishable thermally from surrounding surface waters. However, cold water persists below the surface, sometimes extending down to the ocean floor at depths of more than 4000 m (13,000 ft), and can be detected in vertical profiles of temperature and salinity obtained by instrumented probes. Cold-core rings usually contain more nutrients and marine organisms than the biologically barren Sargasso Sea waters that surround

FIGURE 6.9
In this NASA Nimbus-7 CZCS (Coastal Zone Color Scanner) satellite image of ocean biological production, a prominent warm-core ring shows up as a nearly circular blue/violet region in ocean waters east of Delaware. Relatively low levels of phytoplankton pigment are indicated by blue/violet and relatively high levels are indicated by orange/red. White areas are clouds. [Source: NASA]

them. Thus, they can also be identified in the subsurface by their unusually abundant marine life.

Rings move slowly (typically 5 to 6 km or 3 to 4 mi per day), drifting southwestward in the weaker currents on either side of the northeast flowing Gulf Stream. The proximity of the Gulf Stream to the coast limits the southward movement of warm-core rings. Typically, after a few months to a year, a warm-core ring becomes caught between Cape Hatteras, NC and the Gulf Stream; the ring is then reabsorbed back into the Gulf Stream. Cold-core rings are not as restricted in their movements as warm-core rings and may persist for several years; on average, individual cold-core rings last for about 18 months.

Some of the ocean's largest warm-core rings, with diameters up to 400 km (250 mi), form in the Gulf of Mexico. These rings spin off the Loop Current at highly irregular intervals ranging from several months to 1.5 years. The Loop Current enters the Gulf from the Caribbean by flowing through the Yucatán Strait between Cuba and Mexico, heads northwestward in the general

direction of Louisiana, then makes a clockwise turn, and exits the Gulf through the Florida Strait (between Florida and Cuba). Rings drift westward across the Gulf at 2 to 5 km (1.2 to 3.1 mi) per day. Bordering currents of up to 4 knots (4.6 mph) can play havoc with offshore oil platform operations, damaging equipment and increasing the risk of accidents.

The Agulhas Current, the Indian Ocean's western boundary current, also spawns rings. This relatively fast southward-flowing current averages about 7 km per hr (4 mph). As it reaches Africa's southern tip, part of the current is caught up in the eastward flow around Antarctica and abruptly shifts direction back into the Indian Ocean. Some of the flow continues around South Africa as narrow (50 km or 30 mi wide) filaments that cool rapidly and mix with the surrounding waters in the large upwelling zone off Africa's Namibia coast. The Agulhas Current periodically sheds rings about 320 km (200 mi) across from its westernmost end. Rings in the Southern Hemisphere rotate in the opposite direction of those in the Northern Hemisphere. The Agulhas Current's warm-core rings rotate counterclockwise and contain Indian Ocean waters that are about 5 Celsius degrees (9 Fahrenheit degrees) warmer than nearby South Atlantic surface waters. They retain their identity as they move into the South Atlantic and transport heat, salt and organisms from the Indian Ocean into the South Atlantic. Over a two-year period in the mid-1990s, 14 rings were reported.

UPWELLING AND DOWNWELLING

In some coastal areas of the ocean (and large lakes such as the Great Lakes of North America), the combination of persistent winds, Earth's rotation (Coriolis Effect), and restrictions on lateral movements of water caused by shorelines and shallow bottoms induces upward (upwelling) and downward (downwelling) movements of water.

As explained above, the Coriolis Effect plus the frictional coupling of wind and water (Ekman transport) cause net movement of surface water at about 90 degrees to the right of the wind direction in the Northern Hemisphere and to the left of the wind direction in the Southern Hemisphere. **Coastal upwelling** occurs where Ekman transport moves surface waters away from the coast; surface waters are replaced by water that wells up from below (Figure 6.10). Where Ekman transport moves surface waters toward the coast, the water piles up and sinks in the process known as **coastal downwelling** (Figure 6.11). Upwelling and downwelling illustrate *mass continuity* in the ocean; that is, water is a continuous fluid so that a change in distribution of water in one area is accompanied by a compensating change in water distribution in another area.

FIGURE 6.11
Where Ekman transport moves surface waters toward the coast, the water piles up and sinks in the process known as downwelling.

Upwelling is most common along the west coasts of continents (eastern sides of ocean basins). In the Northern Hemisphere, upwelling occurs along west coasts (e.g., coasts of California, Northwest Africa) when winds blow from the north (causing Ekman transport of surface water away from the shore). Figure 6.12 shows the influence of upwelling on sea surface temperatures along the central and northern California coast. Winds blowing from the south cause upwelling along continents' eastern coasts in the Northern Hemisphere,

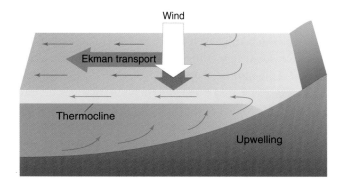

FIGURE 6.10
Where Ekman transport moves surface waters away from the coast, surface waters are replaced by water that wells up from below in the process known as upwelling.

FIGURE 6.12
An infrared satellite image shows the relatively cold upwelling waters along the coast of central and northern California in response to the Ekman transport caused by winds blowing from the north. According to the color scale, the lowest sea surface temperatures are plotted as blue and purple. Note how in places, strong upwelling extends well offshore from the coast. [NOAA Ocean Explorer]

although it is not as noticeable because of the western boundary currents. Upwelling also occurs along the west coasts in the Southern Hemisphere (e.g., coasts of Chile, Peru, and southwest Africa) when the wind direction is from the south because the net transport of surface water is westward away from the shoreline. In the Southern Hemisphere, winds blowing from the north cause upwelling along the continents' eastern coasts.

Upwelling and downwelling also occur in the open ocean where winds cause surface waters to diverge (move away) from a region (causing upwelling) or to converge toward some region (causing downwelling). For example, upwelling takes place along much of the equator (Figure 6.13). Recall that the deflection due to the Coriolis Effect reverses direction on either side of the equator. Hence, westward-flowing, wind-driven surface currents near the equator turn northward on the north side of the equator and southward on the south side. Surface waters are moved away from the equator and replaced by upwelling waters; this is known as **equatorial upwelling**.

FIGURE 6.13
Equatorial upwelling. (A) In this plan view of the ocean from 5 degrees S to 5 degrees N, the trade winds of the two hemispheres are shown to converge near the equator. The consequent Ekman transport away from the equator gives rise to upwelling as shown in (B) a vertical cross section from 5 degrees S to 5 degrees N.

Upwelling and downwelling influence sea-surface temperature and biological productivity (Chapter 9). Upwelling waters originate at considerable depth and are usually colder than the surface waters they replace. You may experience this phenomenon at the beach on a windy day when the warm surface water is blown offshore and replaced by chilly water from below. Coastal upwelling also transports waters rich in dissolved nutrients (nitrogen and phosphorus compounds) from the ocean depths into the photic zone where sunlight penetrating the water supports the growth of phytoplankton populations. The world's most productive fisheries are in areas of coastal upwelling (especially in the eastern boundary regions of the subtropical gyres); about half the world's total fish catch comes from upwelling zones (Chapter 10). On the other hand, in zones of coastal downwelling, the surface layer of warm, nutrient-deficient water thickens as water sinks. Downwelling reduces biological productivity and transports heat, dissolved materials, and surface waters rich in dissolved oxygen to greater depths. This occurs, for example, along the west coast of Alaska in the eastern boundary region of the Gulf of Alaska sub-polar gyre.

Alternate weakening and strengthening of upwelling off the coast of Ecuador and Peru are associated with El Niño and La Niña episodes in the tropical Pacific (Chapter 11). During an El Niño event, upwelling wanes, and cold nutrient-rich water remains so deep that weak upwelling brings only warm, nutrient-poor water into the photic zone. In extreme cases, nutrient-deficient waters coupled with over-fishing cause fisheries to collapse bringing about severe economic impacts.

Coastal upwelling and downwelling also influence weather and climate. Along the central and northern California coast, upwelling lowers sea surface temperatures (Figure 6.12). Relatively cold surface waters chill the overlying humid marine air to saturation so that thick fog develops, especially in summer. Also, seasonal upwelling and downwelling reduce the annual temperature range along the west coasts of the Americas. During El Niño and La Niña, changes in sea-surface temperature patterns associated with weakening and strengthening of upwelling off the northwest coast of South America and along the equator in the tropical Pacific affect the distribution of precipitation in the tropics and elsewhere. Upwelling cold water also inhibits formation of tropical cyclones (e.g., hurricanes and tropical storms) there. As we will see in Chapter 8, tropical cyclones derive their energy in the form of latent heat from warm surface waters.

Monitoring the Ocean Depths

While ocean scientists have measured surface and near-surface temperature, salinity, and currents for more than a century, probing the ocean depths to determine the vertical structure and circulation of the ocean has been much more challenging. Accurate measurements of deep currents and water temperature and salinity at various depths not only require instruments that can withstand the stresses of the ocean environment, but also appropriate platforms that provide a means of delivering the instruments to the desired depth and retrieving the data once measurements are made. In the past few decades, however, systematic surveys of the deep ocean have greatly expanded our knowledge of the properties of seawater and water movements. Deep-sea casts from oceanographic research ships have produced most of these data.

Atmospheric scientists traditionally use the term *sounding* to denote a sequence of measurements obtained at various altitudes in the atmosphere. Ocean scientists use the term *cast* (as in net cast or CTD cast) for measurements made at various depths in the ocean. This term likely originated with boat pilots (such as Mark Twain) who used a weighted measured line thrown overboard to determine water depth.

New promising ocean sensing technologies include submersible, instrumented *floats* that obtain vertical profiles of temperature, pressure (a measure of depth), and conductivity (a measure of

salinity) (Figure 6.14). A widely spaced array of 3000 plus instrumented floating profilers were deployed across the ocean at 3-degree latitude/ longitude intervals. The primary purpose of the float array, known as *Argo (Array for real-time geostrophic oceanography)* is to monitor the climate (long-term average conditions) of the wind-driven layer and pycnocline (not the thermohaline circulation) on denser spatial and temporal scales than previously available. The long-term observations

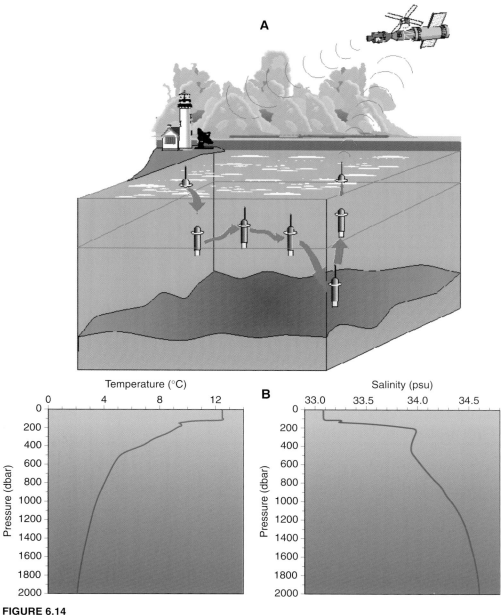

FIGURE 6.14
An Argo float (A) obtains continuous profiles of ocean temperature and salinity to a maximum depth of about 2000 m. The instrument surfaces and sends data to a satellite for downloading. (B) This is a sample plot of float-derived temperature and salinity profiles obtained at a location in the eastern North Pacific, west of Northern California, on 1 February 2008. [Courtesy of the U.S. Global Ocean Assimilation Experiment]

provided by Argo are the basis for mapping the large-scale average oceanic flow.

Research ships, commercial vessels, and low-flying aircraft drop floats into the sea. Typically, a float is programmed for a 10-day cycle during which it sinks to a prescribed depth of 1000 m (3300 ft), drifts with the current for 9 days before sinking to a maximum depth of 2000 m (6600 ft), and then returns to the surface monitoring ocean water properties along the way. At the surface, the float relays its collected data via satellite to computer databases. Tracking the position of the float over time also records water movements.

While the Argo global-scale array is an international effort, various institutions in the U.S. deployed about half the floats. Among the other 22 participating nations are Australia, Canada, Japan, France, and the United Kingdom. The U.S. portion of the Argo program includes floats that are under the auspices of the University of Washington, Scripps Institution of Oceanography, and the Woods Hole Oceanographic Institution. Argo data are archived at NOAA's Atlantic Oceanographic and Meteorological Laboratory in Miami, FL.

In Chapter 3, we described another technology that uses changes in the speed of sound to measure temperature over great distances within the ocean (*acoustic thermometry*). In addition, the distribution of various tracer materials, such as dissolved oxygen, CFCs (chlorofluorocarbons), or radioactive substances from both atmospheric and oceanic testing of nuclear devices have been used to track movements of subsurface waters. For more on oceanographic casting methods, refer to this chapter's second Essay. For a description of a unique way to track ocean currents, go to this chapter's third Essay.

Thermohaline Circulation

As we have seen, the upper portion of the ocean is put into motion by wind forcing at the surface. Below the pycnocline, the deep ocean is shielded from the direct action of the wind, and ocean currents are driven primarily by density differences in water masses. These density contrasts are caused by variations in water temperature and salinity with cold salty water being the densest combination (Chapter 3). The deep-ocean circulation driven by variations in density is termed **thermohaline circulation**, the name coming from *thermo* meaning heat and *haline* referring to salinity. An equivalent name for this circulation is the **meridional overturning circulation**

(MOC) because this is the primary mode of water motion (sinking at high latitudes and upwelling at low latitudes). Recall from Chapter 5, our discussion of the intra-annual variation in the poleward heat transport by the MOC.

The MOC consists of two western boundary currents, the warm Gulf Stream flowing northward and the Deep Western Boundary Current flowing southward. The Gulf Stream is a heat source for the atmosphere until eventually in the subpolar North Atlantic some surface waters become sufficiently cold and dense to sink to the ocean bottom. This cold deep water then flows southward along the continental slope of the eastern U.S. as the Deep Western Boundary Current. The thermohaline circulation (or the meridional overturning circulation) is the dominant type of flow in the deep ocean.

The thermohaline circulation is a significant player in the Earth system for several reasons. Although deep-ocean currents are relatively weak, the volume of deep water is much greater than the volume of surface waters so that the magnitude of water transport is about the same. The temperature difference between the warm surface waters and the cold deep waters controls the basic stratification of the ocean. The deep circulation contributes to poleward heat transport (Chapter 5) and its circulation varies over a broad range of temporal scales from years to millennia. This variability helps modulate climate change (Chapter 12).

FORMATION OF DEEP WATER

Density gradients in the deep ocean are established by dense waters sinking in a few select locations. These deep-water formation regions are generally characterized by very low temperatures and, in some cases, high salinity. In the Northern Hemisphere, deep water is formed in the Greenland-Norwegian Sea and Labrador Sea. Deep water forms in late winter when the surface water has reached its lowest temperature and hence its greatest density. The primary mechanism of deep water formation in the Northern Hemisphere is **open ocean convection**. Cold winds cool the surface water to the extent that its density becomes greater than that of all the water beneath it creating an unstable water column and driving overturning. Deep waters formed in the Greenland-Norwegian Sea are separated from the main body of the Atlantic Ocean by a submarine ridge running east from Greenland, through Iceland, and on to Europe. Dense waters overflow through gaps in this ridge, cascading down-slope into the Atlantic Ocean and entraining overlying waters along the way. In contrast, convection in the Labrador Sea directly injects water into the mid-depth Atlantic. Unlike other sources of deep water in the Atlantic, deep water formation in the Labrador Sea undergoes considerable inter-annual variability. Some winters lack any deep convection whereas other winters are characterized by vigorous overturning.

A third source of deep waters in the North Atlantic Ocean consists of very salty outflows from the Mediterranean Sea. These waters originate in the northwestern Mediterranean in winter as cold, dry *Mistral winds* cool the surface waters and enhance evaporation. This dense salty water fills the deep Mediterranean basin to a depth of about 400 m (1300 ft) and spills over the sill at the Strait of Gibraltar.

In the Southern Hemisphere, deep waters form at several regions around the Antarctic continent but primarily in the Weddell Sea. Unlike the Northern Hemisphere, much of the deep water formation occurs underneath floating sea ice and details are not as well known. The water is cooled by cold winds acting on openings in the cracks (leads) in the sea ice cover. In addition, the water becomes denser during formation of sea ice. As noted in Chapter 3, salt left behind during freezing of seawater increases the salinity of the surrounding waters, a process called **brine rejection**. Water made denser by cooling and brine rejection sinks along the continental slope of Antarctica into the deep ocean. As this cold, dense water sinks, it entrains additional water thereby increasing the total flow. In addition to the Weddell Sea, cold dense bottom waters are created in the Ross Sea as well as other scattered locations along the continental shelf of Antarctica.

WATER MASSES

Currents in the deep ocean are very weak, typically averaging less than 1 mm per sec. Such currents are difficult to observe directly; hence, much of what we know about the circulation of the deep ocean is inferred from the study of water properties. Water properties such as temperature and salinity are only altered by interaction with the atmosphere at the surface of the ocean. Thus, after sinking, the characteristic temperature and salinity of the water is conserved. A large, homogeneous volume of water having a characteristic range of temperature and salinity is known as a **water mass**. Water masses are typically identified based on their source region at the ocean surface (Figure 6.15). Hence, deep convection in the North Atlantic forms a water mass called *North Atlantic Deep Water (NADW)*. Likewise, the water mass formed around Antarctica is called *Antarctic Bottom Water (AABW)* (Table 6.1).

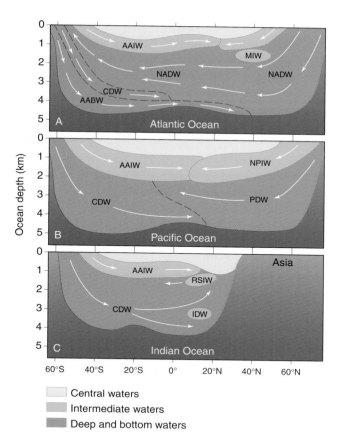

FIGURE 6.15
Vertical distribution of water masses in the (A) Atlantic, (B) Pacific, and (C) Indian Oceans.

TABLE 6.1

Water Masses of the Atlantic, Pacific, and Indian Oceans

Atlantic Ocean
Antarctic Intermediate Water (AAIW)
Mediterranean Intermediate Water (MIW)
Circumpolar Deep Water (CDW)
North Atlantic Deep Water (NADW)
Antarctic Bottom Water (AABW)

Pacific Ocean
Antarctic Intermediate Water (AAIW)
North Pacific Intermediate Water (NPIW)
Pacific Deep Water (PDW)
Circumpolar Deep Water (CDW)

Indian Ocean
Antarctic Intermediate Water (AAIW)
Indian Deep Water (IDW)
Red Sea Intermediate Water (RSIW)
Circumpolar Deep Water (CDW)

In addition to the deep waters discussed above, the other principal type of water mass in the thermohaline circulation is *intermediate water*. As the name implies, intermediate waters rest above the deep waters but below the wind-driven circulation (at a depth of 1 to 2 km). Intermediate waters are formed by a variety of processes. The most extensive of the intermediate waters, *Antarctic Intermediate Water (AAIW)* is formed by open ocean water cooling in the Southern Ocean. Other intermediate waters are formed in marginal seas. Examples include *North Pacific Intermediate Water (NPIW)* formed in the Sea of Okhotsk, *Red Sea Intermediate Water (RIW)*, and *Mediterranean Intermediate Water (MIW)*.

As discussed above, AABW, the densest waters in the Southern Ocean, forms in the Weddell Sea. AABW does not flow into the other ocean basins as it is trapped close to the Antarctic continent by submarine ridges. Lying above AABW is a large water mass that encircles the entire Southern Ocean: *Circumpolar Deep Water (CDW)*. CDW results from the mixing of AABW with overlying deep waters of the Atlantic, Pacific, and Indian Ocean basins. The Antarctic Circumpolar Current efficiently mixes and spreads this water mass around Antarctica. CDW flows from this southern starting point northward as bottom water in all three ocean basins (Atlantic, Pacific, and Indian).

The Atlantic Ocean is the primary site of deep water formation in the Northern Hemisphere. This is due to both the high salinity of the Atlantic as well as the extent of the ocean at high latitudes which exposes surface waters to cold winter winds. NADW is characterized by high salinity compared to other deep water masses. This high salinity signature can be used to trace the spread of NADW throughout the world ocean. Deep water formed in the North Atlantic spreads south across the equator and becomes entrained into the circumpolar flow around Antarctica. From the Southern Ocean, this water spreads into both the Indian and Pacific Oceans. Flowing northward underneath the NADW in the Atlantic is a wedge of deep waters formed in the Southern Ocean. CDW reaches into the Northern Hemisphere in the Atlantic, gradually mixing and entraining into the NADW lying above.

In contrast to the Atlantic Ocean, the Pacific Ocean has no sites of deep water formation. Although surface waters in the northern Pacific are cooled to very low temperatures, the low salinity of the surface waters (due to precipitation and runoff) prevents the water density from becoming sufficiently great to initiate sinking to the bottom. Additionally, the shallow Bering Strait at a depth of only about 50 m (165 ft) effectively isolates the deep Pacific Ocean from the deep Arctic Ocean. The only water mass locally produced in the Pacific is *North Pacific Intermediate Water (NPIW)*, formed in moderate quantities in the Sea of Okhotsk. Lacking any deep water formation in the North Pacific, the deepest portions of the Pacific basin are filled with *Circumpolar Deep Water*, originating in the Southern Hemisphere. Over time, this CDW mixes with the overlying waters forming a third water mass: *Pacific Deep Water (PDW)*. Note that unlike other deep waters, PDW is not formed by cooling at the surface, but rather the mixing of other water masses. PDW flows slowly south with a portion eventually upwelling into the pycnocline while another portion returns to the Southern Ocean.

The meridional overturning circulation in the Indian Ocean is broadly similar to that of the Pacific Ocean. Most of the Indian Ocean, occupying the smallest of the three major ocean basins, is located in the Southern Hemisphere. No deep water masses form along its northern boundaries, where the climate is tropical and subtropical. Small amounts of intermediate water form from the saline outflow of the Red Sea but this flow is most notable for its effect on salinity rather than the net mass input. Deep flow consists of CDW flowing north along the bottom, gradually upwelling and mixing to form a water mass known as *Indian Deep Water (IDW)*.

IMPLICATIONS FOR CLIMATE

The ocean is a key component of Earth's climate system. In Chapters 3 and 5, we discussed the implications of the ocean's great thermal inertia for maritime climates and Chapter 5 focused on the key role of the ocean in the global radiation budget. In this chapter, we described how wind-driven surface currents and the deep-water thermohaline circulation (meridional overturning circulation) transports heat energy and thereby influences climate over a broad range of spatial and temporal scales. Changes in the operation of the meridional overturning circulation (MOC) could have important implications for future climate as it may have had in the past.

An essential component of the MOC is formation of bottom water in the far northern reaches of the North Atlantic Ocean. As noted earlier, dry, cold winds that blow east and southeast from northern Canada chill surface waters. The combined cooling of surface waters, evaporation, and sea-ice formation produces cold, salty North Atlantic Deep Water (NADW). The newly formed relatively dense NADW sinks and then flows southward along the continental slope of North and South America toward Antarctica. Ultimately, continued production of NADW is essential to maintain the MOC and northern Europe's moderate climate.

The MOC could weaken if the North Atlantic surface-water salinity were to drop too low to allow the formation of deep-ocean water masses. (An influx of large amounts of fresh water into the North Atlantic might be responsible for such an event.) This may have happened in the past. For example, some scientists argue that weakening of the MOC was responsible for the Little Ice Age (about CE 1400 to 1850) when the climate of northern Europe was markedly colder than now. Mountain glaciers advanced, growing seasons became shorter, and sea ice cover increased. Paintings from this era show Dutch skaters on frozen canals—something that would not occur during today's climatic regime. Cores extracted from deep-sea sediment deposits contain evidence of earlier cold episodes that may be linked to weakening of the MOC; such episodes include the Heinrich events described in the first Essay of Chapter 4. There is more on climate change and this topic in Chapter 12.

Conclusions

The surface ocean, its currents driven by winds, is the part of the ocean that is most directly involved in Earth-system processes. It transports heat globally, supplies water vapor to the atmosphere, dissolves and transports salts, nutrients, and gases, supports fisheries, and plays major roles in day-to-day weather and short-term climate variability. The deep-ocean is isolated from the atmosphere by the mixed layer and pycnocline except at high latitudes; it is mostly cold and dark. The relatively slow thermohaline circulation is driven by density contrasts between water masses and involves about 90% of the ocean's waters. The deep circulation is important in long-term climate change, may play an important role in sequestering or buffering greenhouse gases such as carbon dioxide, and is important in transporting dissolved nutrients. We continue our investigation of the dynamic nature of the ocean in the next chapter where we examine waves and tides.

Basic Understandings

- The ocean is divided into three depth zones based on density: the surface mixed layer of uniform or near uniform density, the intermediate pycnocline where density increases markedly with depth because of changes in temperature and/or salinity, and the deep layer. The pycnocline is very stable and inhibits mixing of ocean waters between the mixed layer and the deep layer.

- Two circulation regimes dominate the ocean: wind-driven currents in the surface layer and the relatively slow thermohaline circulation in the deep ocean.

- Wind-driven currents are maintained by kinetic energy transferred from the horizontal winds to ocean surface waters. Once the wind sets surface waters in motion as a current, the Coriolis Effect and the configuration of the ocean basin modify the speed and direction of the current.

- Frictional coupling of the surface winds with the ocean puts surface waters into motion and the Coriolis Effect, combined with the frictional coupling of successively deeper layers of water, cause the horizontal movement of water to change direction and decrease in magnitude with increasing depth, producing the Ekman spiral. In an ideal case, a steady wind causes surface waters to move at an angle of 45 degrees to the right of the wind in the Northern Hemisphere (to the left in the Southern Hemisphere). The Ekman spiral brings about net water movement through a depth of about 100 m (330 ft) at 90 degrees to the right of the wind direction in the Northern Hemisphere and 90 degrees to the left of the wind direction in the Southern Hemisphere.

- Because of the wind circulation in semi-permanent subtropical highs, Ekman transport causes surface waters to converge toward the central region of subtropical gyres, producing a mounding of surface water near the center of the gyre. In response to this horizontal gradient in water pressure, water moves from where the pressure is higher toward where the pressure is lower, that is, downhill and directly opposite Ekman transport.

- Surface water parcels flow outward and down slope away from the center of the gyre and simultaneously the Coriolis Effect causes water parcels to shift direction to the right in the Northern Hemisphere (to the left in the Southern Hemisphere). Eventually, the outward-directed pressure gradient force balances the Coriolis Effect and water parcels flow around the subtropical gyre and parallel to contours of elevation of sea level. This horizontal movement of surface water is known as geostrophic flow.

- Ocean surface currents resemble Earth's long-term average planetary-scale surface wind patterns. Surface currents form subtropical gyres roughly centered in each ocean basin near 30 degrees latitude. Viewed from above, currents in these gyres flow in a clockwise direction in the Northern Hemisphere and a counterclockwise direction in the Southern Hemisphere.

- In the sub-polar gyres of the far north, current directions are opposite that of the Northern Hemisphere subtropical gyres.

- Winds associated with passing storm systems can disturb the ocean surface and cause the flow of ocean surface currents locally to deviate temporarily from long-term average patterns.

- Trade winds of the Northern and Southern Hemispheres drive equatorial currents and warm surface water westward across the tropical ocean.

- On the west sides of the subtropical gyres, surface currents are relatively fast, narrow, and deep. These are the western boundary currents and include, for example, the Gulf Stream, Kuroshio Current, and Brazil Current. On the eastern sides of the subtropical gyres, surface currents are slower, much wider, shallower, and not as close to the coast. These eastern boundary currents include, for example, the Canary, California, and Peru Currents.

- The contrast in characteristics of the western versus eastern boundary currents is due to the conservation of angular momentum, the variation of the Coriolis Effect with latitude, and the current's frictional interaction with the coast.

- Western boundary currents spawn warm- and cold-core rings (eddies). Rings develop when a meandering current forms a large loop that pinches off and separates from the main current. In the Northern Hemisphere, warm-core rings form on the current's landward side and rotate clockwise whereas cold-core rings form on the current's ocean side and rotate counterclockwise.

- In coastal areas, the combination of persistent winds blowing parallel to the coast, the Coriolis Effect, and restrictions on lateral movements of water caused by shorelines and shallow bottoms induces upward and downward movements of water. Where winds generate Ekman transport of surface waters away from the coast, colder nutrient-rich water wells up from below, a process called upwelling. Upwelling supplies nutrient-rich waters to the sunlit, surface zone of the ocean spurring biological productivity.

- Where winds generate Ekman transport of surface waters toward a coast, water piles up and sinks; this is called downwelling.

- Upwelling also occurs along the equator in response to Ekman transport associated with the trade winds of the two hemispheres.

- Over the past few decades, systematic surveys of the deep ocean have greatly expanded our knowledge of the properties of seawater and water movements. Casts denote a sequence of measurements (e.g., temperature, conductivity) obtained vertically through the ocean depths such as obtained by Argo profilers.

- Deep-ocean currents are driven primarily by slight differences in seawater density, caused by variations in water temperature and salinity with cold salty water being the densest combination. The deep-ocean circulation driven by variations in density is termed the thermohaline circulation or the meridional overturning circulation (MOC).

- A water mass is a large, homogeneous volume of water having a characteristic range of temperature and salinity. Water masses are typically identified based on their source region at the ocean surface and their ocean depth.

- The surface and thermohaline ocean circulation regimes transport heat and salt on a planetary scale. They are important components of Earth's climate system.

Review

1. Describe the vertical structure of the ocean in middle latitudes based on temperature variation with increasing depth.
2. How does water density vary with depth within the pycnocline? Under what conditions is a pycnocline also a thermocline?
3. In the Northern Hemisphere, how does the direction of Ekman transport of ocean water compare to the surface wind direction?
4. Distinguish between the directions of the trade winds in the Northern versus Southern Hemisphere. What is the significance of the intertropical convergence zone (ITCZ)?
5. Compare the surface ocean currents on the eastern and western sides of the subtropical gyres.
6. Compare the rotation direction and productivity in warm- and cold-core rings of the Northern Hemisphere. Do cold-core rings associated with the Gulf Stream entrain waters from coastal areas or the Sargasso Sea?
7. Describe the role played by Ekman transport in coastal upwelling. Distinguish between coastal and equatorial upwelling.
8. How does the speed of water motion in the thermohaline circulation compare to that of surface ocean currents?
9. What is a water mass? How are water masses classified?
10. Describe the thermohaline circulation and its significance for Earth's climate system.

Critical Thinking

1. Suppose that the surface wind is blowing from the north along the Oregon coast. Predict the direction of Ekman transport of surface waters. Would you expect coastal upwelling or downwelling?
2. Compare the direction of Ekman transport in the subtropical gyres of the Northern Hemisphere versus the Southern Hemisphere. Explain the difference.
3. How might rings (warm-core and cold-core eddies) influence the intensity of storm systems over the ocean?
4. How and why do coastal upwelling and downwelling affect sea surface temperature?
5. Define thermohaline circulation and describe how it is maintained in the ocean.
6. What role is played by the Coriolis Effect in western boundary currents?
7. Describe the relationship between trade winds and biological productivity along the equator.
8. How does a semi-permanent subtropical high pressure system influence the salinity of the underlying surface ocean waters?
9. Describe the weather conditions that would favor upwelling along the Wisconsin coast of Lake Michigan.
10. How does the wind direction over the Arctic Ocean compare to the direction of motion of the underlying ice floes?

ESSAY: Global Positioning System

Satellite navigation was the brainchild of the U.S. Department of Defense. Similar to the 18th century governments who offered prize money for anyone who could solve the longitude problem (Chapter 5), the U.S. government spent over $12 billion to develop a satellite-based system that would determine location precisely, at all times and in all types of weather. The *Global Positioning System (GPS)* was intended originally for military use and dates to the 1978 launch of the first Navstar satellite. GPS can provide near pinpoint location accuracy globally for a wide variety of military and civilian applications. Not to be outdone by its then Cold War adversary, the former Soviet Union developed a similar system called GLONASS. This system has suffered maintenance problems but now appears to be on the verge of rejuvenation via agreements with India for launch of additional satellites and talks with the U.S. about changing certain radio frequency standards which would allow a certain amount of interoperability with the U.S. GPS as well as the relatively new commercial Galileo system of the European Union.

Civilian use of GPS began in the 1980s, mostly on large ships. At least 24 Navstar satellites are needed to provide continuous service. Once this was achieved in the early 1990s, inexpensive, small portable receivers were developed and marketed, and civilian use of GPS soared. Today the civilian sector accounts for about 92% of GPS equipment sales. (Worldwide, sales of GPS equipment reached $17 billion in 2003 and are projected to climb to $50 billion by 2010.) GPS is widely used for navigation by ships, planes, delivery trucks, and automobiles, and is increasingly being used to provide location in cellular telephones.

The principle behind GPS is *trilateration* (related to triangulation) from satellites that are in view of the receiver (Figure 1). At least four satellites are needed for maximum precision. The time it takes for a ranging signal to travel from a satellite to a receiver is determined using accurate clocks. Atomic clock times are embedded in the code of a signal that is continuously transmitted by the satellites. When the timed signals arrive at the receiver they are compared with a code generated by the clock of the receiver. The time difference between the codes is the important factor. Radio signals travel at a finite speed (300,000 km per sec, or 186,000 mi per sec, the speed of light) so that elapsed time can be converted to distance. All GPS satellites are identifiable by their coded signals and their orbits are regular allowing a refinement of the triangulated distances. Using an inexpensive widely available receiver, a person can readily locate his/her position within a few meters. More sophisticated military receivers can achieve location accuracy in centimeters.

FIGURE 1
To determine its location on Earth's surface, a GPS receiver measures the travel times of radio signals sent by three satellites of known orbital location. Travel times are converted to distances. This trilateration technique is more precise when a fourth satellite is used to synchronize the clocks on the GPS satellites and receiver

Using one satellite, a person's location must be some point on a sphere centered on the satellite with the radius of the sphere equal to the distance to the satellite. Knowing our distance from a second satellite, our location must be some point on a sphere having a radius equal to the distance to that satellite. The two spheres have different radii and geometry indicates that the intersection of two spheres is a circle. Our location must be somewhere on that circle. A third satellite describes yet another sphere that intersects with the other two spheres, narrowing our location to one of two possible points, that is, where all three spheres intersect. Usually one of the two points is either in space or in Earth's interior. Hence, the other point is determined to be our location on the surface of Earth. A computer in the GPS receiver has algorithms that can distinguish between locations likely to be correct and locations that are spurious.

Use of a fourth (or additional) satellite is intended to compensate for the imprecision caused by slight differences in timing between the precise atomic clocks flown onboard the GPS satellite and the less accurate quartz clocks in the GPS receiver. Measurements made by the fourth satellite are used to synchronize the two clocks. Actually, most GPS receivers will choose the best signals from many satellites and use four of them to fix the position so that assumptions about which one of two points of intersection is correct never have to be made. A mariner at sea level does not need to know altitude, and this further simplifies the procedure.

Plans are currently underway to increase the location accuracy of GPS by broadcasting new signals from the navigation satellites. One of the anticipated benefits of these new signals is a reduction in interference caused by Earth's ionosphere (a region of the upper atmosphere containing a relatively high concentration of electrically charged particles). These improvements to GPS soon should be in place and are essential for completion of the transition of civilian aviation to GPS-based navigation and air traffic control.

ESSAY: Profiling the Ocean Depths

In situ sampling at various depths in the ocean provides profiles of water transparency, temperature, salinity (from electrical conductivity), and density. Sunlight is essential for photosynthesis and an easy way to estimate the maximum depth in the water column reached by visible light utilizes a simple instrument known as a Secchi disk. The *Secchi disk* is a plate-like device about 20 cm (7.9 in.) in diameter—although they come in different sizes depending upon the anticipated range of clarity. The disk is hung from a weighted line marked off in one-meter increments and is divided into alternate black and white quadrants to make it easier to see at depth. As close to mid-day as possible, the Secchi disk is gradually lowered into the water (oriented parallel to the sea surface) on the sunny side of the boat until the observer can no longer see the disk (i.e., cannot distinguish between the black and white quadrants) and the depth is recorded. The disk is then raised slowly until it just reappears, and this depth is recorded. The Secchi depth is the average of these two depth readings and is a reasonable estimate of the compensation depth of 0.1% to 1% light penetration. It is semi-quantitative method that is still used today. Of course, with modern electronics, very precise measurements of the transparency of ocean water to sunlight are made from profiling instruments.

Some of the first temperature and salinity casts made in the early 20th century employed collection bottles and reversing thermometers that were attached to a wire. The specially designed bottles obtained seawater samples at designated water depths and their contents were sent to a ship or onshore laboratory for chemical analysis. Thermometers recorded seawater temperature which when combined with salinity readings yielded water density and depth. Two liquid-in-glass thermometers were used at each sampling depth, one accounting for pressure at depth and the other protected from the effects of pressure at depth. A collection bottle plus thermometers were attached to the wire at fixed depth intervals. To obtain data, a messenger (metallic weight) slides down the wire, tripping the shallowest collection bottle so that it flips over, captures a seawater sample, and closes. At the same time, the thermometers reverse thereby fixing their readings. This action releases another messenger that slides down the wire to the next deeper bottle where the process of data collection is repeated. Although this casting method is time consuming, reversing thermometers and collection bottles are still used today for calibrating other instruments.

In the 1970s, electronic sensors were introduced for more rapid and reliable measurements of CDT: conductivity (a measure of salinity), depth, and temperature. A CDT instrument package is linked to an oceanographic research ship via a hydrographic cable. As the CDT is lowered and raised in the water, its sensors provide a continuous stream of data at specific depths. An additional component is a series of a dozen or more Niskin collection bottles plus thermometers arranged in a rosette pattern (Figure 1). Ship-based researchers are able to open and close collection bottles at designated depths of the cast.

FIGURE 1

A rosette of Niskin water collection bottles being lowered over the side of an oceanographic research ship. The purpose of this experiment is to determine the concentration of chlorophyll and biological productivity. [NOAA Ocean Explorer]

In the mid 20th century, a mechanical instrument called a *bathythermograph (BT)* was developed that could obtain a nearly continuous temperature profile with depth from a slowly moving ship. As this torpedo-shaped device sinks into the water, a temperature-sensitive element (typically a deformation or bimetallic thermometer) inside the BT moves a stylus (a needlelike marking device) across a metal- or smoke-coated slide recording temperature as a function of depth (obtained from pressure bellows). The resulting temperature trace was interpreted after the instrument was retrieved from the water.

Since the 1970s, newer electronic technologies have permitted more rapid castings that produce an almost continuous profile of temperature. An *expendable bathythermograph (XBT)* is a non-recoverable instrument package deployed from fast moving ships or airplanes that obtains a nearly continuous ocean temperature profile to a depth of approximately 1800 m (5900 ft). This torpedo-shaped device consists of a thermistor (electronic thermometer) housed in an expendable casing. A thin conducting wire connects the XBT to the ship or plane and transmits the temperature signal to an onboard recorder. The electrical conductivity of seawater is used to complete the electrical circuit. As the device sinks into the ocean at a known rate, data are transmitted electronically at regular intervals, permitting the recording of ocean temperature as it changes with depth. A slightly different profiling instrument is an *expendable conductivity-temperature-depth profiler (XCTD)* that provides essentially continuous profiles of ocean conductivity (salinity) in addition to temperature and pressure.

NOAA's Atlantic Oceanographic and Meteorological Laboratory in Miami, FL oversees the XBT program. Volunteer commercial ships deploy as many as four XBTs daily along selected shipping lanes. The data are compiled by a computer onboard ship and then transmitted via satellite relay to the Laboratory for global distribution. More than 70 ships voluntarily produce 26 monthly transects across the three major ocean basins.

In 1985, the ten-year international *Tropical Ocean Global Atmosphere (TOGA)* program commenced. One of TOGA's projects was deployment of *TAO (Tropical Atmosphere/Ocean)*, an array of moored buoys (small, non-piloted, instrumented platforms) in the tropical Pacific Ocean. Data from this array have been extremely valuable in detecting and predicting such atmospheric/oceanic episodes as El Niño and La Niña (Chapter 11). This instrument array, renamed *TAO/TRITON* in 2000, presently consists of approximately 70 deep-sea moorings that measure several atmospheric variables (air temperature, wind, relative humidity) as well as oceanic parameters (sea surface and subsurface temperatures at 10 depths in the upper 500 m or 1640 ft). Several newer moorings also have salinity sensors, along with additional meteorological sensors. Five moorings along the equator also measure ocean velocity using a Subsurface Acoustic Doppler Current Profiler. The data are collected and relayed in near real-time to shore via satellite. Real time data displays from the TAO/TRITON array are available on the Internet from NOAA's *Pacific Marine Environmental Laboratory (PMEL)* in Seattle, WA.

Over the last decade or so, a variety of autonomous instrumented profilers have been developed and deployed to measure large-scale subsurface currents and make repeated near real-time vertical measurements of ocean variables. Early versions of these free-drifting profilers were identified by the term *PALACE (Profiling Autonomous Lagrangian Circulation Explorer)* whereas a subsequent version was called *APEX (Autonomous Profiling Explorer)*. Elsewhere in this chapter, we describe the Argo array.

An Argo float (profiler) is about 1 m (3.3 ft) long and less than 20 cm (8 in.) in diameter. A profiler moves vertically between the ocean surface and a maximum depth of about 2000 m (6600 ft) by pumping hydraulic oil between an internal reservoir and an external bladder. The profiler ascends when the relatively lower density oil (as compared to the density of sea water) flows into (and expands) the bladder (decreasing the density) and descends when oil flows in the opposite direction. During the float's ascent, onboard sensors record the temperature, pressure (depth), and conductivity (salinity) nearly continuously. Upon returning to the ocean surface, the float telemeters these data to a satellite for subsequent relay to data collection stations (Figure 6.14). The float's position is determined by satellite, and ocean current information is inferred from the horizontal displacement of the float between subsequent surfacings. The geostrophic assumption is used to compute ocean currents at depth. Following a programmed interval at the surface, hydraulic oil is pumped back to the internal reservoir, and the float returns to depth for the next cycle. The anticipated lifetime of one Argo float is 100 cycles.

ESSAY: Bottles and Rubber Duckies, Tracking Currents with Flotsam and Jetsam

The classic message-in-a-bottle is one of the simplest ways to determine ocean surface currents. Bottles, examples of *jetsam*, the traditional term for floating objects intentionally tossed from a ship, are released into the ocean at a known time and place and left to float along with the surface current. Inside the bottle is a message intended for whoever finds the bottle at a later date. Typically the message requests that the finder notify the sender of where and when the bottle was found.

Prince Albert I of Monaco (1848-1922), an early amateur oceanographer, employed this elementary technique to map the currents of the North Atlantic subtropical gyre in the late 1800s. From his yacht, the *Hirondelle*, he dropped hundreds of bottles throughout the North Atlantic. In addition to his bottles, Albert collected the accounts of other bottles dropped from commercial ships making trans-Atlantic voyages. One such bottle, recovered in the Caribbean off the coast of the Yucatán Peninsula in 1890 contained a typical message: *"This bottle was thrown from the S.S. Cephalonia of the Cunard Line on the 24th of November, 1887, by W.C. Lippard about 400 miles from Boston. Anybody finding this will please send it to the Boston newspapers."*

A drawback of the message-in-the-bottle method of tracking ocean currents is that typically only one or two percent of the bottles are ever recovered. Hence, many bottles must be tossed into the ocean to obtain a small amount of data. An alternative method, used more recently, is to take advantage of accidental spills of floating objects into the ocean. Such *flotsam*, the traditional term for goods lost over the side of a boat, can also provide useful data if spilled in large quantities at a known time and place.

One such example of flotsam occurred in May 1990 when 21 cargo containers were washed off the container vessel *Hansa Carrier* during a heavy storm in the North Pacific. Five containers held shipments of Nike® shoes and it is estimated that 80,000 shoes were released as the containers fell into the sea. Unfortunately, the loss of containers at sea is routine and this particular loss would not have been noteworthy except that 10 months later hundreds of shoes began washing up on the shores of Oregon, Washington, and Vancouver Island. Stories of the large flotilla of shoes caught the attention of oceanographer Curtis C. Ebbesmeyer who had made a career of tracking currents using buoys and jetsam. Ebbesmeyer used code numbers from the shoes to confirm that they originated from the *Hansa Carrier* spill. Knowing the exact date and location that the shoes were released, Ebbesmeyer and W. James Ingraham Jr. used the locations of found shoes to test predictions made by a computer model of ocean currents in the same area.

Another example of a large flotsam release began in January 1992 when a freighter crossing the Pacific from Hong Kong to Tacoma, WA lost several cargo containers near the International Dateline during a heavy storm. One container held 28,800 plastic floating bathtub toys manufactured by Floatees. The container broke open as it fell into the sea and seven months later beachcombers near Sitka, Alaska began finding hundreds of plastic ducks, turtles, frogs, and beavers. Over the next decade, these floating toys continued to be recovered along beaches—nearly 1000 as of 2007. Data from this spill indicate that the typical "trip" around the sub-polar gyre of the North Pacific takes 2 to 4 years. The toys would not be confined to the North Pacific, however. Eventually some began drifting into the Arctic Ocean and by the year 2000 the first plastic ducks showed up in the North Atlantic as well.

Although worldwide an estimated 10,000 cargo containers are lost overboard each year, only a fraction of flotsam ends up washing up on beaches. Much of it collects at the center of the large subtropical gyres. Subtropical gyres are characterized by convergent Ekman transport. The wind forcing pushes surface waters toward the middle of the gyre. Convergence causes a large-scale sinking of the water, i.e. *Ekman pumping*. Although the water sinks, objects floating on the surface are left behind causing a gradual accumulation of flotsam. This is true for both flotsam and naturally occurring floating objects. The Sargasso Sea, at the center of the North Atlantic subtropical gyre, derives its name from the high concentration of floating sargassum weed which accumulates because of convergent Ekman currents.

While the use of flotsam to study ocean currents is a novel way of obtaining useful results from unfortunate accidents, it also highlights the long-term hazard of plastics in the marine environment. After more than a decade of exposure at sea, the plastic ducks and frogs continue to float and pose hazards to marine life. The North Pacific lacks sargassum weed, thus the most distinctive objects accumulating in the subtropical gyre are floating plastic objects. This has given rise to a rather unfortunate name for this region, the "North Pacific Trash Vortex."

CHAPTER 7

OCEAN WAVES AND TIDES

Case-in-Point
Driving Question
Wind-Driven Waves
    Wind-Wave Generation
    Deep-Water and Shallow-Water Waves
    Seiche
    Wave Mediated Atmosphere-Ocean Transfer
Internal Waves
Ocean Tides
    Tide-Generating Forces
    Types of Tides
    Tides in Ocean Basins
    Tidal Currents
    Observing and Predicting Tides
    Open-Ocean Tides
Tsunami
Conclusions
Basic Understandings/Review/Critical Thinking
ESSAY: The State of the Sea
ESSAY: Monitoring Sea Level from Space
ESSAY: Power Generation from Ocean Tides and Waves

Coast and Geodetic Survey Ship LESTER JONES aground on the Nushagak River mudflats at low tide. [Family of Captain John Ellerbe, C&GS NOAA]

Case in Point

Unusually high waves, known as **rogue waves**, occur in the open ocean as well as some coastal areas. In the early morning of 7 February 1933, a huge wave with an estimated height of more than 34 m (112 ft) struck the stern of the USS *Ramapo*, a Navy tanker. While en route from the Philippines to San Diego, CA, the 146-m (478-ft) ship encountered the freak wave during an intense storm with near hurricane-force winds and high seas. In September 1965, while crossing the Atlantic, one of the world's largest ocean liners, the *Queen Elizabeth 2 (QE2)*, was hit by a giant wave. She had changed course to avoid a hurricane and appeared to be out of serious danger, although seas were rough. Estimating the height of waves from onboard a ship is extremely difficult, but the wave that struck the *QE2* was level with the captain's line of sight from the ship's bridge, some 29 m (95 ft) above the sea surface. An instrumented buoy in the same area recorded extreme waves of similar height. On the morning of 16 April 2005, a wave the height of a seven-story building crashed into the bow of the cruise ship *Norwegian Dawn* off the coast of Georgia.

The *Ramapo, QE2,* and *Norwegian Dawn* survived their encounters with rogue waves, experiencing only minor damage, but many ships, including modern supertankers, which were struck by rogue waves were not so fortunate and were extensively damaged or sunk with loss of life. Rogue waves can also be destructive in coastal areas where they can destroy off-shore oil-drilling platforms.

When does an ocean wave qualify as a rogue wave? The criterion depends on a comparison of the wave with the **significant wave height**, defined as the average height of the tallest one-third of the waves observed in a patch of ocean. By one convention, a wave is considered rogue if its height is 2.2 or more times the significant wave height. Another definition sets the minimum height of a rogue wave at 25 m (82 ft). Rogue waves exhibit a distinctive form unlike other sea waves—a deep trough followed by a steep forward face. Some mariners describe their encounter with a rogue waves as "sailing into a hole in the sea" and then "hitting a wall of water." Although most common during stormy weather, rogue waves sometimes develop even when sea/air conditions are tranquil and appear with little or no warning.

Rogue waves have been reported from all ocean basins. Until recently, ocean scientists assumed that they were a relatively rare phenomenon, estimated to be a once-in-10,000-year or so event at any location in the ocean. However, wave data collected from instruments on a gas-drilling platform off the southern coast of South Africa indicate that the probability of a rogue wave is about 3.1% during any hour. A similar probability of 3.7% was reported from an instrumented buoy in the South Atlantic Ocean east of Rio de Janeiro, Brazil.

What causes rogue waves? Mariners have long attributed exceptionally high waves to an amplifying interaction between waves, called *constructive interference*. With constructive interference, the crests of different waves coincide to produce a wave that is higher than either of the individual component waves. The shape of the sea floor and coastline configuration may also help direct the movement of swells from different sources and bring about an amplifying interaction. Constructive interference may explain the relatively high frequency of rogue waves off the coast of South Africa where large storm swells driven by southwest winds from the Southern Ocean meet the swift Agulhas Current flowing from the northeast. The oppositely directed currents shorten the distance between waves and build wave crests. Another explanation for rogue waves is that eddies (rings) formed by the Agulhas Current may focus wave energy, much like an optical lens focuses light. Such focusing could also occur near the Gulf Stream. This could partially account for the ominous reputation of the region near the Gulf Stream known as the "graveyard of ships" or even more colorfully as the "Bermuda Triangle" where ships have been known to vanish mysteriously.

With a better understanding of the genesis of rogue waves, scientists are hopeful of developing techniques to predict the likely location of these potentially destructive waves and issue warnings to mariners. In this way, ships can alter their course, and lives and cargo will be saved.

Driving Question:
What are sea waves and tides and what causes them?

In thinking about the ocean, most people visualize a vast water surface disturbed by continually changing and sometimes seemingly chaotic patterns of waves. Ceaselessly, waves break against the shore; waves and sea spray buffet a small fishing boat bobbing in the water just offshore; and waves the height of a three-story building batter a supertanker plying through storm-tossed waters a thousand kilometers at sea. Potentially destructive waves are not limited to the ocean. A huge wave may have contributed to the sinking of the ore carrier *Edmund Fitzgerald* on Lake Superior on 10 November 1975 with the loss of its 29 member crew.

What are sea waves and what causes them? Most sea waves are the product of an interaction between the ocean and atmosphere in which *kinetic energy* (the energy of motion) of the wind is transferred to surface waters. Hence, these waves are often called **wind-waves**. Wind-waves are part of the current-generating processes described in the previous chapter. In this chapter, we discuss the formation and life cycle of these waves, their generation as wind-waves or "sea," plus their existence at sea as free waves and swell before expending their energy as breakers on a distant reef or shoreline. We also describe internal waves and tsunamis.

Coastal residents are very familiar with not only sea waves but also the periodic rise and fall of sea level known as tides. Tides are also a type of wave but with very long wavelengths approaching the dimensions of an ocean basin. Because of their importance to marine interests, tides were among the earliest ocean characteristics to be monitored on a regular basis. In fact, elaborate mechanical computers were developed early on to predict tides. In this chapter, we examine tide generation, types of tides and tide prediction.

Wind-Driven Waves

In a general sense, a **wave** is a regular oscillation that occurs in a solid, liquid, or gaseous medium as energy is transmitted through that medium. A pebble tossed into a still pond disturbs the water surface creating waves that move outward in all directions away from the point where the pebble entered the water. The principles of water

waves apply regardless of the size of the body of water. A **sea wave** is an oscillation on the ocean surface that propagates along the interface between the atmosphere and ocean (Figure 7.1). A schematic drawing of an idealized sea wave is shown in Figure 7.2. The highest point reached by the oscillating water surface is called the **wave crest** and the lowest point is the **wave trough**. The **wave height** is the vertical distance between trough and crest. The horizontal distance between successive wave crests (or equivalently between any other two corresponding points of two consecutive waves) is the **wavelength**. The time needed for two successive wave crests (one wavelength) to pass a fixed point is the **wave period**. The number of waves passing a fixed point over an interval of time is the **wave frequency**, the inverse of the wave period.

WIND-WAVE GENERATION

If the air over the ocean were always calm, the sea surface would be smooth and motion-less, a condition sailors refer to as *flat calm*. Wind disturbs this equilibrium

FIGURE 7.1
Storm waves as seen from the MV Noble Star. A sea wave is an oscillation of the ocean surface that propagates along the interface between the ocean and atmosphere. [Courtesy of NOAA]

FIGURE 7.2
Vertical cross-section of an idealized sea wave.

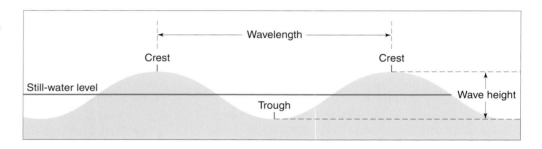

state as some of its *kinetic energy* is transferred to surface ocean waters as the wave-generating force. Restoring forces return the ocean surface to its original horizontal equilibrium state. Waves begin as small ripples, called **capillary waves**, with wavelengths of less than 1.7 cm (0.7 in.). At these short wavelengths, water's surface tension is the restoring force that smoothes out and flattens these relatively small waves.

Surface tension, the attraction between molecules at or near the surface of a liquid, is a property of water arising from hydrogen bonding (Chapter 3). The density of water molecules in the air above the water surface is relatively low. Hence, H_2O molecules in the surface water layer are more strongly attracted by hydrogen bonding to each other and to the layer of water molecules immediately below. Surface tension explains why we can pour water into a glass to a level that is slightly above the rim of the glass, without the water spilling out. Among liquids, water is second only to mercury in the strength of its surface tension.

Strengthening winds increasingly disturb the water surface, producing larger waves having longer wavelengths and greater wave heights. For these larger waves, *gravity* is the restoring force working to level the wave crests and fill in the wave troughs. Gravity pulls the crested water downward, but momentum causes the water to continue downward and a trough is formed. The lowered water is buoyed upward and the next crest rises.

Wind and gravity are responsible for most waves observed on the ocean surface.

As a wave propagates along the air/ocean interface, water particles oscillate, thereby affecting the motion of neighboring water particles (Figure 7.3). In this way, waves (i.e., the changing shape of the water surface) move away from the disturbance that caused them. Water particles oscillate in approximately circular orbits. As long as the wave is travelling through relatively deep water, the orbital diameter of a water particle at the ocean surface equals the wave height. As a complete wave (from crest to trough to crest) passes a fixed point, a water particle completes one orbit and returns to approximately its original location. Oscillations of water particles become smaller (orbits decrease in diameter) with depth below the water surface and eventually dissipate completely. This depth of no wave motion, called **wave-base**, approximately corresponds to one-half the wavelength.

No net horizontal transport of water mass occurs with each wave cycle. Much more significant is the propagation of the changing shape of the water surface (the wave) and its energy. A wave crest travels twice as fast as the wave energy. If you carefully observe the movement of wind-generated waves on a lake, you will notice that they travel as "packets" of several waves. These are actually packets of energy. After a period of observation, you will be able to single out a particular wave crest and follow its movements. You will note that

FIGURE 7.3
For waves passing through relatively deep water, the nearly circular orbits of water particles weaken with increasing depth and essentially disappear at a water depth of one-half the wavelength.

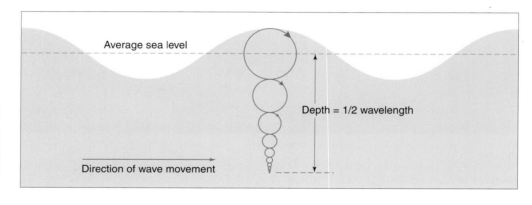

a wave arises in the back of the packet, grows in height, moves through the packet twice as fast as the packet, and disappears at the front of the packet. This same behavior is exhibited by intermediate and deep ocean waves as they also propagate at twice the speed of the wave energy.

Water wave formation and evolution depend primarily on the wind's speed, turbulence, and duration as well as fetch. With increasing speed, the wind becomes more turbulent, that is, it consists of increasingly energetic irregular whirls of air motion known as *eddies*. We experience eddies as wind gusts and lulls on a windy day. Turbulent eddies have both horizontal and vertical components of motion so that the wind exerts forces that act parallel and perpendicular to a water surface. Forces acting parallel to a water surface drag surface water particles laterally whereas forces acting perpendicular to a water surface push the water up and down. At low wind speeds (less than a few km per hr), weak eddies produce capillary waves on the water surface and, as noted earlier, the primary restoring force for these tiny waves is water's surface tension. However, these ripples roughen the water surface, thereby increasing the wind's drag on the ocean surface. Furthermore, growing waves present an increasingly sloped surface area against which the wind blows, creating even greater wind resistance and wave growth. Increasing wind speed translates into more kinetic energy available for transfer to the ocean surface, therefore creating higher waves.

For the same wind speed, higher waves are produced with a longer **fetch,** the distance the wind blows over a continuous water surface. *Duration* refers to the length of time the wind blows from the same direction. For the same wind speed and fetch, waves grow higher and longer the longer the wind blows from the same direction. Together, wind speed, fetch, and duration largely determine the amount of available kinetic energy that is transferred from the atmosphere to the surface waters.

In general, waves continue to build in height and length as long as the energy supplied to the waves by winds exceeds the amount of energy dissipated in breaking waves. Conversely, when the energy supplied by wind is less than that dissipated by the waves in breaking, waves decay (become weaker and smaller). When the amount of dissipated energy equals the amount of energy supplied by the wind, no further wave build up (growth in wave height) occurs.

Wave interference also influences the growth and decay of sea waves. Waves generated by winds associated with two or more storm systems at sea may interfere constructively or destructively. In **constructive wave interference**, two or more wave crests coincide to form composite waves having heights greater than any of the original wave components (e.g. rogue waves). On the other hand, sets of waves can also interact such that the crests in one set of waves coincide with the troughs in another set, partially canceling both sets. The product is a composite wave whose height is smaller than that of the original wave components. This interaction is known as **destructive wave interference**. Both types of wave interference are almost always happening at sea and contribute to the continually changing pattern of waves on the open ocean.

DEEP-WATER AND SHALLOW-WATER WAVES

An ocean surface disturbed by storm winds becomes a confused mass of sharp-crested waves of various heights and lengths, moving in many different directions. This condition is known as **sea**. These are *forced waves*, that is, waves that are forced by the wind (while gravity is the restoring force). Waves continue to propagate well beyond the area of strong storm winds. Such waves, called **swell**, are lower and more rounded than waves forming directly under the storm winds. Swell consists of *free waves* where the only force acting on them is gravity.

Waves in water that is deeper than their wavebase (one-half the wavelength) are known as **deep-water waves**. **Celerity** is the speed of the wave relative to the water. The celerity of deep-water waves depends on wavelength and gravity and can be computed using the formula:

$$C = \sqrt{(1.56 \times \text{wavelength})},$$

where C is the celerity in m per sec and the wavelength is given in meters. For example, the energy of a 10-m (33-ft) long wave travels at 3.9 m per sec (9 mph) whereas that of a 100-m (330-ft) long wave travels at 12.5 m per sec (28 mph).

In relatively deep water, waves with longer wavelengths travel faster than waves with shorter wavelengths so that in the swell, waves sort themselves out with longer waves outdistancing shorter waves. With little dissipation due to friction, swell can travel thousands of kilometers from its source. This is why you sometimes observe swell from a distant storm striking a coastline even while the local weather is tranquil.

Recall from above that with deep-water waves, there is no interaction between the orbital motions of the wave and sea bottom. However, as water waves approach the coastline, they encounter increasingly shallow water.

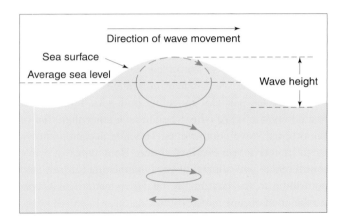

FIGURE 7.4
In shallow-water waves, the orbits of water particles gradually flatten with increasing depth, changing from circular to elliptical and ultimately to a back-and-forth motion near the ocean bottom. Figure not drawn to scale.

FIGURE 7.5
A wave propagating through shallow water becomes steeper and unstable. When the ratio of wave height to wavelength approaches 1 to 7, the crest plunges forward as a breaker. [Photo by J.M. Moran]

Eventually waves enter waters shallower than wave-base and they begin to "feel" the ocean bottom. At this point, these waves are no longer the free waves of the open ocean but are restricted by water depth. These are now **shallow-water waves** where the orbits of water particles gradually flatten with increasing depth, changing from circular to elliptical and ultimately to a back-and-forth motion near the bottom (Figure 7.4). Wave period is unchanged so that a wave interacting with the ocean bottom slows down, its wavelength shortens, and its wave height increases. (With constant period, the water and energy have no place to go but up!) A shallow-water wave occurs in water shallower than one-twentieth the wavelength, whereas **transitional wave** is the name given to a wave entering water having a depth that is between one-twentieth and one-half of the wavelength.

When waves enter waters having a depth of less than one-half the wavelength, the wave celerity depends on water depth and gravity but not wavelength. Shallow-water wave celerity can be computed using the formula:

$$C = \sqrt{(g \times depth)}$$

where C is the celerity in m per sec, g is gravity, and depth is given in meters. For example, the energy of waves in 10 m (33 ft) of water travels at 9.9 m per sec (22 mph) whereas the energy of waves in 2 m (7 ft) of water travels at 4.4 m per sec (9.8 mph). Hence, shallow-water waves slow as they enter shoaling water (water that becomes shallower).

As the water shoals, particles of water in the building wave crest move forward faster than the wave propagates toward shore. The wave becomes steeper and eventually unstable. The crest plunges forward, forming a **breaker**, dissipating wave energy in the process (Figure 7.5). Waves break when the ratio of wave height to wavelength approaches 1 to 7; at this point, the wave-crest angle (a measure of the steepness of the wave) is close to 120 degrees. Surfers take advantage of the fact that breakers are often much higher than deep-water wave crests. Breakers 2 m (7 ft) high exert a pressure equivalent to 15,000 kg per m², significantly impacting both natural and artificial features along the coast. A nearly continuous train of waves breaking along a shore is called **surf**.

Over the years, mariners have developed methods of describing the state of the sea and relating that state to near-surface winds. For more on this, see this chapter's first Essay.

SEICHE

If you've ever sloshed water back and forth in a bathtub, you produced a seiche, a wave phenomenon first studied in Lake Geneva, Switzerland in the 1700s. A **seiche** (pronounced *say-sh*) is a rhythmic oscillation of water in an enclosed basin (e.g., bathtub, lake, or reservoir) or a partially enclosed coastal inlet (e.g., bay, harbor, or estuary). During a seiche, the water level in a basin commonly rises at one end while simultaneously falling at the other end. A seiche episode may last from only a few minutes up to a few days.

A seiche is a **standing wave**. This is in contrast to the wind-driven waves (described above) that are **progressive waves** in that they move through a body of water. With wind-driven waves, crests and troughs travel along the water surface but with standing waves, crests alternate vertically with troughs but at fixed locations. Gravity is the restoring force for both progressive and standing waves.

With a typical seiche in a simple enclosed basin, the water level near the center does not change at all (Figure 7.6). This location, called a *node*, is where water moves fastest horizontally. At either end of an enclosed basin, vertical motion of the water surface is greatest and horizontal movement of water is minimal; these are locations of *antinodes*. The motion of the water surface during a seiche is somewhat like that of a seesaw. The pivot point of the seesaw does not move up or down (analogous to a node) while people seated at either end of the seesaw move up and down (analogous to an antinode). Partially enclosed basins usually have a node at the mouth (rather than near the center) and an antinode at the landward end. Furthermore, some basins are complex and have several nodes and antinodes.

Wind, air pressure gradients, earthquakes, or astronomical tides can induce a seiche. For example, wind blowing persistently in the same direction across the broad expanse of a bay (or lake) causes water to pile up at the downwind shore. When the wind slackens, the piled up water is released and the water surface oscillates back-and-

forth from one end of the bay (or lake) to the other as a seiche until eventually the water calms to a horizontal surface. The natural period of a seiche generally ranges from minutes to hours and is directly proportional to basin length. Hence, the natural period of a seiche in a large coastal inlet is considerably longer than in a small pond. Also, for the same basin, the natural period is inversely proportional to water depth; that is, the period shortens as water deepens.

Usually a seiche in a harbor or lake causes little concern because typically the vertical movements of water level are small—often only a few centimeters. Under certain conditions, however, a seiche may grow to great heights with serious consequences including coastal flooding and damage to moored vessels such as has happened in San Diego Bay and Los Angeles/Long Beach, CA. A seiche grows as a consequence of **resonance** meaning that the period of the disturbance (e.g., earthquake, wind) matches the natural period of oscillation of the basin. By timing your rhythmic disturbance of the water in a tub to match the natural period of the tub (about 1 second), you can cause the seiche to build until water splashes out of the tub and onto the floor. Through resonance, vibrations from the Northridge, CA earthquake of 17 January 1994 caused swimming pools to overflow throughout Southern California. In bays open to the ocean, if the period of tidal forcing equals the natural period of the bay, resonance can greatly increase the *tidal range* (difference in water level between high and low tide).

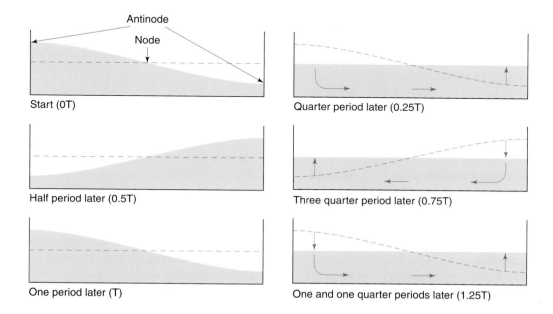

FIGURE 7.6
A seiche in an enclosed basin with a single node. The maximum vertical motion of the water takes place at the antinodes and the maximum horizontal motion occurs at the node.

Sea waves help bring about transfer of energy and matter between the atmosphere and ocean, a major interaction among subsystems of the Earth system. The largest wind-generated waves on the ocean surface are important in driving ocean currents by transferring momentum from the wind to ocean surface waters. Waves with shorter wavelengths play a major role in heat transfer from the ocean surface to the atmosphere through *latent heating* and *sensible heating* (Chapter 5). Latent heat derived from ocean's surface waters powers storms such as thunderstorms and tropical cyclones (e.g., hurricanes) (Chapter 8).

Waves with shorter wavelengths (especially breaking waves) also deliver tiny salt particles to the atmosphere where they function as cloud condensation nuclei spurring development of clouds (Chapter 5). Droplets of ocean spray can also transfer microscopic marine algae and viruses into the atmosphere where winds can transport them long distances. Breaking waves also capture myriads of air bubbles that are carried tens of meters below the ocean surface. Gases in these bubbles dissolve in seawater; this process, known as **bubble injection**, is an important source of dissolved oxygen and carbon dioxide for surface waters (Chapter 3).

Internal Waves

Internal waves form within the ocean along interfaces where the change in density with depth is relatively abrupt. Fridtjof Nansen (1861-1930) is credited with discovering internal waves in the Arctic Basin in the late 1800s.

Fundamentally, waves are pulses of energy that travel along surfaces separating fluids having different densities. Hence, wind-driven waves and seiches occur at the interface between air and water. Similar interfaces also occur beneath the ocean surface. As described in Chapter 6, the ocean is not homogeneous; water density changes with depth principally in response to variations in temperature and salinity. Favorable sites for development of internal waves include the base of the mixed layer and interfaces (pycnoclines) between water masses having different densities. Internal waves also form in estuaries along the pycnocline between fresh river water and salty ocean water (Chapter 8).

The smaller the density contrast between two fluids in contact, the slower the internal wave propagates and the greater the wave height. Density contrasts between different water masses are about 1000 times less than that between air and water so that internal waves propagate more

slowly than surface waves but have much greater wave heights. Simply put, with internal waves there is a much smaller density difference for gravity to act upon. Typically, internal waves have lengths in the hundreds of meters and heights of several meters but sometimes are considerably higher (100 m (330 ft) or more). Besides astronomical tides, slumping on the ocean floor, turbidity currents, and water masses slipping over one another also can generate internal waves. Even ships moving across the sea surface can generate internal waves on shallow pycnoclines.

Ocean Tides

Astronomical tides are the regular rise and fall of the sea surface caused by the gravitational attraction between the rotating Earth and the moon and sun. Tides can be thought of as progressive planetary-scale waves that propagate across ocean basins; wave crests are high tides and wave troughs are low tides. The length of a tide wave is considerably greater than the depth of the ocean so it behaves as a shallow-water wave.

In the hypothetical case of an ocean-covered Earth of infinite depth with no continents, tides can be visualized as waves having lengths of one half of the circumference of the planet. Astronomical tides are *forced waves* in that they always follow the driving force of the moon and sun. Tide crests would be located directly below the celestial body (moon or sun) responsible for the tide-generating force. On our hypothetical Earth, the speed of propagation of the tide crest depends, at least in part, on the rotation of the planet relative to the sun or moon. On the equator where the planet's circumference is about 38,600 km (24,000 mi), the tide crest would travel at about 1600 km per hr (1000 mph).

On the real Earth, continents break up the ocean into separate basins and the ocean has a variable depth. Tides are shallow-water waves so that wave celerity depends on water depth. For an average ocean depth of 4000 m (13,000 ft), tidal celerity is about 200 m per sec (400 mph). Tides speed up where the ocean is relatively deep and slow over ridges where the ocean is shallower. At sea, the amplitude of the tide wave is well under a meter but increases as it enters shallower coastal waters. Tides are measured mostly at coastal locations as local changes in water level through time. The average vertical difference in height between water levels at high and low tides is called the **tidal range** and generally varies between less than a meter to several meters (Figure 7.7). The time between successive high tides is the **tidal period**.

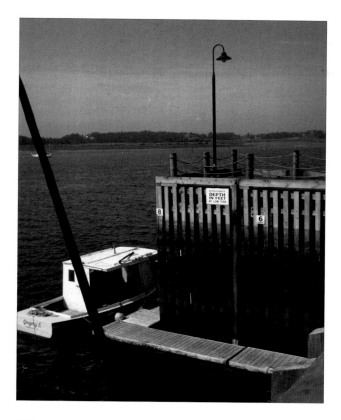

FIGURE 7.7
Low tide at a mooring in a harbor along the coast of Maine. Note the watermark on the dock indicating the level of the water at high tide. [Photo by J.M. Moran]

Tides are important because of their effects on ecosystems, local navigation, moorings, coastal structures, legal boundaries, fisheries, and recreation. Today, considerable scientific research focuses on the global nature of tides, including their influence on other physical processes in the ocean such as circulation, mixing, and wave generation. Furthermore, ocean and atmospheric scientists are interested in how storm-driven waves and surges combine with tides to affect the potential for coastal flooding and the rate of coastal erosion (Chapter 8). In the following section, we focus on some fundamentals of ocean tides and their prediction.

TIDE-GENERATING FORCES

The tide-generating force is produced by the combination of (1) the gravitational attraction between Earth and the moon and sun, and (2) the rotations of the Earth-moon and Earth-sun systems. Forces combine to deform Earth's ocean surface into a roughly egg-shape with two bulges. One ocean bulge faces towards the moon and the other is on the opposing side of the planet, facing away

from the moon (Figure 7.8). A similar interaction between Earth and sun produces two other ocean bulges that line up towards and away from the sun.

According to the **law of universal gravitation** (Isaac Newton, 1642-1727), the *gravitational attraction* between two bodies is directly proportional to the product of the masses of the two bodies and inversely proportional to the square of the distance between them. Simply put, the greater the mass, the greater is the force of attraction whereas the greater the distance, the smaller the force of attraction. Although the sun is 10^7 times more massive than the moon, the moon is much closer to Earth and for that reason exerts a greater gravitational pull on Earth. In fact, the tide-generating force of the moon on the Earth is more than twice that of the sun on the Earth. For now, we will ignore the influence of the sun and focus on the moon.

The gravitational pull of the moon on Earth is primarily responsible for the bulge in the ocean surface that is oriented toward the moon. (Actually, Earth's rotation drags the bulge ahead of the position directly under the moon.) On the opposing side of the planet, the gravitational pull is weaker and the rotation of the Earth-moon system is primarily responsible for the tidal bulge. Earth and moon revolve around a common center of mass. Because Earth is much more massive than the moon, the center of mass of the system is within 4700 km (2900 mi) of Earth's center, that is, 1700 km (1060 mi) below the Earth's surface. This has been likened to a seesaw with an adult seated at one end and a child at the other end. The pivot point (center of mass of the adult-child system) must be moved toward the adult for the two individuals to balance the seesaw.

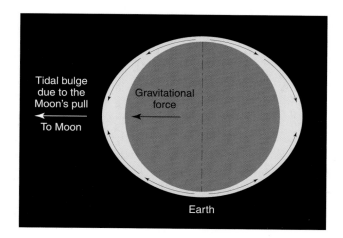

FIGURE 7.8
Two ocean tidal bulges produced by the gravitational attraction of the moon combined with the rotation of the Earth-moon system on an idealized water-covered Earth.

Newton's first law of motion predicts that a net force must operate in any rotating system and this net force in the rotating Earth-moon system gives rise to the tidal bulge on the side of the planet opposite the moon. Recall from Chapter 4 that according to Newton's first law of motion, an object in constant straight-line motion remains that way unless acted upon by an unbalanced (net) force. In a rotating system, the net force confines an object to a curved (rather than straight) path. Consider an analogy. Suppose that you are a passenger in an auto that rounds a curve at high rate of speed. You feel a force that pushes you outward from the turning auto. Actually, you are experiencing the tendency for your body to continue moving in a straight path while the auto follows a curved path. In the same way, the rotation of the Earth-moon system causes the ocean to bulge outward on the side of the planet opposite the moon.

So far in our discussion of tide-generating forces, we have used the *equilibrium model of tides*, which assumes a frictionless Earth entirely covered by water. With this model, ocean bulges would always align with the celestial body that caused them. Furthermore, any location on the planet that is moved by Earth's rotation through these bulges would experience rising and falling sea level (i.e., tides). If only one celestial body (moon or sun) were present, each day a low-latitude locality would experience two high tides (when bulges pass) and two low tides (when halfway between the bulges). If the positions of the Earth and the other celestial body remained the same in space, the period of these waves would be the time it takes for one half a rotation of Earth, about 12 hrs.

While Earth is rotating, however, the moon is revolving around Earth. The moon revolves around Earth once each lunar month (averaging 29.5 days, between new moons) and in the same direction as Earth's daily rotation. Hence, Earth must make more than a full rotation in order for a specific location on the planet to line up again with the advancing moon. Catching up with the advancing moon requires 24 hrs plus 1/29.5 of a day, which is approximately 24 hrs and 50 min. This moon-based day (24 hrs, 50 minutes) is also called the **tidal day**. Because the tidal day is longer than the solar day, the times of high and low tide change by about 50 minutes from one solar day to the next.

The ocean's tidal bulges produced by the moon remain in the same alignment relative to the moon, but change their latitudinal (north-south) positions on Earth from day to day as they follow the moon during its monthly revolution about Earth. The plane of the moon's orbit is inclined by 5 degrees to Earth's equatorial plane so that during one lunar month, the moon's latitudinal position moves from directly over the equator northward to 28.5 degrees N (5 degrees beyond the Tropic of Cancer), back to the equator, on southward to 28.5 degrees S (5 degrees beyond the Tropic of Capricorn), and then back to the equator where another cycle begins.

When the moon is at its maximum latitudinal position, the center of one tidal bulge is just north of the Tropic of Cancer and the center of the other tidal bulge is on the other side of the planet just south of the Tropic of Capricorn. Hence, a location along or near the Tropic of Cancer or Tropic of Capricorn experiences only one significant tidal bulge in 24 hrs.

Sun-related ocean tidal bulges are produced in the same way as those caused by Earth-moon interactions. That is, the gravitational attraction between Earth and sun plus Earth's annual revolution around the mutual center of mass of sun and Earth generate a second set of similar but smaller tidal bulges that are aligned with the sun. As noted earlier, because of the sun's much greater distance from Earth, the sun's tidal pull on the ocean is less than half (about 46%) of the moon's tidal pull. These tidal bulges follow the sun (just as moon-related bulges track the moon), their locations changing as Earth rotates and follows its yearly orbit about the sun (Figure 5.1). The period of the solar tide is 24 hrs.

The tide-generating force diminishes rapidly with increasing distance so that celestial bodies at greater distances from Earth than the sun are too far away to exert a significant tidal pull on Earth's ocean. The *tide-generating force* (arising from a combination of gravitational and rotational forces) is inversely proportional to the cube of the distance between Earth and any other celestial body. Hence, doubling the distance between two bodies reduces the tide-generating force by a factor of 2^3 or 8 times.

TYPES OF TIDES

Based on the number of high and low tides and their relative heights each tidal day, tides are described as diurnal, semi-diurnal, or mixed (Figure 7.9). When the moon is directly over Earth's equator, its associated tidal bulges are centered on the equator. In theory, all locations on the planet except at the highest latitudes would rotate through the two tidal bulges and experience two equal high tides and two equal low tides per tidal day; this is known as a **semi-diurnal tide**. A semi-diurnal tide has a period of 12 hrs and 25 min, and theoretically has a wavelength of more than half the circumference of Earth.

On an ocean-covered Earth, different types of tides occur when the moon is either north or south of the equator. Whereas semi-diurnal tides would theoretically occur at

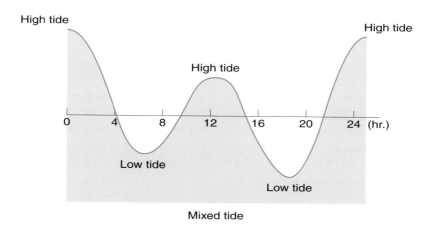

FIGURE 7.9
Types of astronomical tides observed in coastal locations

the equator at all times, most locations north or south of the equator would experience two unequal high tides and two unequal low tides per tidal day; this is called a **mixed tide** and the difference in height between successive high (or low) tides is called the **diurnal inequality**. When the point on Earth directly under the moon is near the Tropic of Cancer or Tropic of Capricorn, the diurnal inequality is at its maximum and the tides are called *tropic tides*. When the moon is above or nearly above the equator, the diurnal inequality is at its minimum and the tides are known as *equatorial tides*. When the moon and its associated tidal bulges are either north or south of the equator, most points

at high latitudes in theory would be impacted by one tidal bulge and would experience one high tide and one low tide per tidal day. This so-called **diurnal tide** has a period of 24 hrs and 50 min.

The separate sets of ocean bulges related to the moon and sun act at times together and at other times in opposition. About every two weeks, the positions of the sun, moon, and Earth fall along a straight line (Figure 7.10A). At these times of new and full moon phases as viewed from Earth, the lunar- and solar-related ocean bulges also line up (and add up) to produce tides having the greatest monthly tidal range (that is, the highest high

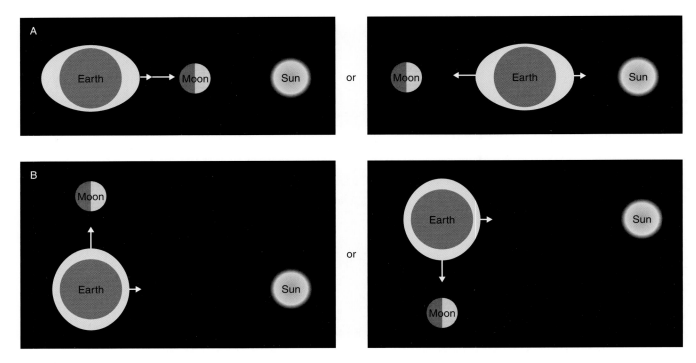

FIGURE 7.10
Configurations of Earth, moon, and sun responsible for (A) spring tides, and (B) neap tides.

tide and lowest low tide); these are called **spring tides**. Between spring tides, at the first and third quarter phases of the moon, the sun's pull on Earth is at right angles to the pull of the moon (figure 7.10B). At this time, tides have their minimum monthly tidal ranges (that is, unusually low high tide and unusually high low tide); these are called **neap tides** or *fortnightly tides*. Furthermore, the moon's orbit about the Earth is an ellipse (rather than a circle) so that the moon is closest to Earth (stronger tide-generating force) at *perigee* and farthest from Earth (weaker tide-generating force) at *apogee*. The moon completes one perigee-apogee-perigee cycle every 25.5 days. Similarly, tides due to the sun vary annually because Earth's yearly orbit around the sun is an ellipse so that Earth is closest to the sun around January 3 each year (*perihelion*) and furthest from the sun on July 4 each year (*aphelion*).

TIDES IN OCEAN BASINS

To this point in our discussion of ocean tides, we have assumed a water-covered Earth that rotates on its spin axis through the tidal bulges. In a more realistic situation, many non-astronomical factors modify tides, including ocean bottom topography, the presence of continents, coastline configuration, the Coriolis Effect, winds, and water depth. Tidal bulges move relatively

unimpeded around the globe only in the Southern Ocean near Antarctica. Consider, for example, the idealized case of tides in a Northern Hemisphere ocean basin of uniform depth that is completely surrounded by land (Figure 7.11). Assume also that the moon is providing the only tide-generating force and initially is situated directly above the ocean basin.

As Earth rotates from west to east, the tidal bulge shifts toward the western boundary of the ocean basin and the water surface slopes gently downward toward the east. The western boundary of the basin experiences high tide while the eastern boundary experiences low tide. Tide waves are shallow-water waves. Hence, as noted earlier in this chapter, the orbits of water particles flatten with increasing depth, changing from circular to elliptical and ultimately to a back-and-forth motion near the ocean bottom. The horizontal motion of water particles in a tide persists for long periods (because the tide wave is constantly being forced) so that the tide wave is subject to the Coriolis Effect. As the tidal bulge at the western boundary begins to move down slope toward the east, the Coriolis deflects water particles to the right (in the Northern Hemisphere) so that the tidal crest (high tide) rotates into the southern portion of the basin. Now, the water surface slopes downward toward the north. The tidal crest continues to rotate around the basin in a counterclockwise direction (viewed from above).

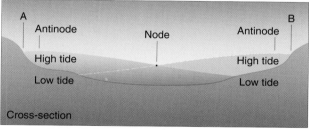

FIGURE 7.11
In this idealized Northern Hemisphere ocean basin bordered on all sides by land (top), a tide wave rotates in a counterclockwise direction (viewed from above). Lines radiating outward from the central node are cotidal lines that join points where high tide occurs at the same time of day. This is a semi-diurnal tide. Also shown (bottom) is a vertical cross-section from point A to point B. Note that the tidal range varies from zero at the node to a maximum at the antinodes (along the coast).

When the tide is high on one side of the basin, it is low on the opposite side. In Southern Hemisphere basins, reversal of the Coriolis Effect causes the tide wave to rotate in a clockwise direction (viewed from above).

This so-called *dynamic model of tides* applies reasonably well to seas and large embayments as well as the open ocean. Ocean scientists graphically represent the rotary motion of the standing tide wave in a basin by a series of cotidal lines radiating outward from a central node like the spokes in a bicycle wheel (Figure 7.11). A **cotidal line** joins points where high tide occurs at the same time of day; they are usually drawn at one-hour intervals. The tidal range varies from zero at the node to a maximum at the antinode along the coast.

Diurnal tides make one complete circuit per tidal day whereas semi-diurnal or mixed tides complete two circuits per tidal day. The period of the rotary tide waves is 12 hrs 25 min for semi-diurnal tides and 24 hrs 50 min for diurnal tides. For an ocean of average depth (about 4000 m or 13,000 ft), a tide wave progresses as a shallow-water wave at about 645 km per hr (400 mph). (As with wind-generated shallow-water waves, this is the speed of the wave crest, not the water.) Actual wave celerity along the coast varies greatly due to changes in bathymetry. Along the west coast of the U.S., tide waves travel at about 565 km per hr (350 mph), whereas along the west coast of Africa in the Northern Hemisphere, speeds are about 360 km per hr (225 mph). For coastal residents, however, these relatively high speeds are not apparent because for a diurnal tide, a 2-m (6.5-ft) rise in water level may take slightly more than 6 hrs.

The natural period of oscillation of a shallow basin may match the period of the tide-generating force causing resonance. The extraordinary tidal range (up to 16 m or 53 ft during spring tide) in the Bay of Fundy (Figure 7.12) is a two-step amplification involving the Gulf of Maine (12-hr period) and the Bay of Fundy (6.2 hr period). The Gulf of Maine resonates with the semi-diurnal lunar tide and the Bay of Fundy resonates with the Gulf of Maine.

Although tide characteristics may vary during the month at a specific locale, all coastal areas have primarily diurnal, semi-diurnal, or mixed tides. Non-astronomical factors help explain why locations on the U.S. Atlantic coast have predominantly semi-diurnal tides whereas many places on the Gulf Coast have mostly diurnal tides, and localities on the Pacific Coast have mostly mixed tides. Portions of Canada's Atlantic coast also have mixed tides.

TIDAL CURRENTS

Alternating horizontal movements of water accompanying the rise and fall of astronomical tides in coastal areas are known as **tidal currents**. Along the boundaries of an ocean basin (the location of antinodes), tidal ranges and hence tidal currents reach their maximum speed. Irregularities along the coast can modify the rotary motion of tide waves so that tidal currents move more directly into and out of rivers and harbors (Figure 7.13). Tidal currents flow in one direction during part of the tidal cycle and in the opposite direction during the remainder of the tidal cycle. When tidal currents are directed toward the land, water levels rise in harbors and rivers; these are called **flood tides**. Tidal currents flowing seaward with falling sea levels are called **ebb tides**. Between flood and ebb tides are slack water periods with little or no horizontal movement.

FIGURE 7.12
ASTER satellite image of the Bay of Fundy, Nova Scotia, Canada, at high tide (top) on 20 April 2001, and low tide (bottom) on 30 September 2002. The world's highest astronomical tides (tidal range of 16 m) occur in Minas Basin at the eastern extremity of the Bay of Fundy due to resonance of the Bay of Fundy-Gulf of Maine system; that is, the natural period of oscillation of about 13 hrs is close to the 12 hrs 25 min period of the lunar tide of the Atlantic Ocean. The scene covers an area of about 347 sq. km (134 sq. mi). [Courtesy of NASA/GSFC/METI/ERSDA/JAROS, and U.S./Japan ASTER Science Team.]

In some coastal areas where the tidal range is relatively large and the flood tide enters a narrow bay or channel, a tidal bore forms and moves upstream in a river or shallow estuary. A **tidal bore** is a wall of turbulent water, usually less than a meter in height. Tidal bores are well known at the mouth of the Amazon River in Brazil, on the Severn River in England, in Turnagain Arm off Cook Inlet, Alaska, in the Qiantang River in China, and in the upper embayments and rivers of the Bay of Fundy, Nova Scotia.

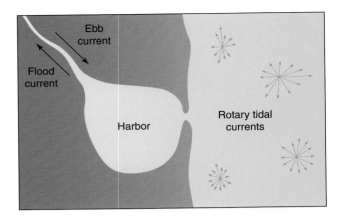

FIGURE 7.13
Ebb tide and flood tide in a harbor viewed from above.

OBSERVING AND PREDICTING TIDES

Observing the changing water levels caused by astronomical tides is relatively simple and has long been important for major ports. Knowing tide levels helps pilots and ship captains avoid running aground in shallow stretches of harbor channels. In the 1850s, the port of New York began operating a real-time tide gauge that indicated to ship operators the tide level and whether it was rising or falling. Today government agencies (e.g., NOAA, Canadian Hydrographic Services, and the British Admiralty) maintain tide observing and prediction systems that advise mariners based primarily on the output of numerical models and computers. On the other hand, fewer sources of information exist on tidal currents in harbors because they are much more difficult and expensive to monitor than tide levels. Whereas tide levels are nearly uniform over broad areas, tidal currents change quickly with variations in wind and river discharge. Furthermore they are affected by complex shorelines and bottom topography. Nonetheless, NOAA's *Physical Oceanographic Real Time Services (PORTS)* provides real-time information on tides and tidal currents to ship operators for 13 major U.S. ports. In the U.S., tide and tidal current predictions are made by NOAA's National Ocean Service CO-OPS (*Center for Operational Oceanographic Products and Services*) for more than 3000 locations and are available to the public online. Consider how tide predictions are made.

Periods of motions of the Earth, sun, and moon in space (i.e., orbit and rotation) are fixed and known precisely. The predictability of the movements of tide-generating celestial bodies means that astronomical tides can also be predicted with great accuracy. Tides are waves so that local tides can be resolved mathematically into their various components, or tidal constituents, called **partial tides**. Each partial tide describes a unique individual or combination of periods of motion (e.g., spring-neap cycle, perigee-apogee cycle). Partial tides are predicted individually and added together to forecast the height and timing of future local tides. Although as few as four partial tides can account for 70% of the total tidal range in the open ocean, some 60 components are commonly used (to account for both astronomical and non-astronomical factors including the effects of shallow water). More than 100 components must be considered to predict accurately the tides along a complex coastline, such as that of Cook Inlet, Alaska or in the upper portion of a tidal river such as at Philadelphia, PA. Predictions of local astronomical tides are most reliable when based on data collected for at least 18.6 years (i.e., a *nodal cycle*) a period that encompasses most of the astronomical configurations of the Earth-moon-sun system that generate the tides. However, only a single year of tide station observations

usually suffices for very reasonable tide predictions once they are adjusted for the nodal cycle. In most cases, local winds and atmospheric pressure variations are the primary causes of the difference between the actual and predicted tide (Figure 7.14). In upper tidal estuaries, seasonally high river discharge may also cause significant differences between actual and predicted tides and tidal currents.

OPEN-OCEAN TIDES

An Earth-orbiting satellite routinely measures tides over the deep-ocean. Such a satellite is equipped with a radar-altimeter that bounces microwave signals off the sea surface and precisely measures sea level. With such data, it is possible to determine what happens to tide waves and their energy as they travel across deep-ocean basins. The *TOPEX/Poseidon satellite*, a joint venture of the U.S. and France accurately measured global sea level every 10 days. However, this mission finally ended in January 2006 after 13 years and 5 months of service when the spacecraft

FIGURE 7.14

Observed (red) and predicted (blue) water level (in feet above Mean Lower Low Water) for the tide station at Southport, NC from 1 to 4 December 2007. Vertical dashed line marks the "present" time. [From NOAA, National Ocean Service, Center for Operational Oceanographic Products and Services.]

lost its ability to maneuver. The *Jason satellite* which was launched in December 2001, now measures global sea level. For more on measuring sea level from space, refer to this chapter's second Essay.

As shallow-water waves, tides lose energy through frictional drag with the ocean floor, especially in shallow seas and along continental margins. Satellite measurements show that about three quarters of the global tidal energy dissipates in shallow seas bordering northern Europe, in the Yellow Sea off Asia, in the shallow seas around Australia, near Argentina, and in Canada's Hudson Bay.

Open-ocean tides are important in mixing deep-ocean water. Ocean scientists long assumed that wind was the principal mixing agent of the open ocean, but satellite altimeter data now show that tidal mixing in the deep ocean is about as important as the wind. Perhaps as much as half of the tidal energy in the ocean is dissipated in mixing processes when tidal currents in the deep ocean flow over seamounts, ridges, and other rugged features on the ocean floor or weave through passages between islands.

Tidal currents flowing over topographic irregularities on the ocean floor generate internal waves that propagate away from their source. These internal waves arise from the fact that water density increases gradually with increasing depth. As tidal currents encounter a seamount or submarine ridge, relatively dense water is forced upward into slightly less dense water. Then to the lee of the obstacle gravity pulls the denser water downward. However, the descending water gains momentum and overshoots its equilibrium level and descends into denser water. The water then ascends thereby forming an oscillating wave that propagates horizontally. Because these waves are generated by tides, they occur at tidal frequencies and are called **internal tides**. Internal tide waves can travel thousands of kilometers beyond the obstruction that formed them and can have very large wave heights. They also break like surf on a beach but under water, locally mixing waters above and below the internal wave. Internal tides are important in mixing cold bottom waters with warmer surface waters as part of the global oceanic circulation (Chapter 6).

Ocean scientists have evidence that internal tides influence the gradient of the continental slope (Chapter 2). The inclination of the continental slope varies from very gentle (as small as one degree) to precipitous (up to 25 degrees where submarine canyons cut into the slope). About 80% of the continental slope is inclined at less than 8 degrees and the average inclination is about 4 degrees. According to geological studies, however, the sediments supplied to the continental slope (mostly by rivers) would support a stable average slope of perhaps 15 degrees or greater. Data acquired from model studies, dives in piloted submersible vessels, and moored instruments show that internal tides produce strong currents that prevent accumulation of sediment that would add to the steepness of the continental slope. In fact, the internal waves ascending the continental slope apparently behave very much like ordinary sea waves entering the shoaling waters of a coastal area (with changes in amplitude, wavelength, and water velocity). Whereas the influence of internal tides is widespread along the continental slope, turbidity currents and tectonic forces can be important locally and regionally in shaping the slope.

A vast amount of energy is involved in ocean tides and waves so it is not surprising that there is some interest in developing technologies to tap this energy to generate electricity. Although the potential is enormous, very little of this energy resource has been developed to date. For more on tidal power, see this chapter's third Essay.

Tsunami

On 1 April 1946 in a span of 27 minutes, two earthquakes shook the Scotch Cap Lighthouse on Unimak Island in Alaska's Aleutian chain (Figure 7.15). Shortly afterward, a huge sea wave appeared and obliterated the lighthouse, killing the five-man crew and hurling debris 35 m (115 ft) above sea level. All told, this destructive sea wave, known as a **tsunami** (from *tsu-nami*, the Japanese word for harbor wave and pronounced *sue-nah-mee*), was responsible for more than 165 fatalities and $26 million (1946 dollars) in property damage.

During the 1990s, 82 tsunamis were reported worldwide; 10 of them together claimed more than 4000 lives. An average 57 tsunamis occur each decade; the apparent recent increase in tsunami frequency is likely due to better global communications systems. The highest reported tsunami wave during the 1990s reached 31 m (102 ft), one of a series of huge waves that struck the small island of Okushiri, Japan on 12 July 1993, taking 239 lives. More recently, on 26 December 2004, a tsunami devastated portions of the coastal area rimming the Indian Ocean claiming an estimated 230,000 lives, the greatest death toll ever recorded by a tsunami. At least 2 million people were made homeless. (This tsunami is described in the Case-in-Point of Chapter 1). During the 20th century, the 141 most damaging tsunamis killed more than 70,000 people. Over the past 2000 years, tsunamis may have claimed the lives of more than 460,000 people in the Pacific region.

FIGURE 7.15
The Scotch Cap Lighthouse on Unimak Island, Alaska before and after the earthquake and tsunami of April 1946. A magnitude 8.0 (Mw) earthquake with the source to the south of Unimak Island generated a tsunami that destroyed the five-story lighthouse, located 9.8 m above sea level. [Courtesy US Coast Guard]

Although the media sometimes refers to a tsunami as a "tidal wave," a tsunami has nothing to do with astronomical tides. Most tsunamis (about 85% of the total) originate in the Pacific Ocean (perhaps 25% near Japan) and are generated by undersea earthquakes occurring along convergent plate boundaries and associated subduction zones (Chapter 2). As the lower plate subducts into the mantle, the upper plate abruptly shifts upward. Tectonic movements of the ocean floor disturb the overlying water column, generating a long-wavelength sea wave. The size of a tsunami generated in this way depends on the amount of movement of the sea floor. In addition to earthquakes in a subduction zone, volcanic eruptions, meteorite impacts, submarine landslides, and even calving glaciers can produce a tsunami. The violent eruption of the Indonesian volcano Krakatoa on 26-27 August 1883 spawned huge tsunami waves (one reported to be the height of a 12-story building) that killed at least 36,000 people. Once formed, a tsunami radiates outward in all directions. Typically generated near a coastline, nearby beaches are first to be subjected to an event. Potential for tsunami-producing submarine landslides also exists on the unstable volcanic slopes of the Canary Islands.

The tsunami hazard is much less in the Atlantic Ocean than in the Pacific Ocean except perhaps around the Caribbean plate boundary. For example, in 2006 scientists surveying the ocean floor off the northern coast of Puerto Rico discovered remnants of past submarine landslides. Some of these landslides were large enough to trigger a tsunami similar in height (2.5 m or higher) to one that struck Puerto Rico in 1918.

In the open ocean, a tsunami propagates as a series of waves having wavelengths that can exceed 750 km (465 mi) and periods of 10 to 30 minutes. Tsunamis are shallow-water waves; that is, their wavelengths are much greater than the depth of the ocean. For the average depth of the ocean of about 4000 m (13,000 ft), wave celerity is about 645 km per hr (400 mph)—approaching the speed of a commercial jetliner. A tsunami can have a long reach, transporting potentially destructive energy from its source to coastlines many thousands of kilometers away. But with an open-ocean wave height of only 0.5 m or so and taking 10 to 30 minutes to pass, a tsunami would be unnoticed moving under a ship at sea.

In the deep water of the open ocean, tsunami wave energy is distributed through a huge volume of water. But like any other wave, when a tsunami enters shoaling coastal waters, it slows and its energy is forced into a decreasing volume of water. The wavelength shortens to perhaps 15 to 20 km (9 to 12 mi) and wave height increases, sometimes building to extraordinary heights as the tsunami approaches the coastline. The December 2004 tsunami had a maximum height of at least 30 m (100 ft) when it first came ashore in Sumatra's Aceh Province. The initial arrival of a tsunami is often marked by a trough that draws water off the beach. This unusual sight can entice curious people to head for the beach where they are caught by the tsunami crest pushing ashore. Often the first wave is followed by a succession of other powerful tsunami waves. Tsunamis inundate dry land as huge breaking waves, a flood similar to a flood tide, or a wall of water, taking lives and obliterating property. Tectonic movements sometimes aid the inland propagation of a tsunami; that is, the ocean bottom rises in the offshore subduction zone while coastal lands sink.

In the United States, coastal residents of Hawaii and Alaska are at greatest risk from a tsunami although tsunamis have struck elsewhere along the West Coast. Hawaii has reported a dozen damaging tsunamis since 1895, the most destructive of which occurred on 1 April 1946. A tsunami destroyed most of the waterfront of Hilo and caused 159 deaths. (This was the same tsunami that destroyed the Scotch Cap Lighthouse mentioned earlier.) A tsunami that struck the Seward, Alaska area on 28 March 1964 took more than 100 lives. Although tsunamis are rare along the West Coast of the U.S. outside of Alaska, geological evidence suggests that the Cascadia subduction zone located off the Pacific Northwest Coast may be the site of tsunami-generating earthquakes about every 300 to 700 years. In April 1992, a magnitude 7.1 earthquake at the southern end of that subduction zone triggered a small tsunami that caused property damage near Cape Mendocino, CA. This event spurred scientific interest in the tsunami hazard all along the West Coast of North America.

The Hawaiian tsunami of 1946 led to the establishment of the *Pacific Tsunami Warning Center* in Ewa Beach, Hawaii in 1948. The tsunami that struck Prince William Sound during the 1964 Alaskan earthquake led to formation of the *West Coast and Alaska Tsunami Warning Center* in 1967 in Palmer, Alaska. Scientists at these centers warn the public of an approaching tsunami based on earthquake occurrences detected by seismic networks around the Pacific Rim plus tide gauge readings in coastal areas. However, these methods have not been very successful—the false alarm rate has hovered around 75% since the 1950s. Undersea earthquakes do not always generate a tsunami and warnings provided by coastal tide gauges generally arrive too late for adequate warning of the public.

Saving lives through improved early warning of an approaching tsunami is the goal of the NOAA *Deep-ocean Assessment and Reporting of Tsunamis (DART)* system. Each DART station has a *tsunameter*, consisting of a pressure sensor anchored to the ocean floor at depths to 500 m (1640 ft) that measures slight variations in pressure exerted by the overlying water column in response to a passing tsunami wave. The sensitive pressure sensor is capable of detecting water pressure changes associated with a tsunami wave as small as one centimeter. An acoustic

signal transmits pressure data from the tsunameter to a companion moored buoy floating on the ocean surface, and then to a satellite for downloading by forecasters at the two NOAA Tsunami Warning Centers to permit more timely warnings for coastal residents.

At the time of the December 2004 tsunami, NOAA was operating only 6 DART stations, all in the Pacific Ocean. As of January 2008, the U.S. had deployed 39 Dart stations mostly in the Pacific Rim; others are located in Hawaii, the Caribbean, the Gulf of Mexico, in the Atlantic off the southeast U.S., and near the equator between Hawaii and Chile (Figure 7.16). Additional sensors are planned for the near future. Data from DART sensors are essential components of the *U.S. National Tsunami Hazard Mitigation Program*, a partnership that includes representatives of various federal agencies (i.e., NOAA, FEMA, and the U.S. Geological Survey) and the Pacific Coast states. In recent years, this program has also installed new shore-based tide gauges and upgraded seismometers operated by the USGS. Together these program components should provide the public with adequate advance warning of both local- and remote-source tsunamis and substantially reduce false alarm rates. Furthermore, another essential outcome of the program is public awareness of the tsunami hazard and the construction of maps that identify coastal areas most susceptible to inundation by a tsunami (Figure 7.17)

Prior to the devastating December 2004 tsunami, there was no tsunami warning system in the Indian Ocean. Since then an international effort, coordinated by the United Nations Educational, Scientific, and Cultural Organization (UNESCO), has been rectifying that situation by putting in place an improved seismic network for detecting large earthquakes, a number of tsunameters, and a real-time coastal tide gauge network. According to UNESCO, the Indian Ocean network is intended to be the first phase of a global tsunami warning system. The U.S. network, in turn, could become part of the global observing system. These real-time data will be fed into numerical models to provide the public with advance warning of a tsunami. One of the outcomes of the extensive scientific documentation of the December 2004 tsunami was an opportunity to use real-time data to test existing tsunami numerical models and make appropriate refinements. With information on the location of tectonic activity plus the volume of displaced seawater, these models simulate propagation of a tsunami through the open ocean and the pattern of flooding as the wave moves onshore. Developed by Japanese and American researchers, the models are designed to forecast when and where a tsunami is likely to strike along the coast and how far inland its waters might flood.

FIGURE 7.16
Location of completed and planned DART and Tsunameter Stations as of November 2007 for real-time detection of tsunamis. [NOAA, National Data Buoy Center]

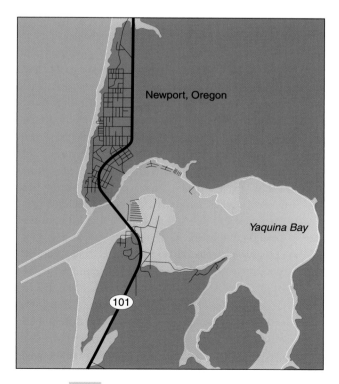

Potential Tsunami inundation area

FIGURE 7.17
Tsunami-risk map for Newport, OR, identifying areas of greatest potential for tsunami flooding. Such maps inform local planning for tsunami hazard mitigation. [Produced by the Oregon Department of Geology in collaboration with the Oregon Graduate Institute of Science and Technology]

Conclusions

Winds supply the kinetic energy that forms waves on the ocean surface, which then propagate horizontally until they expend their energy by breaking on a distant shore. As noted in Chapter 6, this is an important aspect of ocean-atmosphere interaction that provides energy to drive surface currents and mix surface waters. Wave behavior depends on wind speed, fetch, and duration as well as water depth. In terms of interaction with the ocean bottom, a distinction is made between deep-water waves and shallow-water waves.

The gravitational attraction of the moon and sun combined with the rotations of the Earth-moon and Earth-sun coupled systems generate planetary-scale shallow-water tide waves in the ocean basins. The consequence is a periodic rise and fall of sea level that is so familiar to coastal dwellers as ocean tides. Tides also cause currents that are among the strongest of all currents in coastal regions and are responsible for some water movements in the deep ocean. In Chapter 8, we take a closer look at waves and tides in the coastal zone, where the majority of the human population lives.

Basic Understandings

- Kinetic energy of air in motion (the wind) is transferred to the ocean surface causing surface waves. Wind-driven ocean waves are oscillations of the sea surface that propagate horizontally along the ocean/atmosphere interface away from where they were generated. Energy is propagated with the wave—not the water (except where the wave breaks).

- The life cycle of a sea wave begins with input of kinetic energy that disturbs the ocean surface. Water's surface tension is the restoring force for capillary waves—small waves having wavelengths less than 1.7 cm (0.7 in.). For sea waves longer than capillary waves, the restoring force is gravity. Open ocean deep-water waves propagate away from their energy source with little energy loss through friction. Waves expend their energy as they encounter the ocean bottom and shore, finally dissipating their energy in breaking.

- Wave height, the vertical distance between wave trough and wave crest, depends on wind speed (and turbulence), duration of the wind

in the same direction, and the distance (fetch) over which the wind blows. Wave interference also affects the growth and decay of sea waves. Wind-driven waves associated with two or more storm systems at sea may interfere constructively or destructively. In active wave-forming areas, waves (called a sea) have a mixture of wavelengths and periods, plus sharp crests, giving the ocean surface a chaotic appearance. As waves move away from the area where they formed, they become more rounded and sort themselves by wavelength; these are called swell.

- Waves are either shallow-water waves or deep-water waves depending on the ratio of wavelength to ocean depth. The depth of no-wave action is approximately one-half the wavelength of a surface wave. Shallow-water waves are affected by interaction with the ocean bottom. In deep-water (depths greater than one-half the wavelength), waves are unaffected by the ocean bottom.

- As a wave moves into water depths of less than one-half its wavelength, the wave shortens and slows. With no change in period, wave energy has no place to go but up, so the wave builds and becomes steeper as the top of the wave moves faster than the bottom. The wave becomes unstable and breaks expending its energy in the surf zone.

- A seiche is a rhythmic oscillation of water in an enclosed basin or a partially enclosed coastal inlet. During a seiche, the water level in a basin typically rises at one end while simultaneously falling at the other. Under certain conditions, a seiche grows to great heights with serious consequences including coastal flooding and damage to moored vessels. A seiche grows through resonance, that is, amplification that occurs when the period of the disturbance (e.g., earthquake, wind) matches the natural period of oscillation of the basin.

- Astronomical tides are planetary-scale shallow-water waves responsible for the regular rise and fall of the ocean surface. Tides typically are measured at coastal locations as local changes in sea level as a function of time. The difference in height between water levels at high and low tides is called the tidal range and the time between successive high tides is the tidal period.

- Tides are caused by the gravitational attraction

between the Earth and the moon and sun combined with the rotations of the Earth-moon and Earth-sun coupled systems. Although its mass is considerably smaller than that of the sun, the moon exerts a greater influence on ocean tides because it is much closer to Earth. The tide-generating force produces two bulges of water on Earth's ocean surface, one facing the moon (or sun) and one on the opposite side of the planet. Earth's rotation through these two tidal bulges causes the regular rise and fall of the water level.

- Depending on factors such as specific location and phases of the solar and lunar cycles, a coastal locality may experience two equal high tides and two equal low tides per tidal day (semi-diurnal tide), two unequal high tides and two unequal low tides per tidal day (mixed tide), or one high tide and one low tide per tidal day (diurnal tide). Many non-astronomical factors modify ocean tides, including the presence of continents, the Coriolis Effect, winds, and variations in coastline configuration, water depth, and bottom topography.

- In a Northern Hemisphere basin, the Coriolis Effect causes the shallow-water tide wave to rotate around the basin in a counterclockwise direction (viewed from above). When the tide is high on one side of the basin, it is low on the opposite side. In Southern Hemisphere basins, the reversal of the Coriolis Effect causes the tide wave to rotate in a clockwise direction (viewed from above).

- Ocean scientists graphically represent the rotary motion of the tide wave in an ocean basin by a series of cotidal lines radiating outward from a central node. A cotidal line joins points where high (or low) tide occurs at the same time of day.

- Alternating horizontal movements of water accompanying the rise and fall of tides in coastal areas are called tidal currents. Tidal range and tidal currents are at a maximum along the boundaries of an ocean basin (coasts). In coastal embayments and harbors, tidal currents are constrained to flow back and forth as flood tides (flowing toward land) or ebb tides (flowing away from land).

- Treated as a wave, the tide at a particular location can be resolved into many component tidal constituents or partial tides. Partial tides are predicted individually and added together to forecast the local astronomical tide.

- Internal waves form and propagate below the ocean surface on interfaces between water masses of different densities. Density contrasts between different water masses are about 1000 times less than that between air and water so that internal waves propagate more slowly than surface waves but wave heights are much greater.

- A tsunami is a shallow-water ocean wave that develops when a submarine earthquake or, less frequently, a landslide or volcanic eruption disturbs the ocean water. In the open ocean, tsunami wave height is typically less than 0.5 meters with a period of 10 to 30 minutes. Its wavelength usually ranges from 100 to 200 km (60 to 120 mi) and its speed is hundreds of kilometers per hour. With small heights, long wavelengths, and long periods, tsunamis are imperceptible to ships at sea. However, when they reach shore, the wavelength shortens and waves can build to tremendous heights and take many lives and cause considerable property damage.

- Improved early warning of an approaching tsunami is the goal of the NOAA Deep-ocean Assessment and Reporting of Tsunamis (DART) system. Each DART station has a *tsunameter*, consisting of a pressure sensor anchored to the ocean floor at depths to 500 m (1640 ft) that measures slight variations in pressure exerted by the overlying water column in response to a passing tsunami wave.

Review

1. What is the immediate energy source for most waves on the ocean surface? What type of energy is transferred from this source to the surface waters?
2. Distinguish between wave height and wavelength.
3. For deep-water waves, the diameter of the orbit of a water particle at the ocean surface is equivalent to the _____.
4. For deep-water waves, the depth of no wave motion (wave-base) is approximately equal to _____ the wavelength.
5. Define fetch. For the same wind speed, higher sea waves are generated with increasing or decreasing fetch?
6. What is a seiche? How does a seiche differ from wind-driven ocean waves?
7. Astronomical tides are caused by the gravitational attraction between the rotating Earth and what other two bodies in space? Which one of these celestial bodies produces the greater tide-generating force and why?
8. Do astronomical tides behave as deep- or shallow-water waves? Explain your answer.
9. Distinguish between semi-diurnal and mixed tides.
10. Most tsunamis originate in which ocean basin? What type of tectonic activity is responsible for most tsunamis?

Critical Thinking

1. Compare the restoring force for capillary waves versus that of longer wind-driven ocean waves.
2. How does frictional interaction with the ocean bottom influence sea waves?
3. Explain how wave interference influences the height of wind-driven sea waves.
4. How does bathymetry affect a shallow-water wave such as a tsunami?
5. Distinguish among a forced wave, standing wave, and progressive wave. Also provide an example of each.
6. How and why does the tidal range vary between a spring tide and a neap tide?
7. Explain how tectonic activity can affect the inland progression of a tsunami.
8. Compare the types of tides usually experienced along the U.S. Pacific coast and Atlantic coast. What might explain the difference?
9. What is the significance of resonance for the tidal range in coastal inlets?
10. Why are tsunamis more common in the Pacific Ocean basin than the Atlantic Ocean basin?

ESSAY: The State of the Sea

Experienced sailors are usually adept at describing the state of the sea. The term *sea state* refers to the overall appearance of the ocean surface, including the dimensions of wind-generated waves and the presence of surface phenomena such as white caps, foam, or spray. Because the wind is largely responsible for the appearance of the sea surface, approximate wind speed can be inferred from the sea state. The sea state also provides an indication of wind direction because wave crests tend to move in approximately the same direction as the near-surface wind.

In the 19th century, prior to the invention of accurate instruments for measuring wind speed (anemometers), mariners developed a method to estimate the wind speed from the observed sea state. This method evolved from a wind force scale proposed in 1805 by Francis Beaufort (1774-1857), later an Admiral in the British Royal Navy. Initially, Beaufort devised a method for estimating the force of the wind using the amount of sail needed by a fully rigged sailing vessel, a British frigate of the day. He divided his scale into 13 increments, ranging from 0 (calm) to 12 (hurricane). Hence, for example, a wind of force 1 (light air) was described as "just sufficient to give steerage way" for a frigate, whereas a force 12 (hurricane) was "that which no canvas could withstand." By 1838, the *Beaufort scale* was modified to specify the sea state and was adopted by the British Navy. On this scale, force 1 winds produce "ripples with appearance of scales; no foam crests" (wave heights of about 7.5 cm or 3 in.) whereas a force 12 wind produces a chaotic sea state described as "air filled with foam; sea completely white with driving spray; visibility greatly reduced."

In the 20th century, the first reliable anemometers allowed mariners to quantify the Beaufort scale in terms of wind speed. For example, a force 1 wind is 1.6 to 4.8 km per hr (1 to 3 mph) whereas a force 12 wind is 119 km per hr (74 mph) or higher (see Figure for examples). In 1926, the Beaufort scale was extended to include the effects of wind on land (Table 1). In addition to wind speed, the state of the sea depends on swell and the fetch and duration of the wind. Other factors such as water depth, heavy rain, or ice can also affect wave height. Furthermore, the Beaufort scale applies to waves on the open sea; waves in enclosed waters tend to be smaller and steeper.

Experience tells us that waves do not have a single wave height or wavelength, but occur in a spectrum of sizes. This variation is partly due to the inherent variability of wind speed and direction over a continuum of space and time scales. One of the most useful statistics for describing wave characteristics is *significant wave height*, the average height of the highest one-third of waves observed in a patch of ocean. Because smaller waves are usually not visible against the background of larger waves, we can assume that significant wave height approximates the visually observed mean wave height. Statistical analysis of waves indicates that the largest individual wave that one might encounter in a storm would be roughly twice as high as the significant wave height. The *dominant wave period* represents the period of waves exhibiting the maximum wave energy.

Spurred by the need for better weather and climate forecasts, the meteorological and oceanographic communities have expanded their monitoring of wind and wave conditions over the open ocean. These observations utilize more sophisticated techniques than visual observations from ships of opportunity traversing limited regions of the ocean. Today, sensors on moored automated buoys and orbiting satellites as well as ships at sea gather near-surface wind and wave data.

Moored buoys, deployed by various nations in their coastal waters, serve as instrumented platforms for making automated weather and oceanographic observations. The *National Data Buoy Center (NDBC)*, part of NOAA's National Weather Service, operates approximately 70 moored buoys in the coastal and offshore waters of the western Atlantic Ocean, Gulf of Mexico, and the Pacific Ocean from the Bering Sea to southern California, around the Hawaiian Islands, and in the South Pacific, as well as the Great Lakes. Buoys are equipped with accelerometers or inclinometers that measure the heave acceleration or the vertical displacement provided to the buoy by waves passing during a specified time interval. An onboard computer uses statistical wave models to process these measurements and generate wind-sea and swell data that are then transmitted to shore stations. These data include significant wave height, average wave period, and dominant wave period during each 20-minute sampling interval. Selected buoys also measure directional wave data, such as mean wave direction.

Measuring the winds at sea has always been difficult and the historical database has very sparse coverage. Today, Earth-orbiting satellites equipped with radar scatterometers use the sea state to estimate near-surface wind speed and direction and provide the first global map of the surface wind field over the ocean. A *scatterometer* is a sensor that measures the return reflection or scattering of a microwave (radar) signal sent to Earth's surface. A rough sea surface reflects back (backscatters) to the antenna on the satellite a stronger signal than does a smooth sea surface. Backscatter is proportional to roughness because more water surface faces directly at the radar when the water is rougher (with waves) than when the water is smooth. Computer algorithms estimate wave height and then the wind speed from differences measured in the strength of the return signals. If two emitted beams are spaced with a precise angular distance, slight variations in the return signals from the roughened surface permit determination of wind direction. As a feasibility study, the first spaceborne scatterometer was onboard the U.S. Skylab Mission in 1973-74. From June to October 1978, the U.S. SEASAT-A Satellite Scatterometer (SASS) demonstrated that accurate winds could be obtained remotely from space. The NSCAT (NASA Scatterometer) was flown onboard the Japanese satellite ADEOS, launched into orbit in 1996 and operational until mid-1997. SeaWinds sensors accompanied the U.S. QuikSCAT (Quick Scatterometer) launched in 1999 and the Japanese Midori 2 satellite in December 2002.

FIGURE 1
The state of the sea corresponding to Beaufort Force 1 wind speed: 1 to 3 knots (top) and 10 wind speed: 48 to 55 knots (left). [From NOAA's National Weather Service, Milwaukee/Sullivan, WI]

TABLE 1
Beaufort Scale of Wind Force

Beaufort Number	General description	Sea and land observations for estimating wind speed	Wind speed 10 m above ground in km/hr (mph)
0	Calm	Sea like mirror; smoke rises vertically.	< 1 (< 1)
1	Light air	Slight ripples at sea; smoke but not wind vane shows direction of wind.	1-5 (1-3)
2	Light breeze	Small, short wavelets; wind felt on face, leaves rustle, wind vane moves.	6-11 (4-7)
3	Gentle breeze	Large wavelets, scattered whitecaps; leaves and small twigs move constantly, small flags extended.	12-19 (8-12)
4	Moderate breeze	Small waves, frequent whitecaps; dust and loose paper raised, small branches moved.	20-28 (13-18)
5	Fresh breeze	Moderate waves; small leafy trees swayed.	29-38 (19-24)
6	Strong breeze	Large waves, some spray; whistling heard in utility wires, large branches in motion.	39-49 (25-31)
7	Near gale	White foam from breaking waves; whole trees in motion.	50-61 (32-38)
8	Gale	Moderately high waves of great length; twigs break off trees.	62-74 (39-46)
9	Strong gale	Crests of waves begin to roll over, spray may impede visibility; slight structural damage.	75-88 (47-54)
10	Storm	Sea white with foam, heavy tumbling of sea; trees uprooted, considerable structural damage.	89-102 (55-63)
11	Violent storm	Very rare, unusually high waves; widespread damage.	103-118 (64-73)
12	Hurricane	Very rare, much foam and spray greatly reduce visibility; disastrous.	119 (74) and higher

ESSAY: Monitoring Sea Level from Space

Flown onboard a polar-orbiting satellite, a *radar altimeter* measures the apparent distance to the sea surface based on the travel time of a pulse of microwave energy directed downward by the instrument. When the microwave pulse strikes the ocean surface, part of the signal is reflected back to the satellite's radar instrument. The time between initial transmission of the pulse and receipt of the reflected signal, coupled with the known speed of the microwave signal allows calculation of the distance between the satellite and the ocean surface. Using the latest satellite altimeters, ocean scientists can determine the height of the ocean surface with an accuracy of a few centimeters. Remote sensing of the height of the sea surface takes into account different factors including those arising from the satellites' orbit, the atmosphere's influence on propagation of the microwave pulse, variations in the strength of gravity, and astronomical tides.

Many variables affect sea level, with changes in local gravitational attraction being one of the most important. The local gravitational attraction between the solid Earth and overlying ocean water depends on both distance and mass of Earth's lithosphere. The greater the mass, the greater is the gravitational attraction, whereas the greater the distance, the smaller is the attraction. Ocean water is attracted horizontally toward areas of stronger gravitational attraction, piling up and increasing sea-surface height, and away from areas of weaker gravitational attraction, decreasing sea-surface height. Density differences in Earth's lithosphere can cause significant variations in sea-surface height. Sea level drops about 4 m (13 ft) for every 1000 m (3300 ft) increase in ocean depth, owing to local gravitational effects of Earth's crust on the overlying ocean water. Ocean bottom features such as ridges and trenches can cause sea height to vary by tens of meters. However, the mounds and depressions in the sea surface are not readily apparent when sailing or flying over them because the ocean's horizontal dimensions are so great that slopes are small.

Variations in sea-surface elevation are measured relative to Earth's geoid. The *geoid* is the equipotential surface of the planet's gravitational field which coincides with global mean sea level in the absence of any disturbance such as winds, currents, or tides. (Gravity everywhere acts downward and perpendicular to a geopotential surface.) The geoid's height variation is less than 200 m (650 ft). For example, sea level rises about 1 m in the subtropical gyres and drops about 2 m across the Antarctic Circumpolar Current. The somewhat irregular surface of the geoid contrasts with the *reference ellipsoid*, an idealized mathematical representation of Earth' surface as a smooth oblate spheroid, somewhat flattened at the poles and bulging at the equator.

Although efforts at remote sensing of sea surface topography by satellite were conducted in the 1970s and 1980s, the technique was not fully developed until the early 1990s. Sensors on the TOPEX/Poseidon satellite, launched in 1992 as a joint venture of the U.S. and France, measured sea heights with an accuracy of a few centimeters. Today, the Jason series of satellites continues to provide ocean altimetry data that has many valuable applications. The satellite radar altimeter has proven to be a versatile and powerful tool for remote sensing of the ocean. Analysis of satellite altimeter derived sea-surface elevations provides the most complete data set on the bathymetry of the ocean floor. Physical oceanographers also use satellite altimetry to measure changes in the height of the ocean surface due to wind and density differences. This enables them to calculate patterns of surface currents (*geostrophic flow*) from observed sea-surface slopes (Chapter 6). Altimeter data are also used to determine wave heights, estimate surface wind speed, and track surface water masses including movement of surface water across the tropical Pacific basin during El Niño and La Niña (Chapter 11). The Jason-1 satellite altimeter proved valuable in tracking the propagation and height of the December 2004 tsunami (Figure 1).

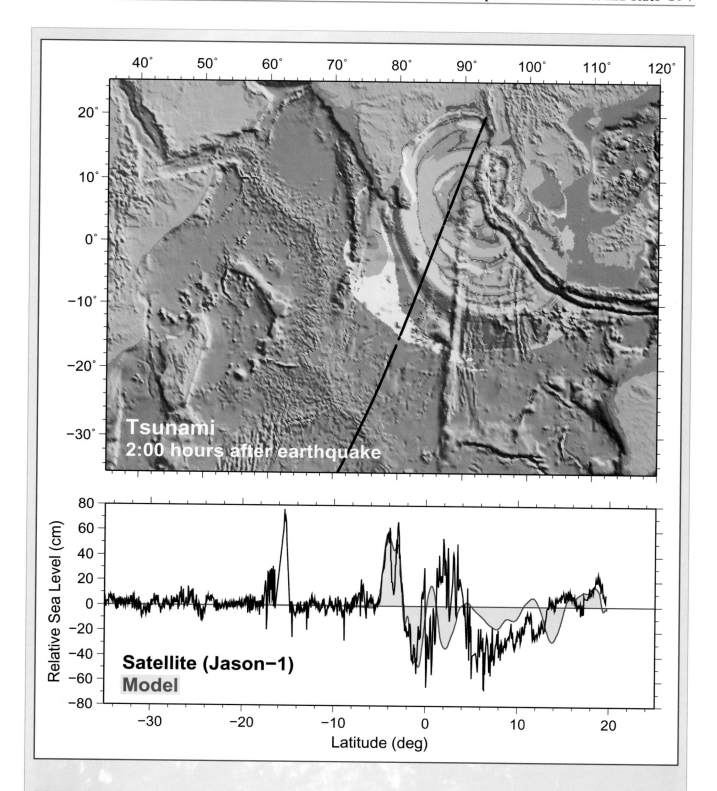

FIGURE 1
Sea-surface height measurements obtained by the altimeter onboard the Jason-1 satellite enabled NOAA scientists to track and measure the height of the December 2004 Indian Ocean tsunami. The image represents the wave pattern two hours following the earthquake. [Courtesy of NOAA]

ESSAY: Power Generation from Ocean Tides and Waves

Ocean tides and waves have long interested scientists, engineers, and conservationists as energy sources for generating electrical power and "clean" energy alternatives to lessen our dependence on fossil fuels. Tidal power has received the most attention—both the regular rise and fall of the sea surface as well as strong tidal currents. Indeed, tidal power was used for milling grain as early as the 11th century in Britain and France and the 17th century in Boston.

In the last half of the 20th century, large tidal-power installations were built in France, Canada, Russia, and China. These plants operate much like hydroelectric facilities except that water flows in both directions. Suitable coastal sites must have tidal ranges greater than 5 m (16 ft) and relatively fast tidal currents that flow through a constricted inlet into a large basin. A dam (called a barrage) is constructed across the inlet with turbines submerged at the base of the dam. The ocean is on one side of the barrage and the basin is on the other side. The incoming flood tide is channeled through the turbines and the basin fills with water. During the slack water period the gates on the barrage are closed. Then, with the outgoing ebb tide, the gates are opened and the exiting water again drives the turbines that generate electricity.

The downside of this technology is the fact that electrical generation is not continuous at the same level of output 24-hrs a day, diminishing during slack periods when tidal currents are weak. Very few locations possess the ideal combination of coastal configuration and tidal range. Furthermore, where such a combination does exist (e.g., Bay of Fundy, Nova Scotia), the barrage is likely to disrupt the local ecology, fishery, and tourism.

The most successful of the tidal-power installations is La Rance Plant on the Brittany coast of France just south of Saint-Malo where the tidal range varies from 9 m (30 ft) to more than 13 m (43 ft). This 240 megawatt (MW) plant has 24 turbines that generate about 90% of Brittany's electricity. The 18 MW facility at Annapolis Royal, Nova Scotia has been less successful and never operated commercially. A small, tidal power plant was built on the sea floor near the Arctic tip of Norway to generate power from the area's strong tidal currents and provide electricity for Hammerfest, one of the world's most northerly towns. The power plant uses large windmill-like turbines mounted on the sea floor and transmits electricity to the local power grid via submarine cables. Initially the plant generated enough electricity for about 300 homes but is planned for expansion to power perhaps 1000 homes.

Many engineering schemes have been proposed for generating electrical power from ocean surface waves. A few have been built and operated briefly as demonstration projects. One demonstration plant was built in the mid-1990s on the remote island of Islay in the Western Islands of Scotland, an area known for its high waves. The plant operated for a short time before being destroyed by high waves in a storm. Small-scale wave-powered generators are often used to power navigation aids on offshore buoys.

The world's first commercial wave energy conversion project is based on a new technology known as the *Pelamis Wave Energy Converter*. From a site off the north coast of Portugal, the system initially produced 2.25 MW of electricity; anticipated expansion is expected to bring electrical output to a level that will meet the needs of 1500 homes. The Pelamis system consists of four cylindrical tube segments, each 120 m (395 ft) long and 3.5 m (11.5 ft) in diameter. The segments float semi-submerged and moored in waters 50-60 m (165-200 ft) deep and about 5 km (3.1 mi) from the coastline. Hinged joints link together the segments and it is the wave-induced motion of these joints that is the immediate source of energy. This motion, in turn, drives hydraulic rams that pump high pressure oil that powers hydraulic motors that, in turn, run electrical generators. An ocean-floor cable delivers electricity to the shore. The Pelamis device is moored in such a way that its tube segments orient toward oncoming waves thereby optimizing the harvesting of energy. Production of 30 MW would require many interconnected tubes covering an ocean area of about 1 square km.

Because of its long coast facing the waves of the open Atlantic, wave energy conversion may be Portugal's most promising alternative energy source. Costs are significantly less than both wind power and solar photovoltaic power. Interest in this technology is also growing in the United Kingdom.

CHAPTER 8

THE DYNAMIC COAST

Case-in-Point
Driving Question
Coastline Formation
Coastal Features
  Beaches
  Barrier Islands
  Rip Currents
  Salt Marshes and Wetlands
  Human Alterations
Estuaries
Coastal Storms and Storm Surge
Tropical Cyclones
  Hurricane Characteristics
  Where and When
  Hurricane Life Cycle
  Hurricane Hazards
  Evacuation
Extratropical Cyclones
Conclusions
Basic Understandings/Review/Critical Thinking
ESSAY: The Great Lakes and the Ocean
ESSAY: Moving the Cape Hatteras Lighthouse

Arch rock at Depoe Bay, Oregon. [NOAA]

Case in Point

Many of the world's most populous cities are located along the coast, and efforts to protect them against flooding from storm-generated surges are becoming more challenging as global sea level rises. In many instances, the problem is not new as demonstrated by what has happened to Venice, a city in northern Italy situated on a cluster of 120 salt-marsh islands in a large coastal lagoon at the head of the Adriatic Sea (Figure 8.1). Bridges connect the islands and a causeway and ferries link Venice to the mainland. A long narrow barrier island separates the lagoon from the sea (Gulf of Venice) except for three major tidal inlets. At one time, the sea and the lagoon protected the city from foreign invaders. In fact, tradition has it that Venice was founded in CE 452 by people from northern Italian cities who fled to the islands seeking protection from invading Teutonic tribes. Today, however, the encroaching sea threatens Venice's art and architectural treasures and perhaps the city's continued existence.

Slow subsidence of Venice combined with rising sea level has increased the frequency of flooding. Venice has been sinking slowly under its own weight for centuries. From the 1930s to 1970s, withdrawals of large quantities of groundwater for industrial use exacerbated the problem. Groundwater occupies the tiny pore spaces

FIGURE 8.1
ASTER satellite image of Venice, Italy, located in the saltwater lagoon between the mainland and barrier islands. The image was acquired on 9 December 2001. ASTER (Advanced Spaceborne Thermal Emission and Reflection Radiometer) is flown on NASA's Terra Satellite orbiting Earth at an altitude of 705 km (430 mi). [Courtesy of NASA/GSFC/METI/ERSDAC/JAROS, and U.S./Japan ASTER Science Team]

in sediment and as the water is pumped out, the sediment compacts and the ground subsides. Land subsidence is also occurring because of oxidation of organic-rich soils in fertile farmland that was reclaimed from marshland at the southern end of the Venice Lagoon. A drainage system that keeps the soil relatively dry promotes oxidation and consequent loss of soil mass. Reclamation of marshland began in the late 19th century and continued into the late 1930s. Cumulative land subsidence since reclamation is up to 2 m (6.5 ft) and is currently taking place at a rate of 1.5 to 2 cm per year. According to estimates by the *Venice Organic Soil Subsidence (VOSS)* project, in 50 years oxidation could remove all the organic soil with additional land subsidence of 75 to 100 cm (30 to 40 in.).

Ten major floods inundated Venice over the past 70 years and smaller floods became much more frequent in the same period. During the often stormy months of November through January, some areas of the city are under water almost every day. Portions of Venice, including the historic Piazza San Marco, are flooded about 100 days per year; a century ago, the flood frequency was about 7 days per year. Flooding forces businesses to close and inconveniences residents and tourists alike but more significantly, the salt water corrodes the brick underpinnings of historic churches and other buildings along the Grand Canal and elsewhere in the city.

To protect Venice from future flooding, the Italian government embarked on a $5 billion project to construct a total of 78 floodgates at the three tidal inlets. Each gate measures up to 5 m (16 ft) thick, 20 m (66 ft) wide, and 27 m (89 ft) in length. Most of the time, the hollow gates will be filled with seawater and lie horizontally within a foundation (caisson) on the sea floor so as not to impede tidal currents or navigation. But when a storm surge is predicted to elevate the tide to a height of 110 cm (43 in.) or more, the floodgate system will be activated. (By comparison, the water level reached 194 cm, or 6.4 ft, during the disastrous flood of November 1966.) Compressed air will be pumped into the gates expelling the water. The gates are hinged at one end so that the free end can swing to the surface and block the flow of floodwaters through the inlets. This system is designed to protect Venice from a 60-cm (24-in.) rise in mean sea level and a 3-m (10-ft) flood. Locks will allow passage of ocean-going container-cargo and cruise ships as well as the fishing fleet. Similar flood-control structures have been built on the Thames River in England to protect London and at the mouths of estuaries to protect the low-lying Dutch coastal plain.

Although the idea for the Venice floodgates dates back to at least the mid 1980s, it was not until May 2003 that a stone-laying ceremony signaled the beginning of construction on the *Moses Project* (known in Italian as *Mose* for Modulo Sperimentale Elettromeccanico). As of this writing, the project is almost one-third complete and is slated for completion in 2011. However, environmental protests have slowed construction. Opponents of the Venice floodgate scheme argue that closing the inlets will cause substantial environmental damage, especially to the lagoon ecosystem. Most of Venice's sewage empties untreated into the many canals dissecting the city or directly into the lagoon. Normally tidal currents dilute and transport these wastes out to sea but if the gates are closed for extended periods, wastes will accumulate in the city's canals or in the lagoon. Some scientists speculate that the gates could be closed for as many as 50 days per year.

Driving Question:
Why and in what ways is the coastal zone a particularly dynamic and vulnerable portion of the Earth system?

The **coast**, the primary focus of this chapter, encompasses the relatively narrow region transitional between land and ocean. Although on a given day the coast can appear stable and benign, the many components of the Earth system (ocean, atmosphere, geosphere, cryosphere, and biosphere) continually interact in the coastal zone making it an exceptionally active environment. Forces operating at the land/sea interface include tides, breaking waves, glacial processes, sea-ice conditions, near-shore currents, sediment discharged by rivers and streams, changing sea level, tectonic and other geological processes, and the impact of living organisms including humans. These interactions are responsible for the wide variety of coastline types worldwide including, for example, rocky beaches, cliffed headlands, barrier islands, mangrove swamps, estuaries, sand dunes, coral reefs, and fjords.

Rapid human population growth is stressing the coastal zone. In 2005, the National Oceanic and Atmospheric Administration (NOAA) reported that the coast is now home to about 53% of all Americans. Some 153 million people currently reside in coastal counties—about 33 million more than in 1980—and the population is expected to swell by 12 million in the next decade. According to NOAA, a county is described as coastal if

it is on a coast (i.e., Atlantic, Gulf, Pacific, Great Lakes) or at least 15% of the county's land area is in a coastal watershed. The 673 coastal counties represent 17% of the nation's land area and have three times the nation's average population density. Population growth is most rapid from Texas through the Carolinas with Florida leading the nation in population growth (and hurricane potential). The population of Florida's coastal counties increased 73% between 1980 and 2003.

Increasing human population density in the coastal zone translates into greater demands for electrical power, fresh water, wastewater treatment, and roads. Environmental stressors that accompany population growth include waste disposal, recreational activities, tourism, infrastructure needs, industrial expansion, homes, and power plants, and the exploitation of fisheries, minerals, oil, and natural gas deposits. Adverse impacts on coastal ecosystems include shrinking plant and animal habitats, surface- and ground-water pollution, and more frequent algal blooms due to enhanced runoff of fertilizers and other nutrients. Furthermore, population growth along the Atlantic and Gulf coasts exposes more people to the hazards of hurricanes and powerful extratropical storms.

In this chapter, we examine the various types of coasts and the processes responsible for their evolution and distinguishing features, and how human activity is altering the coastline. Special attention focuses on beaches, barrier islands, salt marshes, and estuaries. We describe hazards posed to coastal residents by tropical and extratropical storm systems and the key role played by air-sea interactions in powering these weather systems. We begin with coastline forming processes. A coastline also borders the Great Lakes. For more on the Great Lakes and how their properties and processes compare with those of the ocean, refer to this chapter's first Essay.

Coastline Formation

As shown schematically in Figure 8.2, the farthest inland extent of storm waves is one way of delineating the **coastline**, in some cases marked by sand dunes or wave-cut cliffs. Another definition is the mean high water level. Land exposed at low tide up to the coastline is the **shore** and the average low tide line is the **shoreline**. The **intertidal zone**, the shore area between high and low tides, is alternately under water and exposed to the atmosphere as the tide rises and falls. Moisture, temperature, and salinity fluctuate dramatically so that organisms living in the intertidal zone are equipped with special adaptations enabling them to survive drastic changes in their environment (Chapter 10).

A fundamental distinction among coastlines is whether they occur in tectonically active or inactive (passive) continental margins (Chapter 2). Mountain building and volcanic activity are dominant geological processes in tectonically active coastlines such as those that rim much of the Pacific Ocean basin. These processes can elevate coasts so rapidly that waves and

currents cannot erode or deposit sediment fast enough to significantly modify long stretches of the shoreline. The few beaches that exist are small, isolated and usually restricted to near wave-cut cliffs or the mouths of rivers, which supply sand and gravel. For example, subduction is causing uplift along the Pacific Northwest coast. The Juan du Fuca plate is created at the submerged Juan de Fuca Ridge and is moving eastward, subducting beneath Washington, Oregon, and Northern California. Along the southern Oregon coast, the rate of tectonic uplift is greater than the global rise in sea level. Wave-cut benches are visible in the cliffs well above present high-water level. Meanwhile, along the northern Oregon coast, the rate of sea level rise is keeping pace with tectonic uplift.

Erosion, transport, and deposition of sediment are dominant geological processes along passive shorelines such those that border the Atlantic Ocean and Gulf of Mexico. In passive continental margins, sediments (mostly sand and silt) are deposited by rivers and streams entering the ocean and supplied by breaking waves undercutting shoreline cliffs that subsequently slump or slide into the ocean. Waves and currents transport these sediments along the shore, forming beaches, spits, and offshore barrier islands.

Rocky shorelines that are common in New England and Atlantic Canada formed during the Pleistocene Ice Age (1.7 million to 10,500 years ago) when huge lobes of glacial ice scoured the land numerous times, eroding soils and bedrock. As the ice retreated, sea level rose (Figure 8.3). The time since the ice retreated has been too short for accumulation of significant quantities of

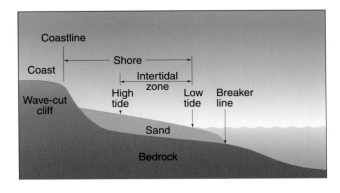

FIGURE 8.2
Idealized cross-section of a coastal zone, in this case bordered on the land side by wave-cut cliffs.

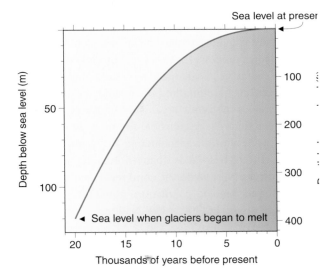

FIGURE 8.3
Smoothed post-glacial curve showing rise in global sea level from about 20,000 years ago to the present.

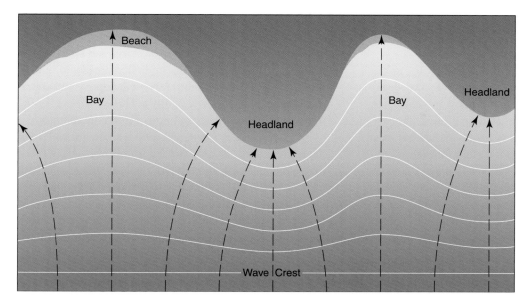

FIGURE 8.4
Viewed from above, waves slow in shoaling water and undergo refraction as they approach an irregular coastline. Solid white lines are wave crests; dashed lines are orthogonals to wave crests.

sands and gravels on most rocky shorelines. Furthermore, the retreating glacial lobes left behind many lakes and bogs that trap the little sediment produced, preventing the remainder from reaching the shore. Hence, not enough sediment is available for waves and tides to smooth the complex coastlines. Such recently de-glaciated coastlines feature many small harbors and inlets, with rocky islands offshore.

As waves enter coastal waters of varying depth, they usually undergo **refraction**, bending of a wave in response to changing wave speed. Along the coast, wave refraction influences patterns of erosion, sediment transport, and deposition. Consider some examples. Suppose that the shoreline is straight and coastal waters shoal uniformly in a direction perpendicular to the coastline. If wave crests approach the shoreline at an angle other than 90 degrees, the wave bends. The segment of the wave moving through deeper water progresses toward shore at its original speed while the segment of the wave entering shoaling water begins to "feel" the bottom and slows (Chapter 7). Consequently, the wave crest is refracted toward the shallower water. Refraction causes approaching wave crests to come into near alignment with the depth contours (bathymetry) of the ocean bottom and to closely conform to the shape of the shoreline.

On the other hand, suppose that the coastline is irregular and coastal waters do not uniformly shoal toward the shore. This situation is shown in Figure 8.4 viewed from above. Well offshore in deep water, approaching wave crests (continuous white lines) are essentially straight and parallel. Waves eventually enter water that is not uniformly deep and are refracted toward shallower water. Hence, waves approaching an irregular coastline are refracted (converge) toward headlands (rocky cliffs that project seaward) and away from coves or bays. Convergence concentrates wave energy causing undercutting and erosion of headlands whereas spreading out (divergence) of wave energy in bays weakens wave action and favors deposition of sediment and expansion of the beach. Eventually, the forces of erosion cut back the headlands and sediment fills in coves and bays so that the coastline straightens. Figure 8.5 shows the remnants of a headland that was extensively eroded by wave action.

FIGURE 8.5
These rocky knobs along the Washington coast are what remains of a headland eroded by wave action. [Photo by J.M. Moran]

Coastal Features

Erosive and depositional processes impact to some degree both tectonically active and passive coastlines. The immediate source of energy for these processes is breaking waves. As we saw earlier in this book, the sun drives atmospheric circulation (Chapter 5) and winds transfer kinetic energy to the ocean surface forming waves (Chapter 7). Hence, solar energy ultimately powers erosive and depositional processes operating along the coast. In this section, we focus on selected features of the coast, that is, beaches, barrier islands, salt marshes, and wetlands. We also consider how and why humans alter the coastal zone.

BEACHES

A **beach** is an accumulation of wave-washed sediment (usually sand and gravel) at the landward margin of the ocean (or a lake). At the mean high-water mark, most beaches feature a prominent **berm**, a platform of sand that is nearly flat-topped and slopes steeply seaward. A beach is a changing system in which erosive and depositional forces continually do battle. Waves, tides, and currents erode cliffs, wash away dunes, and transport sand to and from the beach. The balance between sediment reaching a beach and sediment leaving a beach is always in flux.

A beach functions as a buffer that minimizes erosion by storm-driven ocean waves. As storm waves push ashore, water movement spreads the sand flattening the beach surface. In this way, wave energy is distributed over a broader area of the beach thereby dissipating energy and reducing erosion. Following a storm, sand transported to the beach by currents fills in eroded areas and returns the beach to a steeper profile. Nonetheless, especially at middle and high latitudes, significant differences are noted in the appearance of a beach in winter versus summer.

In winter, erosive forces tend to prevail over depositional forces as powerful storm waves cut back the beach, moving sands onto shallow submerged bars near the shoreline. Hence winter beaches have a steeper slope. Strong storm winds blow sands from dry areas of the beach to dunes building behind the beach or into a lagoon. In summer, the weather often is more tranquil and depositional forces tend to prevail over erosive forces. Waves transport sand from offshore bars back onto the beach and the beach widens. Summer beaches feature a gentler slope.

Sediment is delivered to the shore by rivers and streams and eroded from seaside cliffs by ocean waves. As rivers and streams enter the sea, their current slows and diverges, depositing much of their suspended sediment load near their mouths (Chapter 4). Breaking waves attack the base of seaside cliffs, carving out a notch. The cliff slope becomes too steep and rock debris slumps or slides into the ocean (Figure 8.6). A number of factors govern the propensity of a cliff to slumping or sliding including composition (e.g., consolidated versus unconsolidated sediment), geological structure (e.g., presence or absence

FIGURE 8.6
Wave-eroded cliffs along the Oregon coast. [Photo by J.M. Moran]

of fractures), and rainfall. Furthermore, the relentless pounding of waves breaking against the coast fragments exposed rock. Coastal currents then transport these sediments to and from the beach. Even the rock debris that accumulates at the base of a seaside cliff is eventually removed, exposing the cliff to more erosion.

Earlier in this chapter, we noted that waves approaching the shore bend (are refracted) toward shallower water causing their crests to closely conform to the shoreline. Despite the effects of refraction, wave crests rarely line up perfectly parallel to the beach, often striking the beach at oblique angles up to 10 degrees or so (the angle between wave crests and the shoreline). Breaking waves striking the shore at an oblique angle give rise to sediment-transporting currents along the shore. If a breaking wave approaches the shore directly, a thin sheet of water rushes straight up the sloping beach face as *swash*, stops briefly, and then flows straight down slope as a *backwash* (Figure 8.7). If, on the other hand, a breaking wave approaches the shore at an oblique angle, the swash follows a diagonal up the beach face, then straight down slope (Figure 8.8). Together, the upwash and backwash constitute the zigzag or saw tooth motion that rolls particles along the beach face, known as *beach drift*. The oblique approach of waves to the shore produces a component of water motion that flows parallel to the shore known as a **longshore current** (Figure 8.9). A longshore current transports sediments as **littoral drift** (a river of sand) along the coast, either nourishing or cutting back beaches. In some cases, littoral drift transports sediment offshore into the head of a submarine canyon where it is permanently lost to the beach.

FIGURE 8.8
Wave crests approaching the beach at an oblique angle at the Assateague Island National Park, VA. [NOAA Corps]

The **beach sediment budget** is summarized in the following word equation:

Sediment Budget = Sediment Input − Sediment Output

In summary, sediment input processes include delivery by rivers, streams and wind, erosion of seaside cliffs, longshore current supply, and onshore transport. Sediment output processes encompass removal by longshore currents, wind erosion, and offshore transport. If the sediment balance is

FIGURE 8.7
Swash on a sloping beach face at Gaviota State Park about 33 miles west of Santa Barbara, CA. [Photo by Edward Hopkins]

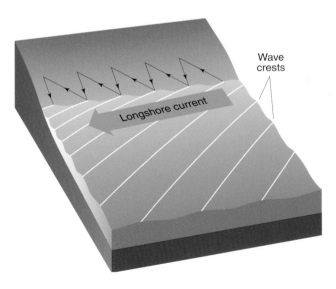

FIGURE 8.9
Viewed from above, waves approaching the coastline at an oblique angle produce a component of water motion roughly parallel to the shore (longshore current) that transports sediment (littoral drift). Zig-zag arrows represent the flow of water up and down the beach face.

positive, (e.g., in summer) the beach grows; with a negative balance, (e.g., in winter) the beach is cut back. If input and output are equal, the beach is in a steady state.

Along the Atlantic coast, different geologic processes account for significant differences in beaches. From South Florida north to the south shore of Long Island, NY, beaches are located mostly on the shorelines of barrier islands. As discussed in the following section, a **barrier island** is an elongated, narrow accumulation of sand oriented parallel to the coast and separated from the mainland by a lagoon, bay, or estuary. Chains of barrier islands lie offshore of a broad coastal plain that extends to a relatively smooth continental shelf. The coastline of *barrier island beaches* is segmented by estuaries such as Chesapeake Bay. North of Long Island, NY, the coastal plain is mostly absent and the Appalachian Mountain bedrock continues to the shore and beyond. In this region, the combination of bedrock and numerous episodes of glaciation and de-glaciation have shaped beach formation. Much of the New England coast is rocky and irregular, overlain in places by unconsolidated glacial deposits, and featuring small pocket beaches between rocky headlands. Offshore are small islands, shoals, submerged basins, and ledges. Most New England beaches are *mainland beaches*, that is, they are on the mainland and not offshore islands. On Cape Cod, for example, most beaches are on the ocean side with sand dunes on the landward side. Some beaches occur on **sand spits**, finger-like ridges of sand or gravel that protrude from the shore into a body of water, or a **tombolo**, a spit linking an offshore island to the mainland or another island.

BARRIER ISLANDS

Nearly 300 barrier islands fringe much of the Atlantic and Gulf Coasts primarily from Texas to Long Island, NY, the longest and best developed of any barrier island chain in the world. (The number of barrier islands worldwide exceeds 2500.) They occur where the supply of sand is abundant, the sea floor is gently sloping, waves are energetic and the continental margin is passive. Barrier islands vary in length from a few hundred meters to more than 100 km (62 mi) whereas the width is often a kilometer or less. Padre Island is the longest of the nation's barrier islands extending more than 180 km (112 mi) along the Texas Gulf Coast. Tidal inlets segment barrier islands. Recall from this chapter's Case-in-Point that three major tidal inlets link the Gulf of Venice to the lagoon where the island city of Venice, Italy is located.

Beginning at the ocean side of a typical undeveloped barrier island and working our way toward the mainland, we would encounter successively a beach, dunes, flats, marsh, lagoon, flats, marsh, and upland areas (Figure 8.10). The near-shore and beach zones are high-energy environments with the potential for considerable impact from waves, longshore currents, and onshore winds. Just inland from the beach is a dune field consisting of one or more parallel ridges of wind-blown sand from the beach (Figure 8.11). The next zone is the back-island flat, an extensive plain consisting of grassland (marsh) or woodland, depending on the age and size of the island and its exposure to storms and high winds. This area is prone to wash over by high waves generated by the winds of powerful coastal storms. The flat grades into a salt marsh that borders a lagoon, estuary, or bay; it is a low-energy environment where fine sediments accumulate. A **lagoon** is a partially enclosed body of water separating a barrier island from the mainland. Normally, lagoons receive essentially no input of river water and tidal fluxes maintain salinities near that of seawater. (In this way, lagoons differ from estuaries—discussed later in this chapter.) Where evaporation rates are relatively high, the salinity of water in some isolated lagoons may exceed the usual seawater salinity. In an extreme example, Laguna Madre between Padre Island and the Gulf coast has salinities as high as 60 psu.

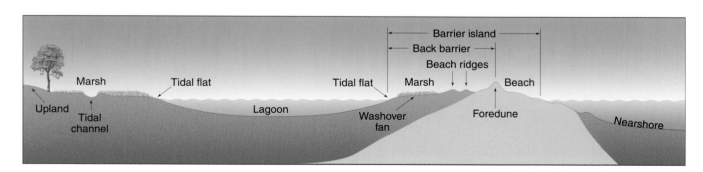

FIGURE 8.10
A cross-sectional profile of a typical undeveloped barrier island with the mainland to the left and the open ocean to the right.

FIGURE 8.11
Sand dunes located just inland from a beach on a barrier island on North Carolina's Outer Banks. [Photo by J.M. Moran]

Scientists recognize several different ways whereby a barrier island may form. Many (especially along the southeast Atlantic and Gulf Coasts) date from the mid Holocene epoch (about 5000 years ago) when sea level was somewhat higher than it is now. (The Holocene epoch covers the past 10,500 years.) Higher sea level submerged beaches isolating the tops of dune ridges as offshore islands while flooding lower areas landward of the dune ridges, which became lagoons. Some barrier islands (e.g., small Gulf Coast islands) are the product of the vertical growth of a submarine sand bar that emerged from the sea as an island. Along an irregular coastline, sand spits can lengthen into barrier islands through longshore sand transport. During intense storms, the spit many be breached, forming barrier islands. This is the origin of barrier islands along some segments of the New England coast.

A barrier island is a continually changing system. Waves breaking on the shores of a barrier island dissipate their energy by shifting sands and modifying the shape of the island. As sea level gradually rises, episodes of storm-induced wash-over become more frequent. Sand is removed from the ocean-side of the island and transported to the lagoon-side and in this way a barrier island migrates toward the mainland—eventually becoming a mainland beach.

Barrier islands absorb the brunt of powerful storm-driven sea waves thereby providing some protection for coastal beaches, estuaries, wetlands, and shoreline structures. But many barrier islands have been developed, especially for cottages and resorts, and their sands are now temporarily stabilized under layers of asphalt or concrete. Some coastal cities, including Atlantic City, NJ, Miami Beach, FL, and Virginia Beach, VA are built entirely on barrier islands. Such exposed locations are particularly vulnerable to the ravages of the high winds and floodwaters associated with tropical cyclones (discussed later in this chapter). On developed barrier islands, much of the energy of storm waves may be expended in demolishing buildings and roads instead of shifting sands. Conflict is inevitable between rigid structures such as roads and buildings and the inherently changeable platforms (i.e., barrier islands) upon which they are built.

RIP CURRENTS

In the *surf zone* (where shoreward moving waves break in shoaling coastal waters), water moves toward and usually along the shore. Whereas the shoreward transport of water occurs over broad areas of the surf zone, the return seaward flow of water tends to concentrate in narrow widely spaced belts often corresponding to depressions in the seafloor or breaks in sand bars. The narrow seaward flow of water must balance the broad shoreward flow of water so that the offshore flow occurs as a relatively swift surface or near-surface current with speeds up to 2 knots (1.7 mph) or so. This is known as a **rip current**. (Sometimes, a rip current is referred to as a *rip tide*, but this is a misnomer; rip currents have nothing to do with astronomical tides.) Usually the strength of a rip current increases as wave height and wave period increase.

A rip current flows at nearly right angles to the shoreline and spreads seaward a few meters to hundreds of meters beyond the line of breaking waves (Figure 8.12).

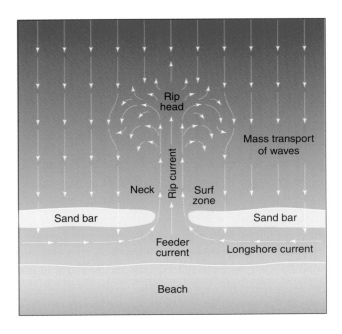

FIGURE 8.12
A rip current viewed from above.

Viewed from above, a rip current is marked by choppy water made turbid by suspended sand and floating debris being transported seaward. Conventional thinking was that rip currents were transient phenomena lasting from a few minutes to a few hours. However, field studies conducted by University of Florida scientists indicate that a rip current may persist for weeks or even months at essentially the same location along the shore, varying in strength during that period.

A rip current is hazardous for people swimming in the surf zone and can develop offshore of any surf beach including those bordering the Great Lakes. Most people are unable to swim against the strong current and are swept into deeper offshore waters. According to the U.S. Lifesaving Association, rip currents claim an estimated 150 lives on average each year along the nation's beaches. Perhaps as much as 80% of all rescues performed by surf beach lifeguards involve rip currents. In Florida, during 1989-1999, drowning deaths due to rip currents averaged 19 annually—more than the combined yearly death toll from hurricanes, tornadoes, and lightning for the same period. As noted above, however, a rip current is narrow. If caught in the current, swimmers are advised not to fight the current but to swim parallel to the shore until they escape into calmer waters and can swim back to shore.

In coastal areas, NOAA's National Weather Service issues a daily rip current outlook that rates the risk of rip currents as low, moderate, or high. These outlooks plus increased public awareness of the hazards of rip currents contributed to a recent decline in rip current fatalities at the surf beaches of southeast Florida. From 1979 to 1991, the year the Miami National Weather Service office began issuing outlooks, the average annual death toll declined from 12 to 5.

SALT MARSHES AND WETLANDS

A **salt marsh** is composed of salt-tolerant plants that colonize shores that are protected from wave action. Along the New England coast, the dominant plant species in undisturbed salt marshes are cordgrass (along the shore), marsh hay, black rush, and shrubs (inland often bordering trees). Tidal creeks meander through most salt marshes allowing seawater to flood the marshes on rising tides and drain on ebbing tides (Figure 8.13). Vegetation slows the movement of water through a salt marsh thereby inducing deposition of suspended fine sediment and the plants anchor the sediment in place. A salt marsh offers many benefits including protecting the coastline from storm wave erosion, filtering runoff thereby reducing the input of pollutants and excess nutrients into estuaries, and providing habitat for organisms such as crabs and oysters.

FIGURE 8.13
A tidal creek meanders through a Massachusetts salt marsh. [Photo by J.M. Moran]

In the tropics and subtropics, such as South Florida and Puerto Rico, coastal wetlands support thick growths of salt-tolerant woody trees called **mangroves**. Mangroves have extensive root systems that trap sediments. They also provide habitat for both marine and land animals. Some organisms are especially adapted for survival in mangrove thickets, such as mangrove oysters, which attach themselves to roots and branches. Mangrove forests protect low lying coastal areas from storm surges and tsunamis. Unfortunately, in many areas, development activities are destroying the forests. For example, during a recent 100-year period, Tampa Bay, FL lost an estimated 44% of its coastal wetland area, including mangrove forests and salt marshes.

Wetlands are among the most productive natural ecosystems on Earth, providing food-rich nursery grounds for estuarine and other coastal organisms, including many commercially important fish. Roots of wetland plants (both grasses and trees) trap sediment and organic matter. Where sea level is rising, wetlands can build up fast enough that their surface remains at sea level, assuming an adequate supply of sediment. If sea level is rising too rapidly and the sediment supply is limited, marshes are eroded as is presently the case on the Mississippi River delta and around the Chesapeake and Delaware Bays. Where sea level is stable, wetland plants can trap enough sediment (if available) to build the marsh surface above normal sea level. Where this happens, the shore advances and grasslands or forests eventually replace the coastal wetland.

HUMAN ALTERATIONS

Human alteration of the coastal zone has many purposes including preservation of recreational beaches, flood control, maintenance of harbors and navigation channels, and protection of homes, roads, and other structures built near the beach, in the dunes behind them, or on the top of seaside cliffs. When erosion threatens to damage or destroy shoreline structures, three protective strategies are available: armor, artificial beach nourishment, and strategic retreat. *Armor* includes construction of dams, breakwaters, jetties, groins, and sea walls. *Artificial beach nourishment* refers to the addition of sand to a beach, and *strategic retreat* involves inland displacement of a structure threatened by rising sea level and storm waves.

Coastal armor has both costs and benefits, but research suggests that the overall costs outweigh the benefits. Armor can disrupt littoral drift and alter the natural flow of sediments to and from a beach. Sediments settle out of suspension in the reservoir behind a dam, reducing the river's sediment load below the dam and the sand supply for the beach. Longshore currents transport existing sands away from the beach, sometimes to the extent that all that remains is rocky rubble (cobbles and boulders).

A **breakwater** is a long, narrow offshore structure, usually constructed of large blocks of rock or concrete and oriented parallel to the shoreline. Its purpose is to provide calm waters for docking boats or to protect beaches from erosion by absorbing the energy of breaking waves or reflecting waves back to sea. Some breakwaters are built on open coastlines where no natural harbors exist. However, sediments settle to the bottom of the relatively calm waters on the landward side of the breakwater and costly dredging may be required to keep the harbor open for navigation.

Breakwaters also disrupt littoral drift. Most sediment accumulates in the harbor and is unavailable for deposition on down-current beaches. Just such a situation occurred at Santa Barbara, CA after a breakwater was built in 1928. To keep the harbor open and maintain longshore sand transport, sand is continually dredged from the harbor and piped as slurry (sediment and water mixture) to the down-current side of the harbor. A pipeline now transports sand formerly conveyed by natural longshore currents.

A **jetty** is similar to a breakwater except that it is oriented perpendicular to the shoreline and extends seaward up to a kilometer or more. In some cases, a jetty serves the same function as a breakwater by protecting harbors from storm waves. Often jetties are also used to keep a barrier island inlet open for navigation into and out of a harbor on the mainland side of the island. Jetties constructed on either side of the ocean-side entrance of a tidal inlet constrict the flow of tidal currents. Constriction accelerates the flow of water, reducing sediment deposition and perhaps eroding the channel bottom. On the other hand, jetties disrupt littoral drift across the inlet.

Up current from a jetty, beaches widen due to enhanced sediment deposition (*beach nourishment*) whereas beaches disappear down current from a jetty due to lack of sand input and wave erosion. Consider an example.

Ocean City, MD is a beach resort that has undergone considerable development since the 1950s. The resort is located at the south end of Fenwick Island, a barrier island. Although steps were taken in the late 1970s to curb further development by limiting dredging and filling of wetlands (intended to create more land for dwellings), the resort remains a popular destination. Most residents and visitors are probably unaware that in August 1933 a hurricane made a direct hit on the Middle Atlantic region, the only one to do so during the 20th century. (For a direct hit, the storm must approach the coast from the southeast.) Although at landfall, the hurricane intensity was moderate, the air pressure pattern caused strong onshore winds that made it the most damaging hurricane in the history of the area. Hurricane-force winds devastated the coast from Virginia to New Jersey, fatalities numbered 47, and property damage was $40 million (in Depression era dollars). The hurricane lashed Fenwick Island and opened an inlet at its southern end linking the backwater bay with the Atlantic Ocean. Subsequently, the U.S. Army Corps of Engineers erected two rock jetties to maintain the inlet for navigation. However, the jetties also altered the southward flowing littoral drift causing the beach to widen north of the jetty at Ocean City while the beach at Assateague Island, south of the inlet, was deprived of sand and eroded back.

Other structures called **groins** resemble jetties but are smaller and usually more closely spaced along a beach (Figure 8.14). Their purpose is to widen a beach by trapping sand moving downstream as littoral drift.

FIGURE 8.14
Viewed from above, closely-spaced groins disrupt the longshore drift so that sand is deposited on the up-current sides (D) and eroded from the down-current side (E). In this way, groins trap sand along a beach and the beach widens locally.

But once again, sand trapped by groins is not available to beaches down current so that local beach widening is at the expense of beach erosion elsewhere.

A **seawall** is a concrete or rock embankment intended to protect beaches, roads, buildings, and shoreline cliffs from erosion by storm waves. However, seawalls also cut off a source of sediment for the beach by preventing erosion of bluffs. Furthermore, evidence suggests that wave energy, rather than being mostly absorbed, is actually reflected by a seawall, stirring up the water and sand at the base of the structure, accelerating erosion, and causing beaches to narrow. Deeper water in the near shore area means that rather than breaking well offshore, storm waves break against the seawall, further exacerbating erosion and ultimately destroying the seawall.

Beaches are the economic life-blood of many coastal communities, attracting visitors for a variety of recreational activities. Perhaps 70% of all vacationing Americans spend time at a beach. Breakwaters, jetties, groins, and seawalls are often constructed to preserve beaches, protect seaside property, and support the local economy. But for reasons discussed above, these strategies to *armor* or *harden* the coastline have serious drawbacks. In fact, these drawbacks convinced many coastal states to prohibit armoring of the coast to prevent beach erosion.

An alternate and widely used strategy to maintain existing beaches or restore badly eroded beaches is **artificial beach nourishment**. Sand is usually dredged from nearby lagoons or inlets or deep waters just offshore and then spread on the beach. In some cases, sand is trucked to the beach from an inland sand pit. On the plus side, artificial beach nourishment attempts to re-establish the natural balance between sediment inputs and outputs. On the negative side, beach nourishment is expensive. The new sand is not the same as the original and tends to erode at a faster rate so that beach nourishment is often short-lived (typically lasting 5 years or less) and must be repeated regularly to maintain the beach.

Today's large-scale beach nourishment projects are rooted in the Ash Wednesday storm of 1962 which caused considerable beach erosion along the New Jersey shore. Congress authorized the U.S. Army Corps of Engineers to repair the damage by dredging sand and pumping it on the beach. As of this writing beach nourishment projects have taken place on more than 125 East Coast beaches at a total cost in excess of $2.5 billion. In many cases, the process had to be repeated.

The transient nature of artificial beach nourishment is illustrated by what happened at Folly Beach, SC, a barrier island southeast of Charleston,

SC. In September 1989, Hurricane Hugo's storm surge severely eroded the beach. In 1992, the U.S. Army Corps of Engineers spent $15 million to restore the beachfront through artificial beach nourishment. But only two months after the project was complete, a coastal storm washed away 80% of the new sand. Similar experiences are common along U.S. coastlines.

When erosion threatens shoreline buildings, strategic retreat is an alternative to artificial beach nourishment or armoring the coast with seawalls, groins or other structures. *Strategic retreat* refers to the physical relocation of a building inland. In 1999, this strategy was used to preserve the historic Cape Hatteras Lighthouse. (For more on this, refer to this chapter's second Essay.) In some cases, entire settlements are moved inland. For example, the town of Port Valdez in Alaska's Port Valdez fjord (terminus of an oil pipeline) was relocated after being heavily damaged by a tsunami triggered by the 1964 Alaska earthquake (Chapter 7). Originally, the town was situated at the head of the fjord and was moved to one side for greater protection.

Human activity also has modified salt marshes and other coastal wetlands either intentionally or unintentionally. For centuries most people considered wetlands to be wastelands and reclaimed them by ditching, draining, or filling. In this way, former wetlands were developed for airports, agriculture, housing, and shopping malls. Over the past 250 years, more than half of the original wetland acreage in the United States was converted to other purposes. But we now know that wetlands provide habitats that are necessary to support coastal marine ecosystems and efforts are underway to reclaim damaged wetlands. For example, restoration efforts are underway to return the area of saltpans in southern San Francisco Bay to its original wetland condition by removing dikes, grading, and replanting grasses. Comparable projects are underway in the Netherlands where polders (reclaimed continental shelf areas) are also being restored to their original condition. Wetlands are complex ecosystems, however, and it is difficult to re-establish a wetland that will function as well as an undisturbed one.

Estuaries

An **estuary** is a partially isolated body of water where fresh water (from rivers and streams) mixes with seawater—from the lower extent of the photic zone to the most inland reach of tidal action. As pointed out in Chapter 1, estuaries are among the most productive ecosystems on Earth because of their special combination of physical and biological characteristics. They receive a continual supply of nutrients and organic matter delivered by river water and ocean tides. In Chapter 10, we focus on biological production in estuaries; in this chapter, we consider the origins of estuaries and their circulation patterns.

Most estuaries developed during the post-glacial (Holocene) sea level rise that inundated the land drowning the mouths of rivers. Other estuaries developed through glacial erosion of mountain valleys, tectonic processes, or from the action of longshore sediment transport. In high latitude mountainous regions during the Pleistocene Ice Age, tongues of glacial ice occupied former river valleys and eroded those valleys below present sea level. With subsequent deglaciation and concurrent rise in sea level, ocean water flooded the valleys. Such a steep-walled enclosure of water is known as a **fjord** (Figure 8.15). Along some tectonically active coasts, the sea surged over down-faulted blocks of crust. And in other coastal locations, sand spits grew via littoral drift and partially isolated a body of water from the ocean.

Although some mixing of fresh river water and seawater occurs in all estuaries, the characteristic circulation of an estuary depends on the amount of river inflow versus the strength of tidal currents. Based on circulation type, ocean scientists distinguish among salt-wedge estuaries, partially mixed estuaries, and well-mixed estuaries. At one extreme (salt-wedge estuaries), inflow of river water is the dominant factor and mixing is minimal and at the other extreme (well-mixed estuaries), tides are the dominant factor and mixing is extensive.

FIGURE 8.15
A fjord along the mountainous coast of Norway. [Photo by J.M. Moran]

FIGURE 8.16
Circulation in a salt-wedge estuary. The charts at the bottom show the variation in salinity (S) with depth at three water-sampling stations.

In estuaries where river inflow is relatively strong and tidal currents are weak, the low-salinity river water is quite distinct from the high salinity ocean water. That is, the two layers of water remain stratified. Where they meet, the wedge of less dense fresh water overlies the wedge of denser seawater; the thin vertical transition zone between the two layers is a *halocline*. This is known as a **salt-wedge estuary** (Figure 8.16). Seaward flow of the fresh water is much stronger than the landward movement of the seawater. The only mixing that takes place is due to internal waves that develop and propagate along the halocline (Chapter 7). Breaking of these internal waves mixes relatively small amounts of saltwater (from below) with the fresh water (above) so that strong stratification persists. During peak flow, a salt-wedge estuary forms near the mouth of the Columbia River but when river discharge is low, the salt-water wedge migrates upriver. Other examples of salt-wedge estuaries occur at the mouth of the Mississippi and Hudson Rivers. The Amazon River in Brazil is an extreme case of mixing in that the river's discharge is so great that seawater does not penetrate into the river's mouth and mixing of seawater and river water is confined to the continental shelf.

With declining river discharge and strengthening tidal currents, vertical mixing within an estuary becomes more vigorous so that stratification and the halocline weaken. In these **partially mixed estuaries**, salinity typically varies by less than 10 psu from the bottom water

FIGURE 8.17
Circulation in a partially mixed estuary. The charts at the bottom show the variation in salinity (S) with depth at three water-sampling stations.

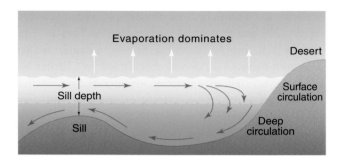

FIGURE 8.18
Anti-estuarine circulation characterizes the Mediterranean and Red Seas.

to the surface water (Figure 8.17). That is, the flow of fresh water seaward (above the halocline) and the flow of seawater landward (below the halocline) are both stronger than in a salt-wedge estuary. Chesapeake Bay is a classic example of a partially mixed estuary and is the largest estuary in the United States. It is almost 300 km (185 mi) long, 65 km (40 mi) at its broadest, and averages about 20 m (66 ft) deep. The estuary was formed during the post-glacial rise in sea level that flooded the ancient Susquehanna River Valley. The Bay receives about half its water from the Atlantic Ocean and the other half from the more than 150 rivers and streams draining a 166,000 square km (64,000 square mi) land area encompassing portions of New York, Pennsylvania, West Virginia, Delaware, Maryland, Virginia, and the District of Columbia. Other examples of partially mixed estuaries include San Francisco Bay and Puget Sound.

In a **well-mixed estuary**, strong tidal currents dominate the inflow from rivers and thoroughly mix the fresh water and saltwater. With no vertical stratification and no halocline, the only salinity gradient is a horizontal gradient from fresh water up estuary to seawater in the ocean. Delaware Bay is an example of a well-mixed estuary.

In broad estuaries, the Coriolis Effect influences the circulation and mixing. In the Northern Hemisphere, both seaward and landward flowing currents are deflected to the right of their initial direction. That is, the two currents are deflected toward opposite banks of a broad

estuary, such as Chesapeake Bay, resulting in fresh river water flowing to the sea on one side and saltwater flowing up river on the other side. This results in a tilted halocline and lateral mixing in contrast to the vertical mixing in estuaries that are too narrow to be significantly influenced by the Coriolis Effect.

Sediment distribution within an estuary depends on the relative strength of river discharge compared to tidal currents. River-borne sediments dominate salt-wedge estuaries whereas the sediment in well-mixed estuaries comes mostly from offshore sources. Partially mixed estuaries have a mixture of sediments from both sources. The two-layered circulation pattern in salt-wedge and partially mixed estuaries trap fine river-borne sediment. River-transported sediments eventually encounter the weaker current associated with the halocline. Coarser sediments settle to the bottom of the estuary while finer sediments (clays) remain suspended and concentrate near the halocline, forming a *turbidity maximum*.

In arid coastal regions that receive less fresh water input than is lost through evaporation, vertical circulation patterns are opposite those in most estuaries (Figure 8.18). In these systems, called *anti-estuarine circulations* or *reverse estuaries*, landward-flowing surface waters replace waters lost through evaporation. Intense evaporation produces highly saline waters that sink and flow seaward. Such circulation systems characterize the Mediterranean and Red Seas.

Coastal Storms and Storm Surge

People who live in the coastal zone are vulnerable to a variety of natural hazards and those hazards can be exacerbated by human activity. Among these coastal hazards are sea level rise, tsunamis, land subsidence, beach or shoreline erosion, salt-water intrusion into aquifers, and storm surge. In this section we describe the storm surge that can be produced by coastal storms. In Chapter 12, we consider the threat of coastal flooding caused by climate change and rising sea level.

Atmospheric scientists distinguish between two types of storm systems that pose a threat to the coast: tropical cyclones and extratropical cyclones. Both of these low-pressure weather systems are characterized by surface winds that blow in a counterclockwise and inward direction viewed from above in the Northern Hemisphere (Chapter 5). A **tropical cyclone** originates in a uniform mass of warm humid air over the tropical ocean but may track into higher latitudes; it includes hurricanes, tropical storms, and their precursors. An **extratropical cyclone** forms in middle latitudes and spends its entire life cycle in middle and high latitudes; its circulation brings together contrasting warm and cold air masses to form fronts and frontal weather (clouds and precipitation).

Potentially the most devastating impact of tropical and extratropical storms on the coastal zone is ocean water driven ashore by strong onshore winds (blowing from sea to land) associated with an intense storm system centered over or near the ocean. Strong winds (coupled with low air pressure) pile up a dome of seawater 80 to 160 km (50 to 100 mi) wide that sweeps across the coastline bringing floodwaters inland that can take lives and cause considerable property damage (Figure 8.19). A **storm surge** can erode beaches, wash over barrier islands, cut new tidal inlets, wash out roads and railway beds, and demolish marinas, piers, cottages, and other coastal structures.

Many factors influence the potential for a storm surge, including storm intensity, timing of astronomical tides, bathymetry, and shoreline configuration. In general, a storm surge of 1 to 2 m (3 to 6.5 ft) can be expected with a weak hurricane, whereas the storm surge accompanying a violent hurricane may top 5 m (16 ft). Lower air pressure contributes to the wind-driven mounding of water, with sea level rising about 0.5 m (1.6 ft) for every 50-millibar drop in air pressure. A storm surge is superimposed on astronomical tides so that the impact is greatest when the storm surge coincides with high tide and especially spring tide (Chapter 7). In addition, wind-driven waves having heights of 1.5 to 10 m (5 to 33 ft) top the storm surge, further exacerbating the impact on coastal areas (Figure 8.20). All other factors being equal, the more gradual the slope of the ocean bottom in coastal areas, the greater is the storm surge. Low-lying coastal plains are most vulnerable to a storm surge especially if no barrier islands are present to dissipate the energy of the surge.

A numerical model developed in 1979 by NOAA accurately predicts the location and height of a storm surge. Weather forecasters report considerable success with the **SLOSH (Sea, Lake, and Overland Surges from Hurricanes)** model. Analysis of SLOSH output and local topographic maps enables forecasters to identify areas most likely to be inundated by floodwaters when a hurricane threatens. Hypothetical hurricanes are simulated using various combinations of storm intensity, forward speed, and expected landfall location to predict the maximum high water level for various SLOSH basins along the coast. Public safety officials use this

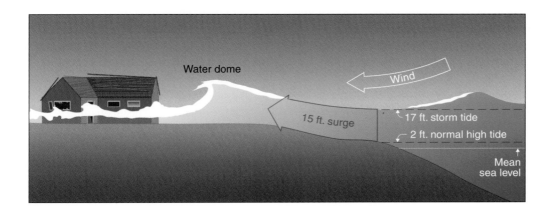

FIGURE 8.19
A storm surge is a dome of seawater 80 to 160 km (50 to 100 mi) that is driven onshore by strong winds associated with tropical or extratropical cyclones. The storm tide is the sum of the storm surge and the prevailing astronomical tide. [Adapted from NOAA]

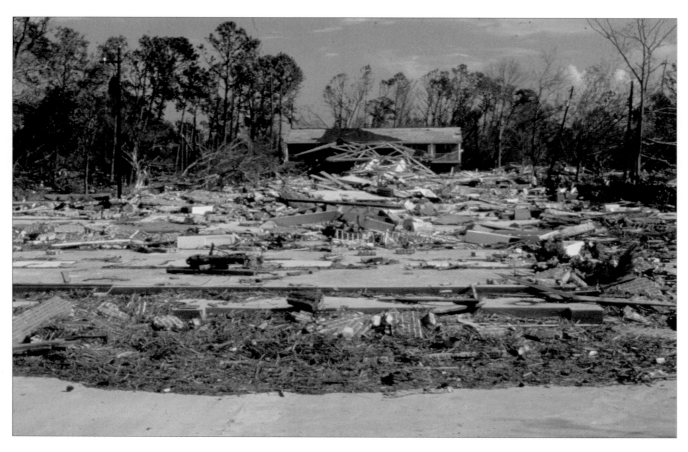

FIGURE 8.20
Damage produced at Gulfport, MS by the storm surge of category 5 Hurricane Camille in August 1969. [Photo Courtesy of NOAA]

information in developing evacuation plans. SLOSH model coverage includes the entire U.S. East and Gulf Coasts, as well as parts of Hawaii, Guam, Puerto Rico, and the Virgin Islands.

Understanding storm surges and why some coastal areas are more prone to storm surges than others requires a closer look at the basic characteristics of tropical and extratropical cyclones.

Tropical Cyclones

The most catastrophic storm surges are associated with hurricanes that make landfall, that is, hurricanes that track from sea to land. On 2 May 2008, Cyclone Nargis (Figure 8.21A), tracking northeast from the Bay of Bengal, slammed into the western coast of Myanmar (formerly known as Burma). Packing maximum sustained winds of 210 km per hr (130 mph), the cyclone (the name given hurricanes in this part of the world) produced a storm surge of 3.5 m (11.5 ft) that pushed across the low

lying Irriwaddy Delta, devastating a 30,000 square km area that is home to 25% of the nation's population of 57 million. After striking Yangon (Rangoon), Cyclone Nargis weakened and finally dissipated near the Myanmar/Thailand border. Several tens of thousands lost their lives and up to 2 million were left homeless. In addition, Irawaddy Delta agriculture, which normally grows almost two-thirds of the nation's rice crop, was destroyed by the cyclone, likely causing long-term food shortages in Myanmar and beyond.

In the most deadly natural disaster in U.S. history, more than 8000 people perished, mostly by drowning, when a hurricane storm surge devastated Galveston, TX on 8 September 1900. Ocean waters flooded the entire city located on a barrier island. Some 3600 homes were destroyed; a dam of wreckage that built up some six blocks inland from the beach probably spared the business district total destruction. To protect the city from future storm surges, the U.S. Army Corps of Engineers elevated the city an average of 3 m (10 ft) and erected a massive concrete seawall along the city's Gulf shore.

On the evening of 28 August 2005, the effects of the approaching Hurricane Katrina were beginning to be felt along the north central Gulf Coast as the storm's outer rain bands swept ashore. Within 24 hrs, Katrina's ferocious winds, storm surge, and heavy rains would devastate the Gulf Coast of Louisiana and Mississippi, obliterating coastal communities and devastating New Orleans. According to the National Weather Service, Katrina was the third most intense hurricane (minimum central air pressure of 920 mb) to make landfall on the United States since reliable records began in 1851. Katrina claimed at least 1300 lives and, in terms of economic loss, Katrina ranks as the most destructive hurricane to strike the United States.

Katrina began in the southeastern Bahamas on 23 August 2005 as the twelfth tropical depression of the season; the next day the system strengthened to a tropical storm and was assigned its name. Katrina intensified as it slowly moved northwestward and then westward through the Bahamas. On 25 August, Katrina made landfall in south Florida as a weak category 1 hurricane on the Saffir-Simpson Hurricane Intensity Scale (described later in this chapter), producing maximum sustained winds of 130 km per hr (80 mph) and heavy rain (more than 12.5 cm or 5 in. in southeast Florida). Tracking almost due west and fueled by the warm waters of the Gulf of Mexico, the

storm quickly intensified and gradually turned toward the northwest and then north. By the afternoon of 26 August, Katrina was a major hurricane. As a precaution, public officials issued mandatory evacuation orders for the people of New Orleans, LA, Gulfport, MS, and sections of Mobile, AL. Earlier, personnel on platforms and oil rigs in the Gulf were evacuated.

By the morning of 28 August, Katrina (Figure 8.21B) was a category 5 hurricane with maximum sustained surface winds of 282 km per hr (175 mph). The system weakened to category 4 prior to making landfall on the morning of 29 August in southern Plaquemines Parish just south of the town of Buras, LA at the mouth of the Mississippi River. Maximum sustained winds were 226 km per hr (140 mph) to the east of the storm center with hurricane force winds extending 195 km (120 mi) from its center, driving a 6 to 9 m (20 to 30 ft) storm surge that reached well inland (to the 30-ft contour line) along the Louisiana and Mississippi Gulf coast and as far east as Mobile, AL, flooding parts of the city. Several hours later, after passing over Breton Sound and Lake Borgne, the storm made another landfall at the mouth of the Pearl River on the Louisiana-Mississippi border. By then, Katrina had weakened to a category 3 hurricane. At 11 p.m., EDT, the north/northeast moving system was centered near Columbus, MS, downgraded to a tropical storm. Along

FIGURE 8.21
(A) NOAA satellite image of Tropical Cyclone Nargis, a category 4 storm which devastated the low-lying coastal plains of Myanmar (Burma) including the capital city Yangon (Rangoon) on 2 May 2008. Extensive flooding from the associated storm surge and heavy rains, and winds killed tens of thousands, made millions homeless, and destroyed an extensive rice growing region. (B) NOAA geostationary satellite image of Hurricane Katrina taken on Aug. 28, 2005, at 11:45 a.m. EDT, as the powerful storm churned in the Gulf of Mexico as a category 5 storm with sustained winds near 175 mph, a day before the storm made landfall on the U.S. Gulf Coast. [Photos courtesy of NOAA].

much of Katrina's path, total rainfall exceeded 20 to 25 cm (8 to 10 in.).

Topography made New Orleans particularly vulnerable to Hurricane Katrina. The city occupies a bowl between the Mississippi River and Lake Pontchartrain. Much of the bowl, home to more than 1 million residents and businesses, is up to 1.8 m (6 ft) below sea level. The people of New Orleans depend on earthen levees and concrete floodwalls to keep the water out and pumps to remove flood waters. However, the combination of strong winds, storm surge, and heavy rainfall caused numerous breaches in the levee system, the pumps failed, and up to 80% of New Orleans was flooded to depths that in many places reached 6 m (20 ft).

Although warned in advance of the approaching potentially catastrophic storm, thousands of people either were unable or chose not to evacuate New Orleans. As weather conditions deteriorated and floodwaters began to rise, many people fled to the Louisiana Superdome, the city's shelter of last resort. On 29 August, winds gusting to more than 160 km per hr (100 mph) ripped off part of the roof of the Superdome and knocked out electricity. An estimated 30,000 people spent many days in overcrowded, deplorable conditions without adequate food, water, sanitary facilities, or air conditioning. Other residents of New Orleans fled the rapidly rising waters, climbing to the upper floors, attics or roofs of their homes where they awaited rescue by boat or helicopter. The damage to New Orleans was so extensive that recovery is taking years.

HURRICANE CHARACTERISTICS

Hurricane is likely derived from *Haracan*, the name of the storm god of the Taino people who inhabited Caribbean islands at the time of Spanish exploration of the New World. A **hurricane** is an intense cyclone that originates over tropical ocean waters, usually in late summer or early fall (when sea-surface temperatures are highest), and has a maximum sustained wind speed of at least 119 km per hr (74 mph). By convention in the United States, *sustained wind speed* is a one-minute average measured at the standard anemometer height of 10 m (33 ft).

Hurricanes develop in a uniform mass of very warm and humid air. Typically, the central pressure at sea level is considerably lower and the horizontal air pressure gradient is much greater in a hurricane than an extratropical cyclone. A hurricane is usually a much smaller system, averaging a third the diameter of a typical extratropical cyclone. Rarely do hurricane-force winds extend much more than 120 km (75 mi) beyond the system's center. The circulation in a hurricane weakens rapidly with altitude and usually becomes anticyclonic (clockwise in the Northern Hemisphere) in the upper troposphere at altitudes above about 12,000 m (40,000 ft).

At the center of a hurricane is an area of almost cloudless skies, subsiding air, and light winds (less than 25 km per hr or 16 mph), called the **eye** of the storm. The eye generally ranges from 10 to 65 km (6 to 40 mi) across, shrinking in diameter as the hurricane intensifies and winds strengthen. At a hurricane's typical rate of forward motion, the eye may take up to an hour to pass over a given locality. People are sometimes lulled into thinking the storm has ended when skies clear and winds abruptly slacken following a hurricane's initial blow. They may be experiencing passage of the hurricane's eye; heavy rains and ferocious winds soon will resume but blow from the opposite direction.

Bordering the eye of a hurricane is the **eyewall**, a ring of thunderstorm (cumulonimbus) clouds that produce heavy rains and very strong winds. The most dangerous and potentially most destructive part of a hurricane is the portion of the eyewall on the side of the advancing system where the wind blows in the same direction as the storm's forward motion. On that side, hurricane winds combine with the storm's forward motion producing the system's strongest surface winds. In the Northern Hemisphere, this dangerous semicircle of high winds and high ocean waves is on the right side of the hurricane when facing in the direction of the system's forward movement. Cloud bands, producing heavy convective showers and hurricane-force winds, spiral inward toward the eyewall.

WHERE AND WHEN

Three conditions are required for a tropical cyclone to form: (1) high sea-surface temperatures, (2) adequate Coriolis Effect, and (3) weak winds aloft. To a large extent, these requirements dictate where and when tropical cyclones are most likely to develop.

Tropical cyclone formation requires a sea surface temperature (SST) of at least 26.5 °C (80 °F) through an ocean depth of about 45 m (150 ft) or more. Such exceptionally warm ocean waters sustain the system's circulation by the latent heat released when water vapor, evaporated from the ocean surface, is conveyed upward and condenses within the storm system. Temperature largely governs the rate of evaporation of water, so the higher the SST, the greater is the supply of latent heat for the storm system. Furthermore, the spray from breaking ocean waves readily evaporates, adding to the supply of water vapor that condenses and releases latent heat in the developing tropical cyclone.

As a tropical cyclone makes landfall or moves over colder water, however, it loses its warm-water energy source and weakens. The strong winds of a tropical cyclone stir up surface ocean waters. Cyclonic winds induce Ekman transport and divergence of surface waters under the storm system, bringing cold water to the surface. Until the normal thermal structure of the ocean is restored, lower than usual sea-surface temperatures can inhibit development of subsequent tropical cyclones over the same region of the ocean. Water welling up to the surface is also nutrient-rich spurring biological production (stimulating algal blooms) often in portions of the ocean (e.g., Sargasso Sea in the Atlantic east of Bermuda) that normally are low in productivity. In 2004, Steven M. Babin and his colleagues at Johns Hopkins University reported that their analysis of satellite imagery revealed an enhancement of chlorophyll concentration at the ocean surface in the wake of each of the 13 hurricanes that passed over the Sargasso Sea from 1998 to 2001.

In recent years, atmospheric scientists discovered that changes in SST associated with warm- and cold-core ocean rings influence tropical cyclone development. Recall from Chapter 6 that rings are eddies that break off western boundary currents such as the Gulf Stream. Tropical cyclones may intensify over warm-core rings and weaken over cold-core rings. For example, the Loop Current in the Gulf of Mexico is a source of warm-core rings that may intensify tropical cyclones passing overhead.

The second condition for tropical cyclone development is a significant Coriolis Effect; that is, the influence of Earth's rotation must be sufficiently strong to initiate a cyclonic circulation. As noted in Chapter 5, the Coriolis Effect weakens toward lower latitudes and is zero at the equator. With very rare exceptions, tropical cyclones do not form within 5 degrees of the equator (a distance of about 480 km or 300 mi).

The first two conditions that favor tropical cyclone formation (i.e., high SST and sufficient Coriolis Effect) occur only over certain portions of the ocean. The main ocean breeding grounds for tropical cyclones along with average storm trajectories are plotted in Figure 8.22. Most hurricanes form in the 8- to 20-degree latitude belts. Major breeding grounds are: (1) the tropical North Atlantic west of Africa (including the Caribbean Sea and Gulf of Mexico), (2) the North Pacific Ocean west of Mexico, (3) the western tropical North Pacific and China Sea, where a hurricane is called a *typhoon* (from the Cantonese *tai-fung*, meaning great wind), (4) the South Indian Ocean east of Madagascar, (5) the North Indian Ocean (including the Arabian Sea and Bay of Bengal), and (6) the South Pacific Ocean from the east coast of Australia eastward to about 140 degrees W. In the Indian Ocean and near Australia, hurricanes are called simply *cyclones*.

The requirement of high sea-surface temperatures makes the occurrence of tropical cyclones distinctly seasonal. For reasons presented in Chapter 3, the temperature of surface ocean waters lags the regular

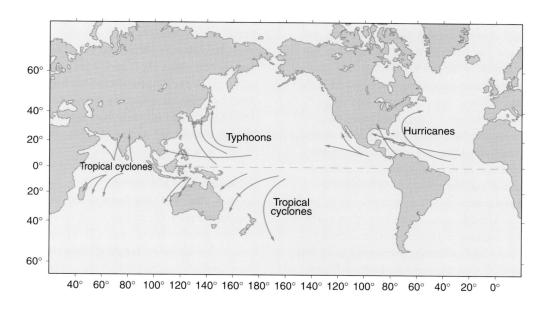

FIGURE 8.22
Tropical cyclone breeding grounds are located only over certain regions of the world ocean. Arrows indicate average hurricane trajectories.

seasonal variations in incoming solar radiation. Sea-surface temperatures reach a seasonal maximum roughly 6 to 8 weeks after the date of most intense solar radiation. Most Atlantic hurricanes develop when surface waters are warmest, that is, in late summer and early autumn; the official hurricane season runs from 1 June to 30 November, with the peak hurricane threat for the U.S. coastline between mid-August and late October.

The third condition for tropical cyclone development is relatively weak winds aloft (in the middle and upper troposphere) over oceanic breeding grounds. Weak winds aloft allow a cluster of cumulonimbus clouds to organize over tropical seas, the first step in the evolution of a hurricane. By contrast, strong west-to-east winds aloft shear off the tops of westward tracking thunderstorms, preventing the systems from building vertically and organizing. Vertical *wind shear* is the principal reason hurricanes rarely form off the east or west coasts of South America (although Caribbean hurricanes occasionally impact the north coast of Venezuela).

A worldwide average of about 88 tropical cyclones develops each year and approximately one-half attain hurricane strength. The western Pacific Ocean, with its vast expanse of warm surface waters, is the most active area for tropical cyclones, with roughly 24 systems each season (1945-2004), of which about 16 intensify into typhoons.

Only hurricanes spawned over the tropical Atlantic, Caribbean Sea, and Gulf of Mexico pose a serious threat to coastal North America. Based on the period 1931 to 2004, a seasonal average 10.2 named tropical storms (precursors to hurricanes) form over these waters. Of these systems, on average about 6 intensify into hurricanes and of these an average 2.4 become major hurricanes. On average, two hurricanes strike the U.S. coast each year. The 2005 Atlantic hurricane season set a new record with 27 named tropical cyclones; the previous record was 21 set in 1933. In 2005, 14 Atlantic tropical cyclones became hurricanes (a new record) and 4 major hurricanes struck the U.S. (also a record). However, the annual number of hurricanes may have little bearing on the number of landfalling hurricanes and their impact. Whereas only 4 hurricanes occurred during the 1992 hurricane season, one of them, Hurricane Andrew, was the second most costly in terms of property damage in U.S. history, amounting to $34.3 billion (in year 2000 dollars). Hurricanes have hit every Atlantic and Gulf Coast state from Texas to Maine. Florida is the most hurricane-prone of all the states, with 64 hurricanes crossing its coastline between 1900 and 2004. In the same period, Texas was second with 38 followed by North Carolina (29) and Louisiana (27).

The primary breeding ground for hurricanes in the Atlantic shifts east and west with the seasons. Early in the hurricane season (May and June), hurricanes form mostly over the Gulf of Mexico and the western Caribbean. By July, the main area of hurricane development begins to shift eastward across the tropical North Atlantic. By mid-September, most hurricanes form in a belt stretching from the Lesser Antilles (in the eastern Caribbean Sea) eastward to south of the Cape Verde Islands (off Africa's West Coast). After mid-September, hurricanes again originate mostly over the Gulf of Mexico and the western Caribbean.

The Pacific Ocean west of Mexico and Central America ranks second to the western North Pacific in the average annual number of tropical cyclones (averaging 15.2 between 1966 and 2004); the majority of these cyclones (8.4) develop into hurricanes. And yet, the Pacific Coast of North America is rarely a target of hurricanes. Prevailing winds (northeast trades) are directed offshore and usually steer tropical cyclones that form west of Central America away from the coast. Also, the southward flowing cold California Current plus upwelling just off the Southern California (and Baja California) coast produce sea-surface temperatures that normally are too low to sustain tropical cyclones that travel toward the northeast. However, during unusual atmospheric/oceanic circulation regimes, hurricanes have struck coastal Southern California and even tracked over the Desert Southwest.

The Hawaiian Islands are sometimes threatened by tropical cyclones that develop over the central tropical Pacific or track into that region from the Pacific hurricane breeding grounds west of Mexico. Fortunately, in an average year, only 3 to 4 tropical cyclones affect the central Pacific and since 1957 only 4 hurricanes have struck the islands. However, the most recent one, Iniki in September 1992, devastated the island of Kauai. Seven people lost their lives. Total property damage was estimated at $2.3 billion, making this the most costly natural disaster in the history of the State of Hawaii.

HURRICANE LIFE CYCLE

The first sign that a hurricane may be forming is the appearance of an organized cluster of thunderstorm clouds over tropical seas. This region of convective activity is labeled a **tropical disturbance** if a center of low pressure is detected at the surface. If atmospheric/oceanic conditions favor hurricane development and if those conditions persist, the surface air pressure falls and a cyclonic circulation develops. Water vapor condenses within the storm, releasing latent heat of vaporization, and the heated buoyant air rises. Expansional cooling of the ascending air triggers more condensation, release of even more latent heat, and a further increase in buoyancy. Rising temperatures in the core of the storm, coupled with an anticyclonic outflow of air aloft, cause a sharp drop in surface air pressure, which in turn, induces more rapid convergence of humid air at the surface. The consequent uplift surrounding the developing *eye* leads to additional condensation and release of latent heat.

Through this process, a tropical disturbance intensifies and its winds strengthen. When maximum sustained wind speeds reach 37 km per hr (23 mph) or higher, the developing system is called a **tropical depression**. When maximum sustained wind speeds reach at least 63 km per hr (39 mph), the system is classified as a **tropical storm** and assigned a name, such as Alberto or Beryl. Once maximum sustained winds reach 119 km per hr (74 mph) or higher, the storm is officially designated a hurricane. As a hurricane weakens and decays, the system is downgraded by reversing this classification scheme.

Hurricanes that form over the Atlantic Ocean near the Cape Verde Islands usually drift slowly westward with the trade winds (along the southern flank of the North Atlantic subtropical high) across the tropical North Atlantic and into the Caribbean. At this stage in the storm's trajectory, it is not unusual for the system to travel at a mere 10 to 20 km per hr (6 to 12 mph) and take a week to cross the Atlantic. Once over the western Atlantic, however, the storm usually picks up speed and begins curving northward along the western flank of the North Atlantic subtropical high, and northeastward as the system is caught in the middle latitude westerlies. Precisely where this curvature takes place determines whether the hurricane enters the Gulf of Mexico (perhaps then tracking up the lower Mississippi River Valley or over the Southeastern States), moves up the Eastern Seaboard, or curves northeastward into the Atlantic.

Upon reaching about 30 degrees N, an Atlantic hurricane may begin to acquire extratropical characteristics as colder air circulates into the system and fronts develop. From then on the storm resembles an extratropical cyclone and completes its life cycle usually over the North Atlantic. Many hurricanes, however, depart significantly from the track just described. Some of the hurricane tracks plotted in Figure 8.23, for example, are very erratic. A hurricane can describe a complete circle or reverse direction. In addition, some hurricanes, fueled by warm Gulf Stream waters, maintain tropical characteristics far north along the Atlantic Coast. Coastal New England and Atlantic Canada, for example, have been the targets of hurricanes.

FIGURE 8.23
Tropical cyclone trajectories are sometimes erratic as shown by these samples. As indicated by the darker blue shaded area, however, most Atlantic tropical cyclones initially drift westward and then curve toward the north and northeast when they reach the western Atlantic. [From NOAA, *Hurricane*, Washington, DC: Superintendent of Documents, 1977.]

HURRICANE HAZARDS

In addition to storm surge (discussed earlier in this chapter), hazards of hurricanes are extremely heavy rain and inland flooding, strong winds, and occasional tornadoes. Hurricanes and tropical storms can produce very heavy rainfall with amounts typically in the range of 13 to 25 cm (5 to 10 in.). Even when the system tracks well inland, heavy rains often persist and may trigger costly and life threatening flooding. According to research conducted by scientists at NOAA's Tropical Prediction Center/National Hurricane Center in Miami, FL, freshwater flooding was responsible for almost 60% of the 600 U.S. deaths attributed to tropical cyclones or their remnants during the period from 1970 to 1999. In those three decades, far more people (351) died from inland flooding than from coastal storm surge flooding (only 6 fatalities). On the other hand, the majority of the more than 1300 fatalities associated with Hurricane Katrina in August 2005, were caused by the storm surge. The storm surge remains as the most serious potential impact of a landfalling hurricane and is the primary reason people are evacuated from low-lying coastal areas and barrier islands.

From 1970 to 1999, about 12% of tropical cyclone fatalities were wind related. Winds pushing on the outside walls of buildings exert a pressure that increases dramatically as winds strengthen. Furthermore, debris carried by the wind and hurled against structures exacerbates the damage potential of strong winds. Hurricane winds diminish rapidly once the system makes landfall, so that most wind damage is confined to within about 200 km (125 mi) of the coastline. Two factors account for the abrupt drop in wind speed once a hurricane makes landfall. A hurricane over land is no longer in contact with its energy source, warm ocean water. In addition, the frictional resistance offered by the rougher land surface slows the wind and shifts the wind direction toward the low-pressure center of the system. This wind shift causes the storm to begin to fill; that is, its central pressure rises, the horizontal air pressure gradient weakens, and winds slacken.

Although winds weaken once a hurricane makes landfall, the system may produce tornadoes. (A *tornado* is a small column of air that whirls rapidly and violently about a nearly vertical axis and is made visible by clouds, dust and debris). Usually only a few tornadoes occur with a hurricane but in 1967, Hurricane Beulah reportedly spawned as many as 115 tornadoes across southern Texas. Tornadoes are most probable after the hurricane enters the westerly steering current and curves towards the north and northeast; they form mostly to the northeast of the storm center, often outside the region of hurricane-force winds.

In the early 1970s, H.S. Saffir (1917-2007), a consulting engineer, and R.H. Simpson, former director of the National Hurricane Center, designed a rating system for hurricanes known as the **Saffir-Simpson Hurricane Intensity Scale** (Table 8.1). Hurricanes are rated from category 1 to 5 corresponding to increasing intensity. The scale, first included in hurricane advisories in 1975, provides an estimate of potential coastal flooding and property damage from a hurricane landfall. Wind speed is the primary determining factor for a hurricane's rating on the Saffir-Simpson scale as storm surge heights are highly dependent on bathymetry and other factors in the region of landfall. Each intensity category specifies (1) a range of central air pressure, (2) a range of maximum sustained wind speed, (3) storm surge potential, and (4) the potential for property damage.

Of the 176 hurricanes that struck the U.S. Atlantic or Gulf Coasts between 1901 and 2004, 65 (about 37%) were classified as major; that is, they rated 3 or higher on the Saffir-Simpson scale. Property damage potential rises rapidly with ranking on the Saffir-Simpson scale. In fact, destruction from a category 4 or 5 hurricane can be 100 to 300 times greater than that caused by a category 1 hurricane. The 25 major hurricanes that made landfall along the Gulf or Atlantic Coasts between 1949 and 1990 accounted for three-quarters of all property damage from all landfalling tropical storms and hurricanes during the same period.

Scientists at the National Hurricane Center watch for the development of tropical cyclones over the Atlantic, Caribbean, Gulf of Mexico, and the Eastern Pacific. The Center operates the SLOSH model for prediction of storm surges, prepares and distributes hurricane watches and warnings for the public, conducts research on hurricane forecasting techniques, and sponsors public awareness programs.

EVACUATION

From 1981 through 2000, only ten major hurricanes (category 3 or higher) struck the U.S. mainland. This was similar to the 1971 through 1990

TABLE 8.1
Saffir-Simpson Hurricane Intensity Scale

Category	Central pressure mb (in.)	Wind speed km/hr (mph)	Storm surge m (ft)	Damage potential
1	>980 (>28.94)	119-154 (74-95)	1-2 (4-5)	Minimal
2	965-979 (28.50-28.91)	155-178 (96-110)	2-3 (6-8)	Moderate
3	945-964 (27.91-28.47)	179-210 (111-130)	3-4 (9-12)	Extensive
4	920-944 (27.17-27.88)	211-250 (131-155)	4-6 (13-18)	Extreme
5	< 920 (< 27.17)	> 250 (> 155)	> 6 (> 18)	Catastrophic

period when only nine major hurricanes made landfall on the U.S. coast. From 10 August 1980 to 17 August 1983, no hurricanes struck the United States. The infrequency of major hurricanes during the 1970s and 1980s lulled many coastal residents of the Southeast U.S. into a false sense of security and encouraged development and population growth in areas that could be devastated by a major hurricane. More and more resort hotels, high-rise condominiums, and expensive homes were constructed perilously close to the shoreline and even among coastal sand dunes (Figure 8.24).

A

B

FIGURE 8.24
The relative infrequency of hurricanes in the 1970s and 1980s lulled some residents of the U.S. Gulf and East Coast into a false sense of security and inspired construction of resort hotels (A) and vacation homes (B) within meters of high-tide level. [Photo by J.M. Moran]

About 45 million permanent residents inhabit hurricane-prone portions of the nation's coastline, and the population continues to climb. Until the recent upturn in hurricane frequency, most Atlantic and Gulf Coast residents never experienced the full impact of a major hurricane. Some of them may have weathered with relative ease a weak hurricane or the fringes of a strong system. But such an experience may lull them into complacency so that they are less likely to prepare adequately should a major hurricane threaten. Compounding the problem of the growth of the resident population in the Southeast is the arrival of holiday, weekend, and seasonal visitors to seaside resorts. The human population in some of these locales swells ten- to one-hundred-fold during vacation periods. Many of these resorts are in low-lying coastal areas or on barrier island beaches that are subject to rapid inundation by a storm surge.

Evacuation of people from barrier islands, as well as other low-lying coastal areas, is the traditional strategy in the event of a major storm threat (Figure 8.25). Since the 1985 hurricane season, evacuation has proved its value in lives saved. But the potential downside of evacuation was illustrated in September 1999 when Floyd, an unusually massive hurricane, threatened much of the Eastern Seaboard. In the greatest evacuation in U.S. history, more than 2 million residents of the Atlantic coastal area from south Florida to South Carolina took to the roads and fled inland. In many areas the result was grid-lock—too many vehicles on too few highways. As it turned out, Floyd spared most of the evacuated area and made landfall near Cape Fear, NC on 16 September 1999 as a category 2 system. Torrential rainfall, totaling as much as 38 to 50 cm (15 to 20 in.) over portions of

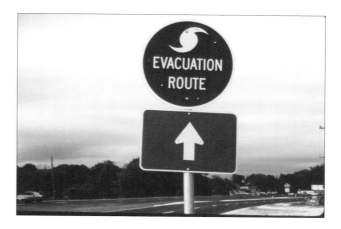

FIGURE 8.25
In hurricane-prone areas, special road signs mark evacuation routes. [Photo by J.M. Moran]

eastern North Carolina and Virginia caused extensive inland flooding, 56 deaths, and property damage of at least $6 billion.

Successful evacuation of coastal communities hinges on sufficient advance warning of a hurricane's approach but hurricanes are notorious for sudden changes in direction, forward speed, and intensity. (In retrospect, perhaps 75% of all coastal storm evacuations prove to be unnecessary.) A hurricane's erratic behavior is especially troublesome for people living in isolated localities (e.g., a barrier island linked to the mainland by a single bridge) and congested cities where highway systems have not kept pace with population growth. In such places the time required for evacuation may be lengthy. The Federal Emergency Management Agency (FEMA) estimates evacuation times during the peak tourist season as 50-60 hrs for New Orleans, LA and Fort Myers, FL, 40-49 hrs for Ocean City, MD, 30-39 hrs for the Florida Keys and Cape May County, NJ, and 20-29 hrs for Long Island, NY, Atlantic City, NJ, the Outer Banks of NC, and Galveston, TX.

As coastal communities continue to grow, more time is required for evacuation of their population. Evacuations must begin earlier when a storm is farther away and greater uncertainty surrounds its likely track. Such uncertainty necessitates a broader zone of evacuation that translates into greater economic losses associated with evacuation (e.g., closed businesses). Cognizant of the problem of lengthy evacuation times, some coastal communities are looking into alternative strategies such as establishing shelters in public and commercial buildings and growth control ordinances.

Extratropical Cyclones

Of all the extratropical cyclones to affect the U.S. coastal zone, the so-called nor'easter receives the most attention because of its severity and the number of people impacted. A **nor'easter** is an intense extratropical cyclone that tracks along the East Coast of North America and is named for the direction from which the most destructive winds blow. Unlike hurricanes, nor'easters may originate over land, forming along the boundary between air masses that contrast in temperature and humidity. Like hurricanes, they often intensify over warm ocean waters. Nor'easters are most frequent from October through April, when the seasonal contrasts in air mass characteristics (temperature and humidity) are greatest. The system moves toward the northeast and, if centered just offshore, strong onshore

winds on the northern and northwestern flanks of the system (blowing from the east and northeast) can cause a storm surge and high waves resulting in considerable coastal erosion, flooding, and property damage.

Although rarely attaining the strength of even a category 1 hurricane, a nor'easter can pack a powerful punch. In an intense nor'easter, winds can produce wave heights of 1.5 to 10 m (5 to 33 ft) superimposed on a storm surge of up to 5 m (16 ft). A nor'easter often impacts a much greater swath of coastline than a typical East Coast hurricane. As noted above, the diameter of an average extratropical cyclone is three times that of an average hurricane. Whereas a hurricane tends to track directly from sea to land, impacting perhaps only about 100 to 150 km (60 to 90 mi) of coastline, a nor'easter often moves parallel to the coast so that its onshore winds may sweep over more than 1500 km (900 mi) of coastline. A less intense but slower-moving nor'easter can actually cause more damage than a more intense but faster-moving nor'easter. Winds in the slow-moving system blow in the same onshore direction for a longer period than is the case with the fast-moving system. Persistent onshore winds increase the likelihood of a destructive storm surge and high waves.

Strengthened by latent heat acquired from evaporation of relatively warm ocean water, some nor'easters develop very rapidly. By convention, a rapidly intensifying extratropical cyclone is labeled a *bomb* if its central pressure drops at least 24 millibars in 24 hrs. Few cyclones actually meet this criterion, and most of those that do, develop over warm ocean currents such as the Gulf Stream or the Kuroshio Current. An extreme example of an East Coast bomb was observed during early January 1989. An incipient cyclone was first identified off of Cape Hatteras, NC at about 7:00 p.m. (EST) on 4 January; its central air pressure was 996 mb. Twenty-four hours later, the storm was centered about 700 km (435 mi) south of Newfoundland with a central pressure of 936 mb. The storm had intensified (pressure decreased) by 60 mb in 24 hrs, 2.5 times the criterion for a bomb.

One of the most noteworthy nor'easters of the 20th century in terms of its widespread impact on human activities occurred on 12-14 March 1993 (Figure 8.26). A major storm system tracked from the Gulf of Mexico up along the Eastern Seaboard. Although the system's size and central pressure were not particularly unusual, its human impact was enormous primarily because of its track along the East Coast. This track enabled the storm to draw into its circulation a tremendous amount of moisture evaporated from the warm ocean waters just off the coast,

FIGURE 8.26
One of the greatest winter storms in United States' history, a nor'easter blizzard, struck the eastern third of the nation between March 12 and 14, 1993. Colorized infrared mage taken March 13, 1993. [NOAA]

FIGURE 8.27
A downed tree and snow-covered car attest to the magnitude of snowfall in the Asheville, North Carolina area during the nor'easter of March 1993. Some snowfall totals were: Mt. Mitchell, NC, 50 in.; Grantsville, MD, 47 in.; Syracuse, NY, 43 in. [NOAA]

while the cold air inland helped the storm produce heavy snow over the highly populated areas to the north and west of its track from Alabama to Maine (Figure 8.27). In addition to property damage caused by heavy snow and high winds, a *squall line* (an elongated group of strong to severe thunderstorms) associated with the storm produced 27 tornadoes in Florida, and a 3-m (10-ft) storm surge in the Gulf of Mexico flooded the Apalachicola area. All told, this nor'easter claimed about 208 lives, more than three times the combined death toll of Hurricanes Hugo and Andrew, and caused damage estimated at $6 billion, the costliest extratropical cyclone in U.S. history.

Many people visiting Ocean City on Fenwick Island, MD are probably unaware of the impact of the great nor'easter of 5-8 March 1962. This slow moving and intense storm system produced waves as high as 9 m (30 ft) superimposed on a 2-m (7-ft) storm surge. Coastal erosion and flooding were extensive. During five successive high-tide cycles over two days, storm waves washed over almost all of Fenwick Island. Property damage at Ocean City was estimated at $7.5 million. In view of the considerable development that has occurred on the island since 1962, can you imagine the impact of a similar storm today?

R. Dolan and R.E. Davis of the University of Virginia proposed an intensity scale for nor'easters that is analogous to the Saffir-Simpson Scale for hurricanes. Their scale was derived from research conducted along the Outer Banks of North Carolina. Dolan and Davis recognized that sea waves generated by a nor'easter largely govern the storm's coastal impact and based their classification scheme on a wave power index. The *Dolan-Davis wave power index* is computed by multiplying a

storm's duration by the square of the maximum significant wave height. (All other factors being equal, waves are higher where the continental shelf is relatively narrow.) Storms are classified into 5 categories, ranging from Class I (very common weak systems) to Class V (very rare extreme systems). A Class I storm might last for 4 hrs with an average peak wave height of 2 m (6.6 ft) and produce minor beach erosion and little or no property damage. At the other extreme, a Class V storm might last for 4 days or longer with an average peak wave height of 7 m (23 ft) and produce extreme beach erosion, destroy dunes, and cause region-wide property damage.

Conclusions

Essentially all components of the Earth system come together and interact in the coastal zone: ocean, atmosphere, cryosphere, geosphere, and biosphere (including humans). The land/sea interface is a particularly dynamic portion of the Earth system where numerous forces shape the coast. Beaches, barrier islands, cliffed headlands, and estuaries are among the many features of the coastline. People are increasing their presence in the coastal zone and their activities sometimes conflict with the forces of nature including rising sea level, storm surges, and littoral drift.

Having examined the physical properties of the ocean, we next focus on life in the ocean. The next chapter covers marine ecosystems and the processes that support life in the ocean. Chapter 10 considers marine organisms and how they have adapted to the varying physical conditions of their environment.

Basic Understandings

- The coast encompasses the relatively narrow region that is transitional between land and the ocean. Although the coast may appear stable and unchanging, the many components of the Earth system (ocean, atmosphere, biosphere, geosphere, and cryosphere) interact in the coastal zone making it an exceptionally active environment.

- The farthest inland extent of storm waves defines the coastline, in some cases marked by sand dunes or wave-cut cliffs. Another definition is the mean high water level. Land exposed at low tide up to the coastline is the shore and the average low tide line is the shoreline. The intertidal zone, the area of the shore between high and low tides, is alternately under water and exposed to the atmosphere as the tide rises and falls.

- Mountain building and volcanic activity are dominant geological processes in tectonically active coastlines such as those that rim the Pacific Ocean basin. Sediment erosion, transport, and deposition are dominant geological processes along passive shorelines such as those that surround the Atlantic Ocean and the Gulf of Mexico.

- As sea waves move into coastal waters of varying depth, they undergo refraction, that is, bending of a wave in response to changing wave speed caused by changing water depth. Wave crests bend toward shallower water. In this way, waves approaching an irregular coastline are refracted (converge) toward headlands (rocky cliffs that project seaward) and away from coves or bays. Convergence concentrates wave energy causing erosion of headlands whereas spreading out (divergence) of wave energy in bays reduces wave action favoring deposition of sediment and expansion of a beach.

- A beach is an accumulation of wave-washed sediment (usually sand and gravel) at the landward margin of the ocean (or lake); it is a system in which erosive and depositional forces continually do battle.

- When breaking waves approach the shore at an oblique angle, a zigzag motion of the swash moves particles along the beach face; this is known as beach drift. Waves approaching the shore at an oblique angle also produce a component of water motion that is directed parallel to the shore known as a longshore current. A longshore current transports sediments as littoral drift along the coast, either nourishing or cutting back beaches.

- A barrier island is an elongated, narrow accumulation of sand oriented parallel to the coast and separated from the mainland by a lagoon, estuary, or bay. They occur where the supply of sand is abundant, waves are energetic, and the sea floor is gently sloping. Barrier island beaches border the Atlantic Coast from south Florida to Long Island, NY. Mainland beaches occur from there northward through coastal New England and Atlantic Canada. Beginning at the ocean side of a typical undeveloped barrier island and working our way toward the mainland, we would encounter a beach, dunes, flats, marsh, and lagoon.

- Along the coast, the narrow seaward flow of water must balance the broad shoreward flow of water so that the offshore flow occurs as a relatively swift surface or near-surface current. This is known as a rip current.

- A salt marsh is a nearly flat, low-lying, protected coastal area where fine-grained sediment accumulates and salt-tolerant plants grow. Tidal creeks meander through most salt marshes allowing seawater to flood the marshes on a rising tide and to drain on the ebb tide.

- Artificial structures (including dams, breakwaters, jetties, groins, and sea walls) disrupt littoral drift and alter the natural flow of sediments to and along a beach. An alternate strategy to maintain existing beaches or restore badly eroded beaches is artificial beach nourishment. With this approach, sand is usually dredged from deep waters and then spread on the beach. Artificial beach nourishment is an expensive and temporary solution; however, it does provide substantial protection for coastal property and businesses.

- An estuary is a partially isolated body of water where fresh water (from rivers and streams) mixes with seawater. Most estuaries developed during the post-glacial (Holocene) rise in sea level. Other estuaries developed through glacial erosion of mountain valleys, tectonic processes, or longshore sediment transport. Based on differences in circulation regime, a distinction is made among salt-wedge estuaries, partially mixed estuaries, and well-mixed estuaries.

- A tropical cyclone originates in a uniform mass of warm humid air over the tropical ocean but may track into higher latitudes; it includes tropical storms and hurricanes. An extratropical cyclone forms in middle latitudes and spends its entire life cycle in middle and high latitudes; its circulation brings together contrasting warm and cold air masses to form fronts and frontal weather.

- Potentially the most devastating impact of tropical and extratropical storms in the coastal zone is a storm surge, a dome of ocean water driven ashore by strong onshore winds associated with an intense storm system centered over or near the ocean. Factors that influence the potential for a storm surge include storm intensity, timing of tides, bathymetry, and shoreline configuration.

- A hurricane is an intense tropical cyclone that originates over tropical ocean-waters, usually in late summer or early fall with a maximum sustained wind speed of at least 119 km per hr (74 mph). In addition to storm surge, hazards of hurricanes are flooding rains, strong winds, and tornadoes.

- The three conditions required for a tropical cyclone to form are (1) relatively high sea-surface temperatures, (2) adequate Coriolis Effect, and (3) weak winds aloft. To a large extent, these requirements dictate where and when tropical cyclones develop. The energy source for tropical cyclones is latent heat released when water vapor evaporated from the ocean condenses in the system. As a tropical cyclone intensifies, the successive stages in its life cycle are designated tropical disturbance, tropical depression, tropical storm, and finally hurricane.

- The Saffir-Simpson Hurricane Intensity Scale rates hurricanes from category 1 to 5 corresponding to increasing intensity and provides an estimate of potential coastal flooding and property damage from a hurricane landfall.

- A nor'easter is an intense extratropical cyclone that tracks along the East Coast of North America and is named for the direction from which its most destructive winds blow. Unlike hurricanes, nor'easters may originate over land, forming along the boundary between air masses that contrast in temperature and humidity. They are most frequent from October through April.

Review

1. Explain why the coastal zone is a particularly dynamic part of the Earth system.
2. What are the dominant geological processes operating in tectonically active coastlines and passive coastlines? Of North America's Atlantic and Pacific coasts, which one is more tectonically active?
3. Why does a wave crest bend (refract) as it approaches the shoreline at an angle other than 90 degrees?
4. How and why does the width of an East Coast beach change from winter to summer?
5. Briefly describe the origins of a longshore current.
6. Describe rip currents and why they are potentially hazardous for swimmers.
7. Are barrier islands found on tectonically active or passive continental margins? Justify your choice.
8. Distinguish among the types of estuaries in terms of fresh water and seawater flow and vertical stratification.
9. Identify the hazards to the coastal zone posed by landfalling hurricanes.
10. What is the "fuel" that powers both tropical cyclones and extratropical cyclones?

Critical Thinking

1. Explain how wave refraction affects erosion and sediment deposition along an irregular coastline.
2. Why does an irregular coastline tend to straighten with time?
3. What is the origin of the sediment that forms a beach and how do human activities disrupt the supply of that sediment?
4. Identify some of the costs and benefits of coastal armor.
5. List some of the advantages and disadvantages of artificial beach nourishment.
6. Explain how an undeveloped barrier island is a continually changing system.
7. What role is played by the ocean in the development of tropical cyclones?
8. Why do hurricanes rarely strike Southern California?
9. Under what conditions might an extratropical cyclone cause more coastal erosion than a hurricane?
10. Speculate on some of the ways whereby a rising sea level might impact the coastal zone.

ESSAY: The Great Lakes and the Ocean

The Great Lakes of North America are components of the Great Lakes of the World (GLOW). GLOW also includes Great Bear Lake and Great Slave Lake of Canada, Lake Baikal of Russia, Lakes Victoria and Malawi of Africa, Lake Titicaca in South America and others. GLOW and particularly the Great Lakes are often referred to as "models of the ocean." How accurate is this statement?

Combined, the Great Lakes constitute one of the largest reservoirs of surface fresh water on the planet, accounting for about 18% of the total. (Only the polar ice sheets and Lake Baikal contain more fresh water.) The Great Lakes are a chain of lakes (Figure 1). Lake Superior, the largest and deepest of the five lakes (Figure 2), drains into Lake Huron via the St. Marys River. Lake Michigan waters also empty into Lake Huron through the Straits of Mackinac. From Lake Huron, water flows via the St. Clair and Detroit Rivers into Lake Erie, the smallest and shallowest of the five lakes. Water then flows from Lake Erie through the Niagara River and Welland Canal into Lake Ontario and empties into the St. Lawrence River, the Gulf of St. Lawrence, and ultimately the North Atlantic Ocean. Water draining into Lake Superior along its western shore travels some 3600 km (2230 mi) to the Gulf of St. Lawrence. *Residence time* of water in the Great Lakes ranges from 2.6 years in Lake Erie to 191 years in Lake Superior.

The Great Lakes are a legacy of the Pleistocene Ice Age that began about 1.7 million years ago and ended about 10,500 years ago. Prior to the Pleistocene, rivers likely flowed through valleys where lake basins are now located. Huge

FIGURE 1
The Great Lakes of North America with the drainage basin shaded in green. Weather and climate over the lakes and the drainage basin control lake levels.

FIGURE 2
Shoreline of Lake Superior near Munising, MI, the largest of the Great Lakes. [Photo by J.M. Moran]

lobes of glacial ice advancing southward from what is now Canada widened and deepened the river valleys, and the weight of the ice further depressed the evolving lake basins. Ocean basins, on the other hand, are much older (hundreds of millions of years) and are the products of tectonic processes (Chapter 2).

The Great Lakes are small compared to ocean basins; their dimensions are similar to those of the continental shelf, that is, 10s to 100s of kilometers (10s to 100s of miles) in the horizontal, and 10s to 100s of meters (10s to 100s of yards) in the vertical. Like the ocean, the Great Lakes are sufficiently large that the Coriolis Effect plays a role in the circulation of their waters (Chapter 5). The Coriolis Effect along with winds and stratification generate circulation phenomena that are the same as those observed in the ocean (e.g., wind-driven Ekman transport, coastal upwelling and downwelling, and geostrophic flow).

Unlike small lakes but like the ocean, the Great Lakes are sufficiently large and deep that much of their water mass is unaffected by frictional interaction with the coast and bottom. If wind sets the surface water in motion at the nearly frictionless center of the lake basin, inertia keeps the water in motion. (Recall from Chapter 4 that according to *Newton's first law of motion*, an object in constant straight-line motion or at rest remains that way unless acted upon by an unbalanced force. *Inertia* is the name given to this tendency for an object to continue moving or to remain at rest.) With no other forces operating, the flow is governed by the Coriolis Effect. In the Great Lakes, Coriolis deflection is to the right, so that a surface current describes a loop, called an *inertial circle*, having a period of about about 17 hrs at 45 degrees North—near the middle of Lake Michigan. (Actually, the current follows a straight path while the basin rotates with the spinning Earth). For a current speed of 10 cm per sec (0.2 mph) at 45 degrees N, the radius of an inertial circle is 1 km (0.6 mi), whereas for a current speed of 100 cm per sec (about 2 mph), the radius is 10 km (6 mi).

Ekman transport operates in the Great Lakes. If the wind blows parallel to the coast, depending upon the direction of the wind, Ekman transport causes either coastal upwelling or coastal downwelling (Chapter 6). In response to upwelling or downwelling, the thermocline tilts near the coast creating a horizontal gradient in density (or pressure). The balance that develops between this horizontal density gradient and the Coriolis Effect produces *geostrophic flow* (Chapter 6). In the Great Lakes, geostrophic flow is observed as a coastal current or *jet*.

When winds slacken, the release of the tilted thermocline (caused by upwelling or downwelling) generates two types of free internal waves involving the Coriolis Effect: inertial waves or oscillations and Kelvin waves. Inertial oscillations occur in the thermocline across the entire lake but with maximum currents at the center of the lake. A *Kelvin wave* is an *edge wave*, meaning that maximum wave height is at the coast but diminishes to lake level within 5 to 10 km (3 to 6 mi) offshore. Kelvin waves depend upon the Coriolis Effect and progress cyclonically around the lake with the "edge" to the right of the direction of motion. Crests and troughs of a Kelvin wave are not readily observed except by temperature readings at municipal water intakes. A Kelvin wave crest brings deeper cooler water to the intake whereas a Kelvin wave trough delivers shallower warmer water. The period of a Kelvin wave is typically much longer than the period of an inertial oscillation. Large scale eddies are also observed in the Great Lakes coastal waters that resemble those on the shelf and in the open ocean.

Both inertial oscillations and Kelvin waves also occur in the ocean. Kelvin waves develop in the equatorial Pacific when the trade winds weaken during El Niño and the water piled up in the western tropical Pacific sloshes back toward South America (Chapter 11). The sloshing consists of Kelvin waves with maximum height on the equator where the Coriolis Effect changes sign. When these Kelvin waves strike the South American coast, they split into two waves, one progressing northward and the other southward along the coast. The northward moving Kelvin wave eventually reaches the U.S. West Coast.

An obvious difference between the Great Lakes and the ocean is salinity: Great Lakes waters are fresh whereas seawater is saline. In the Great Lakes, water density depends on temperature and maximum density is at 4 °C (39.2 °F). On the other hand, seawater density depends on both temperature and salinity and its temperature of maximum density is below its initial freezing point (Chapter 3). An important implication of this contrast in physical properties is the occurrence of seasonal turnover in lakes but not the ocean. Spring and fall turnover of lakes in temperate latitudes is important for organisms living in lakes because turnover replenishes the dissolved oxygen supply of those water bodies. Lake turnover also recycles nutrients, especially nitrogen and phosphorus compounds, from bottom sediments to the overlying water, where they become available to aquatic plants, especially algae.

Bright summer sunshine penetrates a lake to shallow depths, warming the surface layer of water. Meanwhile, the dark deep water does not benefit from solar heating and remains cold, with an average temperature as low as 4 °C. This stable stratification (layering) of warm, less dense surface water and colder, denser water at depth persists through most of the summer, with little mixing between the layers. The upper layer of the stratified lake is known as the *epilimnion* and the lower layer is known as the *hypolimnion*, with the transition zone between the two layers being the *thermocline*.

In a stratified lake, oxygen that is supplied by the atmosphere and photosynthetic organisms replenishes the dissolved oxygen supply of only the epilimnion. In the hypolimnion, cellular respiration by decomposers and other organisms removes dissolved oxygen. With very little transfer of oxygen from the epilimnion, dissolved oxygen levels in the hypolimnion steadily decline. If lake stratification were to persist, the dissolved oxygen concentration would fall to levels that would severely stress cold-water fish species (e.g., trout, whitefish) living in the hypolimnion. Fortunately, these fish and other inhabitants of the hypolimnion usually do not perish because lake stratification eventually breaks down, lake waters turn over, and the dissolved oxygen content of the hypolimnion is replenished.

As summer gives way to autumn, the sun becomes lower in the sky, daylight shortens, and air temperatures drop. Heat is lost from the warm surface waters to the overlying cool air and ultimately to space. Eventually the temperature of the epilimnion cools to that of the hypolimnion, the thermocline disappears, and the lake has a uniform temperature and density from top to bottom. Winds blowing across the lake transport surface water from the upwind shore toward the downwind shore. Oxygen-depleted water wells up from below on the upwind shore and oxygen-rich surface water sinks at the downwind shore. This *fall turnover* of lake-waters brings oxygen-depleted water from the lake bottom to the surface where it is exposed to the atmosphere and replenished in dissolved oxygen.

Cooling during late autumn and early winter eventually drops the temperature of surface waters to 4 °C and lower. The lake begins to stratify with the coldest and least dense water at the surface. With continued cooling, the lake surface temperature eventually drops to 0 °C and a skim of ice forms. While large areas of the Great Lakes (especially sheltered inlets such as Green Bay) may develop an ice cover, stirring of waters by strong winds brings slightly warmer water to the surface and keeps much of the lake surface ice-free through the winter. For the Great Lakes, the entire water column must overturn to reach maximum density (at 4 °C) before the lake can cool below 4 °C, stratify, and freeze. For Lake Superior, the deepest of the Great Lakes, this is a maximum depth of 400 m (1300 ft). Lake-water temperatures typically vary from 0 °C just under the ice to 4 °C at the lake bottom. Ice forms a barrier that prevents exchange of oxygen between the lake-water and atmosphere, and cellular respiration within the lake causes a gradual decrease in dissolved oxygen levels. When ice finally melts in spring, the lake waters may be seriously depleted in dissolved oxygen.

With the arrival of spring and lengthening daylight, air temperatures rise, and lake surface waters warm. Eventually, the temperature of the surface water reaches 4 °C and once again the temperature and density of the lake become uniform from top to bottom. Just as in autumn, strong winds trigger turnover of lake waters and the mixing that accompanies *spring turnover* brings oxygen-depleted water to the surface where oxygen is replenished directly from the atmosphere and via photosynthesis. As spring gives way to summer, lake stratification is reestablished. What is intriguing and different from ocean water is that in spring the Great Lakes typically begin to stratify in shallower water near shore and stratification progresses toward the center of the Lakes at about 1 km (0.6 mi) per day.

Wind-driven waves are similar on the ocean and Great Lakes although the scales are different. Swells and larger-size waves are more common on the ocean because of more persistent winds and longer fetch (Chapter 7). Through the years, many powerful storms have swept over the Great Lakes, producing huge waves that sank thousands of vessels with a considerable loss of life. Even very large ships may be unable to withstand the fury of storm waves on the lakes. For example, on 10 November 1975, a fierce storm tracking over Lake Superior produced winds gusting to 145 km per hr (90 mph). Waves of 3.5 to 5 m (12 to 16 ft) sank the *Edmund Fitzgerald*, at the time the largest ore carrier on the Great Lakes at 222 m (729 ft) long, 23 m (75 ft) wide, and carrying 26,116 tons of taconite pellets. The *Edmund Fitzgerald* sank in 160 m (525 ft) of water at the eastern end of Lake Superior about 27 km (17 mi) from Whitefish Bay, MI with the loss of its crew of 29. Speculation is that huge waves lifted the bow and stern enough to cause the ship to break amidships and sink before the crew could react.

The ocean and the Great Lakes also share some similarities in long-term changes in water level but there are also fundamental differences. Astronomical tides are evident in the ocean, but are not very noticeable on the Great Lakes. On the other hand, seiches are common on the Great Lakes but are not prominent in the open ocean or on the continental shelves, although they are observed in harbors and embayments. For both tides and seiches the time scale is hours and the height scale is centimeters to meters.

Over the past 3000 to 3500 years, Great Lakes levels have fluctuated in a quasi-periodic manner about an established datum (based on mean lake levels during the modern record of 1918-1998). Departures from this so-called *International Great Lakes Datum (IGLD)* were never much more than a meter during the 3000 to 3500 year period. As of this writing, Great Lake levels are near historic lows (Figure 3). Great Lakes levels are governed by precipitation, runoff from spring snowmelt, and air temperature. Temperature affects the rate of evaporation of water and controls ice cover that also influences evaporation. Should the present global warming trend continue, lake levels are expected to fall whereas sea level is predicted to rise. We have more to say about these prospects and their implications in Chapter 12.

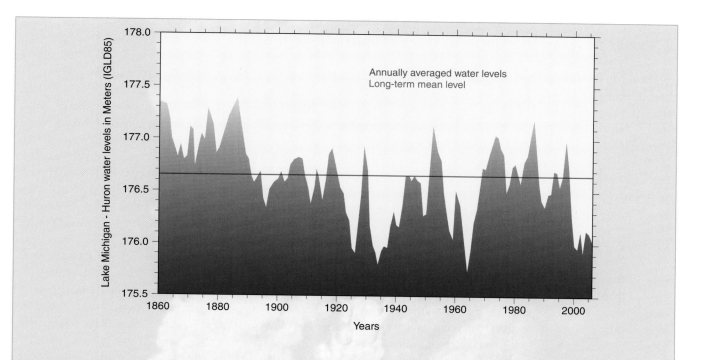

FIGURE 3
Record of water levels (in meters) of Lakes Michigan and Huron beginning in 1860. Horizontal red line is the long-term mean. These data are collected and archived by NOAA's National Ocean Service. [Courtesy of NOAA's Great Lakes Environmental Research Laboratory (GLERL)]

ESSAY: Moving the Cape Hatteras Lighthouse

When beach erosion threatens to damage or destroy coastal structures, three protective strategies are available: *armor* (e.g., groins, seawalls), *artificial beach nourishment*, and *strategic retreat* (relocation of structures inland). At various times, all three strategies were employed to keep the encroaching sea from claiming the historic Cape Hatteras Lighthouse (Figure 1).

In 1870, a 63-m (208-ft) brick lighthouse was built at Cape Hatteras on one of the barrier islands that form North Carolina's Outer Banks. At the time, the lighthouse with its distinctive white and black diagonal stripes was about 460 m (1500 ft) from the shoreline. But the beacon's location on a barrier island and the steady rise in sea level (presently about 2 mm or 0.08 in. per year) made it increasingly vulnerable to attack by powerful sea waves generated by the winds of tropical and extratropical cyclones that often track near Cape Hatteras. In less than 50 years, about 335 m (1100 ft) of the east-facing beach in front of the lighthouse had washed away. In the 1930s and early 1940s attempts to stabilize the beach with groins failed and after World War II, the lighthouse was taken out of service (replaced by a beacon mounted on a metal tower located well inland) and assigned to the National Park Service (NPS).

The Cape Hatteras Lighthouse soon became one of North Carolina's most popular tourist attractions and public support for preserving the lighthouse grew. Artificial beach nourishment was tried many times in the 1960s and 1970s but with short-lived success. The growing threat to the lighthouse was made clear in 1982 when an intense winter storm brought storm waves to the base of the lighthouse. During the height of the storm, quick acting NPS personnel tore up slabs of asphalt from a newly constructed parking lot and piled them around the base of the lighthouse to protect the foundation. Subsequently, sand bags were piled on top of the asphalt slabs.

Coastal engineers advised against a plan to build a seawall around the lighthouse. They pointed out that the structure's brick and stone foundation is less than 2 m (7 ft) deep and rests on yellow pine timbers that must remain submerged in fresh water to prevent decomposition. Surrounded by a seawall, the lighthouse eventually would become an island, saltwater would replace fresh water in the subsurface and rot the pine timbers, the foundation would collapse, and the lighthouse would fall into the sea.

By 1987, the Cape Hatteras Lighthouse was only 49 m (160 ft) from the sea. The only option to save the lighthouse was a strategic retreat inland, a plan endorsed by the National Park Service in 1989. In effect, retreat is a preservation/protection strategy that adapts to rather than confronts the forces of nature. After years of public debate, the lighthouse was physically moved on rollers and iron rails 884 m (2900 ft) to a new location (and a new foundation) some 488 m (1600 ft) from the edge of the Atlantic Ocean. The lighthouse began its journey on 17 June 1999 and arrived at its destination twenty-two days later. The Cape Hatteras Lighthouse again opened to the public on 26 May 2000.

Is this the end of the Cape Hatteras Lighthouse story? Not likely. Sea level will probably continue to rise, tropical and extratropical cyclones will generate storm surges, and barrier islands will migrate toward the mainland. In fact, on 18 September 2003, Hurricane Isabel made landfall on the Outer Banks as a category 2 system causing considerable coastal erosion and flooding. The storm surge cut a new inlet and came precariously close to the Cape Hatteras Lighthouse, damaging roads and parking lots.

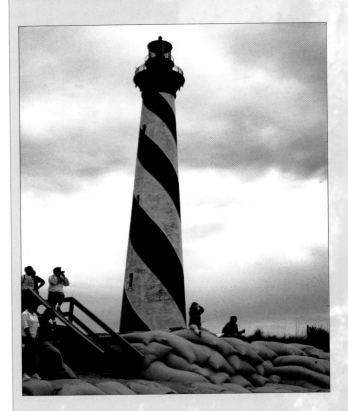

FIGURE 1
This photo of the Cape Hatteras Lighthouse was taken in April 1995. Notice the sandbags at the base of the tower. [Photo by J.M. Moran]

CHAPTER 9

MARINE ECOSYSTEMS

Case-in-Point
Driving Question
Requirements for Marine Life
Structure of Marine Ecosystems
    Producers
    Consumers
    Decomposers
    Trophic Structure of Ecosystems
    Bioaccumulation
Ecosystem Processes
    Energy for Growth and Reproduction
    Production in the Photic Zone
    Nutrients and Trace Elements as Limiting Factors
    Microbial Marine Ecosystems
Ocean's Role in the Global Carbon Cycle
    Physical Pump
    Biological Pump
Ecosystem Observations and Models
Conclusions
Basic Understandings/Review/Critical Thinking
ESSAY: Ocean Iron Fertilization and Climate Change
ESSAY: Methane Hydrates, Future Energy Source
ESSAY: Ocean Color and Marine Production

A school of smallmouth grunt near elkhorn coral. [NOAA]

Case in Point

In December 1987, many people in Montreal, Quebec became ill after consuming farmed mussels later traced to one area of the eastern Canadian province of Prince Edward Island. Their symptoms included abdominal cramps, vomiting, diarrhea, severe headaches, hallucinations, seizures, and memory loss. The disease was later described as *amnesic shellfish poisoning*. Three people died and 105 others experienced acute poisoning.

    Scientists worked around the clock for days at a Canadian government laboratory in Halifax, Nova Scotia to identify the toxin (poison) responsible for the illness and its source. A mussel is a filter-feeding mollusk that siphons large volumes of water, filtering out organisms such as diatoms and other tiny particles for food. Scientists discovered that the mussels had fed on a species of diatom belonging to the genus *Pseudo-nitzschia*. The particular species produces a neurotoxin known as domoic acid. While harmless to the mussels, domoic acid is a naturally occurring amino acid that causes a host of debilitating symptoms in humans who ingest contaminated shellfish. Domoic acid is particularly damaging to the brain's memory centers. Tests for this toxin enable fishery managers to halt immediately the harvesting and sale of mussels from contaminated areas wherever they occur,

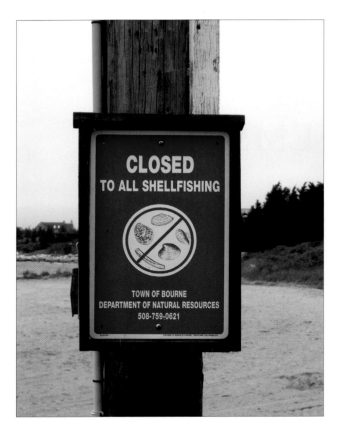

FIGURE 9.1
A harmful algal bloom (HAB) may pose a hazard to human health when a naturally occurring toxin enters the food chain necessitating the closure of commercial shellfish beds. [Courtesy of Woods Hole (MA) Oceanographic Institution]

thereby preventing additional illness and death (Figure 9.1). In fact, commercial supplies of mussels, clams, oysters and scallops from most areas are now rigorously tested for toxins.

Blooms of phytoplankton, microscopic algae, occur widely in surface ocean waters. Under normal conditions, the phytoplankton community consists of many species. Sometimes, however, a bloom of a single species occurs and can cause serious harm to the environment, the demise of marine organisms, economic losses, and human health problems, including illness and death. Amnesic shellfish poisoning is one of the many possible consequences of **harmful algal blooms (HABs)** or **red tides**. Fortunately, of the thousands of species of microscopic algae that inhabit the ocean, only a few dozen or so produce powerful toxins. Not all harmful algal blooms are red or toxic and they have nothing to do with astronomical tides. Furthermore, they are not all caused by algae; many toxic blooms are caused by dinoflagellates, microscopic one-celled organisms that behave like both plants and animals.

Another potentially more deadly illness that is linked to an algal toxin is *paralytic shellfish poisoning (PSP)*. In this case the culprit is a photosynthetic swimming alga, a dinoflagellate known as *Alexandrium catanella*. In sufficient numbers, *A. catanella* may cause the water to take on a luminescent red appearance. It produces saxitoxin, another neurotoxin. In humans, symptoms of PSP include tingling and numbness of lips, fingers, face and extremities, vomiting, diarrhea, slurred speech, headache, and rapid heartbeat. Death is caused by respiratory paralysis. Note that cooking will not destroy algal toxins in shellfish.

Red tides are becoming more frequent worldwide. Some red-tide producing organisms have shown up in the ballast-water discharged by ships far from their port of origin and may contribute to the increasingly widespread occurrence of red tides. For example, poisonous algal blooms increased 10-fold between 1975 and 1995 in coastal waters of China. However, the principal reason for more frequent red tides is probably increased nutrient input into coastal waters due to runoff of nutrients (mostly nitrogen and phosphorus compounds) from agricultural fields and sewage from urban areas. For example, in 2007, NOAA scientists implicated nutrients discharged by the Mississippi River (aided by seasonal wind patterns and Gulf currents) in the development of red tides on the continental shelf off the west coast of Florida. Scientists discovered that a surprisingly small amount of nutrients was needed to initiate a red tide.

Blooms of toxic algae have been blamed for fish kills and the deaths of marine mammals around the world. In late February 2002, the deaths of 20 dolphins that washed ashore in Southern California were attributed to the domoic acid secreted by a species of dinoflagellates. The die-off of significant numbers of the manatee population of southwest Florida in 2005 was attributed to a red tide of *Karenia brevis*. The manatee is an endangered marine mammal.

In addition to toxin-producing blooms, a second type of harmful algal bloom, known as a **high biomass bloom**, depletes the supply of dissolved oxygen in seawater (Chapter 3). If excess amounts of nutrients wash into coastal waters, phytoplankton blooms can become extremely dense. When the algae die, their remains sink to the ocean bottom where they are acted upon by *aerobic decomposers*, organisms that use dissolved oxygen. Eventually the water may become severely depleted of dissolved oxygen, making it impossible for other organisms (except *anaerobic decomposers*) to survive. Such conditions can cause massive fish kills.

Harmful algal blooms develop in the waters of almost every coastal state of the U.S. According to a 2007 NOAA report, harmful algal blooms are responsible for direct economic loss in the United States estimated to average $75 million annually. Besides public health costs, losses due to closure of commercial fisheries, plus management and monitoring costs, harmful algal blooms cost the tourism and recreation industries millions of dollars each year because the decomposing residue of algal blooms washes up on beaches and produces a foul odor and unpleasant appearance that drives away visitors. For example, in 1991 a *Pseudo-nitzschia* bloom forced the closing of Washington State beaches to commercial shellfish harvesting and recreation at an estimated $15-$20 million revenue loss for local communities.

Driving Question:

What are the basic components and structure of marine ecosystems and what is their source of energy?

With this chapter, our focus shifts to life in the ocean. The physical and chemical properties and processes examined in earlier chapters influence all marine organisms and their interactions. In this chapter, we describe how interactions among the biosphere, atmosphere, and ocean govern the distribution and abundance of life in the ocean.

A fundamental subdivision of the Earth system is the *ecosystem*. This chapter examines the components of marine ecosystems including producers, consumers, and decomposers. We emphasize the source of energy (photosynthesis, chemosynthesis) and the transfer of energy among organisms occupying the various feeding (trophic) levels within food webs. We then take a closer look at the processes operating within marine ecosystems including energy supply for growth and reproduction, factors influencing biological production in the ocean, the role of nutrients and trace elements as limiting factors, and the importance of microbes in marine ecosystems. In view of the contemporary interest in the carbon cycle and global climate change, we also examine the physical and biological processes governing the flux of carbon into and out of the ocean over a range of time scales. We begin by identifying the essential requirements for marine life.

Requirements for Marine Life

The ocean is home to a huge number of different types or species of organisms—perhaps as many as 10 million—and many more are yet to be discovered and studied. The wide variety of marine habitats makes possible this great biodiversity. Some marine ecosystems, such as coral reefs (Chapter 10), are structurally complex and provide niches for many types of organisms that have evolved different adaptations to their environment. The discovery of hydrothermal vents and their associated thousands of species of marine organisms dates only to 1979 (Chapter 2).

Many of the fundamental requirements for life in the ocean are the same as those needed by terrestrial organisms. Essential for all life on Earth are a source of energy (e.g., sunlight), liquid water, the appropriate mix of chemical constituents (e.g., nutrients), and the right combination of environmental conditions (e.g., range of temperature). One major difference between life in the ocean and life on land is the much greater space and variety of marine habitats. On land, the tops of the tallest plants are only a few tens of meters above the ground and only a few species of birds can fly higher than 100 m (330 ft). In the ocean, microscopic plants live at depths as great as about 200 m (650 ft) and animals inhabit all depths. Even the deepest trenches (about 10,000 m or almost 33,000 ft deep on the ocean floor) support life. Another important difference is that terrestrial plants typically spend their entire life cycle rooted in the soil at a fixed location whereas those in the ocean are suspended in a continually moving fluid.

All living organisms require energy, which they obtain either as producers (via photosynthesis or chemosynthesis) or as consumers eating other organisms. Photosynthetic organisms use light energy (solar radiation) to convert simple inorganic compounds (carbon dioxide and water) into complex energy-rich organic substances, which provide food. Chemosynthetic organisms live in the absence of light and derive energy from substances such as hydrogen sulfide (H_2S).

In addition to water and energy, marine life forms require nutrients and trace elements in sufficient quantities—just as humans require certain minerals and vitamins in small quantities in their diet. Nutrients that are required by marine organisms in relatively large quantities include phosphorus and nitrogen compounds, calcium, and magnesium—all of which are essential for plant growth. Iron and several other elements, so-called *trace elements* or *micronutrients*, are also required, but in very small quantities. Iron is especially important because it plays a role in the formation of *chlorophyll*, the most common photosynthetic pigment in plant cells, and it is essential for certain plant enzymes. When any one of these essential factors is not available in sufficient quantities, plant growth is limited.

According to the **law of the minimum**, the growth and well being of an organism is limited by the essential resource that is in lowest supply relative to what is required. This most deficient resource is known as the **limiting factor**. For example, trace amounts of iron may be a limiting factor in high nutrient-low chlorophyll (HNLC) areas of the ocean. For more on this topic and the possible implications for mitigating the current upward trend in atmospheric CO_2, see this chapter's first Essay.

Structure of Marine Ecosystems

An **ecosystem** is a fundamental subdivision of the Earth system in which communities of organisms interact with one another and with the physical conditions and chemical substances of their habitats. All ecosystems have both living (*biotic*) and nonliving (*abiotic*) components plus energy sources. Biotic components include producers, consumers, and decomposers whereas abiotic components constitute their physical and chemical environment. As we shall see, ecosystems vary enormously in structure and complexity.

Where sunlight is available, the basis of ecosystems is a group of organisms collectively known as **producers**, photosynthesizing organisms. On land, they are primarily green plants. In the ocean, producers include familiar seaweeds and sea grasses in shallow waters, algae, and some bacteria. Producers are also called *autotrophs* (meaning *self-nourishing*) because they manufacture the food they need by harvesting energy (either light energy or chemical energy) from the abiotic environment. That manufactured food constitutes primary production, the base of most common ecosystems. More precisely, **primary production** is the amount of organic matter

synthesized by organisms from inorganic substances and is usually measured in units of grams of carbon per square m per unit time. Autotrophs store energy-rich organic matter in their cells for use in all life processes, such as growth, maintenance of cells, and reproduction.

Organisms (usually animals) that feed on autotrophs are called **consumers** or *heterotrophs* (meaning *other-feeders*). The organic material produced in the growth of consumers is known as **secondary production**. Heterotrophs may be herbivores, carnivores, or omnivores. *Herbivores* feed exclusively on plants, whereas *carnivores* eat herbivores or other carnivores. *Omnivores* eat both plants and animals. In this section we take a closer look at marine producers, consumers, and decomposers (organisms that break down dead plants and animals).

PRODUCERS

In the sunlit portion of the ocean, producers are plants, algae, and some bacteria. Multi-celled plants are relatively rare in the ocean. Seaweeds (large algae) and sea grasses (true vascular plants) grow attached to some substrate on the ocean bottom. They can survive only in shallow, relatively clear water where light levels are sufficient for photosynthesis. Floating, microscopic unicellular algae, photosynthetic bacteria, and other groups of organisms capable of photosynthesis are responsible for more than 99% of biological production in the photic zone. Collectively these floating organisms are referred to as **phytoplankton**, from the Greek words *phyto* for plant and *plankton* for wanderer.

Compared to terrestrial ecosystems, marine ecosystems have higher rates of production for a given amount of biomass. Phytoplanktonic organisms are very small and make up only 1% of the total mass of plants on Earth, but they are responsible for considerable global primary production. As is typical of very small organisms, phytoplankton reproduces rapidly during favorable environmental conditions (as often as eight times a day) so that populations of phytoplankton species can fluctuate dramatically. Some types have very complex life cycles with numerous stages and different, poorly known forms. This is especially true of certain toxic and otherwise harmful algal species, discussed in this chapter's Case-in-Point.

Here we describe four major groups of phytoplanktonic organisms: diatoms, coccolithophorids, dinoflagellates, and bacteria. Although all are single-celled, some may form colonies or chains of individual cells. Some types of phytoplankton (i.e., dinoflagellates and bacteria) are not simply classified because they have characteristics of both plants and animals. They may carry out photosynthesis and they may also act as heterotrophs. Organisms that can be both autotrophic and heterotrophic are called **mixotrophs**. The various types of phytoplanktonic organisms range in size from less than 2 micrometers to about 2 mm (visible to the naked eye).

Diatoms are a diverse group of *protista* (or *protoctista*) having properties of both plants and animals. They are encased in shell-like cases (called *frustules*) made of silica (Figure 4.9A). These cases can be very ornately decorated. Diatoms contain photosynthetic pigments (primarily *chlorophyll*) and contribute significantly to primary production. When diatoms die, they sink to the bottom where their frustules form a major component of marine biogenous sediment deposits in some areas of the ocean bottom (Chapter 4).

Coccolithophorids are also single-cell photosynthesizing organisms; they are covered with tiny calcium carbonate plates (Figure 4.8A). Coccolithophorids are unusual in that they appear to thrive in nutrient-poor waters, forming large blooms that turn surface waters greenish blue as viewed from space (Figure 9.2). The plates of coccolithophorids are major contributors to marine calcareous sediment deposits including, for example, the

FIGURE 9.3
A large red tide formed by the dinoflagellate *Noctiluca*. [Courtesy of Peter Franks, Scripps Institution of Oceanography, University of California, San Diego]

White Cliffs of Dover on the southeast coast of England. About 70 million years ago a white mud composed of mostly coccolithophorid fragments accumulated at the bottom of a shallow sea and gradually converted to chalk, a fine-grained calcareous rock. Although the chalk was deposited at a very slow rate (about 0.5 mm per year), up to 500 m (1600 ft) of chalk eventually accumulated in some places. Tectonic forces elevated the chalk layers above sea level and later, toward the end of the Pleistocene Ice Age, formation of the English Channel made Britain an island and exposed the White Cliffs, rising up to 90 m (300 ft) or more above sea level.

Dinoflagellates have two flagella (thread-like structures) and no solid covering so that they are not preserved in marine sediment deposits. Many species of dinoflagellates are mixotrophs, many are bioluminescent (Chapter 10), and some species form red tides (Figure 9.3). Species of dinoflagellates that do not contain photosynthetic pigments are exclusively heterotrophs and are considered to be zooplanktonic (described below).

The smallest and probably the most numerous of phytoplanktonic organisms are certain groups of bacteria. They are distinct from the other single-celled organisms just mentioned in that they lack internal cellular structure such as nuclei, chloroplasts and mitochondria. The many types of bacteria play important roles in the functioning of marine ecosystems. Some are autotrophs; others are heterotrophs; and still others are decomposers, breaking down organic material from dead organisms (known as *detritus*) and recycling the nutrients back into the

FIGURE 9.2
Coccolithophorid bloom in the Bering Sea off Alaska, north of the Aleutian Island chain. Bright white areas are clouds or snow covered land. [NASA SeaWiFS image]

FIGURE 9.4
Cyanobacteria are the most abundant photosynthetic organisms in the ocean. [NASA]

FIGURE 9.5
Copepods are tiny crustaceans that are an important food source for juvenile fish and shellfish. [NOAA]

ecosystem. Cyanobacteria have a blue-green pigment and are mixotrophs (Figure 9.4). Some bacteria play an important role in the ocean's nitrogen cycle.

Whereas photosynthesis drives the most familiar marine ecosystems, scientists have discovered extraordinary ecosystems in the deep ocean in which chemical energy, rather than sunlight, drives the basic biological processes. That is, marine organisms in these ecosystems harvest energy from chemical reactions. This method of primary production is referred to as **chemosynthesis**. For example, bacteria oxidize sulfides, such as hydrogen sulfide (H_2S), to obtain energy to fix carbon from carbon dioxide into simple sugars. Regardless of whether an ecosystem is driven by photosynthesis or by chemosynthesis, the total amount of carbon converted from carbon dioxide into organic matter is known as primary production. The process is also referred to as *carbon fixing* because carbon is changed, or fixed, from a simple (inorganic) to a more complex (organic) form, usually energy rich sugars and carbohydrates.

CONSUMERS

Small herbivores are the chief consumers of phytoplankton; small and large carnivores, in turn, prey on herbivores. Single-cell and multi-cellular consumers that drift passively with ocean currents or are weak swimmers are referred to collectively as **zooplankton** (animal plankton). They include bacteria and dinoflagellates as small as 2 micrometers (called *microplankton*). Very large

organisms, such as jellyfish and other gelatinous animals, are also zooplankton; these animals may measure as much as a meter (3 ft) across. Active swimmers can pursue and capture their prey, but most zooplanktonic organisms are suspension or **filter feeders**. They use tiny hairs (called *cilia*) or mucus-covered surfaces to capture particles suspended in the water.

The most ubiquitous members of the zooplankton are **copepods**, a diverse group of tiny crustaceans covered with an exoskeleton made of chitin, a colorless and amorphous substance (Figure 9.5). Copepods include both herbivorous and carnivorous species. In some areas of the ocean, herbivorous copepods inhibit the growth of phytoplankton populations. While nutrient availability typically limits the growth of phytoplankton populations, copepods are exceptional herbivores in that they can reproduce at such a high rate that they provide grazing pressure that limits phytoplankton growth. Copepods play an important intermediate role in marine food chains, feeding on phytoplankton and, in turn, being eaten by larval and juvenile fish.

Larger members of the zooplankton community include **euphausiids** and other shrimp-like crustaceans called **krill** (Figure 9.6). Krill, up to 6 cm (2.5 in.) in length, are so numerous in the ocean that their biomass is equal to the combined weight of all people on Earth! A major reason for their abundance in the Southern Ocean is the upward transport of nutrients in the North Atlantic Deep Water (NADW) around Antarctica. Krill are a direct or indirect food source for a variety of marine organisms including whales, fish, squid, seals, penguins, and seabirds. In fact, krill are regarded as the keystone species in the Southern Ocean. A *keystone species* is an

FIGURE 9.6
Euphausiids (krill) occur in large swarms in the Southern Ocean and feed on algae on the under surface of sea ice. [NOAA Ocean Explorer

essential member of an ecosystem that contributes to biodiversity; its loss would likely lead to the extinction of other forms of life in the ecosystem. Larval forms of fish, crabs, lobsters, starfish and other larger animals are also members of the ocean's zooplankton community.

Zooplankton is the main food source for larger consumers in the sea. These include larval and juvenile fish and even the much larger basking sharks (e.g. whale sharks) and baleen whales (Chapter 10), which filter zooplankton out of the water by passing seawater through comb-like structures in their mouths. It is important to remember, however, that larger animals are rare in the sea compared to the enormous number of smaller zooplanktonic organisms, protozoans, and bacteria. In fact, the size of the average animal in the open ocean is no larger than a mosquito!

DECOMPOSERS

Decomposers, or detritivores (detritus eaters), are consumers that feed on dead organic matter, either on the ocean bottom or in the water column. Decomposers are essential components of all ecosystems because they break down organic matter and recycle nutrients back into the ecosystem. Whereas most decomposers are bacteria size, some decomposers such as worms may be complex organisms living on the sea floor and in ocean bottom sediments.

TROPHIC STRUCTURE OF ECOSYSTEMS

As noted in Chapter 1, a **food chain** is a linear path of feeding relationships among organisms (e.g., producers, consumers) along which energy and materials move within an ecosystem. For example, in a marine food chain, phytoplankton are eaten by herbivores, which in turn are eaten by carnivores, which are then eaten by other carnivores and so on. In reality, such simple food chains rarely exist in the ocean and marine heterotrophs are more likely to feed on a wide variety of prey organisms. Most ecosystems consist of several levels of consumers including fish, marine mammals, and sea birds. Humans tend to feed at the highest levels in marine ecosystems. This complex of linked food chains is more realistically described as a **food web** and each feeding position occupied by an organism within a food web is called a **trophic level** (Figure 9.7).

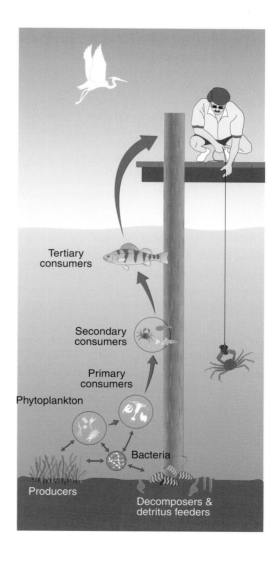

FIGURE 9.7
This simple food web is typical of an estuary. [Adapted from NOAA]

Within food webs, energy is transferred in only one direction: from lower trophic levels to higher trophic levels (e.g., from producers to consumers). But this energy transfer is inefficient. As organisms occupying one trophic level feed on the tissues of its prey, only a small fraction of the energy is passed to the next higher level of the trophic system. We can visualize the energy distribution within a food web as a pyramid with producers forming a broad base containing most of the ecosystem's energy. Each successively higher trophic level contains considerably less energy than the one below it. That is, energy transfer within food webs is much less than 100% efficient. **Ecological efficiency** is defined as the fraction of the total energy available at one trophic level that is transformed into work or some other usable form of energy at the next higher trophic level.

Worldwide, ecological efficiency varies depending on types of organisms and ecosystems but is never very high. In some ecosystems, no more than 5% of the energy at one trophic level becomes incorporated in the tissues of organisms that occupy the next higher trophic level. An ecological efficiency of 10% is typical for the open ocean. In some highly productive marine ecosystems having few trophic levels and where strong upwelling provides an abundant supply of nutrients to surface waters, ecological efficiency can be as high as 20%.

Biomass is easier to measure than energy so that scientists usually follow and describe the flow of energy within food webs in terms of biomass. (*Biomass* is the total mass or weight of organisms.) Applying the *10% rule of ecological efficiency*, some 10,000 grams of primary producers will supply food for 1000 grams of herbivores (e.g., copepods). They, in turn, will feed 100 grams of primary consumers (e.g., fish larvae) and only 10 grams of secondary consumers—salmon, for example. If humans consume the salmon, then only 1 gram of human biomass will result from the original primary production of 10,000 grams of phytoplankton. As we have noted, however, few marine ecosystems are as simple as this example; most marine food webs consist of many different organisms feeding on multiple food sources. Many of the fishes listed on restaurant menus (e.g., tuna, shark, salmon) are carnivores that feed at higher trophic levels and require considerable food energy from the ecosystem. Furthermore, a complex food web with diverse food sources tends to be more stable and less vulnerable to environmental change than is a simple ecosystem. The loss of one species as a food source may not destroy an entire complex food web as it might a simple food chain. On the other hand, a short, simple food chain is more efficient at transferring energy.

Why is ecological efficiency so low? There are many reasons. For one, not all the biomass at each trophic level is harvested. Many organisms have characteristics (adaptations) that enable them to avoid predation thereby reducing the harvest. Not all the harvested biomass is ingested. Parts of the prey organism (e.g., skeleton) may not be eaten even though they contain food energy. Not all the ingested biomass is digested (assimilated). If consumed, indigestible materials are excreted and subsequently broken down by decomposers. Furthermore, not all the assimilated biomass is converted to usable energy. Energy losses occur when assimilated food enters the organism's cells and is processed to liberate energy for maintenance, growth, and reproduction. This process of energy liberation, known as **cellular respiration**, occurs in all living cells. However, cellular respiration is inefficient. Less than half the energy in sugars (the direct source of energy for cellular respiration) is converted to a usable form. The rest is transformed to heat that cannot be used to perform work (biological activities) and eventually is released to the environment. Carbon dioxide and water, the other products of cellular respiration, also escape to the environment.

Low ecological efficiency has implications for *mariculture* such as rearing salmon in *fish farms*. Farmed salmon are generally fed fishmeal, made by grinding up marine fish caught in the wild. Given an ecological efficiency of 10%, it takes at least 10 grams of fishmeal (actually, more than 10 grams of whole fish since it is dried prior to grinding) to produce one gram of salmon.

BIOACCUMULATION

Food webs are pathways not only for energy but also for toxins, especially those that persist in the environment. They persist because they do not break down physically, chemically, or biologically. Examples include polychlorinated biphenyls (PCBs) and heavy metals such as mercury. Such substances tend not to dissolve in water but to concentrate in fatty tissue. These toxins may interfere with the metabolism and reproduction of sensitive organisms and in some cases pose health hazards for humans. We described a tragic example of bioaccumulation in the Case-in-Point of Chapter 4 when mercury contamination of sediments in Minamata Bay, Japan entered the marine food web and caused human illness and death.

Some persistent toxins move from one trophic level to the next, building in concentration along the way as one organism consumes another. This process of continually increasing concentration within a food web is called

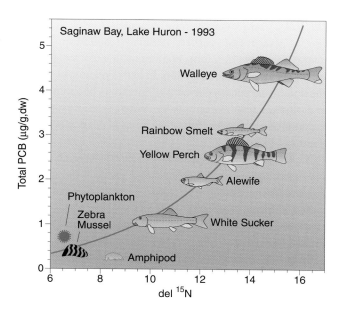

FIGURE 9.8
Field studies in the freshwater ecosystem of Saginaw Bay, Lake Huron, MI found bioaccumulation of PCBs in successively higher trophic levels. Scientists use "del ^{15}N" as a measure of the distance between trophic levels where ^{15}N is an isotope of nitrogen. [Adapted from NOAA Great Lakes Environmental Research Laboratory]

bioaccumulation. Bioaccumulation is a consequence of the ecological inefficiencies that prevail between trophic levels—the biomass declines at each successively higher level but the toxins remain. Furthermore, organisms do not readily break down or excrete persistent toxic substances. Hence, from one trophic level to the next higher trophic level, the amount of toxin lost is small compared to the amount that is transferred. Because most of an ingested toxin is retained and most of the biomass is lost, a toxin becomes more concentrated at successively higher trophic levels (Figure 9.8).

Bioaccumulation is especially pronounced in aquatic (marine and fresh water) food webs, which usually consist of 4 to 6 trophic levels rather than the 2 or 3 levels that are common in terrestrial ecosystems. In addition to contamination via bioaccumulation, some fish and shellfish can absorb certain toxins directly through their gills from the surrounding water. The combination of absorption plus bioaccumulation causes a toxin to become anywhere from 1000 to more than a million times more concentrated in upper-trophic level organisms (compared to the concentration of the toxin in the environment). Hence, people and fish-eating birds (e.g., eagles, osprey) that feed on fish at higher trophic levels run the greatest risk of consuming harmful

levels of toxins with their meal. Especially susceptible individuals (e.g., children, pregnant women, nursing mothers) are advised to restrict their intake of fish that may be exposed to toxins.

Persistent toxic substances can enter the ocean in the discharge of rivers or can settle out of the atmosphere. As we saw in this chapter's Case-in-Point, a toxin may even be a substance that is naturally produced by a marine organism.

Ecosystem Processes

Sunlight provides energy for photosynthetic organisms, which inhabit sunlit surface ocean waters and provide the food for other marine organisms. Chemosynthesizing organisms, which live in dark, deep-ocean waters and within the rock and sediment on the seafloor, obtain their energy through complex chemical reactions involving a mix of chemicals in the hydrothermal fluids circulating through rock fractures. In this section, we examine in more detail the sources of energy for growth and reproduction of marine organisms, marine production, how nutrients and trace elements can be limiting factors, and the important role of microbes in marine ecosystems.

ENERGY FOR GROWTH AND REPRODUCTION

Photosynthesis is represented by the following chemical equation:

$$6H_2O + 6CO_2 + ENERGY \rightarrow C_6H_{12}O_6 + 6O_2$$

Photosynthetic pigments in marine plants and bacteria absorb light energy and use it to combine water and carbon dioxide to form simple carbohydrates ($C_6H_{12}O_6$) and release oxygen gas. That is, photosynthesis converts solar energy into chemical energy. However, less than 0.5% of the available solar energy becomes chemical energy; much of the rest of the solar energy is converted to heat. Chlorophyll is the most common photosynthetic pigment and is the ingredient that makes the leaves on most terrestrial plants green. (Chlorophyll reflects radiation in the green portion of the visible spectrum and absorbs radiation at all other wavelengths.) Other pigments dominate in some plants and are responsible for the brown and red colors of some algae. The complex chemical structure of these pigments enables them to trap the energy of light photons and transfer it to electrons in the sugar or carbohydrate molecules formed during photosynthesis.

Because solar radiation is essential for photosynthesis, this process occurs only during daylight and primarily in relatively shallow waters (Chapter 5). Most sunlight is absorbed very near the ocean's surface; typically 80% is absorbed in the upper 10 m (33 ft) of water. The blue and green portions of the visible spectrum penetrate to the greatest depth in the water column (Figure 5.8) and photosynthesis is most efficient within this range (peaking at wavelengths of about 0.44 and 0.65 micrometers). The depth to which sunlight penetrates ocean water depends on the clarity of the water. Where waters are turbid because of abundant phytoplankton or suspended particles, or discolored by dissolved materials, the depth of the photic zone is reduced. In muddy rivers the photic zone may be only a few centimeters deep, whereas in very clear areas of the open ocean, it may be more than 200 m (660 ft) deep. Coastal waters, with their abundant dissolved and suspended sediments, tend to be more turbid and absorb light at much shallower depths.

Energy-releasing chemical reactions can occur in the ocean without sunlight. Many microbes synthesize organic matter, obtaining energy from chemical reactions fueled by energy-rich substances, such as hydrocarbons (petroleum or methane gas), hydrogen sulfide, and various metals. These energy-rich substances are discharged in the waters of hydrothermal vents (Chapter 2), from sea-floor petroleum seeps, decomposing whale carcasses, or decaying salt-marsh vegetation. For example, hydrogen sulfide (H_2S) takes the place of the sun in supplying energy for chemosynthesis:

$$H_2S + 2O_2 \rightarrow H_2SO_4 + \text{Energy}$$

Hydrogen sulfide (H_2S) combines with dissolved oxygen (O_2) to produce sulfuric acid (H_2SO_4) and releases energy. Chemosynthetic organisms can use this energy to produce carbohydrates (just as in photosynthesis):

$$24H_2S + 6O_2 + 6CO_2 \rightarrow C_6H_{12}O_6 + 24S + 18H_2O$$

Hydrogen sulfide (H_2S) combines with dissolved oxygen (O_2) and carbon dioxide (CO_2) to produce carbohydrates ($C_6H_{12}O_6$), sulfur (S), and water. Hence, chemosynthesis supports ecosystems near hydrothermal vents on the ocean bottom just as photosynthesis in the surface waters supports ecosystems in much of the rest of the ocean. The biomass of such ecosystems on and within the ocean floor is unknown but is probably less than that of photosynthetic marine ecosystems.

PRODUCTION IN THE PHOTIC ZONE

As noted earlier, cellular respiration makes energy available in a form that organisms use for growth, maintenance, and reproduction. In plants photosynthesis is the dominant process during daylight hours but both plants and animals respire continually. Whereas photosynthesis is confined to the photic zone, respiration takes place at all depths in the ocean.

Net production is the amount of organic matter produced during photosynthesis that exceeds the amount consumed via cellular respiration. Because respiration occurs at all depths and at all times in the ocean while photosynthesis occurs only in light, net photosynthetic primary production is confined to surface sun-lit waters. The total amount of carbon fixed into organic matter through photosynthesis in a given unit of time is the **gross primary production** (expressed in units of grams of carbon per square m per day or year). But respiration by producers releases some of the energy stored in these carbon-containing compounds for their own metabolic processes such as growth and reproduction. The amount of carbon remaining is called **net primary production** and this is the total food and energy supply available for the rest of the ecosystem.

No net primary production occurs below the **compensation depth**—usually the ocean depth where the light level diminishes to about 1% of what it is at the surface. The compensation depth varies with location and time of day. At that depth, the amount of carbohydrates and oxygen produced by photosynthesis balances the amount consumed by respiration. Photosynthetic organisms cannot survive for long below the compensation depth because they cannot fix enough carbon or produce sufficient organic carbon based food to meet their own respiratory needs.

When organisms die, their tissues decay and nutrients are remineralized and released back to the water. If decomposition occurs within the surface zone, living organisms quickly recycle nutrients. Primary production using recycled nutrients is called **regenerated production** (Table 9.1). Where decomposition occurs below the pycnocline, nutrients cannot readily mix back

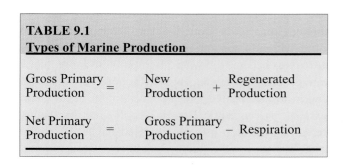

TABLE 9.1
Types of Marine Production

Gross Primary Production	=	New Production	+	Regenerated Production
Net Primary Production	=	Gross Primary Production		− Respiration

up into the photic zone. Therefore, recycling is much slower because little new growth occurs below the photic zone. Primary production based on nutrients brought into the ecosystem by processes such as upwelling or winter mixing is called **new production**. Pulses of phytoplankton growth may occur when storm winds and waves transport nutrients from below the pycnocline upward into the sunlit surface waters.

The present estimate of total gross primary production in the world ocean is 50 gigatons (Gt) of carbon per year, where one Gt equals one billion tons. Given the area of the ocean, this figure translates into about 145 grams of carbon per square m per year—about the same production as terrestrial forests, grasslands, and cropland. To put these numbers into some perspective, a standard paper clip weighs about 0.5 gram so that each square meter of the ocean (summed to the depth where the light level drops to 1% of its surface value) fixes the equivalent of about 290 paper clips of carbon. Actual values of primary production (in grams of carbon per square m per year) range from less than 50 in the open ocean, up to 500 in coastal upwelling zones, and to as high as 1250 in shallow estuaries.

Primary production requires sunlight, nutrients, and phytoplankton (above the compensation depth) and varies with both location and season. Primary production is very low in much of the tropical ocean. The chief reason for this desert-like condition is lack of nutrients. In the tropics, incoming solar radiation is intense throughout the year so that the ocean is stratified year-round thereby inhibiting new nutrients from moving into the photic zone from below. Brief exceptions are caused by the strong winds of a tropical cyclone that mix water to great depths and transport nutrients into sun-lit surface waters. In addition, tropical coral reefs are highly productive. Overall, the tropical ocean has considerable biological diversity but relatively little biomass.

Low productivity in the central subtropical ocean is also due to lack of nutrients. Recall from Chapter 6 that Ekman transport in the subtropical gyres causes surface waters to converge producing net downwelling near the center of the gyres. Downwelling depresses nutrient-rich water to depths well below the photic zone.

At temperate latitudes, production varies with the season. In winter, sunlight is weak and surface waters become more dense and sink. The winds of winter storms mix water to the extent that the shallow seasonal pycnocline disappears and most autotrophs are carried to depths below the photic zone. In spring, more intense solar heating reestablishes the pycnocline

FIGURE 9.9
This satellite image shows the spring bloom around Arctic Canada in May 2003. Areas of high chlorophyll concentration are shown in red, orange, and yellow whereas areas of lower production are in shades of green and blue. [NASA]

and stratification, halting the deep mixing of autotrophs. With abundant nutrients, more sunlight, and a more stable water column, conditions are favorable for a dramatic increase in phytoplankton populations, an event known as the **spring bloom** (Figure 9.9). Once the spring bloom is well underway, there is an explosive growth of zooplankton populations that graze on the phytoplankton. (This is sometimes referred to as a *zooplankton bloom*). In some areas of the ocean, such as the North Atlantic, the spring bloom ends when the zooplankton have reduced the phytoplankton to levels that are not sustainable. In other areas of the ocean, the spring bloom is limited by nutrient supply. Often, a secondary bloom occurs in early fall while sunlight is sufficiently intense and the first storms of the season transport new nutrients upward into the sunlit surface layer.

Phytoplankton populations grow abundantly where upwelling transports nutrient-rich waters into the photic zone. Persistent upwelling occurs along the equator and on the eastern side of ocean basins, due to prevailing winds and offshore Ekman transport (Chapter 6). Such upwelling zones support about one quarter of all fish production in the ocean. For example, upwelling along the west coast of South America supports the rich sardine and anchovy fisheries off Chile, Ecuador, and Peru. These fisheries collapse during El Niño episodes when upwelling lessens and results in surface waters that are relatively low in nutrients and unable to fuel phytoplankton growth (Chapter 11).

In polar regions sunlight limits production although ocean stratification is generally absent and nutrients are abundant. (High latitude seas such as the Bering Sea are seasonally stratified.) In summer after some of the ice cover melts, the long polar day triggers high primary production.

NUTRIENTS AND TRACE ELEMENTS AS LIMITING FACTORS

For much of the world ocean, photosynthetic production continues until the primary nutrients (nitrogen and phosphorus compounds) are exhausted. However, some areas of the ocean have sufficient nitrogen, phosphorus, and sunlight but still have low levels of production. These areas are often in the middle of ocean basins, far from land, and are known as **HNLC regions** (for high nutrients,

low chlorophyll). Note the areas of very low production in the central ocean basins shown in Figure 9.10.

HNLC regions have long puzzled biological oceanographers. If the nutrient supply is sufficient, why is primary production so low? They suspected that this condition might arise from the lack of some element that usually occurs in trace quantities. Research conducted in the 1980s and 1990s demonstrated that iron is often a limiting trace metal in marine ecosystems. Iron is very insoluble in oxygen-rich ocean waters and usually attaches to particles and quickly sinks to the ocean bottom. Winds transport iron-rich dust particles from land sources (e.g., mountains and deserts) to the ocean where they settle into surface waters and often promote phytoplankton blooms (Chapter 4). However, HNLC regions of the ocean may be so distant from terrestrial sources of wind-borne iron particles that input of iron-rich dust is insufficient to make these areas productive. For more on this topic, refer to this chapter's first Essay.

MICROBIAL MARINE ECOSYSTEMS

The traditional view of marine ecosystems is that large organisms such as fish dominate food webs. However, ocean scientists now recognize that such large organisms are actually very rare in the ocean. In fact, microbes, single-celled organisms including bacteria,

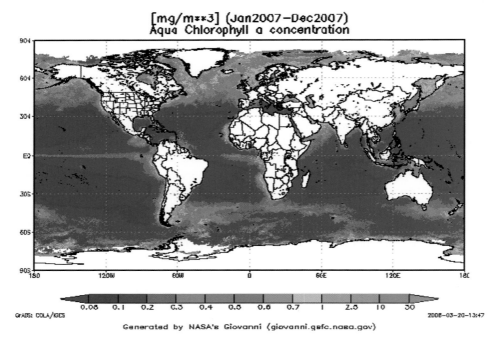

FIGURE 9.10

SeaWiFS image of marine biological production during 2007. Areas of relatively high production are shown in red, orange, and yellow whereas areas of relatively low production are in shades of green and blue. [NASA SeaWiFS image]

apparently dominate life in the ocean along with viruses and a group of organisms known as *archaea*. A single drop (1 milliliter) of seawater contains as many as one million bacteria and 1 billion viruses! The biomass of bacteria and other microbes in the ocean is so large that they are probably responsible for processing and recycling more carbon and nutrients than any other component of the ecosystem.

Now scientists are unraveling the role of these microbes in the ocean. In the 1970s the American oceanographer, John Steele, then at Woods Hole (MA) Oceanographic Institution, found that he could not account for the production of all the fish catches reported in government statistics from around the world. His estimate of total global primary production simply did not provide enough food to support the reported commercial fish catches, let alone all the other organisms in the sea. Where was the extra primary production coming from? Until that time, bacteria and protozoa had been considered to be important in the ocean only for their role in decomposing and recycling materials in ecosystems. Using improved microscopes and microbiological techniques, scientists discovered that microbes act as both producers and consumers. Furthermore, they concluded that microbes contribute enormously to global oceanic primary production and are especially important in open-ocean waters. Consequently, ocean scientists are revising their traditional view of the marine ecosystem in which plants are the major producers.

To observe these one-celled organisms, scientists must use light microscopes or electron scanning microscopes (for the smaller forms). The Dutch scientist Antony van Leeuwenhoek (1632-1723), who ground his own magnifying lenses, was the first to observe microbes in fresh water. Some types of bacteria can be grown in the laboratory by placing a few drops of water on a special jelly (agar, made from marine algae). Hence, a few types of microbes, such as bacteria, are relatively well known.

The ocean is home to three major groups of microbes: bacteria, archaea, and viruses. Archaea and bacteria together form the class of organisms called *prokaryotes*. All prokaryotes are unicellular. They differ from all other organisms (*eukaryotes*) in that their DNA is not enclosed within a cell nucleus. In fact, prokaryotes have essentially no internal cellular structure.

The genetic structure of archaea differs from that of bacteria. They have some different cell structural properties and unusual physiological adaptations that are likely related to the fact that archaea often inhabit extreme environments such as hydrothermal vents, Antarctic sea ice, or extremely salty pools. In the 1980s, Farooq Azam of the Scripps Institution of Oceanography in La Jolla, CA discovered archaea living in ocean water. Subsequent research has shown that archaea play important roles in decomposing simple organic compounds and dissolving organic carbon in the ocean.

Archaea living within the pore spaces of marine sediments appear to be involved in the generation of gas hydrate deposits. Gas hydrates are a potential source of methane (the chief constituent of natural gas), may contribute to global climate change, and may be a factor in the potential for submarine landslides. For more on methane hydrates, refer to this chapter's second Essay. Eleven different types of microbes (nine bacteria and two archaea) dominate life in the ocean in numbers and probably in mass. For example, one photosynthetic bacterium, *Prochlorococus*, accounts for up to half of primary production in the tropical ocean, making it the most abundant and most important primary producer on Earth. This particular organism was discovered in 1988.

Viruses are even stranger organisms. Some question whether they are even living in the traditional sense of the word because they cannot reproduce without a host organism. Their structure is even simpler than that of prokaryotes. They are studied using molecular techniques and may be many times more abundant in ocean waters than bacteria.

Many different types of unicellular *eukaryotes* of very small sizes also inhabit the ocean. These have complex internal cellular structure, similar to the cells of more complex organisms, and are collectively known as *protozoa*. The major groups of protozoans in the ocean include ciliates and dinoflagellates. Many of these single-celled organisms are capable of weak swimming, propelled by hair-like structures.

Scientists now know that bacteria are most abundant in surface ocean waters to depths of about 150 m (490 ft). As we have seen, in addition to their importance as primary producers, bacteria and archaea are significant consumers in marine food webs. They can directly absorb and digest *dissolved organic carbon (DOC)* that cannot be used as food by larger organisms. DOC comes from many sources, including the contents of ruptured phytoplankton cells and microbial cells (as they die or are partially eaten by zooplankton), and from the liquid excretions of zooplankton.

Bacteria and archaea are food sources for the smallest heterotrophs, including dinoflagellates and ciliates. All of these microbes and protozoa may be too small to be a significant food source for most other zooplankton.

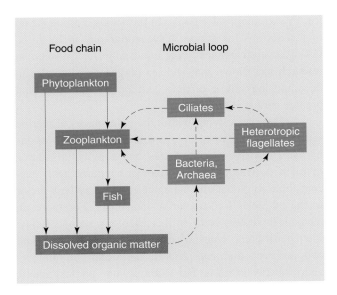

FIGURE 9.11
A simple microbial loop linked to a schematic marine food chain.

Thus, the organic carbon they consume seldom reaches the rest of the marine food web, but is recycled within a semi-separate food web, the so-called **microbial loop** that operates parallel to the larger food web (Figure 9.11). The microbial loop is important in regulating the flow of carbon and energy in the marine ecosystem, particularly in recycling within the photic zone. The microbial loop is a self-sustaining system that scientists are just beginning to understand. It is clear, however, that the ocean is home to large numbers of bacteria, though of only a few types compared to terrestrial ecosystems. Viruses apparently infect bacteria and other microbes, thereby holding their populations in check.

Ocean's Role in the Global Carbon Cycle

One of today's most widely discussed environmental concerns is global climate change and the role played by human-induced changes in the global carbon cycle, one of the chief biogeochemical cycles operating in the Earth system (Chapter 1). The ocean is a major reservoir in the carbon cycle and an important player in Earth's climate system (Chapter 5). Carbon dioxide, a greenhouse gas, is transferred between the atmosphere and ocean as part of the carbon cycle.

In terms of changes taking place over a time frame of a few thousand years, the ocean—primarily the deep ocean—is the most significant reservoir of carbon in the Earth system. The ocean holds about 50 times the amount of carbon dioxide contained in the atmosphere and about 20 times the amount of carbon stored in the biosphere (primarily as organic matter in soils). Over time frames of millions to billions of years the largest carbon reservoir consists of sedimentary rock (e.g., limestone, shale) and fossil fuels (i.e., coal, oil, and natural gas). Together these large reservoirs contain almost 1400 times more carbon than in ocean water. In this section, we focus on the cycling of carbon among the ocean, atmosphere, and biosphere.

On time scales of years to millennia, two different sets of processes, biological and physical, govern the cycling of carbon into and out of the ocean. With both sets of processes, some carbon is cycled with the global thermohaline circulation and is isolated from the atmosphere for centuries to millennia whereas some carbon cycles at a faster pace as in primary production.

PHYSICAL PUMP

An important process controlling the ocean sub-cycle of the global carbon cycle is primarily physical in nature and is known as the **physical pump** or *solubility pump*. The latter name refers to the fact that CO_2 is more soluble in cold water than warm water. Hence, greater amounts of atmospheric CO_2 dissolves in and sinks with the cold dense water masses that form at high latitudes of the North Atlantic Ocean as well as around Antarctica (Chapter 6). In this way, the physical pump acts in concert with ocean heat transport and heat loss to the atmosphere to convey carbon to the deep ocean where it may be sequestered for millennia.

Surface ocean waters take up atmospheric carbon dioxide primarily at middle and high latitudes. The major Northern Hemisphere western boundary currents (Gulf Stream and Kuroshio Current) that originate in the tropics are chilled during their flow northward. (Similar changes occur in Southern Hemisphere currents.) Because of lower temperatures and relatively high biological production in spring and summer, surface ocean waters take up large amounts of CO_2. These dense CO_2-rich waters sink as North Atlantic Deep Water (NADW) in the Greenland-Norwegian and Labrador Seas and as Antarctic Bottom Water (AABW) primarily in Antarctica's Weddell Sea.

As noted in our description of the thermohaline circulation in Chapter 6, situated above AABW is a large water mass that encircles the entire Southern Ocean: *Circumpolar Deep Water (CDW)*. CDW is produced by mixing of AABW with the overlying deep waters of the Atlantic and Pacific Ocean basins. The Antarctic Circumpolar Current spreads this water mass around

Antarctica. From this southern starting point, CDW flows northward as bottom water in all three ocean basins (Atlantic, Pacific, and Indian). Meanwhile, deep water formed in the North Atlantic spreads south across the equator and becomes entrained into the circumpolar flow around Antarctica. From the Southern Ocean, NADW spreads into both the Indian and Pacific Oceans. Flowing northward underneath the NADW in the Atlantic is a wedge of deep waters formed in the Southern Ocean. CDW flows into the Northern Hemisphere in the Atlantic, gradually mixing into the NADW lying above.

Circumpolar Deep Water circulates slowly throughout the ocean on a time scale of 1000 years. It gradually warms and diffuses upward into the surface layer where CO_2 is released (*outgassed*) to the atmosphere because carbon dioxide is less soluble in warmer water. The largest natural releases of CO_2 from the ocean's depths take place in the narrow zones of coastal and equatorial upwelling. As cold water from below moves up into the surface zone, it warms and releases some dissolved carbon dioxide. During El Niño, the presence of a thick layer of warm water in the central and eastern tropical Pacific inhibits upwelling of cold, carbon dioxide-rich waters, thus suppressing the outgassing of CO_2 from deep ocean water (Chapter 11).

BIOLOGICAL PUMP

The second set of processes whereby carbon cycles within the ocean involves biological activity and is known as the **biological pump**, the downward transport of particulate organic carbon (Figure 9.12). Eighty percent of primary production in the ocean takes place in the photic zone of the open ocean and roughly equals the amount of organic matter produced by all land plants annually. Unfortunately, the carbon sub-cycle in the ocean is not well understood, and poorly measured, especially in the intermediate- and deep-ocean zones. Consequently we examine how carbon is fixed as organic matter and then decomposed by bacteria and recycled through the ocean's ecosystems. Consider first the open ocean.

As we have seen, in the photic zone, phytoplankton and other photosynthetic organisms convert inorganic carbon into organic carbon and organisms grow and reproduce rapidly. Having very brief life spans, their cells divide several times a day and individuals die or are eaten by herbivores. In either case, the organic particles they produce sink out of the surface layer as *marine snow*, fecal pellets of zooplankton, or as aggregates of dead phytoplankton cells. The carbon contained in this material plus the carbon in the sinking bodies of zooplankton and other marine animals, is called **particulate organic carbon (POC)**. Up to 50% of the carbon fixed in the photic zone settles out of the surface layer in this form. POC may be eaten by zooplankton or decomposed by bacteria or other microbes. Through this process, some POC quickly converts back to dissolved inorganic carbon. POC that is eaten by zooplankton is repackaged into larger fecal pellets that sink more quickly through the water column (greater terminal velocity). Some organic matter reaches the ocean bottom and is buried by the subsequent rain of particles (Chapter 4).

Only about 10% of the POC that sinks out of the photic zone reaches depths greater than 1000 m (3300 ft). The intermediate zone of the ocean, from just below the photic zone down to a depth of 1000 m is known as the **twilight zone**. Within the twilight zone, light levels

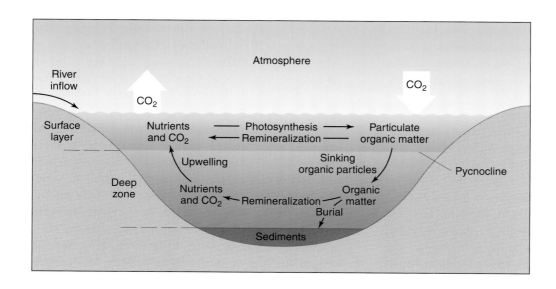

FIGURE 9.12
Biological processes that control the distribution of carbon in the ocean constitute the biological pump.

are too weak for photosynthesis, but sufficient for visual predators to locate prey. This is also the depth where the concentration of dissolved oxygen reaches a minimum because of the higher demand for dissolved oxygen by decomposers of POC in the main pycnocline. The decline in dissolved oxygen begins just below the photic zone and the dissolved oxygen concentration reaches a minimum just beneath the pycnocline.

Particles of organic matter that settle to the sea floor and are not recycled by bottom-dwelling organisms are buried in sediment deposits, removing the carbon they contain from the water and the biosphere for perhaps millions of years. However, only about 3% of the carbon fixed in the photic zone is removed from the ocean in this way for longer than 1000 years; most organic carbon finds its way back to the surface waters and atmosphere in less time via the thermohaline circulation.

Another way in which organic carbon is recycled in the ocean is by *re-mineralization*, that is, by being converted back to soluble inorganic forms. Respiration by all organisms releases CO_2 into the water. If this happens at shallow depths, the CO_2 enters the surface layer and potentially escapes to the atmosphere relatively quickly (within a few years). Dissolved carbon dioxide in the deep ocean remains there for centuries or longer. It may eventually return to the surface via the physical pump described earlier. When a single-celled organism dies, its cell may rupture, spilling the contents into the seawater. Also, zooplankton and other organisms excrete liquid in addition to fecal pellets. These organic carbon-containing substances are ideal food for microbes, which ingest them, returning CO_2 in solution to the water. This process begins in the surface layer and continues through the water column as bacteria and other microbes feed on and decompose organic particles of all sizes. The ocean depth at which decomposition occurs determines the length of time that carbon is retained. Larger and heavier particles are more likely to pass through the mid-ocean depths without significant alteration by microbes until they reach the ocean floor.

Cycling of carbon into and out of the ocean is a key player in Earth's climate system (Chapter 12). Human activities, especially the burning of fossil fuels, the heating of limestone to make cement, and deforestation are adding carbon dioxide to the atmosphere. Based on analysis of ancient air bubbles trapped in polar ice cores, the pre-industrial atmospheric CO_2 concentration was about 280 parts per million by volume (ppmv). By 2007, it was about 383 ppmv and could top 550 ppmv by the close of this century if present trends continue. If there were no photosynthesis or biological pump operating in the ocean, the present atmospheric CO_2 concentrations would be 1000 ppmv and Earth's climate would be much warmer because of a greatly enhanced greenhouse effect (Chapter 5). If the efficiency of the biological pump were perfect, on the other hand, only 100 ppmv of CO_2 would be in the atmosphere.

Carbon dioxide fluxes at the interface between the ocean and atmosphere vary greatly from one region of the ocean to another. For example, across much of the central and eastern equatorial Pacific Ocean, upwelling transports cold deep-ocean waters rich in CO_2 to the sea surface. With intense solar radiation, sea surface temperatures rise, and carbon dioxide is released to the atmosphere. In the North Atlantic, on the other hand, chilling high salinity surface waters forms dense waters that sink, carrying CO_2 from the surface down into the deep ocean. In addition, nutrient-rich waters ensure high primary production in the North Atlantic. Hence, in this region of the ocean, physical and biological processes combine to transport relatively large amounts of carbon dioxide from the atmosphere into the deep ocean. Similar conditions exist seasonally in the Southern Ocean. Decades-long studies of the ocean carbon sub-cycle have shown how the ocean "breathes," that is, where it absorbs CO_2 from the atmosphere and where it returns CO_2 to the atmosphere. This global pattern of breathing changes with the seasons and is affected by ocean circulation.

A mystery that puzzled ocean scientists for some time is the appearance of vast phytoplankton blooms at locales within an otherwise barren portion of the open ocean. These blooms along with high nutrient levels, huge numbers of diatoms, and other marine organisms occur within cold-core eddies (Chapter 6). In the summers of 2004 and 2005 (for a total of 6 months), a team of scientists led by Dennis McGillicuddy, an oceanographer with the Woods Hole Oceanographic Institution (WHOI), conducted ship-based investigations of eddies in the Atlantic's Sargasso Sea. They relied on altimeters onboard NASA satellites to locate eddies and sailed two heavily instrumented research vessels into eddies to obtain basic observational data. In a report issued in 2007 and published in *Science* magazine, the scientific team concluded that the rotating transient eddies interact with wind-driven currents to promote upwelling of nutrients that fuel phytoplankton blooms in the upper layers of water. It had been assumed that within eddies, carbon particles (e.g., from the remains of phytoplankton blooms) in surface waters sink to the deep ocean floor where they are sequestered in sediments. However, the team found that most of the biologically fixed carbon was recycled within the surface waters and not exported to deep water. This discovery points to a mechanism that supplies a major portion of the nutrients that sustains primary production in the subtropical ocean.

To this point, we have been discussing the operation of the carbon sub-cycle in the open ocean. Consider now the carbon sub-cycle in the coastal ocean. The coastal ocean is highly productive, receiving organic matter from many sources including tidal currents that flow through wetlands, the discharge of rivers and streams, wind-borne particles, and erosion of sediment deposits on continental margins. The total amount of organic carbon of terrestrial origin in the coastal ocean is estimated to be equivalent to about one-fifth of the primary production of the open-ocean surface waters. Burial rates of carbon are relatively high in the coastal zone because of a combination of high production and shallow water. This supply of carbon is exacerbated by the discharge of nutrients by rivers and streams that stimulate production.

Ecosystem Observations and Models

Studies of the oceanic carbon sub-cycle on various temporal and spatial scales rely on data obtained remotely by satellite-borne instruments. One of these satellite sensors is NASA's *Sea-viewing Wide Field-of-View Sensor (SeaWiFS)*. SeaWiFS maps ocean color, that is, the distribution of photosynthetic pigments and particularly chlorophyll-a, the most significant photosynthetic pigment in marine algae. With frequent global observations, we can follow annual and seasonal changes in the distribution of chlorophyll-a concentration (Figure 9.10).

Global satellite images obtained from SeaWiFS show the narrow bands of highly productive coastal upwelling waters, especially along the western sides of the continents, and the moderately productive waters of the central and eastern equatorial Pacific and the margins of the Southern Ocean. Using such data, the ocean can be divided into similar biological provinces. In addition, the *Advanced Very High-Resolution Radiometer (AVHRR)* sensor onboard NOAA's polar-orbiting satellites measures sea surface temperatures on a global scale.

By combining remote sensing data from satellite sensors such as SeaWiFS and the AVHRR, one biological and the other physical, scientists can estimate the global (or regional) annual primary production (exclusive of that due to autotrophic microbes or chemosynthesis). In this way, they can deduce the amount of carbon fixed through photosynthesis. This information adds to our understanding of the role of the oceanic carbon sub-cycle in global climate change (Chapter 12). For more on SeaWiFS, refer to this chapter's third Essay.

For information on ocean properties at depths below the range of satellite sensors, ocean scientists rely on in situ observations taken at specific locations over a lengthy period, spanning years, decades, or longer. A major impetus for developing such *time series* of data was the *Joint Global Ocean Flux Study (JGOFS)*. This multi-disciplinary international program (with participants from 20 nations) was established in 1987 under the auspices of the Scientific Committee of Oceanic Research (SCOR). The principal goal of JGOFS was to "assess more accurately, and understand better the processes controlling, regional to global and seasonal to inter-annual fluxes of carbon between the atmosphere, surface ocean and ocean interior, and their sensitivity to climate changes." In late 1988, JGOFS established long-term ocean time series projects at sites near Bermuda and Hawaii, now called BATS and HOT, respectively. At these stations, observations continue to be routinely collected on numerous physical, chemical, optical, biological, and atmospheric variables from the surface through the ocean depths.

These time series data permit scientists to construct numerical models ranging in complexity from those applicable to a single location, to three-dimensional models of the global ocean. The principal goals of these models are to identify processes and explain observations, combine many types of data to improve estimates of biogeochemical fluxes, and improve predictability of future ocean states. Another major goal of ocean modelers is to produce coupled models that integrate biogeochemical and physical processes. However, physical data that drive the models (e.g., solar radiation, wind, cloud cover) currently are more readily available than biogeochemical data. Biogeochemical aspects of ocean modeling are essential and data are being collected, processes are being studied, and the gap between physical modeling and biogeochemical modeling is closing.

When the model results match observational data, researchers can be reasonably confident that they have included most of the major processes affecting ecosystems and biogeochemical cycles and their model accurately reflects what is happening in the real ocean. In cases where the models cannot reproduce the observed data, important processes are still not adequately understood or represented. In some cases, more research on the processes is required and in others, more environmental data must be collected to permit more realistic simulations of ocean processes in time and space.

Conclusions

Although many of the fundamental ingredients of life in the ocean are the same as those required by terrestrial life, the ocean has a larger life zone and a greater variety of habitats than the continents. Marine ecosystems are composed of producers, consumers, and decomposers and their energy is supplied via photosynthesis or chemosynthesis. For several reasons, energy transfer between trophic levels in marine food webs is inefficient. Persistent toxic chemicals may enter marine food webs and bioaccumulate, threatening the well being of organisms (including humans) feeding at higher trophic levels.

We have seen that primary production in the ocean's photic zone varies spatially and temporally because of seasonal changes in sunlight, weather, fluctuations in nutrient supply, the availability of trace elements, stratification of ocean waters, and upwelling. We have also examined the physical and biological processes that govern the role of the ocean in the global carbon cycle. We return to this topic in Chapter 12 where we discuss prospects for an enhanced greenhouse effect and global climate change. Our examination of ocean life continues in the next chapter.

Basic Understandings

- Many of the fundamental requirements for life in the ocean are the same as those needed by terrestrial organisms. Essential for all life on Earth are energy sources, liquid water, the appropriate mix of chemical constituents (e.g., nutrients), and a favorable combination of environmental conditions (e.g., range of temperature).

- Major differences between the ocean and land include the much greater space and variety of marine habitats. Also, terrestrial plants require some sort of substrate to support them, usually soil. In the ocean, stratification plays this role for phytoplankton and is an important part of their ecosystem, to keep them in the photic zone so that they can produce more than they respire.

- When any one of the essential factors (e.g., nutrients) is not available in sufficient quantities, plant growth is limited. According to the law of the minimum, the growth and well being of an organism is limited by the essential resource that is in lowest supply relative to what is required.

This most deficient resource is known as a limiting factor.

- An ecosystem is a fundamental subdivision of the Earth system in which communities of organisms interact with one another and with the physical conditions and chemical constituents of their surroundings. Ecosystems vary in complexity but all have biotic (living) and abiotic (non-living) components.

- The simplest organisms in marine ecosystems consist of producers (or autotrophs), most commonly photosynthesizing plants, algae and bacteria. Autotrophs manufacture their food from the physical and chemical environment. That food constitutes primary production, the base of most common ecosystems. More precisely, primary production is the amount of organic matter synthesized by organisms from inorganic substances and is usually measured in units of grams of carbon per square m per unit time.

- Organisms (usually animals) that feed on autotrophs are called consumers or *heterotrophs*. The organic material produced in the growth of consumers is known as secondary production. Heterotrophs may be herbivores, carnivores, or omnivores. Organisms that function as both autotrophs and heterotrophs are called mixotrophs.

- Marine producers are plants, algae and some bacteria, which use sunlight to produce food through photosynthesis. Floating, microscopic unicellular algae, photosynthetic bacteria, and other groups of organisms capable of photosynthesis are responsible for much of biological primary production in the ocean. Collectively these organisms are referred to as phytoplankton. Four principal groups of phytoplanktonic organisms are diatoms, coccolithophorids, dinoflagellates, and bacteria.

- While photosynthesis drives most marine ecosystems, scientists have discovered ecosystems in the deep ocean in which chemical energy, rather than sunlight, drives the basic biological processes. This method of primary production is referred to as chemosynthesis.

- Unicellular and multi-cellular consumers that drift passively with ocean currents or are weak swimmers are referred to collectively as zooplankton. They include bacteria and dinoflagellates as small as 2 micrometers as well as very large organisms, such as jellyfish and other gelatinous animals.

- Decomposers or detritivores (detritus eaters) are consumers that feed on dead organic matter, either on the ocean bottom or in the water column. They are essential components of all ecosystems because they break down organic matter and recycle nutrients back into the ecosystem.

- Food chains and food webs are sequences of feeding relationships among organisms (e.g., producers, consumers) through which energy and materials move within an ecosystem. Within food chains and food webs, energy transfer occurs in one direction, from lower trophic (feeding) levels to higher trophic levels (e.g., from producers to consumers). But, for a variety of reasons, this energy transfer is inefficient. As an organism occupying one trophic level feeds on its prey, a small portion of the energy stored in the tissues of the prey organism is passed on to the next higher trophic level. In the open ocean, ecological efficiency is about 10% where ecological efficiency is defined as the fraction of the total energy at one trophic level that is transformed into work or some other usable form of energy at the next higher trophic level.

- Food webs are pathways not only for energy but also for toxins, that is, poisons that persist in the environment because they do not break down physically, chemically, or biologically. Some persistent toxins move from one trophic level to the next, building in concentration as one organism consumes another. This process of continually increasing concentration within a food web is called bioaccumulation and is a consequence of ecological inefficiencies.

- Sunlight supplies the energy needed by photosynthetic organisms to convert organic matter from water and CO_2, substances that are readily available from the atmosphere and ocean. Because solar radiation is essential for photosynthesis, this process occurs only during daylight and primarily in relatively shallow waters.

- Other energy-releasing chemical reactions can occur in the deep ocean in the absence of sunlight. Many microbes synthesize organic matter, obtaining energy from chemical reactions fueled by energy-rich substances, such as hydrocarbons (petroleum or methane gas), hydrogen sulfide,

and various metals. This process is known as chemosynthesis.

- The total amount of carbon fixed into organic matter through photosynthesis in a given unit of time is the gross primary production (expressed in units of grams of carbon per square m per day or year). But respiration by producers releases some of the energy stored in these carbon-containing compounds for their own metabolic processes. The amount of carbon remaining is the net primary production and this is the total food and energy supply available for the rest of the ecosystem. No net primary production occurs below the compensation depth—usually the depth where the light level diminishes to about 1% of what it is at the ocean surface.

- Photosynthetic primary production requires sunlight, nutrients, and phytoplankton above the compensation depth and varies with both location and season. Primary production is very low in much of the tropical and subtropical ocean chiefly because of a lack of nutrients or trace elements. At temperate and polar latitudes, productivity varies seasonally.

- Phytoplankton grows abundantly where upwelling brings nutrient-rich waters into the photic zone. Areas of persistent wind-induced upwelling occur along the equator and on eastern sides of ocean basins, due to prevailing winds and Ekman transport.

- Tiny microbes far outnumber large organisms in the ocean. The ocean is home to three major groups of microbes: bacteria, archaea, and viruses.

- An important process controlling the ocean's role in the global carbon cycle is primarily physical in nature. This is called the physical pump or the solubility pump. The latter name refers to the fact that CO_2 is more soluble in cold water than warm water. Hence, greater amounts of atmospheric carbon dioxide dissolves in and sinks with the cold and dense water masses that form at high latitudes of the North Atlantic as well as around Antarctica.

- The second set of processes by which carbon cycles through the ocean constitutes the biological pump. Some of the carbon that is fixed as organic particles in the photic zone sinks to the deep ocean bottom where it is sequestered for an extended period. However, consumption and remineralization within the twilight zone decrease the efficiency of sequestration.

- Studies of the oceanic carbon sub-cycle on large temporal and spatial scales depend on data obtained by remote sensing from satellite-borne instruments. One of these satellite sensors is NASA's Sea-viewing Wide Field-of-View Sensor (SeaWiFS). SeaWiFS maps surface ocean color, that is, the distribution of photosynthetic pigments and particularly chlorophyll-a, the most significant photosynthetic pigment in marine algae.

Review

1. In what general ways do marine ecosystems differ from terrestrial ecosystems?
2. Distinguish among producers, consumers, and decomposers in ecosystems.
3. Define "limiting factor" and briefly explain its significance.
4. Distinguish between photosynthesis and chemosynthesis.
5. Photosynthesis is confined to what portion of the ocean?
6. What is the 10% rule of ecological efficiency?
7. How is cellular respiration one of the reasons for the relatively low ecological efficiency?
8. Define "bioaccumulation" and explain its potential significance for human health.
9. Distinguish between gross primary production and net primary production.
10. Distinguish between the physical pump and the biological pump.

Critical Thinking

1. Summarize the reasons for the relatively low marine ecological efficiency.
2. If no photosynthesis or biological pump operated in the ocean, what is likely to happen to the concentration of atmospheric carbon dioxide?
3. All other factors being equal, how does sea surface temperature affect the rate at which carbon dioxide dissolves in seawater?
4. How might the law of the minimum apply in the event of a major change in climate?
5. How do humans attempt to increase ecological efficiency?
6. Explain why bioaccumulation of toxins often is a more serious problem in marine food webs than in terrestrial food webs.
7. What are the basic requirements for primary production at ocean depths above the compensation depth?
8. Identify factors that reduce the flux of carbon from surface ocean waters to the ocean depths.
9. What are the implications of iron fertilization for ocean acidification?
10. Humans feed at what level of a marine food web?

ESSAY: Ocean Iron Fertilization and Climate Change

As described elsewhere in this chapter, large areas of the open ocean are nearly devoid of one-celled plants (algae) that form the base of marine food webs. In some areas the reason is low concentrations of dissolved phosphorus and nitrogen compounds, nutrients essential for most plant life. Other areas, however, have high concentrations of these nutrients but low concentrations of chlorophyll (plant pigments). Such waters occur in the Antarctic, subarctic, and equatorial Pacific Ocean. Apparently, something is keeping the algae populations from growing. This has implications for climate in that fewer algae reduce the photosynthetic removal of CO_2 dissolved in surface ocean waters. More carbon dioxide in surface ocean waters, in turn, reduces the flux of atmospheric CO_2 into the ocean.

The mystery was solved by John H. Martin (1935-1993), an oceanographer based at Moss Landing (CA) Marine Laboratories. Initially, Martin studied how the classic plant nutrients (nitrogen, phosphorus) limit algal growth. Later his research focused on the role of metals that occur in trace concentrations in seawater and algae. Martin's study of trace metals was made difficult by potential contamination, which usually occurred while sampling seawater aboard ship and during laboratory chemical analyses. To avoid contamination, Martin used special clean rooms with filtered air and ultra-clean plastics. He even made his own ultra-pure chemical reagents so that he could accurately measure concentrations of trace metals in uncontaminated seawater. This work showed that most trace-metal concentrations reported in the scientific literature were too high because of contamination. His fellow scientists were not pleased to have their research criticized and many arguments ensued over Martin's analytical methods and results.

Martin discovered that algal growth normally is inhibited by the presence of copper and zinc in the water, but trace amounts of these metals are necessary for their growth. Martin then proposed that the high-nutrient low-chlorophyll (HNLC) areas of the ocean were deficient in iron and other trace elements. Over about one-third of the ocean, nutrients are abundant but iron concentrations and productivity are low. To test his hypothesis, Martin proposed a field experiment in which he would add large quantities of iron to high nutrient waters to determine if this stimulated algal growth.

Building on his iron limitation hypothesis, Martin also turned his attention to the possible role of marine algae in Earth's climate system. For one, he proposed that algae might have played a role in the large-scale climate fluctuations of the Pleistocene Ice Age. Algae not only give ocean waters a greenish color but also they take up CO_2 via photosynthesis. Martin proposed that during cold, dry glacial climatic episodes, strong planetary-scale winds transported iron and other trace metals in dust blown off mountains and deserts. Plumes of dust moved over the ocean and dust particles settled into the ocean stimulating blooms of phytoplankton. More phytoplankton meant more photosynthesis, less atmospheric CO_2, a weaker greenhouse effect, and a cooler planet. During mild, wet interglacial climatic episodes, less dust reached the ocean and phytoplankton populations declined. Less phytoplankton meant reduced photosynthesis, more CO_2 in the atmosphere, an enhanced greenhouse effect, and a warmer planet.

Lecturing at the Woods Hole (MA) Oceanographic Institution in July 1988, Martin said, "Give me a half tanker of iron, and I will give you an ice age." Martin's hypothesis came at a time of growing scientific interest in the prospects for global warming due to a carbon dioxide-enhanced greenhouse effect. Martin argued that the build up of atmospheric CO_2 (due to fossil fuel combustion and deforestation) could be offset by increasing the ocean's uptake of CO_2. He proposed an experiment in which large amounts of dissolved iron would be released into open-ocean waters where nutrient concentrations are high and chlorophyll levels are low. If successful, a weaker greenhouse effect could cause cooling.

Ocean iron fertilization (OIF) attempts to boost the ocean's biological pump. For this to work as a climate change mitigation strategy, two additional consequences are required. The enhanced biological pump must lead to a lower dissolved CO_2 concentration in surface ocean waters thereby increasing the transfer of carbon dioxide from the atmosphere. Also the carbon transported to the deep ocean by the biological pump must stay there and not be quickly upwelled. Unfortunately, HNLC regions are typically associated with regions of upwelling (e.g., the tropical Pacific Ocean and Southern Ocean) where models suggest that most carbon pumped down would be upwelled and vented to the atmosphere.

Martin died before he could carry out his ocean iron fertilization experiment. In 1993, Kenneth Coale, a researcher at Moss Landing (CA) Marine Laboratories, and his colleagues did carry out Martin's experiment in a patch of HNLC water near the Galápagos Islands in the equatorial eastern Pacific. From their ship, the R.V. *Melville*, they released a half a ton of iron over an ocean area of 64 square km (25 square mi). Within a day the clear water turned soupy green as phytoplankton levels increased three-fold, confirming Martin's hypothesis that at least some species of phytoplankton benefited from the addition of iron. However, the hoped for sequestering of carbon dioxide in the deep ocean did not materialize because zooplankton consumed much of the phytoplankton releasing CO_2 to surface waters. In 1995, Coale and colleagues conducted another OIF experiment in the eastern Pacific Ocean that increased phytoplankton biomass and reduced the carbon dioxide concentration of surface waters. The different result was attributed at least in part to changes in experimental procedures. Subsequently, three open-ocean iron fertilization experiments were conducted in the Southern Ocean. All three experiments increased phytoplankton biomass and reduced the amount of carbon dioxide dissolved in surface waters. However, evidence that particulate organic carbon (POC) sunk to the deep ocean was limited.

As of this writing, the international oceanographic community has conducted a total of 12 OIF experiments since 1993. Although adding to our understanding of the role of iron in marine ecosystems, these experiments did not reveal conclusively how effective OIF is in sequestering carbon in the deep ocean. The next generation of OIF experiments will try to answer some key questions including the fate of the algae blooms: how much is consumed by microorganisms and zooplankton and how much sinks to the ocean floor? The goal is to sequester carbon below the 100-year horizon, equivalent to a water depth of about 500 m (1600 ft). Water below this level does not come into contact with the atmosphere for at least a century. Numerical models predict that HNLC regions of the ocean are not likely to sequester more than several hundred million tons of carbon each year. Furthermore, the scale of these field experiments makes accurate assessment very challenging.

Some scientists and public policymakers vigorously oppose geo-engineering schemes such as ocean iron fertilization aimed at combating human contributions to global climate change. They argue that such quick fixes deflect attention away from the root cause of this global environmental issue, that is, humankind's increasing dependence on fossil fuels. Besides, there are ethical considerations and many uncertainties in tinkering with the Earth system on a grand scale. Not enough is understood about the workings of the Earth system and its numerous feedbacks loops. How might the explosive growth in the populations of certain phytoplankton species impact marine ecology? Might OIF spur the growth of harmful algal blooms (HABs)? Others counter by pointing out that large-scale geo-engineering projects such as iron fertilization may be the only feasible way to stem global warming.

Nonetheless, despite scientific uncertainties surrounding OIF and over the objections of scientists and conservationists, some private companies are going forward with plans for iron fertilization of the ocean. Their goal is to market credits for carbon emission reductions (carbon offsets) based on the amount of CO_2 estimated to be sequestered through phytoplankton blooms stimulated by OIF. In this way, a carbon dioxide emitting industry could reduce its carbon footprint by purchasing carbon credits.

ESSAY: Methane Hydrates, Future Energy Source

Potentially, a major source of clean-burning natural gas in the future is *methane hydrate* (also called *methane ice*). Methane hydrate is a clathrate, an ice-like solid formed from methane (CH_4) and water. The basic chemical structure of *methane hydrate* is a single molecule of methane enclosed in a rigid cage of six water molecules. Cages are linked together forming a crystalline solid that is similar to water ice except that the crystal structure is stabilized by the caged gas molecule. Many gases besides methane can form hydrates such as carbon dioxide, hydrogen sulfide, as well as other light hydrocarbons, but methane hydrates are the most common. Methane is the chief component of natural gas.

As early as 1811 the British chemist Sir Humphry Davy (1778-1829) made the first gas hydrates in his laboratory, but it was not until 1965 that a natural deposit was found (under permafrost in Siberia). Only recently have geoscientists started documenting the presence of methane hydrates in submarine and underground deposits and exploring their potential as an energy source. Ocean scientists first drilled through methane hydrates unintentionally on an expedition in 1970. Although that encounter was uneventful, research-drilling cruises avoided suspected methane hydrate deposits for two decades afterward, fearing they might encounter a pressurized pocket of methane, which could blast away the drilling equipment. Concerns over pressurized gas gradually diminished, and mounting scientific curiosity emboldened researchers to try boring through gas hydrate fields. Starting in 1992, researchers with the international *Ocean Drilling Program (ODP)* intentionally breached methane hydrate deposits several times without incident. Through ongoing exploration and research, marine geologists have identified deposits at numerous sites around the globe along most continental margins of the world ocean (Figure 1).

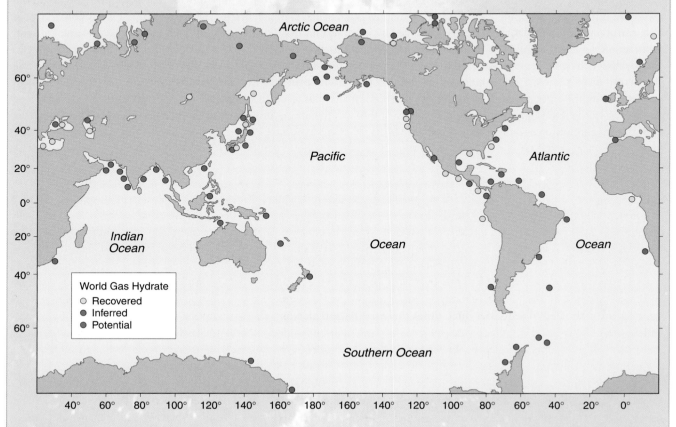

FIGURE 1
Worldwide location of recovered, inferred, and potential methane hydrate deposits. [USGS]

Marine methane hydrates form in pore spaces within ocean sediments. Hydrates are not stable at typical surface temperatures and pressures but are found in sediments at ocean depths greater than 400 to 500 m (1300 to 1600 ft) where temperatures are sufficiently low and/or pressures are sufficiently high to squeeze water and methane into hydrates. When sediment cores containing methane hydrate, or solid chunks of methane hydrate, are brought up from the ocean floor, the reduction in pressure and rise in temperature cause the gas hydrates to become unstable and they decompose, much like ice melting when warmed. Without precautions, gas hydrate will melt and fizz away before reaching the ocean surface. On the other hand, because of its volatility, chunks of methane hydrate will burn at the touch of a match.

The precise origin of submarine methane hydrates is unknown, although scientists suspect that microbes known as archaea living within sediments generate methane from carbon and hydrogen extracted from rich organic materials. That is, biogenic methane is concentrated where organic detritus (from which archaea generate methane) and sediments (which protect detritus from oxidation) accumulate rapidly. At the appropriate temperatures and pressures, the methane molecules are captured within the frozen hydrate structure. By contrast, conventional deposits of methane form through a different process. In that case, seafloor sediments are buried far deeper and are exposed to much higher temperatures, so that the organic material in the sediments simmers until it transforms into petroleum and eventually methane. Free methane then migrates upward through openings between sediments and is trapped below where hydrates might form from biological processes.

Terrestrial deposits of methane hydrates occur at shallow depths at high latitudes where low temperatures (rather than high pressure) keep them stable. For example, petroleum companies have encountered methane hydrates while drilling through permafrost (perennially frozen ground) in Alaska, Canada, and Siberia. In this environment, the flux of heat from Earth's interior generates methane from deeply buried organic matter. The gas migrates upward through openings in the sediments until it reaches the subsurface area where temperatures favor formation of methane hydrates. Methane hydrates formed below permafrost are much more concentrated than submarine deposits.

Methane hydrate deposits are important because of their potential as a future energy resource—both in the immense amounts of methane bound up in hydrates in sea-floor sediments as well as in the free methane trapped beneath hydrate ice layers. As a hydrate, methane is highly concentrated such that breakdown of one unit of methane hydrate ice at sea level pressure produces about 160 units of methane gas. Methane in submarine hydrates is conservatively estimated to contain at least 10,000 gigatons of carbon—about twice the amount of all other fossil fuel reserves on Earth. The United States Geological Survey (USGS) estimates that gas hydrates on the continental margin of North Carolina alone contain about 350 times the energy consumed by the U.S. in one year.

At present, the limiting factor in the exploitation of methane hydrate deposits is the difficulty of bringing the gas to market at competitive prices. Geologists report that most deposits are too thin to be recovered economically. Another major challenge is recovering the methane hydrate from the ocean bottom efficiently without losing the methane to hydrate decomposition.

The first successful extraction of methane from a gas hydrate deposit took place in March 2002 at a site in the Mackenzie River delta in northwestern Canada. Scientists drilled a 1200-m (3900–ft) well through permafrost into sediments containing methane hydrate. Hot water pumped down the well melted the crystals, releasing natural gas that came to the surface where it was flared off. Research continues on methods to mine methane in gas hydrates in continental margin deposits worldwide, but it may be many decades before gas hydrates contribute significantly to the world's energy supply. Meanwhile, Japan is drilling exploratory wells in the Nankai Trough subduction zone in search of gas hydrates.

Methane hydrates could exert their greatest impact on the Earth system by contributing to global climate change. Hydrates may function as a major source or sink for atmospheric methane, a greenhouse gas (Chapter 5). At present, gas hydrates are estimated to sequester three times more methane than exists in the atmosphere. Massive melting of hydrates and the ensuing release of methane gas could raise Earth's surface temperature. On the other hand, cooling could bind up more methane in hydrates, which could further lower Earth's surface temperature by reducing the greenhouse effect. As both temperature and pressure play a role in the stability of methane hydrates, multiple feedback loops are likely.

Consider the following possible feedback scenario: Suppose that rising global temperatures causes methane hydrate to begin to melt, releasing methane to the atmosphere and enhancing the greenhouse effect. More warming leads to melting of glacial ice and sea level rise. However, higher sea level increases pressure on ocean sediments, which could increase the formation of methane hydrates. Gas hydrates form at the expense of atmospheric methane, reducing the greenhouse effect and the Earth cools. Glaciers form and expand and sea level drops. While this scenario is pure speculation, evidence exists for dramatic shifts in methane concentration in the ocean over the past 70,000 years that coincide with episodes when Earth's climate suddenly warmed. For example, release of methane from gas hydrates may have contributed to global warming at the close of the Paleocene Epoch about 55 million years ago.

Methane hydrates may also play an important role in submarine landslides. Gas hydrates cement sediments together, so their formation and breakdown influence the strength of sedimentary deposits and possibly the potential for submarine landslides on the continental slope and rise. Evidence of methane hydrate instability pockmarks the ocean floor along the Blake Ridge off the coast of South Carolina and Georgia. Numerous craters and depressions, 500 to 700 m (1600 to 2300 ft) wide and 20 to 30 m (65 to 100 ft) deep, apparently formed when gas hydrates melted, releasing methane. In other cases, melting at the base of the hydrate layer destabilized seafloor slopes. Hydrate weakness and failure is thought to be a factor in submarine landslides off Alaska, the U.S. Atlantic coast, British Columbia, Norway, and Africa. Such inherent instability could spell problems for future drilling platforms resting on top of hydrate-rich deposits, for example in the Gulf of Mexico. If the gas hydrate collapses are large enough, they could also trigger destructive tsunamis (Chapter 7).

Scientists have discovered ice worms living in methane hydrates. Methane hydrates usually are buried deep in submarine sediments. The Gulf of Mexico is one of the few places where hydrates are found exposed on the ocean bottom, where occasionally solid methane bursts through in mounds, often 1.8 to 2.4 m (6 to 8 ft) across. In 1997, a team of scientists using a mini research submarine on a NOAA-funded research cruise discovered, photographed, and sampled what appears to be a new species of centipede-like worms living on and within mounds of methane ice at a depth of 550 m (1800 ft) about 240 km (150 mi) south of New Orleans. Although it had been hypothesized that bacteria might colonize methane ice mounds, this was the first time that animals have been found living in the mounds (Figure 2). Ice worms, which are 2.5 to 5 cm (1 to 2 in.) in length, flat and pinkish in color, were living in dense colonies burrowed into the methane hydrate. The worms were observed using their two rows of oar-like appendages to move about the honeycombed, yellow and white surface of the icy mound. Researchers speculate that the worms may be grazing off chemosynthetic bacteria that grow on the methane or are otherwise living symbiotically with them. Scientists have also managed to keep a number of the exotic worms alive in shore side laboratories for further study.

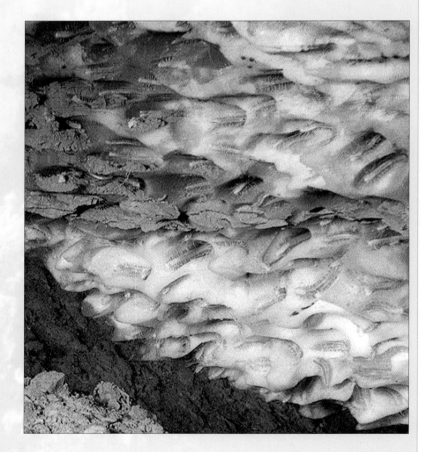

FIGURE 2
Ice worms living in a methane hydrate deposit at a location on the floor of the Gulf of Mexico about 240 km (150 mi) south of New Orleans, LA. [NOAA, Pennsylvania State University]

ESSAY: Ocean Color and Marine Production

Satellite remote sensing of ocean-surface color is contributing to our understanding of the global carbon cycle, other biogeochemical cycles, and global climate change. Ocean-surface color is an index of the global distribution and concentration of photosynthetic organisms living in the upper layers of the ocean. The *Coastal Zone Color Scanner (CZCS)* flown onboard NASA's Nimbus-7 satellite pioneered the technique between 1978 and 1986. SeaWiFS (Sea-viewing Wide Field-of-view Sensor), the successor to CZCS, is on the SeaStar satellite, launched on 1 August 1997 into a sun-synchronous orbit 705 km (438 mi) above Earth's surface. SeaWiFS is an important component of NASA's Earth Science Enterprise, designed to investigate the Earth system from space. These satellite sensors eliminate many of the sampling problems associated with ship-based measurements of marine production—greatly increasing spatial and temporal coverage. (However, remote sensing instruments must be periodically calibrated by surface data.) A satellite sensor can view every square kilometer of cloud-free ocean surface once every 24 hrs.

Ocean color sensors indirectly measure variations in the distribution and concentration of phytoplankton within the upper tens of meters of the open ocean (at somewhat shallower depths in more turbid coastal waters). As noted elsewhere in this chapter, phytoplankton are microscopic, single-celled organisms that form the base of most marine food webs. Chlorophyll-a (and other pigments) in phytoplankton absorbs selected wavelengths of visible solar radiation that penetrate seawater and that energy is used for photosynthesis. (The spectrum of *visible light* is composed of all colors, from violet at the short wavelength end to red at the long wavelength end.) Chlorophyll, the commonest of the phytoplankton pigments, absorbs primarily in red and blue portions of the visible spectrum and reflects green light. Some of that reflected light is scattered to the ocean surface and then into the atmosphere. The more phytoplankton present, the greater is the concentration of plant pigments, and the greener is the water.

Of the scattered radiation intercepted by an ocean-color sensor, only about 10% to 20% actually originates in ocean waters; the rest is sunlight scattered back by atmospheric aerosols and air molecules (primarily nitrogen and oxygen). Ocean waters scatter very little solar radiation having wavelengths in the red (0.67 micrometer) and near infrared (0.75 micrometer). Using these two spectral channels, the atmosphere's contribution to scattered sunlight can be subtracted from the total radiation scattered by the ocean-atmosphere system. The product is a color-coded image of phytoplankton concentration (Figure 1).

SeaWiFS estimates near-surface phytoplankton concentration from measurements of scattered sunlight over a swath width of 2800 km (1740 mi) with a pixel resolution on the order of 1.1 km by 1.1 km. The sensor measures energy in eight spectral bands (six visible, one near-infrared, and one far-infrared) chosen because of their sensitivity to chlorophyll in phytoplankton. From data acquired over a succession of many orbits, SeaWiFS provides a composite global view of variations in marine production. SeaWiFS imagery clearly shows upwelling zones off the coasts of Peru, northwest Africa, and the U.S. West Coast, among the most productive regions of the world ocean. As described in Chapter 6, in these upwelling zones, coupling of the wind with surface ocean waters moves water away from the shore (Ekman transport) and nutrient-rich water wells up from below, spurring marine production. In fact, about 20% of the world fish harvest comes from coastal upwelling zones.

Marine phytoplankton plays an important role in regulating biogeochemical cycles. The atmospheric carbon dioxide concentration has been rising since the beginning of the Industrial Revolution (currently about 1% per year) principally because of the burning of fossil fuels. About half of all CO_2 released to the atmosphere from fossil fuel combustion during that time period has been taken up by ocean waters. Through photosynthesis, phytoplankton removes carbon dioxide dissolved in water and releases oxygen as a by-product. A better understanding of the distribution and concentration of photosynthetic organisms in the sea will improve our understanding of the flux of carbon dioxide into and out of the ocean and the possible implications for global climate change. Furthermore, ocean-color remote sensing is now combined with data from other passive and active satellite-borne sensors for a wide variety of practical applications from locating productive fishing grounds to helping plan the lowest fuel consumption routes for ocean shipping.

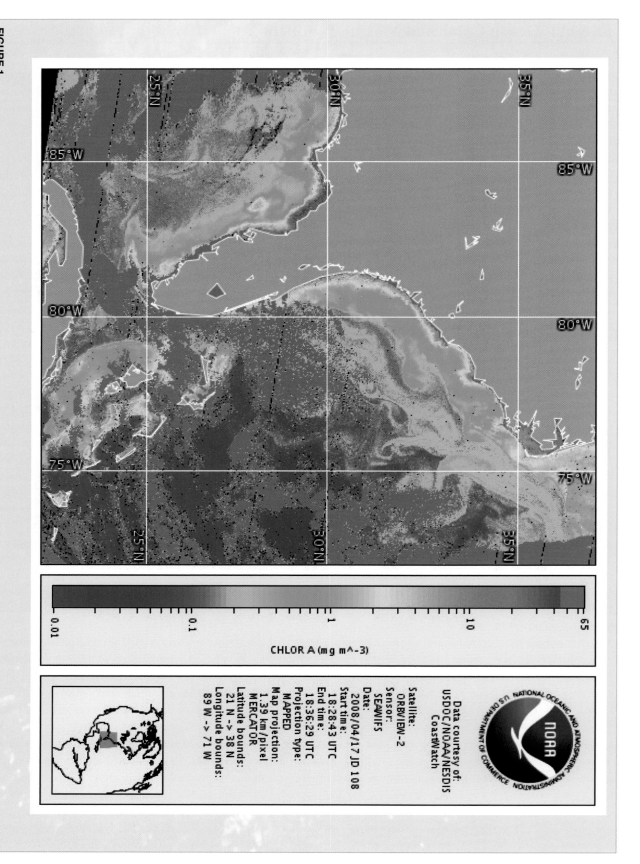

FIGURE 1
SeaWiFS satellite image of biological production for the Gulf Coast, Cuba, Bahamas, and the Eastern Seaboard on 17 April 2008. Red and orange in coastal waters indicate relatively high chlorophyll concentrations; grey patches are clouds. [Courtesy of NOAA CoastWatch and ORBIMAGE]

CHAPTER 10

LIFE IN THE OCEAN

Case-In-Point
Driving Question
Marine Habitats
     Oceanic Life Zones
     Plankton in the Pelagic Zone
     Nekton in the Pelagic Zone
Life Strategies and Adaptations
     Vertical Migration
     Light and Vision
     Sound
     Feeding Strategies
Life at the Ocean's Edge
     Intertidal Zone
     Sea Grass Beds and Salt Marshes
     Kelp Forests
     Coral Reefs
     Benthic Feeding Habits
     Life on the Deep-Sea Floor
Marine Animals
     Fishes
     Marine Mammals
     Marine Reptiles
     Sea Birds
Conclusions
Basic Understandings/Review/Critical Thinking
ESSAY: Life and Sea Ice
ESSAY: Dead Zones
ESSAY: Marine Sanctuaries and Reserves

A Spotted moray eel slithers among the reef growth in the Florida Keys. [OAR/National Undersea Research Program (NURP); University of North Carolina at Wilmington]

Case in Point

Codfish were once so plentiful in the western North Atlantic, especially on the Grand Banks southeast of Newfoundland, that early explorers reported that their ships were slowed by the cod and they could catch them easily using hand nets from small boats. For nearly 500 years the cod fishery was the basis of the economy of Newfoundland and other parts of Atlantic Canada. Some experts argue that the availability of easily transported salt cod provided the food that sustained western European sailors as they explored the North Atlantic and colonized its shores.

Natural fluctuations in cod populations meant periods of low catches but fish stocks always recovered. All that changed after the middle of the 20th century when fishers began using huge factory trawlers to fish intensively for cod on the offshore banks, in waters beyond the limits of Canada's national jurisdiction. In 1977, Canada declared a 323-km (200-mi) exclusive fisheries zone. At that time, Canadian factory trawlers replaced foreign vessels. Although strict regulation ensued, major damage had been done to the cod fishery.

By 1992 cod stocks were so depleted that the Grand Banks fishery was closed. Almost immediately, some 40,000 people lost their jobs in Newfoundland where many small coastal villages depended entirely on the cod fishery for employment. Despite more than 15 years of relief from commercial fishing, the cod population has shown no sign of recovery; in fact, their numbers continue to decrease. Declines in the cod fishery elsewhere prompted the Canadian government in April 2003 to close much of the remaining cod fishery in other areas of the western North Atlantic off Newfoundland and Atlantic Canada. Apparently, the ecosystem that formerly supported cod stocks was altered in such a way as to favor other fish and even lobsters in place of cod. Given our present limited understanding of how this ecosystem functions, it is unclear if the fish stock and the ecosystem that sustained it for centuries can be restored.

In the early years of the 21st century, roughly the same scenario played out as the fisheries authorities of the European Union struggled to find a way to protect the dwindling cod stocks of the North Sea. Heavily subsidized fishing fleets, modern fish finding equipment, and better nets permitted fishers to catch so many fish that stocks fell below the levels needed to maintain the fishery. Efforts to regulate the fisheries were met with strong opposition from the fishers and the fishing industry throughout most of the European Union. Although fish catches were reduced, scientists argue that these cuts were too little and too late to restore stocks sufficiently to permit a sustainable fishery.

The impact of the decline in cod stocks on the fishing industry in northwestern Europe is expected to be serious with the loss of many thousands of jobs and devastation of fishing communities—comparable to what happened earlier in Newfoundland. The effects on the consumer will be significant including, for example, loss of the traditional fish and chips from the menus in British pubs and salt cod from dinner tables in Portugal. Furthermore, extensive disruption of the ecosystem may also lead to the demise of other species, including fish such as haddock that replaced cod on restaurant menus.

The problem of the declining cod fishery also extends into New England where federal courts and NOAA's National Marine Fisheries Service have reduced the length of time that fishers can spend at sea catching cod and other fish. Similar problems also occur off the Pacific coast of the United States where more stringent restrictions on catching groundfish (fish species that live near the sea bottom) have been enacted.

Driving Question:

How have the large and diverse populations of marine organisms adapted to environmental conditions in the ocean?

In the previous chapter we examined the components, structure, functioning, and energy flow of marine ecosystems. In this chapter we continue our look at life in the ocean by describing the various flora and fauna, marine habitats, and some of the ways marine organisms have adapted to the diverse environmental conditions in the ocean.

Marine plants and animals are distributed non-uniformly throughout the ocean, often occurring in scattered patches. We open this chapter by describing marine habitats, oceanic life zones, and the characteristics of plankton and nekton in the open ocean. Central to this discussion is the variety of adaptations evolved by marine organisms including specialized means of floating and moving in the ocean, defense mechanisms to protect against predators, plus feeding and reproductive strategies. We then examine marine plant and animal life at the boundaries of the ocean including organisms living in the intertidal zone, wetlands and estuaries, the deep-sea floor, and coral reefs. Our discussion closes with brief descriptions of marine fishes, mammals, and reptiles plus sea birds.

Marine Habitats

The ocean contains about 99.5% of Earth's potentially inhabited living space; the remaining 0.5% is on land. Living space in the ocean not only vastly exceeds that on land but also consists of many habitats unfamiliar to land dwellers. Ocean scientists know most about life in the ocean's relatively shallow surface layer (especially the coastal zone and over the shelf), and much less about life in the mid-depths, the deepest ocean waters, and the deep-sea floor. We are learning more about life in the ocean, however. In 2000, a 10-year international project was underway to survey the biodiversity of the ocean. Participating in the *Census of Marine Life* are about 2000 researchers representing some 70 nations. The overall goal of the project is to determine life in the ocean: in the past, now, and in the future.

Living organisms inhabit all parts of the ocean, even extreme environments such as Arctic and Antarctic sea ice and hydrothermal vents on the sea floor. The diverse marine habitats include estuaries, coral reefs, polar oceans, and deep-sea trenches. Even sediments and bedrock on the sea floor harbor abundant life. We begin our survey of marine organisms and their habitats by identifying the ocean's major life zones and then examining the plankton and nekton of the open ocean. (For information on life on, within, and beneath sea ice, refer to this chapter's first Essay.)

OCEANIC LIFE ZONES

There are several ways to define *oceanic life zones*. The most commonly used system defines marine habitats in terms of distance from shore and depth (Figure 10.1). In general, open ocean waters constitute the **pelagic zone**, from the ancient Greek *pelagos* meaning the deep or open ocean. Pelagic organisms include **plankton** (passive floaters or weak swimmers such as copepods, larval fish, and jellyfish) and **nekton** (strong swimmers including most fish, squid, turtles, and marine mammals).

The environment of the sea floor at all depths is called the **benthic zone**. Benthic organisms (*benthos*) live either on the ocean bottom or within sediment deposits. They include attached (or sessile), burrowing, and mobile organisms, such as sea stars, crabs, worms, clams, sea cucumbers, sea anemones, urchins, snails, and barnacles.

The pelagic and benthic zones can also be subdivided according to water depth. The upper part of the pelagic zone, up to 200 m (650 ft) deep, is the *epipelagic zone* and roughly corresponds to the photic zone. Below that, from 200 to 1000 m (650 to 3300 ft), is the *mesopelagic zone*, and the deep waters of the open ocean from 1000 to 4000 m (3300 to 13,000 ft) constitute the *bathypelagic zone*. (*Bathy* is a Greek prefix meaning deep). Even greater depths are referred to as the *abyss* or *abyssopelagic zone*.

The area along the shore between high- and low-tide lines is the **intertidal zone**, also known as the *littoral zone*. Two familiar intertidal habitats are rocky shores and sandy beaches. Intertidal zones are home to ecosystems such as salt marshes and mangrove swamps. The area seaward from the shore, across the continental shelf, to the shelf break at a water depth of 120 to 200 m (390 to 650 ft) forms the **neritic zone**. The neritic zone includes the *intertidal zone* and is commonly referred to as the *coastal zone* (Chapter 8).

Oceanic life zones are also defined in terms of nutrient supply (e.g., phosphorus and nitrogen compounds) and productivity. Marine organisms are relatively sparse in the vast open-ocean areas far from land. Many of these areas are lacking in one or more nutrients essential for photosynthetic plants and bacteria. Such nutrient-poor waters having low primary production are described as *oligotrophic*. Waters are

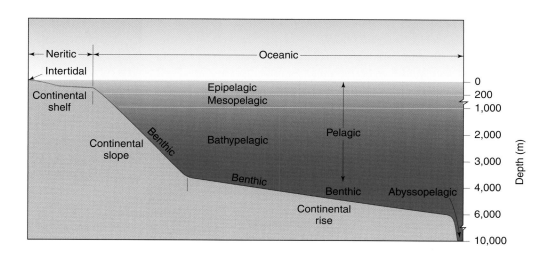

FIGURE 10.1
Life zones in the ocean.

exceptionally clear and appear luminous blue in sunlight due to the lack of organisms and suspended particles. The Mediterranean Sea and large areas of open-ocean within the subtropical gyres (e.g., the Sargasso Sea) are examples of *oligotrophic waters*. On the other hand, ocean waters over continental shelves are especially rich in marine plants and animals. These relatively shallow waters are much more productive than most open-ocean waters because of coastal upwelling and river discharge of nutrients. Nutrient-rich waters having high primary productivity are described as *eutrophic*. In coastal areas where runoff from agricultural lands or sewage discharge enhances the nutrient supply, waters may become excessively eutrophic. Excessive amounts of nutrients promotes an unusually abundant growth of phytoplankton (an algal bloom), which die, sink to the bottom, and deplete waters of dissolved oxygen as they decompose. Each summer, extreme depletion of dissolved oxygen in the Gulf waters off the Louisiana coast eliminates fish and shellfish. For details on the cause of this so-called "dead zone," refer to this chapter's second Essay.

Algal blooms are not always associated with a heavy influx of nutrients. In some cases, blooms arise from disruption of predator/prey relationships within ecosystems. For example, in 1999, massive algal blooms began occurring in San Francisco Bay, a large estuary. Observations over the previous 20 years reported no algal blooms and prior to the 1999 bloom, nutrient loading in the Bay had been declining. Scientists attribute the explosive growth of algae populations to the collapse of the population of bivalves (mollusks), organisms that prey on algae. Without the bivalves to keep their populations in check, algal blooms were inevitable. The loss of bivalves, in turn, was linked to greater coastal upwelling of nutrient-rich waters that favored greater numbers of flatfish and crustaceans, consumers of bivalves.

PLANKTON IN THE PELAGIC ZONE

Most plankton are very small and members of phytoplankton, zooplankton or microbial communities. In Chapter 9, we described the roles of these organisms in the functioning of marine ecosystems. We also saw earlier in this book how their remains are incorporated into marine sediments and sedimentary rocks, thereby linking the biosphere and geosphere through the rock cycle (Chapter 4). In this section we describe strategies and adaptations plankton developed for life in the pelagic zone. Here we define **adaptation** as a genetically controlled trait or characteristic that enhances an organism's chances for survival and reproduction in its environment.

Phytoplankton are slightly denser than seawater and would gradually sink below the sunlit photic zone were it not for characteristics that counteract the tendency to sink. Some species have flattened shapes; others are spiny or occur as long chain-like colonies. These shapes give the cells a relatively large surface area compared to their volume. This adaptation significantly slows sinking, especially in less dense, warm waters, and allows them to remain in the photic zone above the pycnocline. Not surprisingly, the most ornate plankton species inhabit warm tropical waters. Diatoms have a similar adaptation (Figure 10.2). The delicately ornamented outer shell (*frustule*) of diatoms consists of porous silica (SiO_2) that allows for direct uptake of nutrients and gases from seawater as well as rapid expulsion of wastes. One of the most common types of diatoms is shaped like a pillbox; others are elongated or form chains of individual cells. Diatoms are most abundant in cool, nutrient-rich waters, especially at high and middle latitudes and where silica concentrations are relatively high.

The complex shapes and spiny structures of zooplanktonic organisms also increase their surface area to volume ratio, thereby adding to their buoyancy. This is especially obvious in the larvae of many organisms, which have beautifully complex shapes. Another adaptation to increase the buoyancy of planktonic animals is the storage of fats in large, oily globules within their body cavities. Fat is less dense than the surrounding seawater.

Some large planktonic animals have gelatinous bodies, consisting of 95% to 98% water, and are almost neutrally buoyant (having nearly the same density as the surrounding water). Jellyfish, for example, are gelatinous zooplankton having contractile tissues (primitive muscles)

FIGURE 10.2
Although microscopic in size, diatoms can be beautiful and occur in a variety of shapes that provide them with buoyancy in the ocean. [Image courtesy of NASA]

FIGURE 10.3
The bane of swimmers in the Chesapeake Bay, the stinging sea nettle, *Chrysaora quiquecirrha*. [NOAA Photo Library, photo by Mary Hollinger, NODC biologist, NOAA]

NEKTON IN THE PELAGIC ZONE

Larger, free-swimming pelagic animals, collectively called **nekton**, include fish of all sizes, squid, sea turtles, and marine mammals. Some migrate long distances. For example, California gray whales annually migrate from their breeding grounds in warm, shallow waters off the Pacific coast of Baja California, Mexico, to feeding grounds on the Arctic Ocean's continental shelf between Alaska and Siberia, a distance of about 13,000 km (8100 mi). On the other hand, the distribution of many pelagic animals is limited by their tolerance for water temperature, salinity, or food availability.

Except for the smallest zooplankton and jellyfish, marine animals are much denser than seawater. Hence, these animals must swim actively (requiring considerable energy) or utilize other mechanisms to maintain themselves at suitable depths in the ocean. Many adaptations for buoyancy are found in nektonic organisms. The simplest of these are gas bladders. The beautiful chambered nautilus (a primitive relative of squid and octopus) has an external, spiral shell with internal chambers (Figure 10.4). These animals cannot control the air pressure in the chambers—it is always the same as at sea level—so they cannot swim too deep or the shell will collapse under the increasing water pressure. However, they can adjust the amount of fluid, and hence the air volume, in the shell chambers, thereby having some control over buoyancy. In fact, it appears that the nautilus may have been the first large swimming predator to appear in the ocean perhaps 500 million years ago. They are referred to as *living fossils*, that is, organisms that have remained essentially unchanged since their appearance in the geologic past.

that enable them to pulsate their bell-shaped bodies to maintain their position and move slowly in the ocean (Figure 10.3). They swim weakly upward and then sink slowly downward, trapping organisms under their bodies with their tentacles. Jellyfish rely on jet propulsion for locomotion and have been doing so for about 550 million years. The bell-shaped body of a jellyfish is a gelatinous network of nerves and tissue. An extremely thin layer of muscle lines the internal wall of the bell. The jellyfish contracts these muscles ejecting water through the open base of the bell thereby propelling the jellyfish forward. In relatively large jellyfish (which tend to have broader and flatter bodies), jet propulsion is augmented by a paddle-type driving force.

The Portuguese man-of-war (*Physalia physalia*) is a colonial jellyfish-type organism (a siphonophore). It consists of a collection of specialized polyps of four types: a gas-filled float that holds the colony at the surface oriented with the wind, stinging tentacles that trap food, bag-like polyps that secrete enzymes to digest the trapped prey, and reproductive polyps. The specialized stinging cells (nematocysts) in the tentacles produce a powerful toxin, which can be dangerous to humans.

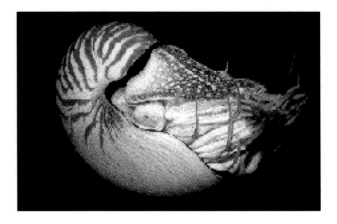

FIGURE 10.4
The nautilus is the only living cephalopod with a shell. They are ancient animals related to squid and octopi. [OceanLink and Bamfield Marine Sciences Center]

Squids are invertebrates; they are mollusks and related to mussels, clams, and snails. They are extremely fast and highly maneuverable swimmers, living at mid-depths of the ocean and migrating to surface waters at night. These fast-growing animals are very successful predators. Most are from 10 to 100 cm (4 to 40 in.) in length and have acute vision. The mysterious giant squid, up to 23 m (75 ft) long, lives in deep waters where it is prey for sperm whales. A few specimens have been caught in fishing nets or have drifted ashore. Their movements are abrupt and powerful and they use their ten long tentacles, covered with suckers, to trap prey and bring it to the mouth, which has a sharp beak-like structure for tearing food apart.

The elusive giant squids are neutrally buoyant and use a special mechanism to prevent sinking. Muscles and cavities in their bodies contain abundant ammonia ions. Since ammonium chloride is less dense than the sodium chloride in seawater, they gain a buoyancy advantage. There is a disadvantage as well. Because they are neutrally buoyant, giant squid gradually float upward if they become trapped in warm water. Their hemocyanin (a form of invertebrate blood) carries oxygen less efficiently in warm water and the squid suffocates and dies. Much of what is known about these mysterious creatures has been learned from dying animals recovered from warm surface waters. Other types of squid must swim continuously in order to maintain their preferred depth in the water column. They are equipped with an internal jet propulsion system. By contracting muscles, the squid forces water into its body through a pipe-like structure called a siphon and then pumps the water out through the siphon as a jet.

Many fishes have gas-filled swim bladders that control buoyancy and regulate the amount of gas in the bladder through a connection to the gut. This makes them sensitive to changes in water pressure with depth, however. Deep-sea fishes with swim bladders are rarely caught alive. If they are brought to the surface too fast, their bladders expand and burst because they cannot adjust to the decreasing pressure fast enough. Fat is less dense than seawater so that another means of increasing buoyancy is to increase the proportion of fat in the body. To achieve neutral buoyancy, about 33% of a fish's tissue must be fat. Some sharks come close to this—their large liver is rich in a fatty substance that is much less dense than seawater. Still, many sharks must swim their entire lives to avoid sinking.

Most pelagic fish rely on active swimming to maintain their level in the ocean and obtain food. Some fish lie on the bottom, waiting for their prey and suddenly lunge to catch it. Others swim all the time, seeking prey over large areas of the ocean perhaps covering hundreds of kilometers each day. The streamlined shape of their body reduces frictional resistance and increases their swimming efficiency. Fish with this feeding strategy require a great deal of energy, efficient muscles, and a rich oxygen supply. Tuna is one such predator. These fish usually feed at a high trophic level and are referred to as *top predators*.

Life Strategies and Adaptations

Marine organisms have evolved many different adaptations to obtain food and avoid being eaten by predators. These include vertical migration, special coloration, eyes sensitive to low light levels, bioluminescence, use of sound, and specialized feeding strategies.

VERTICAL MIGRATION

The photic zone is where photosynthetic primary producers live and food is most plentiful. However, it is also a dangerous place for marine organisms because predators can easily see them. Many types of zooplankton avoid this threat by daily **vertical migration**. Each day at dusk, they come to the surface zone to feed on phytoplankton. As daylight comes, they return to the relative safety of darker, deep waters (the *twilight zone*). These migrations, typically over a vertical distance of about 200 m (650 ft), require expenditure of enormous amounts of energy. In a single daily migration, most small zooplanktonic animals will travel a distance equal to tens of thousands of times their body length. Some fish follow the zooplankton in their daily migration and prey on them. Vertical migration also plays a role in the carbon cycle in that carbon consumed by zooplankton feeding on phytoplankton near the surface at night is transported to deeper water as the animals respire during their return to depth at dawn.

World War II submarine sonars first detected vertical migration as a sound-scattering layer (known as the *deep scattering layer* or *DSL*) that moved up through the water after sunset and down again at sunrise. Sound waves were reflected by the millions of zooplanktonic organisms moving together up and down in the water column to and from the surface. Submarine commanders were able to use this knowledge to hide their vessels beneath the sound-scattering layer.

LIGHT AND VISION

Near the ocean surface, light is abundant and predators have no problem locating prey. Therefore, species of smaller fish that are prey for larger ones have adaptations that make them less visible and therefore less likely to be eaten. The most common adaptation is **adaptive coloration** or camouflage where the animal's color pattern closely matches its background substrate. Hence, they blend in with their surroundings thereby avoiding detection. Many fish exhibit **countershading**, that is, their dorsal side (or back) is a dark color, making it difficult for predators above to see them against the dark, deep water. Their ventral side (or underbelly) is lighter colored, making the fish more difficult for predators to see them from below against the more brightly lit surface waters. Squids and octopi have yet another defense against predators. They can eject a cloud of black or brown "ink" into the water and escape without being seen by a predator.

Marine animals that rely on sight to locate their prey in the dim light of the twilight zone have large, sensitive eyes. In this vast area of the ocean, from 200 to 1000 m (660 to 3300 ft) deep, there is just enough light for predators to locate their prey. In general, the deeper in the twilight zone, the dimmer is the light, and the larger are the eyes of predators living there. Many of these deeper-living fish tend to be reddish in color; red light is absorbed near the surface of the ocean so that red objects are virtually invisible at greater depths.

Below the twilight zone, in the greatest depths of the ocean, light is absent and vision is not useful for locating prey. There is a major exception to this rule, however. Many marine animals (including for example, squid, dinoflagellates, and some species of fish) emit light, a phenomenon known as **bioluminescence** (Figure 10.5). The light usually is a product of a chemical reaction that takes place in specialized cells (*photocytes*)

FIGURE 10.5
Bioluminescence is a property of a wide variety of marine organisms such as the jellyfish *Aequorea aequorea* pictured here. [Courtesy of NSF and Osamu Shimomura, Marine Biological Laboratory, Woods Hole, MA]

or organs (*photophores*). When a substance known as luciferin reacts with oxygen in the presence of the enzyme luciferase, the chemical product gives off blue-green light. In some squid and fish, bacteria living within certain organs are responsible for bioluminescence. Note that bioluminescence differs from *phosphorescence* or *fluorescence* in which light is received from other sources and re-emitted. Bioluminescence is mainly a marine phenomenon and is thought to have evolved a number of different times because it is a characteristic of a broad array of organisms.

Marine animals use light emission to attract mates or prey, frighten or confuse predators, or to disguise themselves. Various deep-sea animals exhibit characteristic patterns of light flashes or luminescent shapes to help them attract a mate. Some fish use bioluminescence to distinguish between male and female. Short bursts of bioluminescent light apparently are especially effective at disorienting prey. Some bathypelagic fishes have strange shapes and many use bioluminescence in their feeding strategies. The female anglerfish has an unusual growth protruding from its head that resembles a fishing rod with a light-producing organ located at the tip of the rod. The structure is a modified dorsal fin that slides along a canal in the back of the fish. When an unwary prey is attracted to the light, the anglerfish consumes it with a sudden snap of its huge mouth.

Light can also be a defensive adaptation for animals in the pelagic environment. The ink ejected by some squid species is luminescent, thereby further confusing a potential predator. Some shrimp emit a luminescent cloudy substance in the direction of an approaching predator while moving rapidly out of sight into the darkness. Also, some marine animals (e.g., squid) are able to camouflage themselves by using bioluminescence to match their body's coloration with that of their background. Even phytoplankton use bioluminescence defensively. Some organisms, such as certain species of dinoflagellates emit light when disturbed. For example, copepods feeding on dinoflagellates stimulate their light emission. But sometimes this attracts the attention of nearby fish to the copepods, allowing the dinoflagellates to escape predation.

SOUND

Marine organisms have other ways of locating prey including sound. Analogous to hearing, many marine animals have evolved ways of sensing the vibrations produced by other organisms moving through the water. A variety of structures and specialized organs have evolved for this purpose. As pointed out in Chapter 3, seawater is essentially transparent to sound. Many marine mammals, including whales, routinely communicate over great distances, even the width of an ocean basin. Scientists are beginning to understand some of their vocabulary. Whales and dolphins possess highly developed auditory senses. In addition to communication and locating prey, they may use sound for navigating over long distances. Fish too are capable of producing sound by using their swim bladders like drums. Predatory seals, dolphins, and whales take advantage of this sound in their search for prey.

Concern is growing over increasing noise levels in the ocean caused by human activities. Sounds such as those produced by large ships, military weapons testing, scientific research, and undersea oil and gas exploration significantly disturb many types of whales. Noise in the ocean may be the reason for some whale strandings in shallow waters or on beaches. Noise need not be very loud to cause problems; low frequency sound waves have higher energy and travel much farther than high frequency sound waves, especially in the ocean's SOFAR channel (Chapter 3).

FEEDING STRATEGIES

Tiny marine animals and the smaller one-cell plants and bacteria mostly move with the waters around them because they cannot swim against ocean currents. Some marine animals have evolved special mechanisms for capturing drifting organisms such as appendages covered with fine bristles that act like strainers to trap small prey. Such structures are very common among copepods and are often very ornate, especially in warm water where they also add buoyancy and act as parachutes to slow sinking out of the photic zone. The general name for marine animals equipped with features that strain food particles out of large volumes of water is **filter feeder**. Even blue whales, the largest animal known to have lived on Earth, are filter feeders. It and eleven other species of baleen whales use plates of fibrous baleen (a substance similar to human finger nails) hanging in a row from their upper jaw to filter plankton from seawater pumped through their mouths by contractions of their massive tongue muscles (Figure 10.6). By feeding directly on primary production phytoplankton, baleen whales shorten the food chain to only two trophic levels.

Filter feeders eat most of the food items trapped in their feeding structures; that is, they are not selective. Other organisms are selective feeders and eat only specific prey organisms. Selective feeding may require special adaptations. For example, some starfish eat mussels, using strong suction to pry open their shells.

FIGURE 10.6
This humpback whale feeds by straining water and trapping food in the baleen plates in its mouth. [NOAA Photo Library photograph]

Some planktonic organisms, such as the planktonic snails called pteropods (also known as sea butterflies), produce a large sticky net of mucus, which functions much like a spider web to trap small water-borne organisms and other food particles. The entire net is then eaten and digested along with the trapped organisms.

Life at the Ocean's Edge

After the pelagic zone, the next largest environment for marine life is the benthic zone, the sea floor at all depths, from the intertidal zone to the deep ocean. The benthic environment is essentially two-dimensional (limited vertically), unlike the vast three-dimensional pelagic zone. Marine organisms that live in the benthic zone collectively are called **benthos**.

Three basic life strategies characterize the benthic zone. Organisms may live attached to a firm surface, they may construct burrows or tunnels or simply dig into sediment deposits, or they may move freely on the sea floor. In general, these habitats dictate their feeding strategies. Attached animals are filter feeders, mobile animals are active predators, and burrowing organisms ingest sediment, digesting the organic material it contains and excreting the rest. Some also dig into the bottom sediments for protection from predators.

Attached organisms include seaweed (technically known as *macro-algae*) and sea grasses, the only truly marine form of the more complex plants (angiosperms). Macro-algae have root-like structures called *holdfasts* that attach to the ocean bottom while they absorb nutrients and water directly from the surrounding seawater. Some familiar attached animals are barnacles, mussels, clams, oysters, corals, and anemones. In general, benthic animals that are not attached move relatively slowly. Starfishes, urchins, and snails are examples of mobile benthic predators. Others are crabs and lobsters, which can move quickly in short spurts to catch their prey or to avoid predation.

Burrowing animals are less familiar to us because they largely disappear beneath the surface of sediment deposits, even in shallow tide pools. They live on sandy and muddy bottoms and include various forms of mollusks and worms. Often their presence can be detected by small holes in the sediment surface and piles of mud or sand ejected from their tunnels during burrowing.

INTERTIDAL ZONE

As mentioned earlier in this chapter, the intertidal (or littoral) zone is the area along the shore between low- and high-tide levels. Most intertidal zones are readily accessible so that properties and components are well known to scientists and amateur naturalists. Because the intertidal zone is where the atmosphere, hydrosphere, biosphere, lithosphere, and cryosphere interface and interact, this zone is among the most changeable portions of the Earth system (Chapter 8). Waves, winds, and tidal currents continually disturb the intertidal zone. With the rise and fall of the tides, the intertidal zone is alternately exposed to seawater and the atmosphere with accompanying drastic shifts in temperature and salinity. In winter, winds, tides, and currents may drive floating pans of sea ice ashore where they abrade and erode the intertidal zone. Special adaptations enable animals and plants to survive in this stressful environment.

Although all intertidal zones share some common characteristics, a distinction is made among intertidal habitats based on the type of substrate (e.g., rocky, muddy, sandy). The most energetic of these habitats are rocky intertidal shorelines where organisms are frequently subject to strong wave action, especially in winter. Rocky shorelines, especially in middle latitudes, are home to complex marine ecosystems with organisms adapted for life in particularly harsh conditions. Where the distance between low and high tide levels is relatively great, organisms may be exposed to dry air and sunshine for many hours at a stretch. Depending on the season, they may have to withstand extremely high or low air temperatures when they are not covered by seawater.

Some intertidal zones feature extensive mud flats. A **mud flat** is a nearly level area of fine silt along the shore. Streams and creeks deliver the sediment and

wave action is typically weak. Mud flats are often ideal habitats for submerged aquatic vegetation, salt marshes, and many forms of benthic animals. In addition, sandy beaches are intertidal habitats (Chapter 8). Seaweeds are important components of the intertidal zone and provide habitat for animals. For example, many snails, sea urchins, and other marine herbivores graze on seaweed and may control its population in some areas. Seaweeds are distributed according to their light requirements and their ability to resist wave action as well as drying and/or freezing conditions during low tide.

All seaweeds are algae and are green, brown, or red, depending on the color of the dominant photosynthetic pigment. In general, brown and red algae are more robust and often have a rubbery feel, whereas green algae are more delicate. Bright green sea lettuce, with thin leaves up to one meter (3.3 ft) long, lives from just above the low tide mark (so it is not exposed to air for very long periods) to depths of about 10 m (33 ft). It requires abundant light. Red algae photosynthesize most efficiently at lower light levels; hence, they are more likely to be found in deeper water or in tide pools that are shaded by rock outcrops or cliffs. They also prefer the higher temperatures of tropical waters.

Brown algae are the most common seaweeds found along the rocky coasts of the northeastern and western United States. They flourish in cold water and usually have a heavier structure that resists strong waves. They often have many small, gas-filled bladders that help keep their blades (not true leaves) floating near the water surface. Another adaptation of brown algae for life in the intertidal zone is the presence of gelatinous substances that helps them retain seawater at low tide when they are exposed to drying air. These substances have many commercial uses as stabilizers in ice cream and as emulsifiers in many food products. Algin extracted from brown algae is also used to thicken textile dyes, in paints, and even by dentists in taking impressions of teeth.

Open-ocean waters are too deep for plants to attach to the bottom and survive. Some plants do survive, however, in an area in the western Atlantic Ocean where Gulf Stream waters flow around the western side of the North Atlantic subtropical gyre (Chapter 6). This area is known as the Sargasso Sea, after the abundant, brown seaweed (*Sargassum*) that floats on the surface. *Sargassum* weed originates in the Caribbean Sea, where it grows attached to hard surfaces in the intertidal zone. It is broken off by storm waves and becomes trapped in the current system of the North Atlantic subtropical gyre where it accumulates as large, floating rafts.

Sargassum weed is supported by bubble-like gas filled structures that keep the plants floating near the surface where light for photosynthesis is abundant. Surface waters of the subtropical gyre are nutrient poor and cannot support large phytoplankton and fish communities. However, rafts of *Sargassum* weed provide a unique habitat for animal life. The small animals that can survive in the nutrient-poor waters maintain a close relationship with the seaweed, either attached to it or swimming within the floating mats. Some small fishes and crabs have color patterns that allow them to blend in with the background of *Sargassum* weed. Many invertebrates such as snails, crabs, and anemones live attached to or moving about the weed. All of these animals are feeding generalists (omnivores), eating whatever comes their way in the water. Sea turtles, especially young ones, also find a protective environment within the *Sargassum* weed of the Sargasso Sea.

As with seaweed, animals are distributed in the intertidal zone according to their tolerance for drying and changes in temperature and salinity. Highly mobile animals, such as crabs, move up and down with the changing water levels as the tide floods and ebbs. Animals such as barnacles and mussels attach themselves to hard surfaces and can shut their shells completely, thereby retaining enough seawater inside to survive until they are covered again by the flood tide. For this reason, barnacles are the dominant animals in the upper, more exposed portion of the intertidal zone. Although they resemble mollusks, barnacles are actually crustaceans. They feed only when covered by water, opening their shells and extending their feathery legs through their shell top to filter food from the water. Barnacles are so firmly cemented to rock surfaces that waves cannot loosen them. Mussels are mollusks that usually live slightly lower in intertidal zones and are firmly attached to rocks by sticky threads.

Other intertidal mollusks include limpets and chitons that attach to rocks with a strong suction created by a muscular foot-like appendage. Both move so slowly that they are unable to keep pace with tidal oscillations. They are fairly resistant to drying out and are only active when they are covered with water. Their food is plant material that they scrape off rock surfaces with a radula, a tongue-like structure consisting of rows of chitinous teeth. Still lower in the intertidal zone is a greater diversity of animals including starfishes, anemones, urchins, and crabs.

While walking along a rocky shore at low tide you may have encountered tide pools sheltering a diverse animal community. A **tide pool** is a volume of water left behind in a rock basin or other intertidal depression by an ebbing tide. If a tide pool is exposed to direct sunshine, organisms inhabiting the pool must contend with great fluctuations in water temperature. Rainfall can also alter the salinity of tide-pool waters. If a tide pool is shaded or in a cave, temperature and salinity variations are much less so that a greater variety of more delicate animals can survive. Typically, tide pools harbor species that have evolved to deal with wide fluctuations in environmental conditions; these organisms include certain algae, sea anemones, starfish, snails, small crustaceans, barnacles, mussels, and fish (Figure 10.7).

Just below low-tide level on rocky shores live the most diverse communities of plants and animals. The complex substrate and the seaweed provide protection for many small animals. Here soft bodied and delicate animals like anemones and sea cucumbers can thrive. Predators, such as lobsters, crabs, small fishes, octopi, and sea otters are important in this ecosystem.

FIGURE 10.7
A tide pool with mussels (submerged) and barnacles (on the exposed rock undersides), located near Bass Harbor Head Lighthouse, Mt. Desert Island, Acadia National Park, Maine. [NOAA Photo Library photograph by Captain Albert E. Theberge, NOAA Corps (ret.)]

SEA GRASS BEDS AND SALT MARSHES

On mud flats and other soft-bottomed habitats (such as along sandy and estuarine shorelines), the most important plants are *sea grasses*, also known as *submerged aquatic vegetation (SAV)* (Figure 10.8). These are *angiosperms*, flowering and seed bearing vascular plants with true roots. They are limited to water depths where light is sufficient for photosynthesis and prefer water that is clear. Sea grass beds are highly productive with some rivaling the primary production of intensively developed agricultural land in the amount of carbon fixed (500 to 1000 gm per square m per year). Sea grass beds export large amounts of organic matter to nearby coastal waters. However, water pollution, sediment runoff from land, and dredging are among the many human activities that threaten sea grass beds. Where nutrient input (nitrogen and phosphorus compounds) is excessive, such as in runoff from agricultural lands, excessive numbers of algae may grow on the blades of sea grasses, shading and eventually killing them.

Perhaps the most extensively studied sea grass ecosystem is the Chesapeake Bay. When Europeans arrived in the Bay area in the early 17th century, sea grasses covered an estimated 240,000 hectares (600,000 acres) of the Bay. By 1978, the sea grass area had shrunk to only 16,000 hectares (41,000 acres). Destruction of sea grass beds is a concern for several reasons. Sea grass anchors sediment and dampens wave action thereby controlling erosion and turbidity. It is a food source for many organisms including waterfowl and small mammals and serves as a primary nursery for crabs and many species of fish.

Reduction of the Chesapeake Bay sea grass habitat along with over-fishing has been implicated in the decline of populations of the blue crab (*Callinectes sapidus*), a mainstay of the Bay fishery for more than a century. Over the past decade or so, the number of adult female crabs plunged by about 80%. Sea grass beds serve young blue crabs as nurseries, a source of food and protection from predators. Without adequate sea grass habitat, the blue crab is more vulnerable to predation by striped bass (i.e., rockfish). Striped bass turned to blue crabs as a food source when fishing reduced the numbers of menhaden, their preferred food. Menhaden is a marine fish in the herring family and the Bay's top fishery by weight. Fortunately, restoration efforts have had some success and by 2005, the area of sea grasses along the shallows and shorelines of Chesapeake Bay had increased to an estimated 31,304 hectares (78,260 acres), up 7% from the previous year but 42% of the bay wide restoration goals. We have more on efforts to restore Chesapeake Bay in Chapter 14 and 15.

Salt marshes commonly occur along sheltered shorelines and are ecologically similar to sea grass beds in estuaries. Salt marsh grasses and bushes differ from sea grasses by being salt-tolerant true land plants, pollinating in the air. Salt marshes are flooded at high tide, but the grasses are never completely covered by salt water. Salt marshes are also home to abundant marine life, and are refuges for waterfowl and other wildlife. They are true transition zones between marine and terrestrial ecosystems (Figure 10.9).

In estuaries, the types of plants and animals vary from marine species near the mouth of the estuary

FIGURE 10.8
A sunlit sea grass meadow in the Florida Keys National Marine Sanctuary. Sea grasses are also known as submerged aquatic vegetation. [NOAA photo by Heather Dine]

FIGURE 10.9
The edge of a salt marsh meeting oak and other higher ground flora on Daniel Island, SC. [NOAA photo by Captain Albert E. Theberge, NOAA Corps (ret.)]

to brackish water species where the salinity is lower, to those that prefer a nearly freshwater environment at the head of the estuary (Chapter 8). The salinity of estuarine waters occasionally changes drastically as when the discharge of fresh water entering the estuary increases abruptly following a period of heavy rainfall. This change in salinity can impact the types of species and their distribution in the estuary depending on how fast they can move or their tolerance.

In the tropics, between about 30 degrees N and 30 degrees S, mangrove swamps are common along muddy, low-lying coastlines and in estuaries. A **mangrove swamp** consists of tropical plant species including trees that grow in low marshy areas and can tolerate salt water flooding of their roots and lower

FIGURE 10.10
Red mangroves are common in Florida. Mangroves roots serve as critical habitat for many species and nutrient filters. [NOAA/OAR/National Undersea Research Program (NURP)]

stems (Figure 10.10). They generally compete successfully with local marsh grasses. Mangroves form dense growths and their aerial roots provide a complex and protective habitat for many organisms. For example, mangrove oysters and other organisms attach to the roots, which trap sediment and organic material. Mangrove swamps are also important nursery grounds for many marine species. However, many hectares of mangrove swamps are lost each year, cleared to create farmland or for coastal development projects such as housing, shopping malls, resorts, airports, and industrial parks. Furthermore, some coastal residents have removed mangrove trees because they obstructed their view of the ocean. Ironically, mangrove swamps may be the final line of defense against a storm surge (Chapter 8).

KELP FORESTS

Seaward of the intertidal zone, kelp forests grow where waters are cool and nutrient-rich (Figure 10.11). **Kelp** includes various species of brown algae that grow to enormous size. In clear waters, individual plants grow at depths of about 30 to 40 m (100 to 130 ft) and their stipes (stem-like structures) and leaf-like fronds reach all the way to the surface. Found in cool waters worldwide, they are especially abundant in coastal upwelling zones off California and the Pacific Northwest.

Kelp plants grow attached to rocky bottoms by root-like structures (*holdfasts*). Holdfasts are quite small so that in many species, the weight of the plant is supported at the surface by a bulbous gas filled float below

the fronds. Hence, strong waves easily destroy kelp beds and huge amounts of detached kelp wash onto beaches following storms. Fortunately, kelp can grow rapidly—up to tens of centimeters per day. Because of this, it can be easily harvested and will regrow if only the tops of the blades are removed. Kelp's primary production is high, rivaling that of some of the richest farmlands.

A dense stand of kelp is like a submarine forest, and it supports a rich community of animals that lives below its canopy. Small fishes, urchins, crabs, and lobsters

FIGURE 10.11
A forest of giant kelp near Baja California. These large brown algae can grow as much as 0.6 m (2 ft) per day in water depths up to 45 m (150 ft). [Image courtesy of NOAA]

are common on the sea floor around the holdfasts of kelp plants. Smaller algae, sea anemones, mollusks, and other invertebrates may attach to these structures. Further up the stipe where light is a little brighter, red and brown algae may live on the surface of the kelp. Sea urchins climb up the kelp plant eating these algae, or even the kelp itself. The canopy protects large schools of young fishes such as herring and sardines. Also, many organisms such as snails graze upon kelp fronds.

Along the Pacific coast of North America, kelp forests are home to large numbers of sea otters. Sea urchins are the favorite food of otters and urchins abound in the kelp forest habitat. In fact, urchins can destroy a kelp forest through grazing if they become too numerous. Sea otters feeding on urchins keep their populations in check. However, when sea otters were hunted (for their fur) to near extinction in the 18th and 19th centuries, sea urchin populations exploded and many kelp beds were lost. A similar relationship exists among kelp, urchins, and lobsters in North Atlantic kelp habitats, and over-fishing of lobsters has had similar results.

In 2007, an international team of ocean scientists reported that kelp forests may be much more widespread in the tropics than previously believed. (Widely scattered reports of kelp in tropical latitudes had circulated for many years.) A computerized kelp-habitat model was developed that incorporates the essential environmental conditions for kelp; that is, cold nutrient-rich water welling up from the deep, adequate sunlight, and a suitable ocean bottom for their holdfasts. The model predicted that kelp forests could be found in various patches of the tropical ocean covering a total area of 23,500 square km (9100 square mi) worldwide. The scientists confirmed the computer prediction when they discovered eight patches of dense kelp forests near the tropical Galápagos Islands.

CORAL REEFS

A **coral reef** is among the ocean's most spectacular biological features. These slow growing structures can be centuries old and may be so large that they are visible from space. In many parts of the tropical ocean, reefs stand hundreds of meters above the sea bottom and can extend hundreds of kilometers along the shoreline. Carbonate-secreting colonial animals are the primary builders of coral-reef frameworks. These open coral structures are bound together by layers of calcareous algae. Coral reefs grow along coastlines or cap extinct undersea volcanoes. They consist of thin veneers of living organisms growing on older layers of dead coral (limestone) or volcanic rock. Whereas corals are found in all ocean basins, large reefs occur only in tropical waters, between about 30 degrees N and 30 degrees S. A few slow growing, small coral reefs occur along shelf breaks in many ocean areas.

The Great Barrier Reef, consisting of about 3000 reefs and 600 low-lying carbonate-sand islands, stretches more than 2000 km (1250 mi) along the Queensland coast of eastern Australia (Figure 10.12). It is the world's most extensive reef system and also the largest structure on Earth made by living organisms. At its northern end, the reef is nearly continuous and is only about 50 km (30 mi.) offshore. In the south, individual reefs are more common with some located up to 300 km (190 mi) offshore. Each year, about 2 million people visit the Great Barrier Reef.

FIGURE 10.12
The Great Barrier Reef extends for 2,000 kilometers along the northeastern coast of Australia. It is not a single reef, but a vast maze of reefs, passages, and coral cays (islands that are part of the reef). [Image courtesy NASA/GSFC/LaRC/JPL, MISR Team]

Most coral reefs are in the tropical Pacific and Indian Oceans. Reef-building corals prefer waters having an average annual temperature of 23 °C to 25 °C (73 °F to 77 °F) and most corals cannot tolerate prolonged exposure to either very low or high water temperatures or to large fluctuations in temperature. For this reason, even small changes in sea surface temperatures—perhaps associated with large-scale climate change—threaten coral reefs. Corals also require clear water and are endangered by sediment runoff from land, oil spills, and other forms of water pollution. Eutrophication caused by excess nutrient input from the land can stimulate the growth of algae on the surface of coral reefs, smothering the coral polyps.

Each type of coral animal builds a characteristic structure that is conspicuous on reef surfaces. Some corals (e.g., brain corals) form robust compact structures; others build delicate, complex branching forms. Many corals have growth rings, much like trees, that can be used to reconstruct past variations in ocean conditions and climate. Scientists use coral growth rings to study past El Niño events in the tropical Pacific Ocean (Chapter 11). Worldwide, coral reefs provide shelter and food for up to 9 million species of marine life (about one-third of the total number of known marine species) including fish, invertebrates, and plants. Coral reefs are among Earth's most productive habitats, ranking second to rainforests in biodiversity. The Great Barrier Reef is home to whales, dolphins, green turtles, fish (1500 species), mollusks (4000 species), and birds (200 species).

Individual coral animals, called *polyps* (Figure 10.13), capture tiny plants and animals floating in the waters flowing over the reef. Reef-building corals also obtain large amounts of energy from microscopic dinoflagellates

FIGURE 10.13
Coral polyps. [NOAA, photo by Brent Deuel]

called *zooxanthellae* living within the tissues of polyps. The photosynthetic pigments in zooxanthellae are responsible for the bright color of corals. More importantly photosynthesis by zooxanthellae provides corals with food, permitting them to grow more rapidly than if they depended only on the food they captured from the water flowing past. Zooxanthellae, in turn, use the metabolic wastes produced by coral polyps as a source of nutrients. Hence, the corals and their zooxanthellae have a symbiotic relationship. A **symbiotic relationship** is a mutually beneficial association in which each organism benefits from the other. The sunlight requirements of zooxanthellae mean that the actively growing parts of a coral reef must be near enough to the ocean surface to receive abundant sunlight.

Without zooxanthellae, corals cannot flourish. As noted above, corals are very sensitive to changes in water temperature. In response to unusually high sea surface temperatures (SST), coral polyps expel zooxanthallae. Without zooxanthallae, coral polyps have little pigmentation and appear nearly transparent on the coral's white skeleton, a condition known as **coral bleaching**. A rise in SST of one to two Celsius degrees (2 to 4 Fahrenheit degrees) is sufficient to cause temporary bleaching. However, if bleaching episodes persist or are unusually severe such as may occur during El Niño, coral polyps and the reef die.

Another potential threat to coral reefs is rising sea level. If sea level rises slowly, healthy coral reefs can grow upward at a rate that will maintain them near the ocean surface and bright sunlight. However, if sea level rises too rapidly, reefs may not be able to grow fast enough. If they are too deeply submerged to receive sufficient sunlight for photosynthesis, they die. Many deeply submerged Pacific seamounts are capped by reef limestone. In these cases, coral growth could not keep pace with the rapid rise in sea level or sinking platforms due to plate movement down slope and away from spreading centers.

Coral reefs growing on volcanic islands typically exhibit a characteristic sequence of forms first described by Charles Darwin (Figure 2.19). A coral reef grows along the shore of an active volcano as a relatively narrow *fringing reef*, similar to those now found on the Big Island of Hawaii. After becoming inactive and eventually extinct, the volcano sinks as the plate under it subsides while being displaced from the hot spot that originally formed the volcano. At first the coral reef grows upward from its original position to form a *barrier reef*, separated from the main island by a shallow lagoon. Barrier reefs occur on the older Hawaiian Islands to the northwest of the Big Island such as off the coast of Oahu. As the volcano erodes and continues to

FIGURE 10.14
Satellite image of an atoll in the western Pacific Ocean. [NOAA Photo Library, photo by Richard B. Mierement, NOAA OSDIA]

sink into the ocean, the volcanic island becomes smaller. Eventually the volcanic island submerges beneath the waves or erodes away, leaving behind only the ring of coral reefs surrounding a shallow lagoon where the island once stood. At this stage, the reef is known as an **atoll** (Figure 10.14). Atolls are shaped like a ring or horseshoe and vary from 1 to 100 km (0.6 to 60 mi) across. Midway and Kure Islands, at the northwestern end of the Hawaiian Island chain, are examples of atolls. Atolls are most common in the Pacific Ocean (Figure 10.15).

Corals described thus far are *hermatypic*, that is, they live in warm, shallow waters and build large reefs, and possess zooxanthellae. Solitary corals and small coral reefs also live in cold, deep water along continental shelf breaks in some parts of the ocean (Figure 10.16). Without light, these so-called *ahermatypic corals* cannot rely on zooxanthellae, so they depend exclusively on trapping food directly from the water using their stinging cells or nematocysts. Some ahermatypic corals are hard structures whereas others are softer and more delicate, branching forms, which do not build limestone structures. They provide excellent habitats for deep-water fishes. But therein is a threat to their survival. Trawlers, fishing boats that drag huge nets along the sea bottom, are destroying these slow growing deep-sea corals. Although little is known about the distribution and biology of deep-sea corals, some nations such as Norway are beginning to ban harmful fishing practices in areas where they occur.

In an effort to preserve coral reefs and other underwater marine resources for present and future generations, the U.S. government has designated certain areas of its jurisdictional waters as *marine sanctuaries* or *marine reserves*. For more on this topic, refer to this chapter's third Essay.

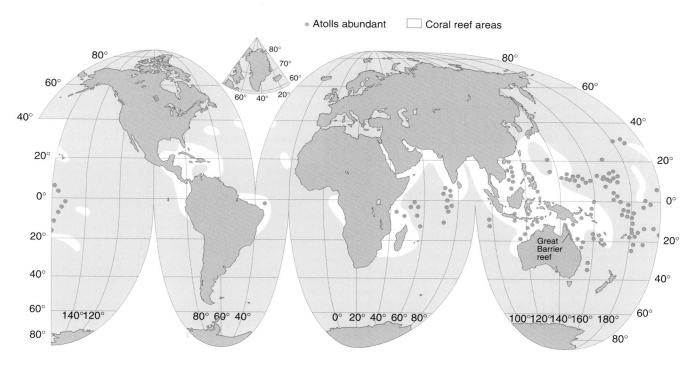

FIGURE 10.15
Location of atolls and coral reefs in the world ocean.

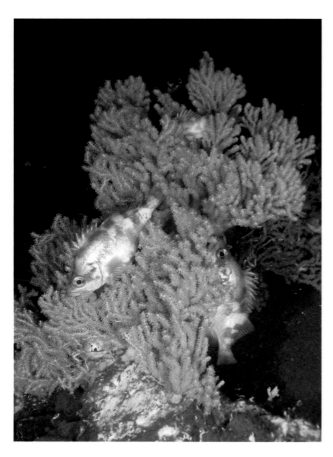

FIGURE 10.16
Darkblotched rockfish nestled in the branches of a deep-sea gorgonian soft coral. [NOAA]

BENTHIC FEEDING HABITS

Animals that live on or in soft-bottomed habitats—whether in the intertidal zone, shallow coastal areas, or in the deep sea—are divided into two categories: infauna and epifauna. **Infauna** inhabit sediment deposits whereas **epifauna** live on the sea floor. Some of these benthic animals are *unselective* in their feeding, moving through or on the mud and simply eating everything. They ingest bottom deposits and digest the organic detritus they contain while the remaining material (mud or very fine sand) is excreted. Other benthic animals are more *selective* in their feeding habits, ingesting food particles from mud and sand, rather than consuming the sediment itself. As benthic animals feed on or in sediment, they disturb the deposits, a process called **bioturbation**. Their feces bind sediments into harder, more durable aggregates that are not readily re-suspended by currents. Close observation of the surface of a water-covered mud flat reveals a variety of feeding structures of infaunal worms and clams extending above the entrances to their burrows.

Soft bottoms also harbor many filter feeders that separate phytoplankton, small zooplankton, and other edible materials from large volumes of water. The distribution of animals in muddy and sandy habitats is controlled primarily by the grain size of the sediment. Filter feeders cannot live in fine-grained mud, because it clogs their feeding apparatus. Hence, they usually inhabit coarser grained sands. Filter feeders are generally rare where deposit feeders are abundant because bioturbation makes the near-bottom water muddy and therefore unsuitable for filter feeding. On the other hand, mud is ideal for unselective feeders. It contains more organic matter brought in from terrestrial sources and raining down from the photic zone plus an abundant supply of decomposing bacteria and other microbes.

Whereas some animals living in the rocky intertidal zone, such as starfish, can absorb dissolved oxygen from the water directly through their body surfaces, benthic animals living in muddy habitats require specialized breathing structures. A respiratory structure may extend outside their burrows or they may pump water through their burrows and past their gills for uptake of dissolved oxygen. Some animals line their burrows with mucus or shell fragments to prevent mud from clogging these breathing structures.

LIFE ON THE DEEP-SEA FLOOR

In the deep ocean, detritus that reaches the sea floor is mostly decomposed and has little nutritional value. For this reason, far fewer organisms can survive in this habitat but it is not the dead zone envisioned by most 19th century scientists. Many unusual creatures live on the deep-sea floor. For example, a starfish-like animal, called a sea lily, lives attached to the bottom by a long, stem-like structure (Figure 10.17). Its arms, covered with a mucous substance, are suspended in the water above the sea floor

FIGURE 10.17
This delicate sea lily (crinoid), a member of the phylum that includes starfish, can orient toward the current to increase food capture. [NOAA Undersea Research Program]

FIGURE 10.18
Tube worms at a hydrothermal vent on the floor of the Pacific Ocean. Discovery of such organisms launched a new avenue of inquiry into our understanding of biological processes operating in the deep ocean (especially chemosynthesis). [OAR/National Undersea Research Program (NURP); College of William & Mary]

and trap particles in the near-bottom waters. The particles are moved along grooves to the mouth. Predatory starfish travel along the bottom on long legs that keep their bodies above the sediment surface. Other filter feeders in the deep ocean include sponges, crustaceans, and some kinds of worms and mollusks. Deposit feeders are similar to those living in shallow benthic habitats, although animals in the deep, cold ocean are generally smaller, an adaptation to the scarcity of food. In these dark waters color has no strategic value so that most animals have a drab appearance.

Communities of specialized animals have evolved to live on the deep ocean bottom near hydrothermal vents (Chapter 2). Large colonies of tubeworms have a symbiotic relationship with bacteria that live within their bodies (Figure 10.18). The bacteria use hydrogen sulfide (H_2S) as an energy source and make food for the tubeworms through chemosynthesis (Chapter 9). These worms can grow to a length of 3 m (10 ft). Also living in this extreme environment are long legged crabs and specialized mollusks and clams.

Marine Animals

In this section, we briefly describe larger marine animals and their adaptations for life in the sea. These organisms include fishes, mammals, reptiles, and birds.

FISHES

Fishes are the most familiar type of nekton. Unlike mammals, which regulate their body temperature, fish are cold blooded and hence are as warm or cold as the surrounding water. (Some fish that live in water at temperatures slightly below 0 °C contain natural antifreeze.) Fishes range in size from the smallest of all vertebrates, a marine goby only 8 to 10 mm long, to the huge whale shark up to 15 m (50 ft) long. Fish may be herbivorous, carnivorous, or omnivorous. They inhabit all parts of the ocean and possess special adaptations for buoyancy, swimming, and life in the dimly lit twilight zone as well as the greatest depths of the ocean. Many open-ocean pelagic fishes are streamlined for swimming fast as they search for prey and flee from predators. Fishes living among plants or rocks often have body shapes and colors that allow them to blend unnoticed with their background. Because the blood and body fluids of marine fish are only about one third as salty as seawater, they need special physiological adaptations in order to survive in the ocean.

There are two major groups of fishes: elasmobranchs (or cartilaginous fishes) and teleosts (or bony fishes). **Elasmobranchs** or **cartilaginous fishes** include sharks, skates, and rays and are considered to be more primitive. Their skeletons lack true bones and consist entirely of cartilage. Their skin feels much like fine sandpaper due to small, embedded tooth-like structures called denticles. Sharks' teeth are large, specialized denticles that occur in rows in the mouth and are continually growing forward, being lost and subsequently replaced from behind.

According to a popular misconception, sharks are ferocious predators who menace swimmers (Figure 10.19). In fact, a few shark species are ferocious but their threat to humans is not significant. Nonetheless, shark attacks—no matter how infrequent—are shocking and frightening. Some sharks are quite selective predators, feeding mostly

FIGURE 10.19
A white-tip shark (*Triaenodon obesus*) swimming northwest of the Hawaiian Islands. [NOAA Photo Library, photograph by Dr. Dwayne Meadows, NOAA/NMFS/OPR]

on preferred types of prey. Other species, such as the tiger shark, are sometimes referred to as "garbage cans of the sea" because they eat almost anything, living or dead. Some types of sharks and rays are bottom feeders, with an upper jaw designed to pick up food from the sea floor. Basking sharks, whale sharks, and many rays are passive filter feeders; that is, they swim continuously, straining plankton from the water passing over their gills. Whale sharks are thus very docile even though they weigh more than 40,000 kg (about 45 tons) and grow to a length of 15 m (50 ft).

Sharks have some unique limitations in that they do not have a swim bladder for buoyancy, their blood pressure is low, and most cannot pump water over their gills to obtain oxygen. To help compensate for all three of these limitations, most sharks swim ceaselessly their entire life. With swimming motion, their pectoral fins provide lift much like an airplane wing. Movement causes a flow of water over their gills to oxygenate the blood (known as *ram ventilation*), and continuous swimming produces muscle action that helps the heart pump blood. Without active swimming, a shark would sink to the bottom and most would asphyxiate. Some sharks, however, possess spiracles, and others have special muscles that force water over the gills, helping them to obtain oxygen even while stationary.

There are over 800 species of cartilaginous fishes. Their reproductive strategies favor survival of their young. Unlike most bony fishes, cartilaginous fishes have internal fertilization. Although they bear very small numbers of young (whereas bony fishes release thousands of eggs), the chance of reproductive success is increased. Some sharks and rays lay their eggs in leathery cases that harden in a few hours. Beachcombers sometimes find these leathery pouches, called "mermaid's purses," washed up on the beach. The young are hatched fully formed; there is no planktonic larval stage among cartilaginous fishes.

Some species of sharks are *viviparous*; that is, embryonic development occurs entirely within the female shark's body and they bear live young. Hammerhead sharks are a viviparous species. Cartilaginous fishes usually lay their eggs or bear their young in coastal nursery areas where there is less danger of predation by larger fishes.

Cartilaginous fishes are *isosmotic* with their environment; that is, the salt concentration in their body is approximately the same as the surrounding seawater. Hence, there can be an equal amount of water leaving the body as enters it. However, the types of salts are different. They have a very high concentration of organic solutes, mostly urea, in their tissues. The concentration of sodium chloride in their body fluids is only about half that of seawater so that a special rectal gland contains a cell that selectively excretes chloride ions into their urine.

Teleosts (or *bony fishes*) have bony skeletons, scales, and a flap covering their gills. This is a large, diverse, and familiar group of fishes that live in a variety of marine and freshwater environments. Most bony fish have a swim bladder, a gas-filled structure that can be inflated or deflated enabling the fish to adjust its buoyancy with changes in water depth. Normally, the salt concentration in bony marine fish is only about one quarter to one third that of seawater. Hence, they must also have a mechanism to regulate the salt content of their bodies. Otherwise they would continually lose water via diffusion through their gills and body surface to the environment. (Ions or molecules tend to migrate from regions of higher concentration to regions of lower concentration.) To prevent this from happening, they must drink a lot of water. Their gills have special chloride excretory cells that transport the excess salt out of their bodies. Their kidneys excrete the larger ions, such as calcium and magnesium, retaining water in the body. Marine teleosts produce only minute amounts of concentrated urine compared to freshwater fish.

Fishes living on or near the ocean bottom are called *demersal fishes* and many of them are commercially important, such as cod, halibut, haddock, and sole. *Flatfishes* are demersal fishes that have a special coloration that camouflages them against the ocean bottom. They include halibut, flounder, and sole. Because these fish spend most of their lives lying on the sea floor, an eye on the lower side would be useless (Figure 10.20). When larval flatfishes hatch as free-swimming zooplankton, they

FIGURE 10.20
Note the two eyes on one side of the head of this flounder photographed at an ocean depth of more than 2600 m (8600 ft) off the North Carolina coast. [NOAA, Office of Ocean Exploration]

have eyes on either side of their head. As larvae mature, however, one eye moves over the top of its head, so that when a young fish finally takes up life on the bottom, both eyes are looking up on the same side of the head. Also its body thins and is laterally compressed. In addition, they have the ability to quickly change the color and pattern of their skin so that they closely resemble their background, another example of adaptive coloration.

As noted above, many pelagic fishes are fast swimmers. Tuna and mackerel are examples of fishes well adapted for strong swimming over long distances in open waters. For example, blue fin and yellow fin tuna typically cruise at 16 km per hr (10 mph) but are capable of brief bursts of 95 to 130 km per hr (60 to 80 mph). Such high speeds require large amounts of energy and these fast swimmers usually occupy a high trophic level in marine food webs. Their dense muscles make their meat very desirable and they are much in demand by humans.

Smaller pelagic fishes such as herring and sardines are abundant in coastal waters and in upwelling areas where nutrients are plentiful. Some of the world's largest fisheries are based on these species. Smaller fishes are converted to fishmeal and used as high protein feed for cattle, poultry, and fish farms and also as fertilizer.

Most marine teleosts spawn; that is, the females release their eggs into the water where they are fertilized after males release sperm. A single female herring can release between 50,000 and 700,000 eggs per breeding season. In general, larger and older fishes are the most productive. The eggs hatch, releasing larvae, which exist for varying periods of time in the plankton as they mature and become stronger swimming juveniles. Only a tiny fraction of the larvae become juvenile fish and far fewer survive to adulthood. There are many reasons for this relatively low reproductive success. Currents can keep the eggs and sperm apart or they may carry the planktonic larvae away from the protective nursery grounds in estuaries. Furthermore, many animals prey upon the eggs, larvae, and young fishes.

Most teleosts broadcast their eggs and sperm into the water and rely upon chance fertilization. By producing thousands of eggs and sperm, they increase the odds of producing a few successful young fishes. Some teleosts have evolved to increase their reproductive success through strategies such as internal fertilization, extended periods of parental care of the young, brooding of the young in the mouth of one of the parents or in a brood pouch (such as in the male seahorse). As mentioned earlier, elasmobranches increase their reproductive success through internal fertilization and protection of

their young, but they produce only a very small number of offspring.

Many environmental factors influence the reproductive success of bony fishes. Some fishes undertake long migrations. **Anadromous fishes** such as salmon, shad, sturgeon, and striped bass are born in rivers and streams, but spend most of their lives in cold regions of the ocean, returning to the same river to breed when they are sexually mature. Pacific salmon may migrate as far as 1300 km (800 mi) to complete this cycle. They reproduce only once, expending considerable energy to reach the headwaters of their particular river. Along the way, they use much of their body mass in this effort or convert it to eggs or sperm. They die after spawning. On the other hand, Atlantic salmon can reproduce many times.

Dams can be formidable obstacles to salmon migration. In the Pacific Northwest, for example, only about 5% of the juvenile salmon survive passage through dams and reservoirs on the Columbia and Snake Rivers. Largely ineffective are fish ladders intended to help the salmon move upstream and other structures that guide them downstream around hydroelectric turbines. These obstacles have been likened to giant food processors for smolt (young salmon) attempting to swim through them. Furthermore, on their downstream passage smolt are held up in reservoirs where they are exposed to predators, pathogens (disease-producing organisms), and water that is too warm. Atlantic salmon suffer a similar fate. More than 900 dams on New England and European rivers prevent most Atlantic salmon from reaching their freshwater spawning grounds. Consequently, their population has declined to less than 1% of historical levels. Today, almost all "Atlantic" salmon sold at fish markets come from fish farms.

Catadromous fishes are not as well known as anadromous fishes; they breed in the open ocean, but spend their adult lives in fresh water. In North America, the American eel is the only catadromous species. For many years the location of their breeding grounds was a mystery. Scientists now know that eels from both European and North American rivers travel thousands of kilometers to congregate in the Sargasso Sea where they spawn. Planktonic eel larvae remain in that location for about a year before migrating to the coastal waters where their parents matured. Young eels mature into adults in the coastal ocean before swimming up river. After 8 to 12 years, they return to the Sargasso Sea where they reproduce once and die. Many questions remain unanswered about how these migratory fishes navigate and identify their home rivers, and how the specifics of navigation are transferred from one generation to the next.

FIGURE 10.21
School of northern anchovies (*Engraulis mordax*). Schooling is a behavioral adaptation of teleosts that may offer protection from predators. [NOAA National Undersea Research Program]

Many species of fish, such as herring and mackerel, reduce predation by swimming together as organized groups, keeping a certain distance between one another (Figure 10.21). This so-called **schooling** behavior is particularly advantageous in the open ocean where hiding places are few and far between. Schooling confuses potential predators and functions as an alarm system when would-be intruders approach. Typically, the individuals in a school disperse in all directions when the alarm is sounded and then reassemble after the danger has past. In addition, fish that form schools swim more efficiently over longer distances using less energy than if each individual were swimming alone. This greater efficiency is accomplished by drafting, similar to the strategy employed by racing car drivers. Fish in a given school are of one species, similar in size, and may be a mixture of males and females or a single sex (depending on the species). A hierarchical structure (leaders and followers) is not evident among individuals in the school. Wide-angle vision or sound vibrations enable each fish in the school to sense the location and movement of its neighbors thereby maintaining order.

MARINE MAMMALS

Marine mammals are warm blooded, air breathing animals that bear live young, which they nurse. They include whales, dolphins, seals, walrus, sea lions, and polar bears (a terrestrial mammal that has adapted to a marine habitat). The largest marine mammals, baleen whales, live primarily in the open ocean where they filter zooplankton from the water as they swim slowly with their mouths open. These filter-feeding whales include the largest animal to have lived on Earth, the blue whale. Grey whales are also very large baleen whales. They forage for crustaceans by sucking up large amounts of sediment from the sea floor and expelling it through their baleen, which retains the food. Smaller whales, such as sperm whales, killer whales, porpoises and dolphins are faster swimming, toothed carnivores that actively hunt their prey. Sperm whales feed on squid captured in the mid-depths of the ocean. Cetaceans (whales, porpoises, and dolphins) spend their entire lives at sea.

Polar bears are unique to the Arctic and are the region's largest land predator growing to a height of 2.5 to 3 m (8 to 10 ft) and weight of 250 to 800 kg (550 to 1700 lb). Polar bears inhabit the waters and coastal areas of Alaska, northern Canada, northern Russia, Greenland, and Norway. These animals depend on sea ice as a platform from which they hunt seals, their principal food source. They will also take walrus and in some cases small whales (e.g., Beluga whales) that have been trapped in small open areas in the ice. They travel across the sea ice and open water to reach their dens on land. About half of all female polar bears bear their cubs in dens on land; the rest build dens on ice floes. Their dense fur and blubber enable them to comfortably swim from one ice floe to another in the Arctic Ocean for distances as great as 100 km (62 mi). In short, polar bears are uniquely adapted to living on Arctic sea ice and are often considered to be marine mammals. However, because of their dependence on sea ice, they face possible extinction as the sea ice cover in the Arctic thins and shrinks (Chapter 12).

Pinnipeds, named for their distinctive swimming flippers, include seals, sea lions, and walruses; many of them inhabit coastal waters (Figure 10.22). Unlike cetaceans, pinnipeds come ashore to breed, give birth, and

FIGURE 10.22
Large walrus (*Odobenus rosmarus divergens*) on the ice of the Bering Sea, Alaska. [NOAA Photo Library photograph by Captain Budd Christman, NOAA Corps]

rear their young. All pinnipeds are fur bearing and many species have been hunted nearly to extinction, although some populations are recovering due to protective legislation.

Manatees and dugongs are large herbivorous mammals that feed on vegetation in shallow waters along the coast and in the estuaries of Florida and many parts of Asia and South America. They are now seriously endangered in many areas because of increasing coastal development and encounters with motorboats whose propellers can severely injure these gentle, slow-moving animals. Loss of sea grass beds, a primary feeding habitat for some manatees and dugongs, is another threat to their survival.

The National Marine Fisheries Service of NOAA, through its Office of Protected Resources, is responsible for enforcing the Marine Mammal Protection Act in the United States. This legislation, enacted in 1972 and re-authorized in 1994, established a moratorium on the hunting of marine mammals in U.S. waters and by U.S. citizens on the high seas.

MARINE REPTILES

The few reptiles that live in the ocean fall into three groups, the best known being sea turtles (Figure 10.23). Marine lizards, such as the iguana of the Galápagos Islands, and sea snakes are examples from the other two groups of marine reptiles.

All sea turtles live in the ocean, but come ashore to lay their eggs. Female sea turtles dig their nests on sandy beaches, lay up to one hundred leathery eggs, and then return to the sea. Newly hatched turtles must fend for themselves

FIGURE 10.23
Leatherback sea turtles occasionally nest on the beach at Canaveral National Seashore in Florida. The leatherback, an endangered species, is one of the largest sea turtles in the world. It can grow to a length of over 2 m (7 ft). [NOAA and the National Park Service, Canaveral National Seashore]

and find their way back down the beach to the sea. Along the way, sea birds and other animals prey upon them. If they make it to the sea, predatory fishes reduce their numbers still further. Only a few hatchlings survive to adulthood. Sea turtles have been hunted for their meat as well as their shells, which are used to make combs and jewelry. Plastic litter in the ocean is a serious threat to sea turtles (as well as other marine animals) that frequently mistake drifting plastic bags for jellyfish, a favorite prey. These bags, when swallowed, can block the digestive tract, eventually killing them. Turtles also get caught in illegal drift nets and on long-lines of hooks intended to catch swordfish. We have more on sea turtles in Chapter 14.

Sea snakes are rare, occurring only in the tropical Pacific and Indian Oceans, usually around reefs. Unlike moray eels, which are actually fishes with gills, sea snakes are reptiles and must come to the surface to breathe; they have special valves that close their nostrils while submerged. Some species of sea snakes go ashore to reproduce and lay eggs; others mate and bear live young without leaving the sea. They are among the most venomous animals on Earth. A single snake can produce about 10 to 15 milligrams of venom at a time, but the fatal dose for humans is only one-tenth this amount. Fortunately sea snakes are extremely shy animals and rarely attack humans unless provoked.

Marine iguanas are herbivores, feeding mostly on seaweeds in the intertidal zone. Large males feed offshore, diving to depths of up to ten meters. They occur only in the Galápagos Islands in the equatorial Pacific Ocean. Having evolved from land lizards, they need a special adaptation to deal with the large amount of salt water they swallow while feeding. A special gland connected to the nostrils excretes excess salt, which the iguana expels by sneezing. Being cold blooded, iguanas regulate their body temperature by spending much time sunning themselves on the rocky shore.

The Galápagos Islands are the product of hot spot volcanism in the eastern tropical Pacific (Chapter 2). Prevailing trade winds cause equatorial upwelling of cold, nutrient-rich waters that provide sufficient production to support marine iguanas. Apparently, the abundant food supply was a factor in the iguana's adaptation to cold, salty ocean waters. During El Niño episodes, however, upwelling of nutrients is reduced thus lowering production so that populations of iguanas and other inhabitants of the Galápagos Islands are threatened (Chapter 11). Upwards of 10% of the iguana population can die of starvation during a lengthy and severe El Niño episode.

SEA BIRDS

Unlike most birds on land, seabirds are carnivorous predators that occupy a high trophic level in marine food webs. They have relatively high metabolic rates and require energy-rich, fatty foods. Wading birds, such as herons, have long legs and inhabit wetlands and shallow soft-bottom habitats where they find prey in the shallow waters and soft sediment. Some, such as flamingos and spoonbills, have specialized bills that allow them to strain bottom deposits to feed on small plants and animals. Herons have a sharp bill enabling them to snatch small fishes from the shallow water. Other seabirds dive for food; these include sea ducks, cormorants, loons, terns, and pelicans (Figure 10.24). Pelicans are among the largest and heaviest birds on Earth, yet they make spectacular dives as they hunt for fish.

No seabird can stay at sea for its entire life. All of them must come ashore to breed and lay eggs on a solid surface. Also, their body heat is necessary to hatch the eggs. The chicks require feeding by their parents until they are ready to fly and hunt for themselves. However, some seabirds spend very long periods flying over the open ocean. The albatross is a classic example, spending years at a time far from land.

Where fishing grounds are exceptionally productive, seabirds establish huge colonies on rocky shores and cliffs, especially during their breeding season. Some seabirds migrate long distances searching for food. Terns migrate from the Canadian Arctic, where they spend the Northern Hemisphere summer, all the way to Patagonia at the southern tip of South America, where they spend the Southern Hemisphere summer.

One type of seabird, however, has lost its ability to fly. Penguins are adapted to live at sea and their streamlined bodies enable them to swim with considerable speed and agility (Figure 10.25). They can dive as deep as 250 m (820 ft) and remain submerged for up to 20 minutes while searching for fish and small squid. They lay eggs and rear their young on land ice. Nearly all species of penguins (17) live in the Southern Hemisphere, mostly around Antarctica and on the southern extremities of Africa, South America, and Australia. One species lives near the equator on the Galápagos Islands. All these areas are nutrient-rich with cold currents. Some penguin species spend up to 75% of their lives at sea, away from land for months at a time. For birds, penguins have unusually dense bones, an adaptation that counteracts their buoyancy problem.

FIGURE 10.24
Brown pelican in breeding colors. [NOAA National Marine Fisheries Service, photo by William B. Folsom]

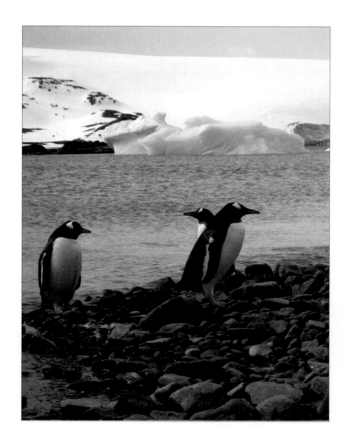

FIGURE 10.25
Although ungainly on land, the flightless penguin is an expert swimmer. Shown here are Gentoo Penguins (*Pygoscelis papua*), largest of the "bush-tail" penguins. They live on Antarctic islands as well as the Antarctic Peninsula. [NOAA/Vents, Korea Polar Research Institute (KOPRI)]

Conclusions

Most of Earth's living space is in the ocean where habitats are many and diverse, ranging from intertidal zones along the coast to soft sediments and hydrothermal vents on the deep-ocean floor. Organisms exploit all these habitats. But survival in the ocean presents many challenges that differ from those faced by terrestrial organisms. Marine plants and animals have evolved many specialized adaptations involving buoyancy, feeding, reproduction, and protection from predators.

Marine plants and animals are distributed nonuniformly in the ocean; their distribution is controlled primarily by environmental factors such as water temperature, salinity, light, and availability of food. Most marine organisms live near the ocean's surface, edges, or on the bottom. In the open ocean, organisms are most abundant in the surface waters, less so at mid-depths, and are least abundant in the deep ocean.

This chapter completes our survey of marine organisms and how they cope with the physical, chemical, and biological properties of the ocean in the Earth system. In the next chapter, we examine some of the large-scale interactions between the ocean and atmosphere and their impacts on the rest of the Earth system including marine life.

Basic Understandings

- Living space in the ocean not only vastly exceeds that on land but also features very different types of habitats. Organisms live in all parts of the ocean, even extreme environments such as Arctic or Antarctic sea ice and hydrothermal vents on the sea floor. Other marine habitats include rocky shores, tide pools, estuaries, coral reefs, polar oceans, deep-sea trenches, and sediments and bedrock on the sea floor.

- Marine life zones are commonly defined in terms of distance from shore and water depth. Open ocean waters constitute the pelagic zone, home to plankton (passive floaters or weak swimmers) and nekton (strong swimmers). The environment of the sea floor at all depths is called the benthic zone, home to organisms that live either on the ocean bottom or within sediment deposits.

- The area along the shore between high- and low-tide lines is the intertidal (or littoral) zone, home to ecosystems such as salt marshes and mangrove swamps. The area seaward from the shore to the shelf break at a depth of about 200 m (650 ft), including the intertidal zone, forms the neritic zone—commonly referred to as the coastal zone.

- Oceanic life zones are also defined in terms of nutrient supply and production. Nutrient-poor waters having low primary production are described as oligotrophic. Broad areas of open-ocean within the subtropical gyres are examples of oligotrophic waters. Nutrient-rich waters having high primary production are described as eutrophic. Coastal upwelling zones and many estuaries have eutrophic waters.

- Plankton, members of phytoplankton, zooplankton or microbial communities, evolved adaptations and strategies for life in the pelagic zone. An adaptation is a genetically controlled trait or characteristic that enhances an organism's chances for survival and reproduction in its environment. For example, the shape of some plankton produces a relatively high surface area to volume ratio that provides buoyancy so that they do not sink below the sunlit photic zone.

- Larger, free-swimming pelagic animals, collectively called nekton, include fish of all sizes, squid, sea turtles, and marine mammals. Some migrate over long distances; the distribution of many others is limited by their tolerance for water temperature, salinity, or food availability. Nektonic organisms also have adaptations for buoyancy—the simplest of these are gas bladders.

- Most pelagic fish rely on active swimming to obtain food. Some fish lie on the bottom, waiting for their prey and suddenly lunge to catch it. Others swim all the time, seeking prey over large areas of the ocean.

- The photic zone is where food is most plentiful but it is also the most dangerous for marine organisms because predators can easily see them. Many types of zooplankton avoid this problem by daily vertical migration. Each day at dusk, they come to the surface zone to feed on phytoplankton. Then, as daylight returns, they return to the relative safety of darker, deep waters.

- Species of smaller fish that are prey for larger ones have adaptations that make them less visible and therefore less likely to be eaten. The most common adaptation is adaptive coloration where the animal's color pattern closely matches its background substrate. Many fish exhibit countershading, that is, their dorsal side is a dark color, making it difficult for predators above to see them against the dark, deep water. Their ventral side is lighter colored, making the fish more difficult for predators to see them from below against the more brightly lit surface waters.

- Some marine animals emit light, a phenomenon known as bioluminescence. The light usually is a product of a chemical reaction that takes place in specialized cells or organs. Marine animals use light emission to attract mates or prey, frighten or confuse predators, or as a disguise.

- The general name for animals that are equipped with features that strain food particles out of large volumes of water is filter feeder. Some planktonic organisms produce large mucous nets, which function much like a spider web to trap small water-borne organisms and other food particles.

- Benthic organisms may live attached to a firm surface, construct burrows or tunnels or simply dig into sediment deposits, or they may move freely on the ocean bottom. Attached animals are filter feeders; mobile animals are active predators; and burrowing organisms ingest sediment, digesting the organic material it contains and excreting the rest.

- A distinction is made among intertidal habitats based on the type of substrate (e.g., rocky, muddy, sandy). The most energetic of these habitats are rocky intertidal shorelines where organisms are frequently subject to strong wave action, especially in winter. Where the distance between low and high tide levels is relatively great, organisms may be exposed to dry air and sunshine for many hours each day. Depending on the season, they may be forced to withstand extremely high or low air temperatures when they are not covered by seawater.

- Seaweeds are important components of the intertidal zone. All are algae and are green, brown, or red, depending on the color of the dominant photosynthetic pigment. They are distributed according to their light requirements and their ability to resist drying and freezing during low tide. Seaweeds provide habitat for many marine organisms living in the intertidal zone.

- On mud flats and other soft-bottomed habitats, the most important plants are sea grasses, also known as submerged aquatic vegetation (SAV). These are angiosperms, flowering and seed bearing vascular plants with true roots. They are limited to water depths where light is sufficient for photosynthesis. Sea grass beds are highly productive.

- Salt marshes commonly occur along sheltered shorelines and are ecologically similar to sea grass beds in estuaries. The salt marsh grasses and bushes differ from sea grasses by being salt-tolerant true land plants, pollinating in the air. Salt marshes are flooded at high tide, but the grasses are never completely covered by salt water. They are home to abundant marine life and are refuges for waterfowl and other wildlife.

- In estuaries, plants and animals vary from marine species near the mouth of the estuary to brackish water types where the salinity is lower, to those that prefer a nearly freshwater environment at the head of the estuary.

- In the tropics, mangrove swamps are common along muddy, low-lying coastlines and in estuaries. They consist of tropical tree species that are salt-tolerant and can withstand tidal flooding of their roots and lower stems. Mangroves form dense growths and their aerial roots provide a complex and protective habitat for many organisms such as mangrove oysters.

- Seaward of the intertidal zone, kelp forests grow where waters are cool and nutrient-rich. Kelp includes species of brown algae that grow to an enormous size. They are especially abundant in coastal upwelling zones off of California and the Pacific Northwest. Kelp grows attached to rocky bottoms by root-like structures known as holdfasts and much of the plant is supported at the surface by a bulbous gas filled float below the fronds. Recent research indicates that patches of kelp also occur in tropical latitudes.

- Coral reefs are among the ocean's most spectacular biological features. They grow along coastlines or cap extinct undersea volcanoes. Coral reefs are only thin veneers of living organisms growing on older layers of dead coral (limestone) or volcanic-rock.

- Hermatypic corals live in warm, shallow water

and build large reefs. Solitary corals and small coral reefs also live in cold, deep water along continental shelf breaks in some parts of the ocean. These are known as ahermatypic corals. Carbonate-secreting colonial coral animals are the primary builders of coral-reef frameworks. Coral reefs provide shelter for many species of fish, invertebrates, and plants and are among the ocean's most productive habitats.

- Coral reefs growing on volcanic islands typically exhibit a characteristic sequence of forms caused by either sea level rise or sinking of the island: fringing reef, barrier reef, and atoll.

- Animals living on and in soft-bottomed habitats consist of either infauna or epifauna. Infauna live within sediment deposits whereas epifauna live on the sea floor.

- Soft ocean bottoms harbor many filter feeders that separate phytoplankton, small zooplankton, and other edible materials from large volumes of water. The distribution of animals in muddy and sandy habitats is controlled primarily by the grain size of the sediment deposits.

- Many unusual creatures live on the deep-sea floor. Sediment feeders are similar to those living in shallow benthic habitats, although animals in the deep, cold ocean are generally smaller, an adaptation to the scarcity of food. In addition, communities of specialized animals have evolved to live on the deep ocean bottom near hydrothermal vents utilizing chemosynthesis.

- Unlike mammals, which regulate their body temperature, fish are cold blooded. Fish may be herbivorous, carnivorous, or omnivorous. They inhabit all parts of the ocean and possess special adaptations for buoyancy, swimming, and life at the surface, in the dimly lit twilight zone, as well as the greatest depths of the ocean.

- The two major groups of fishes are elasmobranchs (or cartilaginous fishes) and teleosts (or bony fishes). Elasmobranchs include sharks, skates, and rays. Their skeletons lack true bones and consist entirely of cartilage. Teleosts have bony skeletons and scales. This is a large, diverse, and familiar group of fishes that live in a variety of marine and freshwater environments.

- Anadromous fishes are born in freshwater rivers and streams, but spend most of their lives in the ocean, returning to the same river to breed when they are sexually mature. Less well known are catadromous fishes that breed in the open ocean, but spend their adult lives in fresh water.

- Many species of fish reduce predation by swimming together in organized groups called schools. This strategy confuses potential predators and functions as an alarm system when would-be intruders approach.

- Marine mammals are warm blooded, air breathing animals that bear live young, which they nurse. The largest marine mammals, baleen whales, live primarily in the open ocean where they filter zooplankton from the water as they swim slowly with their mouths open. Pinnipeds are named for their distinctive swimming flippers and include seals, walruses, and sea lions; many of them live in coastal waters.

- The few reptiles that live in the ocean include sea turtles, marine lizards, and sea snakes.

- Unlike most birds on land, seabirds are carnivorous predators that feed at high trophic levels in marine food webs.

- Penguins are flightless marine birds that are confined primarily to the Southern Hemisphere.

Review

1. Describe the portions of the ocean represented by the pelagic, benthic, and neritic zones.
2. Which areas of the ocean are usually oligotrophic? Which are eutrophic? What is the implication for primary production?
3. Define adaptation.
4. Phytoplankton possesses a special adaptation that significantly slows their sinking motion in the ocean. Identify that adaptation.
5. What is the function of adaptive coloration and countershading for fish?
6. What is bioluminescence and what purpose does it serve?
7. Describe the types of marine organisms found in the benthic zone based on their life strategy.
8. What is the significance of sea grasses?
9. Characterize the environmental conditions most favorable for the growth of coral reefs in tropical ocean waters.
10. Are seabirds herbivorous or carnivorous predators? Explain your answer.

Critical Thinking

1. Why is the ocean's neritic zone likely to be eutrophic whereas the open ocean is more likely to be oligotrophic?
2. What causes an algal bloom and what are the potential consequences for marine life in terms of availability of dissolved oxygen?
3. Describe the daily changes in the environmental conditions of the intertidal zone.
4. Why are adaptations for buoyancy essential for the survival of marine animals.
5. Explain how many types of zooplankton avoid predation through vertical migration.
6. How might shrinkage of the Arctic ice cover (because of global warming) impact polar bears?
7. Provide several examples of how marine organisms avoid sinking to the ocean bottom.
8. Birds feed at a relatively high trophic level in marine food webs. What is the significance of this for bioaccumulation of persistent toxins?
9. What is the source of food energy for marine organisms that live in the deep, dark ocean bottom?
10. Summarize the major differences between marine and terrestrial food webs.

ESSAY: Life and Sea Ice

Marine life forms occupy extreme environments upon, within, and beneath the sea-ice cover of polar oceans. In the Arctic Ocean, for example, sea ice provides habitat for a variety of organisms that are members of an ice-specific food web and include bacteria, viruses, unicellular algae, and small invertebrates. These organisms have adapted to dramatic changes in light intensity, temperature, and salinity. In addition, evidence points to an unexpectedly more diverse marine community in the water column and seafloor under ice shelves.

As noted in Chapter 3, dissolved salts lower the freezing point of seawater. For example, at an average salinity of 35 psu, seawater has an initial freezing temperature of about −1.9 °C. Additionally, salt is excluded as sea ice forms (*brine rejection*). In autumn, as sunlight fades and daylight shortens, the air temperature drops and surface waters cool. Eventually, ice begins to form on the ocean surface as a porous structure of interlocking ice crystals filled with a salty solution called *brine*. Brine, initially accounting for about 10% to 30% of the ice volume, occupies tiny channels and pore space between and within the ice crystals. As winter progresses, the sea ice cover solidifies, pore space decreases, and the salinity of the brine increases. As long as the temperature remains above −5 °C, the ice continues to be riven by tiny passages having diameters ranging from a few micrometers to several centimeters. But when the temperature drops to lower values, the permeability of the ice becomes minimal and the salinity of the brine can approach values near 250 psu.

Ice-dwelling organisms have the same temperature as the surrounding ice so their survival within ice channels and pores depends on adaptations that prevent the growth of ice crystals within their bodies. As mentioned elsewhere in this chapter, an *adaptation* is a genetically controlled trait or characteristic that enhances an organism's chances for survival and reproduction. For example, some ice organisms accumulate fat-like substances in their bodies that prevent freezing.

Sea ice insulates the underlying seawater from the atmosphere so that a considerable temperature difference (*gradient*) develops between the ice/atmosphere interface (where winter temperatures might plunge to −35 °C or lower) and the ice/seawater interface where the temperature is about the same as the seawater (perhaps −2 °C). For this reason, most ice organisms concentrate within the lowermost centimeters of the ice. Beginning in spring with the return of sunlight for photosynthesis and continuing through summer, populations of unicellular ice algae explode. They live in the lowermost portion of the sea ice and often form chains and filaments that extend many meters into the water. Several hundred species of algae living in the ice are the chief primary producers in the Arctic. Ice algae on average account for 4% to 26% of total marine primary production in seasonally ice-covered Arctic waters and up to 50% or more in perennially ice-covered waters.

Dissolved organic matter from the wastes of ice algae is food for ice bacteria. Algae are eaten by crustaceans, rotifers (microscopic invertebrates), and turbellarians (flatworms). Tiny crustaceans (amphipods) live on the underside of the ice, feed on algae, and seek shelter from predators in the brine channels. Juvenile stages of zooplankton also feed on the ice bottom community. With rising temperatures in spring, the solid ice cover breaks up into pack ice and ice floes that can transport organisms thousands of kilometers before melting and releasing their content to the ocean. Melting frees the organic material that has accumulated within the ice crystals to enter the water column and fuel pelagic and benthic food webs.

In recent years, scientists have gathered new information regarding life in and under the polar ice. One fundamental finding is that life in the Southern Ocean is more diverse than previously believed. In December 2003, Australian scientists drilled a hole through the 480-m (1575-ft) thick Amery ice shelf in Antarctica, some 100 km (60 mi) from the ocean. A video camera was lowered to the seafloor at a depth of about 775 m (2550 ft). To their amazement, the scientists identified 24 species of invertebrates (including sponges, mollusks, and sea urchins) within the 2 sq m area of the seafloor within the camera's range. Scientists had assumed that the food supply was insufficient to support life under the ice shelf.

An international scientific team discovered hundreds of new species and greater diversity than expected in the deep waters near Antarctica. During three cruises in 2002 and 2005 onboard the German research icebreaker *Polarstern*, the team scooped up sediment and its inhabitants at 40 sampling sites at depths ranging from 774 to 6348 m (2500 to 20,800 ft). During the Southern Hemisphere summer of 2006-2007, the British Antarctic Survey inaugurated its remotely operated *Isis* vehicle on the deep seafloor surrounding Antarctica. The onboard camera revealed krill (*Euphausia superba*) at a depth of 3000 m (9800 ft). Previously, scientists had assumed that this important member of the polar ecosystem lived at much shallower depths.

Large warm-blooded animals also live on sea ice. Birds (e.g., penguins in the Antarctic), seals, whales, and polar bears utilize sea ice for migration routes, hunting grounds, or rookeries. Seasonal changes in ice cover and thickness make for a dynamic environment and require that animals have excellent navigation skills.

Polar bears have a special adaptation that enables them to survive the extreme cold of the Arctic climate (Figure 1). Scientists became aware of the effectiveness of this adaptation when their plan to take the census of polar bears did not work very well. Because white polar bears blend in with snow-covered ice, scientists decided to locate and count the bears using thermal (infrared) imagery taken from an aircraft. They assumed that polar bears would show up as hot spots in the images. However, scientists discovered that while they often could visually observe the polar bears, the bears were not showing up on thermal imagery. Polar bear fur, made up of hollow tubes, is such an efficient insulating blanket that essentially no body heat gets through the fur and no heat signals reach the infrared sensor on the aircraft.

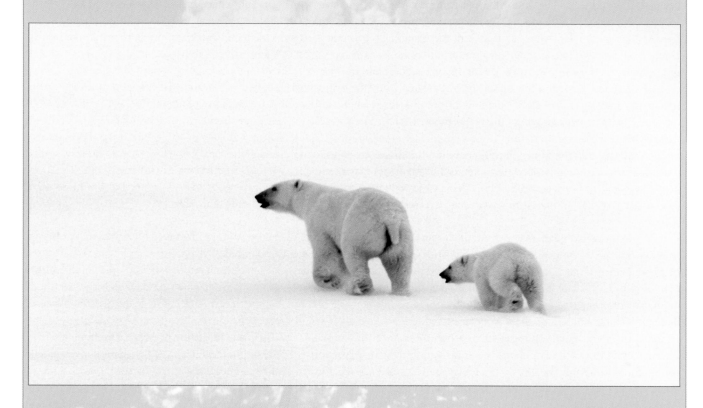

FIGURE 1
Polar bear (*Ursus maritimus*) and cub blend into the background and because of their excellent insulation cannot be detected by airborne infrared sensors. Photograph was taken on the Arctic Ocean ice north of western Russia. [NOAA Photo Library, NOAA Climate Program Office, NABOS 2006 Expedition, photograph by Mike Dunn, NC State Museum of Natural Sciences.]

ESSAY: Dead Zones

Agricultural and urban runoff of excessive amounts of plant nutrients has adversely affected marine ecosystems, especially in coastal seas and estuaries. Since the mid-1970s, each summer a large area of seafloor waters on the continental shelf off the mouth of the Mississippi River and the Louisiana-Texas Gulf coast becomes depleted in dissolved oxygen. These waters can support only bacteria that grow in the absence of oxygen (*anaerobic bacteria*). If they are unable to migrate away in search of food and oxygen, most commercially valuable fish and shellfish (e.g., crabs, oysters) die. For this reason, the impacted area is known as a *dead zone*. In the summer of 2007, the Gulf dead (or hypoxic) zone encompassed an area of nearly 20,450 square km (7900 square mi, about the size of Massachusetts, ranking it as the largest in U.S. ocean waters and one of the largest dead zones in the world.

In 2000, an assessment by the National Science and Technology Council attributed the Gulf dead zone to excess nitrogen compounds (e.g., nitrates) washed into the Gulf in the discharge of the Mississippi River. Synthetic nitrogen fertilizer is routinely applied to agricultural fields in spring and summer. Excess nitrogen from fields runs off into streams and rivers, and eventually reaches bays and other coastal waters causing major pollution problems. This input is supplemented by runoff from urban areas (e.g., the effluent of partially treated sewage). Excess nitrogen triggers explosive growth of algal populations (algal blooms) and the water turns green or brown, shading ocean-bottom sea grasses from essential sunlight. Sea grasses soon die, depriving other organisms of habitat for reproduction and growth and no longer producing oxygen as a product of photosynthesis. After they die, algae also settle to the bottom adding to the accumulating organic matter. Decomposition of organic remains depletes the oxygen dissolved in the bottom waters. The consequence is large volumes of water containing very little dissolved oxygen, a dead zone.

With its strong density gradient, the water column remains stratified throughout the summer so that little mixing takes place between the oxygen-depleted bottom waters and the oxygen-enriched surface waters. The dead zone persists through most of the summer but by late fall, seasonal weather changes help mix the water column, replenishing the dissolved oxygen content of the bottom water.

As shown in Figure 1, the Mississippi River and its tributaries drain a huge area (about 40%) of the coterminous U.S., west to the Rocky Mountains, east to the Appalachian Mountains, and north to the river's headwaters in Minnesota. This drainage basin includes the Corn Belt and much of the runoff responsible for the Gulf dead zone comes from cornfields. The problem is likely to be exacerbated in the future (i.e., a larger dead zone) as more corn is grown for production of ethanol for the biofuels industry.

Until a few years ago, scientists argued that minimizing nitrogen runoff from fertilizer application would be sufficient to bring the Gulf dead zone back to life. For example, in 2001, G.F. McIsaac, an environmental scientist at the University of Illinois at Urbana-Champaign, reported that the dead zone could be alleviated significantly if farmers in the Mississippi River drainage basin cut their application of nitrogen fertilizer by 12%. McIsaac argued that such a reduction would not necessarily reduce crop yields but would decrease the amount of nitrates reaching the Gulf of Mexico by one-third by the year 2010. However, scientists discovered that phosphorus compounds in runoff also contribute to the problem. About 75% of nitrogen and 60% of phosphorus come from fertilizer application. (The balance is from urban sources.) Hence, shrinking the Gulf dead zone requires reducing the input of both nitrogen and phosphorus compounds. Strategies for accomplishing this include (1) limiting fertilizer use, (2) creating buffers (e.g., wetlands, forests) between agricultural fields and rivers that would reduce runoff, and (3) major reductions in sewage runoff from urban areas.

Dead zones occur in coastal seas and estuaries in many parts of the world for essentially the same reason, excess input of plant nutrients. One of the world's largest dead zones developed in the Black Sea near the mouth of the Danube River and covered an area of about 40,000 square km (15,400 square mi). Since 1990, the number of reports of dead zones worldwide has doubled.

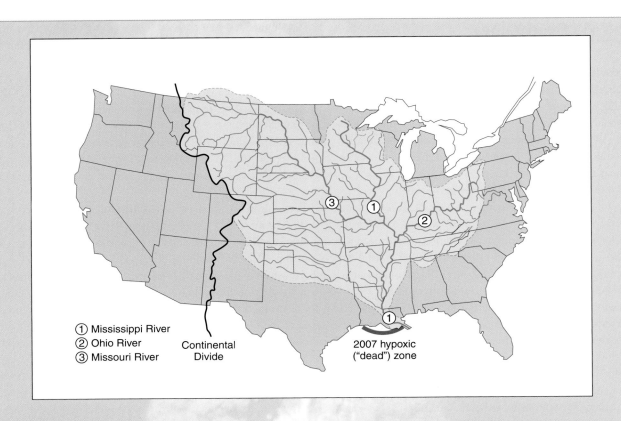

FIGURE 1

In summer, a large volume of bottom water significantly depleted in dissolved oxygen develops in the Gulf of Mexico just offshore of the Louisiana-Texas coast. Hypoxic conditions eliminate many bottom-dwelling organisms (hence the name "dead zone") and are caused by excessive amounts of nitrogen and phosphorus fertilizer washed from agricultural land in the Mississippi River drainage basin (shown in blue on the map). [Courtesy of the U.S. Geological Survey (USGS)]

ESSAY: Marine Sanctuaries and Reserves

In the United States, a major part of the effort to preserve the natural resources of coastal waters and to promote the recovery of underwater communities that have been overfished or heavily disturbed is the *marine sanctuaries* program. At the state level, California has led the way. Point Lobos, CA (near Monterey) was founded in 1960 as the nation's first underwater sanctuary. Since then California has set aside 11 other sites as sanctuaries and has been studying several more potential sites. Although the federal government has moved more slowly than California, federal legislation passed more than 35 years ago holds much promise for the future.

Provisions of the *1972 Marine Protection, Research, and Sanctuaries Act* authorize the President to designate national marine sanctuaries in coastal waters of the continental shelf and in the Great Lakes. Any of several characteristics may qualify a locality as a marine sanctuary, but basically, potential sites must have special biological, aesthetic, archaeological, cultural, or historical significance. The objective of federal legislation is to preserve and protect those areas by managing the multiple demands placed on them. Most marine sanctuaries are not places of refuge for marine life although activities that threaten marine resources are prohibited.

As of this writing, 14 national marine sanctuaries have been designated. They include near-shore coral reefs, whale migration corridors, deep-sea canyons, and historical sites (Figure 1). All are administered by NOAA's National Marine Sanctuary Program. The first national marine sanctuary, established in 1975, is the wreck site of the Civil War ship, *USS Monitor*, off the North Carolina coast. The first sanctuary in the Great Lakes is the Thunder Bay National Marine Sanctuary and Underwater Preserve, resting place of about 160 shipwrecks. It is located in northern Lake Huron near Alpena, MI. The smallest sanctuary is Fagatele Bay, American Samoa, home to a tropical coral reef covering 0.65 square km (0.19 square nautical mi) whereas one of the largest is Monterey Bay, CA with over 13,700 square km (4000 square nautical mi.).

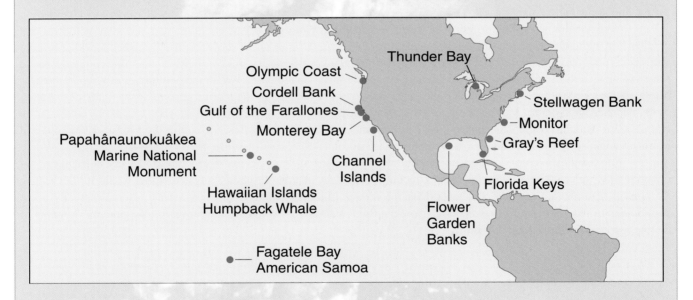

FIGURE 1
Map showing the names and locations of National Marine Sanctuaries in U.S. waters. [NOAA]

The most recent sanctuary is Papahânaumokuâkea Marine National Monument in Hawaii's northwestern waters. Established by Proclamation by President George W. Bush on 15 June 2006, it includes about 70% of all U.S. coral reef habitats, home to more than 7000 marine species, 25% of which live only there. It is the principal habitat for 1400 Hawaiian monk seals. Encompassing 356,894 square km (104,213 square nautical mi) of Pacific Ocean, this sanctuary is the single largest conservation area in the United States and the largest marine conservation area in the world. Any activities, including tourism, which might disturb the ecosystem are prohibited and all commercial and recreational fishing in the region must be phased out by 2011. Such no-disturbance, no-fishing areas are known as *marine reserves*. The "National Monument" designation expedited establishment of the sanctuary and was possible because the region was originally designated a national wildlife refuge by President Theodore Roosevelt (1858-1919) in 1909.

Consider some other examples of national marine sanctuaries. The Channel Islands National Marine Sanctuary is located about 40 km (25 mi) off the coast of Santa Barbara, CA and was designated a sanctuary in 1980. Waters surrounding the five islands of the sanctuary are a rich breeding ground for numerous species of plants and animals and home to a kelp forest. Annually, more than 24 species of whales and dolphins visit the sanctuary. The islands are also home to seabird colonies and pinniped rookeries. The Florida Keys National Marine Sanctuary encompasses the waters immediately surrounding most of the 1700 islands of the Florida Keys. Designated in 1990, the sanctuary forms a 355-km (220-mi) arc extending from the southern tip of Key Biscayne (south of Miami) southwest to, but not including the Dry Tortugas Islands. This complex of subtropical marine ecosystems includes offshore coral reefs, fringing mangroves, and sea grass meadows—home to more than 6000 species of plants, fishes, and invertebrates. The sanctuary covers 9500 square km (2800 square nautical mi).

In November 2000, President Clinton reauthorized the 1972 Marine Protection, Research, and Sanctuaries Act reaffirming the nation's commitment to conserve special areas of the marine environment for the appreciation and enjoyment of present and future generations. However, some conservationists argue that not enough is being done. They point out that at the time of the 1972 legislation the principal threats to the marine environment were oil spills and the plundering of sunken ships. Since then, over-fishing has emerged as the chief threat to marine resources (Chapter 14). Nearly half the U.S. marine fisheries are either depleted or over-fished and, according to the U.S. Department of Commerce, depletion of the fisheries costs the nation's economy billions of dollars in lost revenue each year. Yet, most marine sanctuaries permit fishing and allow recreational boating and mining of some resources—activities that potentially disrupt marine habitats.

Conservationists argue for more "no-take" refuges or *marine reserves* where all fishing and other activities that threaten marine habitats are prohibited. The goal of marine reserves is to allow recovery of over-fished stocks, preserve seafloor communities or rebuild ones destroyed by trawling. Studies of existing marine reserves show that compared to the surrounding waters, biomass and species diversity are greater and fish are larger within the boundaries of a typical refuge. These ecological benefits develop rapidly and occur regardless of the size of the marine reserve. Prior to the designation of the Papahânaumokuâkea Marine National Monument, only about 430 square km (125 square nautical mi) were marine reserves. An example is the 253 square km (74 square nautical mi) Tortugas reserve within the Florida Keys National Marine Sanctuary. Individual states or local municipalities protect other small no-take areas.

The fishing industry has opposed any new or expansion of existing marine reserves. Already beleaguered by dwindling fish stocks (some on the brink of extinction), fishers are adamantly against any action that would further reduce the area of open fishing grounds. However, research reported in 2001 demonstrates that marine reserves actually boost populations of fish in the waters outside their borders. Some fishers are now beginning to realize the potential benefits of marine reserves for the fishing industry.

CHAPTER 11

THE OCEAN, ATMOSPHERE, AND CLIMATE VARIABILITY

Case-in-Point
Driving Question
Earth's Climate System
    Climate Controls
    Role of the Ocean
Tropical Pacific Ocean/Atmosphere
    Historical Perspective
    Neutral Conditions in the Tropical Pacific
    El Niño, The Warm Phase
    The 1997-98 El Niño
    La Niña, The Cold Phase
    Predicting and Monitoring El Niño and La Niña
    Frequency of El Niño and La Niña
North Atlantic Oscillation
Arctic Oscillation
Pacific Decadal Oscillation
Conclusions
Basic Understandings/Review/Critical Thinking
ESSAY: Sea Surface Temperature and Drought in
    Sub-Saharan Africa
ESSAY: El Niño in the Past

Rain shaft in the Caribbean Sea. [Courtesy of NOAA]

Case in Point

In 1982-83, the weather seemed to go wild in many parts of the world and after it was over the total worldwide impacts included thousands of deaths and an estimated $13 billion in property damage. From mid-November 1982 until late January 1983, excessive rains caused the worst flooding of the century in usually arid Ecuador. Strong winds and torrential rains produced by six tropical cyclones lashed the islands of French Polynesia in a span of only three months. (By comparison, on average one tropical cyclone strikes this region of the eastern South Pacific about every

5 years.) At the other extreme, drought parched eastern Australia, Indonesia, and southern Africa. Huge drought-related wildfires broke out in Australia and Borneo. Australia's drought was that nation's worst in 200 years, causing $2 billion in crop losses and the deaths of millions of sheep and cattle. Meanwhile, persistent drought in sub-Saharan Africa grew worse. Over North America, the winter storm track shifted hundreds of kilometers south of its usual location, bringing episodes of destructive high winds and heavy rains to portions of California.

Flooding rains also caused havoc across the southeastern United States. Meanwhile ski resorts in the northern U.S. experienced a snow drought and considerable economic loss as a consequence.

Just prior to these worldwide weather extremes, the ocean circulation off the northwest coast of South America changed drastically with dire implications for marine production. Along the coast of Ecuador and Peru, plankton populations plunged to about 5% of their normal level. The decline in plankton reduced the numbers of anchovy, which feed on plankton, to a record low. Other fishes dependent on plankton, such as jack mackerel, suffered a similar fate. Commercial fisheries off the coast of Ecuador and Peru collapsed. With the decline in fish populations, marine birds (e.g., frigate birds and terns) and marine mammals (e.g., fur seals and sea lions) also experienced major population declines as scarce food supplies caused breeding failures as well as migration or starvation of adults.

The ecological impact of these 1982-83 environmental changes was particularly severe on the remote island of Kiritimati (Christmas Island) at 2 degrees N, 157 degrees W, in the central tropical Pacific. An estimated 17 million seabirds, which feed on fish and squid, normally nest on the island. But scientists arriving on Kiritimati in November 1982 found that nearly all the adult birds had abandoned the island, leaving behind their young to starve. Apparently, sharp declines in food sources forced fish and squid to search for better feeding grounds, and the adult birds followed their prey. By July 1983, the usual ocean circulation returned, plankton populations rebounded, and the adult birds returned to Kiritimati. Nesting began and seabird populations started to recover.

What caused these drastic changes in atmospheric and oceanic conditions? Early on, some scientists attributed the weather extremes to the violent eruption of the Mexican volcano El Chichón in March-April 1982. But it quickly became apparent that the worldwide weather extremes were linked to large-scale ocean/atmosphere circulation changes in the tropical Pacific and soon a new scientific term was added to the public's vocabulary: El Niño. The El Niño of 1982-83 spurred further research on ocean-atmosphere interactions and the deployment of an array of in situ and remote sensing instruments in the tropical Pacific to provide early warning of the development of El Niño. In the late 1990s, when El Niño returned in its full fury, the global community was better prepared thereby lessening the impact.

Driving Question:

How do interactions between the ocean and atmosphere impact worldwide weather and short-term climate variability?

Some weather extremes such as drought and episodes of unusually heavy rains are linked to coupled changes in atmospheric and oceanic circulation. The principal focus of this chapter is short-term climate fluctuations involving interactions between the ocean and atmosphere. One of the most extensively studied of these interactions occurs in the tropical Pacific and is known as El Niño/La Niña. During El Niño, trade winds weaken, upwelling diminishes off the South American coast and along the equatorial Pacific, sea surface temperatures (SST) rise well above long-term averages over the central and eastern tropical Pacific, and areas of heavy rainfall shift from the western into the central tropical Pacific. La Niña sometimes (but not always) follows El Niño and is a period of exceptionally strong trade winds in the tropical Pacific, vigorous coastal and equatorial upwelling in the Pacific, and lower than usual SST in the central and eastern tropical Pacific. Based on changes in SST in the eastern tropical Pacific, some scientists refer to El Niño as the *warm phase* and La Niña as the *cold phase* of this air/sea interaction.

Broad-scale changes in SST patterns over the tropical Pacific that accompany El Niño and La Niña influence the prevailing circulation of the atmosphere in middle latitudes, especially in winter. Weather extremes that most often accompany El Niño are essentially opposite those that usually occur during La Niña. Although we devote much of this chapter to El Niño and La Niña, we also consider other examples of short-term climate variability stemming from air/sea interactions including the North Atlantic Oscillation, the Arctic Oscillation, and the Pacific Decadal Oscillation. We set the stage for this discussion by first describing controls operating within Earth's climate system.

Earth's Climate System

In Chapter 5, we defined **climate** as weather at a particular location averaged over a specific interval of time (by convention, 30 years). A complete description of climate also includes extremes in weather (e.g., highest and lowest temperatures on record, frequency of drought). In a more general sense, climate is the state of the Earth-atmosphere system (Earth's surface plus atmosphere) that gives a locality its characteristic weather patterns.

Climate varies both spatially and temporally. The globe is a mosaic of many different climate types including, for example, the warm, humid tropics, hot and cold deserts, temperate regions, and polar ice caps. Climate changes over a broad spectrum of temporal scales, from years to decades to centuries to millennia. In this section, we describe the various controls operating in Earth's climate system with emphasis on the role of the ocean.

CLIMATE CONTROLS

Many factors work together in shaping the climate of any locality. Controls of climate consist of (1) latitude, (2) elevation, (3) topography, (4) proximity to large bodies of water, (5) Earth's surface characteristics, (6) net incoming solar radiation, (7) long-term average atmospheric circulation, and (8) prevailing ocean circulation. Over a period of at least several million years, all climate controls are variable. On time scales that extend to hundreds of millions of years, continents have drifted to different latitudes, ocean basins have opened and closed, and mountain ranges have risen and eroded away—all with implications for climate. On shorter time scales (e.g., the range of human existence), for all practical purposes, the first four climate controls on our list are essentially fixed and exert regular and predictable influences on climate.

Seasonal changes in net incoming solar radiation, as well as length of daylight, vary with latitude, and air and sea surface temperatures respond to those regular variations (Chapter 5). Air temperature drops with increasing elevation and determines whether precipitation falls in the form of rain or snow. Topography can affect the distribution of clouds and precipitation. For example, the windward slopes of high mountain barriers (facing the oncoming wind) usually are wetter than the leeward slopes (facing downwind). The relatively great thermal inertia of large bodies of water (especially the ocean) moderates the temperature of downwind localities, reducing the temperature contrast between summer and winter and lengthening the growing season. Recall our discussion in Chapter 3 regarding the contrast in maritime versus continental climates. Earth's surface characteristics (e.g., ocean versus land, type of vegetative cover, semi-permanent snow and ice cover) influence the amount of incident solar radiation that is converted to heat and how that heat is used (e.g., raising air temperature, evaporating water).

Atmospheric circulation encompasses the combined influence of all weather systems operating at all spatial and temporal scales ranging from sea breezes to the prevailing winds that encircle the planet (Chapter 5). Although strongly influenced by the other climate controls, atmospheric circulation is considerably less regular and less predictable than the others. This variability is especially evident in weather systems such as thunderstorms and hurricanes that are smaller than the planetary scale. Planetary-scale circulation systems (e.g., the prevailing wind belts, subtropical anticyclones), exert a more systematic influence on climate, determining for example, where precipitation is seasonal and the location of the major subtropical deserts.

ROLE OF THE OCEAN

The ocean is a major player in Earth's climate system operating on temporal scales of days to millennia and spatial scales from local to global. The ocean influences radiational heating and cooling of the planet. Covering about 71% of Earth's surface, the ocean is a primary control of how much solar radiation is absorbed (converted to heat) at the Earth's surface. (Recall from Chapter 5 that the average albedo of the ocean surface is only 8%.) Also, the ocean is the main source of the most important *greenhouse gas* (water vapor) and is a major regulator of the concentration of atmospheric carbon dioxide (CO_2), another greenhouse gas.

On an annual average, the ocean absorbs about 92% of the solar radiation striking its surface; the balance is reflected to space. Most of this absorption takes place within about 100 to 200 m (330 to 650 ft) of the ocean surface with the depth of penetration of sunlight limited by the amount of suspended particles and discoloration caused by dissolved substances. On the other hand, at high latitudes highly reflective multi-year pack ice greatly reduces the amount of solar radiation absorbed by the ocean. The snow-covered surface of sea ice absorbs only about 15% of incident solar radiation and reflects away the rest. At present, multi-year pack ice covers about 7% of the ocean surface with greater coverage in the Arctic Ocean than the Southern Ocean (mostly in Antarctica's Weddell Sea). (The Arctic is an ocean surrounded by continents whereas the Antarctic is a continent roughly centered on the pole and surrounded by ocean. Without an Antarctic continent, much more of the Southern Ocean would be covered by sea ice.)

The atmosphere is nearly transparent to incoming solar radiation but much less transparent to outgoing infrared (heat) radiation. This is the basis of the *greenhouse effect*. Most water vapor, the principal greenhouse gas, enters the atmosphere via evaporation of seawater (Figure 11.1). Carbon dioxide, a lesser greenhouse gas, cycles into and out of the ocean depending on the sea surface temperature, circulation patterns, and biological activity in surface waters (Chapter 9). CO_2 is more soluble in cold water than warm water so that carbon dioxide is absorbed from the atmosphere where surface waters are chilled (at high latitudes) and released to the atmosphere where upwelling brings cool water to the surface and is heated (at low latitudes). Photosynthetic organisms take up carbon dioxide and all organisms release carbon dioxide via cellular respiration. Through the physical and biological pumps, carbon is sequestered in the ocean for varying periods (Chapter 9).

The ocean influences the planetary energy budget not only by affecting the radiational heating and radiational cooling of the entire planet, but also by contributing to the non-radiative latent heat and sensible heat fluxes at the air-sea interface. Recall from Chapter 5 that heat is transferred from Earth's surface to the atmosphere via latent heating (vaporization of water at the surface followed by cloud formation in the atmosphere) and sensible heating (conduction plus convection). On a global average annual basis, about ten times more heat is

FIGURE 11.1
The ocean interacts with the atmosphere exchanging heat energy, water, and gases. The ocean is the primary source of atmospheric water vapor, the principal greenhouse gas, and exchanges carbon dioxide, another greenhouse gas, with the atmosphere. [Photo by J.M. Moran]

transferred from the ocean surface to the atmosphere via latent heating than sensible heating.

The ocean and atmosphere are closely coupled. This coupling is most apparent in the ocean's surface waters where temperatures and wind-driven currents respond to variations in atmospheric conditions within hours to days. On the other hand, the deeper basin-scale thermohaline circulation responds more sluggishly to changes in atmospheric conditions, taking decades to centuries or longer to fully adjust. In turn, ocean currents strongly influence climate. Cold surface currents, such as the California Current, are heat sinks; they chill and stabilize the overlying air, thereby increasing the frequency of sea fogs and reducing the likelihood of thunderstorms. Relatively warm surface currents, such as the Gulf Stream, are heat sources; they supply heat and moisture to the overlying air, destabilizing the air, thereby energizing storm systems. As noted in Chapter 5, ocean surface currents and the thermohaline circulation transport heat from the tropics to higher latitudes.

Although the importance of the ocean in Earth's climate system is apparent, we need to remember that the ocean and atmosphere work together in governing climate. Research findings underscore the ocean-atmosphere climate connection with somewhat surprising observations. At the same latitude, winters are significantly milder in Western Europe than in Eastern North America. Since at least the mid-1800s, scientists have attributed this climate contrast primarily to the moderating influence of the warm Gulf Stream and North Atlantic Current on Western Europe. However, recent research results questioned this assumption. Some scientists argue that while the Gulf Stream continually replenishes the relatively warm waters of the North Atlantic, it may not be as important as atmospheric circulation in explaining Western Europe's relatively mild winters.

In 2002, Richard Seager of Columbia University's Lamont-Doherty Earth Observatory and David Battisti of the University of Washington in Seattle, WA reported that the key to Western Europe's mild winters is the pattern exhibited by the prevailing westerlies. Recall from Chapter 5 that aloft the westerlies blow from west to east in a wave-like pattern of ridges and troughs (Figure 5.20). In winter, a cold pool of air (a *trough*) is anchored over eastern North America resulting in cold northwesterly winds on the western flank of the trough, but an intrusion of warm air over the North Atlantic (a *ridge*) is associated with milder southwest winds over Western Europe. That is, in winter, the westerlies tend to blow from the colder northwest over Eastern North America but from the milder southwest over

Western Europe. In addition, the relatively great thermal inertia of ocean water means that summer heat persists in the North Atlantic surface waters long after the North American continent has cooled in fall. Hence, southwest winds blowing toward Western Europe cross relatively warm waters and are heated from below. The direction of the prevailing winds over the North Atlantic and Western Europe is primarily responsible for delivering relatively mild air masses in winter. This finding also implies that shifts in the direction of the prevailing winds could alter the winter climate of Western Europe.

Broad scale patterns of sea-surface temperature (SST) strongly influence the location of major features of the atmosphere's planetary scale circulation. When SST patterns change so too do the locations of planetary-scale circulation features. For example, changes in the location of the highest sea surface temperatures in the tropical Atlantic affect the north-south shifts of the **intertropical convergence zone (ITCZ)**. The ITCZ is a discontinuous belt of showers and thunderstorms paralleling the equator that marks the convergence of the trade winds of the Northern and Southern Hemispheres (Figure 6.7). The ITCZ encircles the globe and shifts north and south with the seasonal excursions of the sun—more so over land and less so over the ocean—reaching its most northerly location in July and its most southerly location in January. Displacement of the ITCZ over the tropical Atlantic Ocean affects the timing and amount of rainfall along the east coast of South America from Brazil northward into the Caribbean Sea from March to May and in the western part of sub-Saharan Africa in August and September. With north-south shifts in the location of the highest SST, the latitude of the ITCZ changes, and regional rainfall patterns also vary.

Changes in sea-surface temperature patterns in the eastern tropical Atlantic have been implicated in the disastrous multi-decade droughts that have afflicted sub-Saharan Africa. For more on this, see this chapter's first Essay.

Tropical Pacific Ocean/Atmosphere

Scientists have been aware of short-term (inter-annual) variations in climate at many locations for more than a century. One of the regions where these inter-annual variations in the Earth-atmosphere system are readily apparent is the tropical Pacific. There ocean/atmosphere conditions varying on a quasi-periodic basis are identified as El Niño and La Niña. Within the last several decades, the scientific community has realized that these episodes can cause weather extremes not only in the tropical Pacific but also in many other parts of the world.

HISTORICAL PERSPECTIVE

Originally, El Niño was the name given by fishermen to a period of an unusually warm southward flowing ocean current and poor fishing off the coast of Peru and Ecuador that often coincided with the Christmas season. (*El Niño* is the Spanish reference to the Christ child). Typically, these warm water episodes are relatively brief, lasting perhaps a month or two, before sea surface temperatures and the fisheries return to normal. About every three to seven years, however, El Niño persists for 12 to 18 months or even longer and is accompanied by significant changes in SST over vast stretches of the tropical Pacific, major shifts in planetary-scale oceanic and atmospheric circulations, and collapse of important South American fisheries. Today, oceanic and atmospheric scientists reserve the term **El Niño** for these long-lasting ocean/atmosphere anomalies.

An important step in understanding El Niño came in 1924 with the discovery of the so-called southern oscillation by the Englishman Sir Gilbert Walker (1868-1958). Monsoon failure in 1899-1900 caused terrible famines in India and the loss of more than a million lives. In 1904, Walker was appointed director general of observatories in India and charged with developing a method to predict the Indian monsoon. He set out on an extensive search for any possible relationship between monsoon rains and weather conditions in various parts of the world. One of his discoveries was the **southern oscillation**, a seesaw variation in air pressure across the tropical Indian and Pacific Oceans. When air pressure was low over the Indian Ocean and the western tropical Pacific, it was high east of the international dateline in the eastern tropical Pacific. During these conditions, monsoon rains were plentiful over India. With the opposite pressure pattern (high pressure west of the dateline and low pressure east of the dateline), monsoon rains were lighter than usual.

Today, the *southern oscillation index (SOI)* is based on the difference in air pressure between Darwin (on the north coast of Australia at 12 degrees S, 130 degrees E) and Tahiti (an island in the central south Pacific at about 18 degrees S, 149 degrees W). When air pressure is anomalously low at Darwin, air pressure is anomalously high at Tahiti. Conversely, when air pressure is high at Darwin, it is low at Tahiti (Figure 11.2). (Note that some scientists question the consistency and quality of air pressure readings at Tahiti prior to 1935.)

FIGURE 11.2
Variation in the southern oscillation index based on monthly mean sea level pressure anomalies at Darwin, Australia and Tahiti. Strongly positive values of the index indicate La Niña conditions and strongly negative values of the index indicate El Niño conditions. The thick black line is the 10-year running mean (trend line). [Climate Analysis Section, Climate and Global Dynamics Division, National Center for Atmospheric Research, Boulder, CO]

More than four decades would pass before the broader significance of Walker's discovery of the southern oscillation was fully recognized. In 1966, the Norwegian-American meteorologist Jacob Bjerknes (1897-1975), while at the University of California at Los Angeles, demonstrated a relationship between El Niño and the southern oscillation, came up with a possible mechanism whereby they interacted, and identified some of the effects on North American weather. The air pressure difference (*air pressure gradient*) across the tropical Pacific changes as air pressure to the west rises and air pressure to the east falls (and vice versa). These changes in air pressure, in turn, may be linked to changes in SST. Bjerknes analyzed oceanic/atmospheric observations gathered from the tropical Pacific during 1957-58, the *International Geophysical Year*, which happened to coincide with a strong El Niño. He found that an El Niño episode begins when the air pressure gradient across the tropical Pacific starts to weaken, heralding the slackening of the trade winds. Scientists refer to this relationship between El Niño and the Southern Oscillation by the acronym **ENSO**.

ENSO is a *coupled* phenomenon in that its variability in Earth's climate system cannot be explained as exclusively an oceanic or atmospheric event. *Coupled* refers to more than merely something that occurs in both the ocean and atmosphere; in this case, the phenomenon depends on feedbacks between the ocean and atmosphere. Changes in ocean conditions (primarily SST) can and do drive changes in atmospheric circulation and precipitation patterns. What is unique about ENSO is the strong coupling: changes in the ocean drive changes in the atmosphere which then feedback and further alter the ocean.

Not until the El Niño of 1982-83, one of the two most intense of the 20th century, did the scientific community and general public fully realize the potential worldwide impact of ENSO. Some of the effects of the 1982-83 El Niño are described in this chapter's Case-in-Point. That event spurred development of numerical models to simulate ENSO as well as deployment of a network of instrumented buoys and satellites to provide advance warning of a developing El Niño. Also, the last two decades have seen increasing interest in **La Niña** (*the girl*), the name coined in the mid 1980s for an ocean/atmosphere interaction that is essentially opposite El Niño. Some scientists refer to the warm El Niño and cold La Niña as opposite extremes of the *ENSO cycle*.

So important are El Niño and La Niña in year-to-year climate variability that signs of a developing El

Niño or La Niña are now routinely incorporated into long-range seasonal weather outlooks worldwide. Such outlooks identify areas of expected anomalies (departures from long-term averages) in temperature and precipitation and guide development of regional agricultural and water management strategies. Adoption of these strategies helps lessen the impact of attendant weather extremes on water supply and food production in various parts of the world.

NEUTRAL CONDITIONS IN THE TROPICAL PACIFIC

El Niño and La Niña represent departures from the long-term average or *neutral* ocean/atmosphere conditions in the tropical Pacific. Understanding El Niño and La Niña first requires a look at neutral conditions. The prevailing trade winds impact ocean currents, sea surface temperatures, and rainfall across the tropical Pacific.

Prevailing winds blow from the south or southeast along the west coast of South America so that most of the time Ekman transport drives warm surface water to the left (westward), away from the coast (Chapter 6). This causes cold, nutrient-rich water to well up from below the thermocline, which is normally only 50 to 100 m (165 to 325 ft) deep along the coast, and replace the warm, nutrient poor surface water that is transported offshore. Although this zone of *coastal upwelling* is narrow (typically less than 15 km or 10 mi wide), the abundance of nutrients conveyed into the photic zone spurs an explosive growth of phytoplankton populations for an additional 15 km offshore. Those populations in turn, support a diverse marine ecosystem and highly productive fishery.

Upwelling is also responsible for a tongue of relatively cool surface waters along the equator in the eastern tropical Pacific. Near the equator, the northeast trade winds of the Northern Hemisphere converge with the southeast trade winds of the Southern Hemisphere. The associated Ekman transport causes surface waters to diverge away from the equator and colder water wells up from below replacing the departing surface waters. *Equatorial upwelling* produces a strip of relatively low sea surface temperatures along the equator from the coast of South America westward to near the international dateline (180 degrees longitude).

Meanwhile, these same trade winds drive a pool of relatively warm surface waters westward toward Indonesia and northern Australia (both the north and south equatorial current). The wedge of warm water increases the depth of the thermocline and raises sea level in the western tropical Pacific. The thermocline is at a depth of about 150 m (490 ft) in the western tropical Pacific and shoals to a depth of about 50 m (165 ft) in the eastern tropical Pacific. Water expands when heated (as well as being piled up by trans-Pacific trade winds) so that sea level is some 60 cm (2 ft) higher in the west than in the east. The contrast in sea-surface temperature between the western and eastern tropical Pacific (averaging about 8 Celsius degrees or 14.4 Fahrenheit degrees) has important implications for precipitation across the tropical Pacific (Figure 11.3). Relatively cool surface waters in the central and eastern tropical Pacific chill the overlying air and suppress convection so that rainfall is light in that region and along the adjacent western coastal plain of South America. Meanwhile, over the western tropical Pacific, warm surface waters heat the overlying air, strengthening convection that gives rise to heavy rainfall.

Average of ALL AVAILABLE Rainfall mm/dd (3B43) 1998 to 2007

FIGURE 11.3
Benchmark average rainfall in millimeters per day (mm/d) across the tropical Pacific Ocean for the 10-year period 1998 through 2007. The heaviest rainfall is in the western tropical Pacific where sea-surface temperatures are highest. These data were obtained from the TRMM Microwave Imager and IR sensors onboard geosynchronous satellites supplemented by conventional rain gauge measurements. [Source: NASA, Tropical Rainfall Measuring Mission (TRMM)]

The contrast between relatively high air pressure over the central and eastern tropical Pacific and relatively low air pressure over the western tropical Pacific ultimately drives the trade winds. Winds initially blow from regions where air pressure is relatively high toward regions where air pressure is relatively low. The greater the air pressure contrast (i.e., horizontal air pressure gradient), the stronger are the winds. Once in motion, the Coriolis Effect deflects winds to the right in the Northern Hemisphere and to the left in the Southern Hemisphere. Trade winds blow from the northeast in the Northern Hemisphere and from the southeast in the Southern Hemisphere. As long as high pressure and low SST persist over the eastern Pacific basin and low pressure and high SST persist over the western Pacific basin, the trade winds are strong and upwelling remains vigorous along the coast of Ecuador and Peru and the equator east of the international dateline.

High SST in the western tropical Pacific lower the surface air pressure whereas low SST in the eastern tropical Pacific raise the surface air pressure. Hence, during neutral conditions the east-west SST gradient reinforces the trade winds by strengthening the east-west air pressure gradient. In flowing over the ocean surface, the trade winds become warmer and more humid. In the western tropical Pacific warm humid air rises, expands, and cools (Figure 11.4). Water vapor condenses into towering cumulonimbus (thunderstorm) clouds that produce heavy rainfall. Aloft this air flows back eastward and sinks over

the cooler waters of the eastern tropical Pacific. Sinking air is compressed and warmed so that clouds vaporize or fail to develop. This completes the large convective-type circulation known as the *Walker Circulation*, named for Sir Gilbert Walker.

EL NIÑO, THE WARM PHASE

With the onset of El Niño, air pressure falls over the eastern tropical Pacific and rises over the western tropical Pacific as part of the southern oscillation. The air pressure gradient across the tropical Pacific weakens and the trade winds slacken in the western and central equatorial Pacific. During a particularly intense El Niño, trade winds west of the international dateline may reverse direction and blow toward the east.

In response to these shifts in atmospheric circulation over the tropical Pacific, changes occur in surface ocean currents, SST, sea level, depth of the thermocline, and upwelling (Figure 11.5). With relaxation of the trade winds, the westward flow of the equatorial currents weakens and at times reverses direction. Hence, the thick layer of warm surface water normally in the west drifts slowly eastward across the tropical Pacific until deflected toward the north and south by the continental landmasses, sometimes reaching as far north as the coast of western Canada and as far south as central Chile. Eastward drift of warm water is so slow that it may take several months to reach the west coasts of North and South America. In the western tropical Pacific, SST drops,

FIGURE 11.4
Schematic block diagram showing ocean/atmosphere conditions in the tropical Pacific during normal or neutral episodes. Red indicates areas of highest sea-surface temperatures. [NOAA, Pacific Marine Environmental Laboratory (PMEL), Tropical Atmosphere Ocean Project]

FIGURE 11.5
Schematic block diagram showing ocean/atmosphere conditions in the tropical Pacific during El Niño conditions. Red indicates areas of highest sea-surface temperatures. [NOAA, Pacific Marine Environmental Laboratory (PMEL), Tropical Atmosphere Ocean Project]

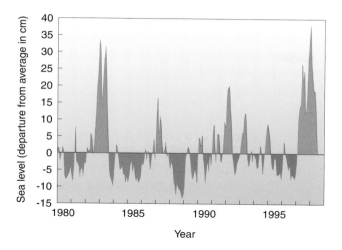

FIGURE 11.6
Sea level record at Galápagos in the eastern tropical Pacific based on tide gauge records and expressed in cm as departure from the long-term average. Relatively high sea levels correspond to El Niño episodes. [NOAA PMEL]

sea-level falls, and the thermocline rises whereas in the eastern tropical Pacific, SST rises, sea-level climbs, and the thermocline deepens (Figure 11.6).

The impacts of these environmental changes can be severe on marine ecosystems. Arrival of warm surface waters in the eastern tropical Pacific reduces upwelling of nutrient-rich waters along the coast of Ecuador and Peru. Deprived of nutrients, phytoplankton populations decline and the commercial fish harvest plummets. Peru's fishing industry boomed in the 1950s and 1960s and by 1970 was one of the largest in the world. At that time Peru accounted for about 20% of the total global catch of anchovies. Most of the catch was exported for poultry feed supplement and accounted for almost one-third of the nation's foreign exchange income. However, over-fishing combined with the effects of the 1972-73 El Niño sent the Peruvian fishery into a tailspin from which it has not recovered.

Warmer surface waters can also severely stress coral reefs living in shallow tropical waters. In response to unusually high sea-surface temperatures, coral expels zooxanthallae, the symbiotic microscopic algae that supply coral with oxygen and some organic compounds produced through photosynthesis. Recall from Chapter 10 that without zooxanthallae, coral polyps have little pigmentation and appear nearly transparent on the coral's white skeleton, a condition referred to as *coral bleaching*. Excessive bleaching can kill coral polyps, destroying habitats for a variety of marine life. Extensive coral bleaching was reported during the 1997-98 El Niño.

The decline of corals due to coral bleaching, ocean acidification (Chapters 3 and 4) and other stresses has serious economic impacts. Coral reefs are valued for fishing, tourism, and protection of shorelines from storm surges. According to Camilo Mora, a coral specialist at Dalhousie University, Halifax, Nova Scotia, the worldwide value of coral reefs amounts to an estimated $30 billion annually.

In a study of Caribbean coral reefs during the summers of 1983 to 2000, Jennifer Gill and colleagues at the University of East Anglia in the U.K. found that atmospheric aerosols may help prevent coral bleaching. Associated with El Niño is a rise in Caribbean SST that favors coral bleaching. But at least partially offsetting this warming is the presence of tiny particles suspended in the atmosphere that scatter and absorb solar radiation thereby causing lower SST. Much of this aerosol load is transported by winds aloft to the Caribbean from the Sahara Desert supplemented by particles from distant volcanic eruptions (Chapter 4). Although El Niño occurred in 1991, the cooling associated with the eruption of Mount Pinatubo in the Philippines that same year appears to have prevented widespread coral bleaching in the Caribbean. According to Gill and her colleagues, El Niño and atmospheric aerosols account for about 70% of the year-to-year variability in Caribbean coral bleaching.

During El Niño, lower than usual SST in the western tropical Pacific and higher than usual SST in the central and eastern tropical Pacific coupled with the change in trade wind circulation give rise to anomalous weather patterns in the tropics and subtropics. Long-term average winds blow onshore over Indonesia so that rainfall is normally abundant, but during El Niño, prevailing winds are directed offshore and the weather of Indonesia is dry. El Niño-related droughts may also grip India, eastern Australia, northeastern Brazil, and southern Africa. Meanwhile, warmer than usual surface waters off the west coast of South America spur convection and heavy rainfall along the normally arid coastal plain, causing flash flooding. Wetter conditions tend to occur in southern Brazil, Uruguay, and equatorial East Africa.

Martin Hoerling, a NOAA meteorologist, and colleagues reported that during the period 1871 to 2002, central India endured 10 severe droughts during the monsoon rainy season (June, July, and August). All 10 droughts occurred during an El Niño episode. However, the converse did not hold; that is, not all El Niño events during the 132-year period were accompanied by drought in central India. In fact, in 13 cases rainy season precipitation was at or slightly greater than the long-term average. In examining the various cases of drought, Hoerling and colleagues found that the greatest SST anomalies during El Niño occurred either in the central equatorial Pacific or in the eastern equatorial Pacific. Drought occurred in central India when the highest SSTs were in the central equatorial Pacific. Numerical models predicted that these exceptionally warm waters would produce warm, humid air that would rise high in the tropical atmosphere, move over central India, and subside. The subsiding air would inhibit development of clouds and precipitation and soon a drought would be underway. This is one of many examples that demonstrate the fact that no two El Niño events are the same.

Apparently, El Niño also influences the intensity, frequency, and spatial distribution of tropical cyclones (e.g., tropical storms, hurricanes). Stronger than usual winds aloft inhibit development of tropical cyclones over the Atlantic Basin (Chapter 8). Those few tropical cyclones that do develop usually are weaker and shorter lived than usual. In the Pacific and Indian Oceans, changes in SST that accompany El Niño appear to alter the intensity and spatial distribution of tropical cyclones rather than their frequency. Because of the extensive area of warmer water over the eastern tropical Pacific, hurricanes that form there can travel farther north and west than usual.

El Niño typically brings dry weather to the Hawaiian Islands. Almost all of Hawaii's major droughts during the 20th century coincided with an El Niño event. As part of the usual atmospheric circulation changes that take place during El Niño, the North Pacific subtropical anticyclone shifts so that the associated region of descending air moves closer to the Islands. The greater than usual frequency of sinking air over Hawaii is responsible for a persistent dry weather pattern.

El Niño also has a ripple effect on the weather and climate of middle latitudes, especially in winter. A linkage between changes in atmospheric circulation occurring in widely separated regions of the globe, often over distances of thousands of kilometers, is known as a **teleconnection**. What causes teleconnections? Latent heat released into the atmosphere during deep convection and the buildup of thunderstorms in the tropical troposphere is one of the major controls of the planetary-scale circulation. Changes in the location of these heat sources alter wind and weather patterns worldwide. Higher than usual SST over the central and eastern tropical Pacific during El Niño heats and destabilizes the troposphere. Deep convection generates towering thunderstorms that help drive atmospheric circulation, governing the course of jet streams, storm tracks, and moisture transport by winds at higher latitudes.

Events in the ocean and atmosphere are somewhat analogous to the effect of large boulders on a swiftly flowing stream. Boulders in the streambed induce a train of turbulent eddies that extends downstream. Moving the boulders will displace the train of eddies. Thunderstorm clouds building high into the tropical troposphere deflect the upper air winds in much the same manner as boulders in a stream; that is, a shift in location of the principal area of convection eastward over the tropical Pacific redirects the atmospheric circulation.

During typical El Niño winters, prevailing storm tracks bring abundant rainfall and cooler than usual conditions to the Gulf Coast states, from Texas to Florida. Over the northern U.S. and Canada, prevailing winds tend to blow from west to east so that extremely cold air masses tend to move eastward across the Arctic and northern Canada. Persistence of this circulation pattern prevents exceptionally cold air masses from invading the northern U.S so that mild weather prevails over much of Canada, Alaska, and parts of the northern U.S. West-to-east flow in the westerlies also diminishes the usual spring contrast between warm, humid air masses moving northeastward from the Gulf of Mexico and cold, dry air masses sweeping southeastward from Canada. Consequently, severe thunderstorms and tornadoes may be less frequent than usual in the Ohio and Tennessee River Valleys.

Although some weather extremes almost always accompany El Niño, no two events are the same because El Niño is one of many factors that influence inter-annual variations in climate. In southern California, for example, heavy winter rains (snows at higher elevations) have occurred during some but not all El Niño events. Record heavy rainfall in Southern California during January 1995 was linked to a shift of the jet stream (and storm track) south of its usual position over the eastern Pacific. In that case, a change in atmospheric circulation associated with El Niño was the culprit. Whereas the 1982-83 El Niño brought severe drought to eastern Australia, dry conditions in Australia during the 1997-98 El Niño were far less severe.

THE 1997-98 EL NIÑO

The 1997-98 El Niño rivaled its 1982-83 predecessor as the most intense of the 20th century (Figure 11.7). Weather extremes and outbreaks of disease (related to rainfall and standing water, such as malaria and cholera) worldwide claimed an estimated 22,000 lives and caused $36 billion in economic losses. This El Niño developed rapidly with the trade winds weakening and eventually reversing direction in the western tropical

FIGURE 11.7
Evolution of the 1997-98 El Niño as derived from changes in ocean surface height (compared to the long-term average) as measured by altimeter sensors onboard the TOPEX/Poseidon satellite. On the color scale, whites and reds indicate elevated areas (warmer than normal water). In the white areas, the sea surface is 14 to 32 cm (6 to 13 in.) above normal; in the red areas it is about 10 cm (4 in.) above normal. Green indicates normal sea level whereas purple corresponds to areas that are at least 18 cm (7 in.) below normal sea level (colder than normal water). [NASA Goddard Space Flight Center]

Pacific in early 1997. Equatorial upwelling ceased during the Northern Hemisphere summer of 1997. A pool of exceptionally warm surface waters (SST greater than 29 °C or 84 °F) migrated eastward from the western tropical Pacific. During the Northern Hemisphere fall of 1997, SST over the eastern tropical Pacific were at least 5 Celsius degrees (9 Fahrenheit degrees) higher than the long-term average. Warming was rapid in the eastern tropical Pacific with SST setting new record highs each successive month from June through December 1997. By late 1997, the thermocline essentially flattened across the tropical Pacific basin, rising some 20 to 40 m (65 to 130 ft) in the west and falling more than 90 m (295 ft) in the east. Somewhat lower surface water temperatures in the west and much higher than usual sea surface temperatures in the east weakened the usual east-west SST gradient. By further reducing the east-west air pressure gradient, the weaker SST gradient contributed to additional slackening of the trade winds.

The 1997-98 El Niño came to an abrupt end in mid-May 1998. Trade winds strengthened rapidly, upwelling resumed along the equator and off the northwest coast of South America, and SST over the eastern tropical Pacific plummeted in response to upwelling of very cold water. At one location along the equator (125 degrees W), the SST fell 8 Celsius degrees (14 Fahrenheit degrees) in only four weeks.

LA NIÑA, THE COLD PHASE

Sometimes, but not always, La Niña follows El Niño. **La Niña** is a period of unusually strong trade winds and exceptionally vigorous upwelling in the eastern tropical Pacific (Figure 11.8). Like its warm counterpart, La Niña tends to persist for 12 to 18 months. During La Niña, SST anomalies are essentially opposite those observed during El Niño; that is, surface waters are colder than usual over the central and eastern tropical Pacific and somewhat warmer than usual over the western tropical Pacific. SST anomalies over the eastern tropical Pacific typically are greater in magnitude during El Niño than during La Niña. SST usually rise about 5 to 6 Celsius degrees (9 to 11 Fahrenheit degrees) above the long-term average during an intense El Niño but drop only 2 to 3 Celsius degrees (3.6 to 5.4 Fahrenheit degrees) below the long-term average during a strong La Niña.

Accompanying La Niña are worldwide weather extremes that are often opposite those observed during El Niño. As with El Niño, the most consistent middle latitude teleconnections appear in winter. In the tropical Pacific, lower than usual SST in the east inhibit rainfall and higher than usual SST in the west enhance rainfall in Indonesia, Malaysia, and northern Australia during the Northern Hemisphere winter and the Philippines during the Northern Hemisphere summer. Elsewhere around the globe, the Indian monsoon rainfall (in summer) tends to be heavier than average (especially in northwest India) and wet conditions prevail over southeastern Africa and northern Brazil (during the Northern Hemisphere winter). Southern Brazil to central Argentina experience a dry winter. In addition, weak winds aloft during La Niña favor tropical cyclone formation over the Atlantic Basin.

Across middle latitudes of the Northern Hemisphere, westerlies tend to be more *meridional* during La Niña; that is, prevailing winds tend to encircle the globe from west to east in great north-south loops. These winds steer cold air masses toward the southeast and warm air masses toward the northeast. Occasionally, a meridional flow pattern becomes so extreme that a broad pool of rotating air essentially separates from the main current and remains over the same geographical area for many weeks to months. (This is somewhat analogous to a whirlpool that forms in a swiftly flowing stream.) A pool of air rotating in a clockwise direction (viewed from above) is known as a *cutoff anticyclone* (or *high*). For as long as a cutoff high persists over the same area, the weather remains dry and the probability of drought increases. Just such an atmospheric circulation pattern was responsible for the severe summer drought that afflicted the central U.S. during the La Niña year of 1988.

La Niña Conditions

FIGURE 11.8
Schematic block diagram showing ocean/atmosphere conditions in the tropical Pacific during La Niña conditions. Red indicates areas of highest sea-surface temperatures. [NOAA, Pacific Marine Environmental Laboratory (PMEL), Tropical Atmosphere Ocean Project]

In spring, a more meridional flow pattern in the westerlies may increase the likelihood of severe thunderstorms and tornadoes across the central U.S. Such a flow pattern brings together air masses that contrast in temperature and humidity, a key ingredient for severe weather development. Also in the U.S., La Niña tends to be accompanied by below average winter precipitation and mild temperatures in a band from the Southwest, through the central and southern Rockies, and eastward to the Gulf Coast. Winter in the Pacific Northwest tends to be cool and wet. Lower than usual winter temperatures also occur in the northern Intermountain West and north-central states.

Changes in the atmospheric circulation pattern associated with a recent La Niña were likely responsible for a persistent cut-off high that brought drought to southwestern Asia, from Iran eastward to western Pakistan. From 1998 to 2001, Afghanistan, near the center of the dry belt, experienced its most severe drought in 50 years, compounding the human misery brought on by decades of political instability and civil strife. Heidi M. Cullen, at the time a climatologist with the National Center for Atmospheric Research (NCAR) in Boulder, CO proposed that changes in the atmospheric circulation pattern were linked to exceptionally low SST in the central tropical Pacific and unusually high SST in the western tropical Pacific. These La Niña conditions brought heavy winter rains to the eastern Indian Ocean (e.g., Malaysia), a shift in the location of the subtropical jet stream, and development of a cut-off high over southwestern Asia. The cut-off high blocked the usual west to east movement of storm systems bringing an extended period of dry weather to portions of southwestern Asia. Cullen cautions, however, that not all La Niña events bring drought to the Iran-Afghanistan-Pakistan region.

PREDICTING AND MONITORING EL NIÑO AND LA NIÑA

Scientists have developed numerical models that simulate El Niño and La Niña. These models approximate oceanic processes that alter sea-surface temperatures, and the atmospheric response, including convection, clouds, and winds. Forecasters rely on two basic types of numerical models to predict the onset, evolution, and decay of El Niño (or La Niña): empirical (or statistical) models and dynamical models. An *empirical model* compares current and evolving oceanic and atmospheric conditions with comparable observational data for periods preceding El Niño (or La Niña) episodes over the prior 40 years. A match or at least some resemblance between

past and present conditions is the basis for a prediction. A *dynamical model* consists of a series of mathematical equations that simulates interactions or coupling among atmosphere, ocean, and land. These so-called *coupled* models are more sophisticated than empirical models and run on supercomputers.

Assessment of the performance of 12 models (6 empirical and 6 dynamical) in predicting the onset, evolution, and demise of the 1997-98 El Niño was somewhat disappointing. The dynamical model operated by the Climate Prediction Center (CPC) of NOAA's National Centers for Environmental Prediction (NCEP) in Camp Springs, MD performed well in predicting the onset of the 1997-98 El Niño. But the NCEP and all other models greatly underestimated (by about 50%) the magnitude of sea surface warming in the eastern tropical Pacific and demonstrated little skill in forecasting the decay of El Niño. The NCEP model predicted gradual cooling in the eastern tropical Pacific through 1998 when in fact sea-surface temperatures plunged in May 1998.

Official forecasts of an impending El Niño appeared in the spring of 1997 (after warming of the eastern tropical Pacific had already begun). Model output strongly influenced the Climate Prediction Center's winter outlook issued in November 1997 for December 1997 through February 1998. That outlook correctly predicted heavier than usual precipitation across the southern U.S. and anomalous warmth over the northern one-third of the nation. Predictions of unusually dry conditions in Indonesia, northern South America, and southern Africa were verified. Above average rainfall predicted for Peru, east Africa, and northern Argentina was also correct. But the extreme drought expected for northeast Australia did not materialize.

Reliable observational data from the tropical Pacific Ocean and atmosphere are essential for detecting a developing El Niño or La Niña, and for initializing numerical models. The accuracy of dynamical models depends on (1) how well their component equations simulate the coupled ocean/atmosphere/land system, and (2) reliable observational data. Numerical models use those initial conditions as a starting point for predicting future states of the ocean and atmosphere and for verifying the model predictions and results. Data are also assimilated into model runs to correct or "nudge" the model as events evolve.

A major reason why dynamical models performed well in detecting the onset of the 1997-98 El Niño was the increasing amount of ocean/atmosphere observational data from the tropical Pacific. Those data

ENSO Observing System

FIGURE 11.9
Components of the ENSO Observing System provide advance warning and monitor the development and decay of El Niño and La Niña events. [NOAA, Pacific Marine Environmental Laboratory (PMEL), Seattle, WA]

were obtained by monitoring systems deployed as part of the 10-year (1985-1994) international *Tropical Ocean Global Atmosphere (TOGA)* study. TOGA was aimed at improving understanding, detection, and prediction of ENSO-related variability. An important product of TOGA, the *ENSO Observing System,* was fully operational by December 1994. The ENSO Observing System consists of an array of moored and drifting instrumented buoys, island and coastal tide gauges, ship-based measurements, and satellites (Figure 11.9).

One component of the ENSO Observing System is the *TAO (Tropical Atmosphere /Ocean)* array of moored buoys (small, unmanned, instrumented platforms) in the tropical Pacific Ocean (Figure 11.10). Buoys are strategically placed over an area bounded by 8 degrees N, 8 degrees S, 95 degrees W, and 137 degrees E. This instrument array, renamed TAO/TRITON in 2000, presently consists of approximately 70 deep-sea moorings that measure several atmospheric variables (air temperature, wind, relative humidity) as well as oceanic parameters (sea-surface and subsurface temperatures at 10 depths in the upper 500 m or 1640 ft). Several newer

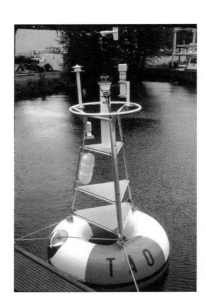

FIGURE 11.10
An instrumented TAO moored buoy photographed at NOAA's Pacific Marine Environmental Laboratory in Seattle, WA. An array of similar moored buoys gathers oceanic and atmospheric data from the tropical Pacific as part of the ENSO Observing System. [Photo by J.M. Moran]

moorings also have salinity sensors, along with additional meteorological sensors. Five moorings along the equator also measure ocean current velocity using Subsurface Acoustic Doppler Current Profilers. Observational data are telemetered to NOAA's Pacific Marine Environmental Laboratory (PMEL) in Seattle, WA via a NOAA polar-orbiting satellite. Those data are available on the Internet in near real-time.

Remote sensing by satellite plays an important role in providing early warning of an evolving El Niño or La Niña. Sensors onboard NOAA and NASA satellites monitor cloud cover and map sea surface temperatures. The TOPEX/Poseidon satellite, a joint mission of NASA and the Centre National d'Etudes Spatiales in France, launched in 1992, provided images of ocean surface topography (sea level) at 10-day intervals until January 2006 when the spacecraft could no longer maneuver (Figures 11.7 and 11.11). Radar (microwave) altimeters onboard the satellite (orbiting at an altitude of 1340 km or 833 mi) bounced microwaves off the ocean surface to obtain precise measurements of the distance between the satellite and the sea surface. These data, combined with data from the Global Positioning System (GPS), produced images of sea surface height. Elevated topography (hills) indicates warmer than usual water whereas areas of low topography (valleys) indicate colder than usual water. Such images can be used to calculate surface ocean currents based on the geostrophic assumption. In December 2001, NASA and its French counterpart

launched Jason 1, the successor to TOPEX/Poseidon, that promises more accurate measurement of ocean surface topography. For more on the technique used to remotely determine ocean surface elevation, refer to the second Essay in Chapter 7.

Another satellite mission that is helping scientists detect the onset and follow the evolution of El Niño and La Niña is the joint U.S.-Japanese *Tropical Rainfall Measuring Mission (TRMM)* launched in November 1997 (Figure 11.3). The TRMM satellite uses active radar plus passive microwave energy sensors to monitor clouds, precipitation, and radiation processes over the area between 40 degrees N and 40 degrees S in the Pacific Ocean. During the 1997-1998 El Niño, sensors on the TRMM satellite recorded reduced precipitation in the western tropical Pacific and increased precipitation east of 150 degrees W longitude. An important feature of the satellite is its TRMM Microwave Imager (TMI), an instrument that "sees through" clouds and measures sea-surface temperatures. The TMI uses the microwave energy emitted by the sea surface to characterize its IR emission spectrum and determine its radiation temperature. Microwaves pass through clouds with little attenuation but are strongly absorbed and reflected by rainfall so that TMI can measure SST only during fair weather.

Increasingly accurate predictions of El Niño and La Niña are enabling humankind to better cope with the impacts of short-term (inter-annual) climate variability. Such forecasts allow informed strategic planning in agriculture, fisheries, and water resource management. Consider an example: Peru's economy, like that of most developing nations, is very sensitive to climate. In Peru, El Niño is bad for fishing and often accompanied by destructive flooding. La Niña benefits fishing but may also mean drought and crop failure. Warning of an impending El Niño or La Niña prior to the start of the growing season allows agricultural interests and government officials to consult on what crops to plant to optimize production. For example, if the forecast calls for El Niño, rice is favored over cotton because rice thrives during a wet growing season whereas cotton is more drought-tolerant and is more suitable during La Niña. Also, in anticipation of the heavy rainfall likely to accompany a full-blown El Niño, water resource managers can direct the gradual draw down of reservoirs to reduce flooding.

FREQUENCY OF EL NIÑO AND LA NIÑA

On 30 September 2003, NOAA scientists announced that they had reached a consensus among

FIGURE 11.11
Sea level record at a location along the equator in the eastern tropical Pacific derived from measurements made by the TOPEX/Poseidon satellite. Sea level is expressed in cm as departure from the long-term average. Relatively high sea levels correspond to El Niño episodes. [From NOAA PMEL]

FIGURE 11.12

Variations in the Multivariate ENSO Index showing the sequence of El Niño and La Niña events since 1950. The Index is based on six variables measured in the tropical Pacific: sea-level air pressure, zonal (east-west) component of surface wind, meridional (north-south) component of surface wind, surface air temperature, sky cloud cover, and sea-surface temperature. Sea-surface temperature anomalies (departures from 1971-2000 averages) are measured for the area in the tropical Pacific Ocean between 5 degrees N and 5 degrees S latitude and from 120 degrees W to 170 degrees W longitude. Warm anomalies (greater than about 0.5 Celsius degree) generally indicate El Niño whereas cold anomalies (less than about –0.5 Celsius degree) generally indicate La Niña. [NOAA/ESRL/Physical Science Division-University of Colorado at Boulder/CIRES/CDC]

experts from the federal government and academia for an index that forms the basis for operational definitions of El Niño and La Niña (Figure 11.12). The Index is based on six variables measured in the tropical Pacific: sea-level air pressure, zonal (east-west) component of surface wind, meridional (north-south) component of surface wind, surface air temperature, sky cloud cover, and sea-surface temperature. Sea-surface temperatures are drawn from an area of the tropical Pacific that includes the equatorial cold tongue and is bounded by longitude 120 degrees W and 170 degrees W, latitude 5 degrees N and 5 degrees S. By this index, El Niño is characterized by a *positive* sea surface temperature departure from normal (based on the 1971-2000 period) greater than or equal to 0.5 Celsius degree, averaged over three consecutive months. La Niña is characterized by a *negative* sea surface temperature departure from normal (based on the 1971-2000 period) greater than or equal to 0.5 Celsius degree, averaged over three consecutive months.

Although El Niño does not always give way to La Niña, La Niña appears more likely to follow an intense El Niño rather than a weak one. This may be explained by the fact that during an intense El Niño, the global water cycle conveys a great amount of heat out of the eastern tropical Pacific and into higher latitudes. Unusually cold water situated just below the warm surface water is poised to well up to the surface as soon as the trade winds strengthen. For example, a significant La Niña followed the intense 1997-98 El Niño.

During the second half of the 20th century, El Niño conditions prevailed 31% of the time and La Niña occurred 23% of the time. The balance of the time neutral or near-neutral conditions prevailed. As of this writing, the most recent El Niño was a weak episode in 2006. Prior El Niño episodes took place in 2004-05, 2002-03, 1997-98, 1991-95, 1986-87, 1982-83, 1976-77, 1972-73, 1969, 1965-66, 1963, 1957-58, 1953, and 1951. During the 1980s and 1990s, La Niña was less frequent than El Niño. The most recent La Niña was in 2007. Prior La Niña episodes took place in 2000-01, 1998-2000, 1995-96, 1988-89, 1973-75, 1970-71, 1964, 1955-56, and 1949-1950. While all El Niño episodes share some common characteristics as described earlier in this chapter, they differ from one another in duration, intensity, and the way they develop. The same applies to La Niña.

El Niño and La Niña are not just recent phenomena. In fact, documentary, archeological, and geological evidence indicates that ENSO has operated over at least tens of thousands of years. For more on this topic, refer to this chapter's second Essay.

North Atlantic Oscillation

Research on El Niño has spurred interest in other regular oscillations involving the interaction of the ocean and atmosphere that impact short-term climate variability. These include the North Atlantic Oscillation (NAO), the

Arctic Oscillation (AO), and Pacific Decadal Oscillation (PDO). In general, NAO, AO, and PDO affect more restricted geographical areas and operate over longer time periods than either El Niño or La Niña.

Over the North Atlantic, the time-averaged planetary-scale atmospheric circulation features a subpolar low pressure system near Iceland (the *Icelandic low*) and a massive subtropical anticyclone centered near 30 degrees N that stretches from Bermuda to near the Azores (Chapter 5). The **North Atlantic Oscillation (NAO)** refers to a seesaw variation in air pressure between Iceland and the Azores. When air pressure is higher than the long-term average over the Azores, it is lower than the long-term average over Iceland and vice versa. The air pressure gradient between the Bermuda-Azores subtropical anticyclone and the Icelandic low drives winds that steer storms from west to east across the North Atlantic.

The North Atlantic Oscillation influences precipitation and temperatures primarily in winter (December to March) over eastern North America and much of Europe and North Africa. The so-called **NAO Index** is directly proportional to the strength of the North Atlantic air pressure gradient, i.e., the difference in sea level air pressure between the Bermuda-Azores high and the Icelandic low. The NAO Index time series in Figure 11.13 is based on the difference in sea level pressure over Gibraltar and the sea level pressure over southwest Iceland. When the NAO Index is relatively high, stronger than usual winter winds blow across the North Atlantic

moving cold air masses over eastern Canada and the U.S. so that winters tend to be colder than usual in that region. But cold air masses modify considerably as they move over the relatively mild ocean surface, warming and becoming more humid so that winters are milder and wetter than usual downstream over Europe. Meanwhile, dry winters prevail in the Mediterranean region. On the other hand, when the NAO Index is low, steering winds over the North Atlantic shift southward so that winters are colder than usual over northern Europe and wet and mild conditions prevail from the Mediterranean eastward into the Middle East. The eastern U.S. and Canada tend to experience relatively mild winters while winters in the southeast U.S. are colder than usual.

The NAO Index varies significantly from one year to the next and from decade to decade and is much less regular than the ENSO cycle. The NAO Index was generally low in the 1950s and trended upward from the 1960s through the early 1990s and then generally downward into the winter of 2006-07.

Changes in winter moisture supply associated with NAO have had varied impacts in Europe and North Africa. During recent decades of relatively high NAO-Index, wetter winters have increased hydroelectric power potential in the Scandinavian nations, lengthened the growing season over northern Eurasia, but also diminished the snow cover for winter recreation. Meanwhile, a moisture deficit has been the problem in the Iberian Peninsula, the watershed of the Tigris and Euphrates Rivers, and the Sahel of North Africa.

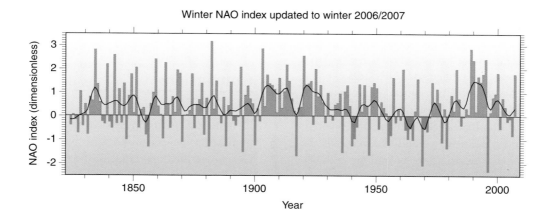

FIGURE 11.13
Record of the North Atlantic Oscillation (NAO) during winter (December to March) through 2006-2007, based on the difference between the normalized sea-level air pressure at Gibraltar and the normalized sea-level air pressure over southwest Iceland. Solid black line is a running mean. [From Tim Osborn, Climate Research Unit, University of East Anglia, Norwich, UK]

Arctic Oscillation

Related to the North Atlantic Oscillation, the **Arctic Oscillation (AO)** is a seesaw variation in air pressure between the North Pole and the margins of the polar region. Associated changes in the horizontal air pressure gradient alter the speed of the band of winds aloft (the *polar vortex*) that blow counterclockwise (viewed from above) around the Arctic. Alternate strengthening and weakening of these polar winds impact winter weather in middle latitudes and contribute to climate variability and changes in ocean circulation.

The Arctic Oscillation shifts between negative and positive phases. During its negative phase, the air pressure gradient is weaker and the polar vortex circulation is not as strong as usual. This allows bitterly cold Arctic air masses to more frequently move out of their source regions in the far north and plunge southeastward into middle latitudes. This brings colder than usual winter weather to most of the U.S., Northern Europe, Russia, China, and Japan. Heavy lake-effect snows around the Great Lakes are more frequent and nor'easters are more likely along the U.S. Eastern Seaboard (Chapter 8). But when the Arctic Oscillation is in its positive phase, the air pressure gradient is greater and winds encircling the Arctic are stronger. These stronger winds act as a dam to impede the southeastward flow of Arctic air. The middle latitude westerlies also strengthen and blow more directly from west to east, flooding much of the U.S. with relatively mild air from off the Pacific Ocean (instead of frigid Arctic air from Canada). Winter temperatures are milder than usual (especially east of the Rocky Mountains) and major snowstorms are less likely. Meanwhile, Alaska, Scotland, and Scandinavia are snowier than usual and California and Spain are drier.

Although during any winter the Arctic Oscillation can shift many times between its negative and positive phases, extended periods occur when either the negative or positive phase dominates the winter season. In the 1960s, the negative phase of the Arctic Oscillation dominated. Since then, the positive phase has been more frequent, a trend that is consistent with observed climate fluctuations in middle latitudes (e.g., less frequent episodes of extreme cold and major snowstorms). Furthermore, during this recent episode of dominantly positive Arctic Oscillation phase, winds have been delivering warmer than usual air and ocean water into the Arctic. As we will see in Chapter 12, this may at least help explain the recent shrinkage of Arctic ice cover.

Pacific Decadal Oscillation

The **Pacific Decadal Oscillation (PDO)** is a long-lived variation in climate over the North Pacific and North America. Sea-surface temperatures fluctuate between the north central Pacific and the west coast of North America. During a PDO *warm phase*, SST are lower than usual over the broad central interior of the North Pacific and above average in a narrow strip along the coasts of Alaska, western Canada, and the Pacific Northwest. In an interesting parallel to what happens off the coast of Ecuador and Chile during El Niño, the layer of relatively warm surface waters off the Pacific Northwest Coast significantly reduces upwelling of nutrient-rich bottom water. Populations of phytoplankton and zooplankton plummet and juvenile salmon migrating to coastal waters from streams and rivers starve (Chapter 10). On the other hand, during a PDO *cold phase*, SST are higher in the North Pacific interior and lower along the coast associated with the return of nutrients, primary production, and salmon.

Key to the climatic impact of PDO is the strength of the subpolar *Aleutian low*, which persists through the winter off the Alaskan coast. During a PDO *warm phase*, the Aleutian low is well developed and its strong counterclockwise winds steer mild and relatively dry air masses into the Pacific Northwest. Winters tend to be mild and dry and water supplies suffer from reduced mountain snow pack. But during a PDO *cold phase*, the Aleutian cyclone is weaker so that cold, moist air masses more frequently invade the Pacific Northwest. Winters are colder and wetter, and the mountain snow pack is thicker. PDO phases tend to last for 20 to 30 years. Cold phases prevailed from 1890 to 1924 and again from 1947 to 1976 whereas warm phases persisted from 1925 to 1946 and 1977 through the 1990s.

Conclusions

El Niño and La Niña involve interactions between the tropical Pacific Ocean and atmosphere. These phenomena underscore the importance of the flux of heat energy and moisture between the ocean and atmosphere. Changes in these fluxes during El Niño and La Niña have relatively short-term (one to two year) impacts on ocean circulation and the weather and climate in various parts of the world with implications for marine life, fisheries, and hydrologic budgets on land (e.g., drought, flooding rains). Short-term fluctuations in climate induced by El Niño and La

Niña as well as the longer-term NAO, AO, and PDO are superimposed on much longer period variations in climate that have longer lasting impacts on the Earth system. The ocean also plays a central role in these long-term climate changes.

ENSO occurs in the tropics because that is the only place where the ocean can drastically alter its structure on time scales of months to years. At higher latitudes, the ocean structure is more strongly confined because of the greater role of Earth's rotation. Therefore, any large-scale ocean-atmosphere coupled variations at higher latitudes will necessarily have a time scale of many years to decades. Scientists are just beginning to piece together the character of these modes of variation in part because studying longer time-scale variations requires longer detailed records which take time to collect. While the current observational record has captured many ENSO events, scientists have only begun to acquire sufficient data to characterize variability at higher latitudes.

In the next chapter, we examine the nature of climate change, causes of climate change, and possible implications of those changes for the ocean and humankind.

Basic Understandings

- Many factors working together shape the climate of any locality. Controls of climate consist of (1) latitude, (2) elevation, (3) topography, (4) proximity to large bodies of water, (5) Earth's surface characteristics, (6) net incoming solar radiation, (7) long-term average atmospheric circulation, and (8) prevailing ocean circulation.

- Climate responds in periodic fashion to the diurnal and seasonal variations in incoming solar radiation. On time scales of millions of years, all climate controls are variable. On shorter time scales, for all practical purposes, the first four climate controls listed above are essentially fixed and exert regular and predictable influences on climate.

- The ocean is a major player in Earth's climate system operating on time scales of days to millennia and spatial scales from local to global. The ocean influences the radiational heating and cooling of the planet and is an active mechanism for the global redistribution of heat energy.

- Ocean currents strongly influence climate. Cold surface currents are heat sinks; they chill and stabilize the overlying air, thereby increasing the frequency of sea fogs and reducing the likelihood of thunderstorms. Relatively warm surface currents are heat sources; they supply heat and moisture to the overlying air, destabilizing the air, thereby energizing storm systems. Furthermore, the global thermohaline circulation contributes to the poleward transport of heat energy.

- In 1924, Sir Gilbert Walker discovered the southern oscillation, a seesaw variation in air pressure between the western and central tropical Pacific. In the mid-1960s, Jacob Bjerknes found that an El Niño episode begins when the air pressure gradient across the tropical Pacific begins to weaken, perhaps in response to changes in SST.

- Over the long-term average (neutral conditions), southerly and southeasterly winds along the west coast of South America drive warm surface waters westward (via Ekman transport), away from the coast. Departing warm surface waters are replaced by cold, nutrient-rich water that wells up from below the thermocline (upwelling) fueling high biological production. Upwelling also occurs along the equator, east of the international dateline, due to convergence of the trade winds of the two hemispheres and Ekman transport.

- During neutral conditions, relatively cool surface waters in the central and eastern tropical Pacific chill the overlying air and suppress convection so that rainfall is light in that region and along the adjacent western coastal plain of South America. Meanwhile, over the western tropical Pacific, relatively warm surface waters heat the overlying air, strengthening convection and giving rise to heavy rainfall. Higher air pressure in the east and lower air pressure in the west result in trade winds blowing from the east piling up a thick layer of warm surface water in the western tropical Pacific.

- At the onset of El Niño, air pressure falls over the eastern tropical Pacific and rises over the western tropical Pacific as part of the southern oscillation. The air pressure gradient across the tropical Pacific weakens and the trade winds slacken and may even reverse direction west of the international dateline. This allows the thick layer of warm surface water piled up in the western tropical Pacific to slosh eastward along the equator into the eastern tropical Pacific, decreasing coastal upwelling.

- As El Niño evolves, in the western tropical Pacific sea surface temperatures decline, sea level falls, and depth of the thermocline decreases. Meanwhile, in the eastern tropical Pacific sea-surface temperatures rise, sea level climbs, and depth of the thermocline increases. Conditions are drier than usual in the western tropical Pacific and wetter than usual in the central tropical Pacific.

- A linkage between changes in atmospheric circulation occurring in widely separated regions of the world is known as a teleconnection. Through teleconnections, El Niño and La Niña have ripple effects on the weather and climate of middle latitudes, especially in winter. During El Niño, prevailing westerlies tend to blow more directly from west to east so that winters are milder than normal in western Canada and across parts of the northern U.S. and wet and cool along the Gulf Coast.

- Although some weather extremes almost always accompany El Niño, no two events are exactly the same because El Niño is only one of many factors that influence short-term variations in climate. The 1982-83 and 1997-98 El Niño events were the two most intense of the 20th century.

- La Niña is a period of unusually strong trade winds and exceptionally vigorous upwelling in the eastern tropical Pacific. During La Niña, sea-surface temperature anomalies are essentially opposite those observed during El Niño. Accompanying La Niña are worldwide weather extremes that are often opposite those observed during El Niño.

- Scientists employ two types of numerical models to predict the evolution of El Niño or La Niña: empirical (or statistical) models and dynamical models. An empirical model bases predictions on records of past ocean/atmosphere conditions. A dynamical model consists of a series of mathematical equations that simulates ocean/atmosphere coupling.

- The accuracy of dynamical models in predicting the evolution of El Niño or La Niña depends not only on how well their constituent equations simulate the coupled ocean/atmosphere system, but also the reliability of observational data used to initialize, correct, and verify the model.

- The ENSO Observing System in the tropical Pacific consists of an array of instrumented moored buoys, current meters, and satellites. Radar (microwave) altimeters onboard the Jason 1 satellite accurately measure ocean surface elevation (sea level) changes that accompany El Niño or La Niña.

- El Niño occurs about once every 3 to 7 years. La Niña appears more likely to follow a strong El Niño than a weak one.

- Other quasi-regular oscillations involving the ocean and atmosphere that impact climate include the North Atlantic Oscillation, Arctic Oscillation, and the Pacific Decadal Oscillation.

- The North Atlantic Oscillation (NAO) refers to a seesaw variation in air pressure between Iceland and the Azores. When air pressure is higher than the long-term average over the Azores, it is lower than the long-term average over Iceland and vice versa. The North Atlantic Oscillation influences precipitation patterns and winter temperatures over eastern North America and much of Europe and North Africa.

- The Arctic Oscillation (AO) is a seesaw variation in air pressure between the North Pole and the margins of the polar region. Associated changes in the horizontal air pressure gradient alter the speed of the band of winds aloft that encircle the Arctic. Strengthening and weakening of these polar winds impact winter weather in middle latitudes and contribute to climate variability and changes in ocean circulation.

- The Pacific Decadal Oscillation (PDO) is a long-lived variation in climate over the North Pacific and North America. Sea surface temperatures fluctuate between the north central Pacific and along the west coast of North America.

Review

1. Define climate.
2. Identify the principal controls of climate. Do any of these controls vary with time?
3. Provide three examples of the role played by the ocean in Earth's climate system.
4. How does the extent of sea ice cover influence the absorption of solar radiation by the ocean?
5. What is the southern oscillation? How is the southern oscillation index calculated?
6. During an El Niño event, how does sea surface temperature and sea level change over the eastern tropical Pacific?
7. Describe the sea-surface temperature anomalies over the tropical Pacific during a La Niña event.
8. Distinguish between the two principal types of numerical models that forecasters rely upon to predict the evolution of El Niño or La Niña.
9. What is the North Atlantic Oscillation and what is its significance?
10. How do negative and positive phases of the Arctic Oscillation relate to winter weather in the U.S.?

Critical Thinking

1. What is the role of the ocean in Earth's greenhouse effect?
2. In what sense are the ocean and atmosphere coupled during an El Niño event?
3. Explain how changes in patterns of sea-surface temperature (SST) can alter the circulation of the atmosphere.
4. What are the early signs of a developing El Niño in the tropical Pacific Ocean?
5. What are the early signs of a developing La Niña in the tropical Pacific Ocean?
6. Why is La Niña more likely to follow a strong El Niño than a weak one?
7. What is meant by teleconnections and what is their significance in forecasting the impact of ENSO?
8. No two El Niño events are the same. Explain what is meant by this statement.
9. How does a horizontal air pressure gradient affect the speed of the horizontal wind?
10. How does the SST influence the temperature and humidity of the overlying air mass?

ESSAY: Sea Surface Temperature and Drought in Sub-Saharan Africa

Perhaps nowhere in the world has prolonged drought caused more human misery than in sub-Saharan Africa, much of which is known as the Sahel. The Sahel, an Arabic term meaning "shore" or "border," is the transition zone in West Africa between the Sahara Desert to the north and the rainforest of the Guinea coast to the south. As shown on the map in Figure 1, the Sahel encompasses all or part of Mauritania, Senegal, Mali, Burkina Faso, Niger, and Chad—the most impoverished nations on Earth. Low average annual rainfall, considerable year-to-year variability in rainfall, and long-term drought have brought considerable hardship to the people of the Sahel. They are particularly vulnerable to the effects of drought because most of them depend on agriculture for their livelihood. Droughts forced them off their lands that, even in the best of times, are marginal for survival of crops and livestock. They migrated to cities in search of food and work, and many ended up in refugee camps. In the worst of times, horrible scenes of starving children, emaciated livestock, and withered crops were televised to a worldwide audience.

FIGURE 1
Changes in sea surface temperature perhaps coupled with human activity may explain the occurrence of multi-decadal drought in the Sahel of North Africa (shaded in light brown), one of the most impoverished regions of the world.

    Drought in the Sahel is the product of interactions involving the atmosphere, ocean, land, and people. The Sahel has a semiarid climate that features a rainy season (Northern Hemisphere summer) and a dry season (Northern Hemisphere winter). The average length of the rainy season and mean annual rainfall increases from north to south across the Sahel. At the northern edge of the Sahel (about 18 degrees N), the rainy season usually does not begin until June and may last only a month or two; mean annual rainfall typically is less than 100 mm (about 4 in.). In the extreme southern Sahel (about 10 degrees N), the rainy season is underway as early as April and persists up to 5 or 6 months; mean annual rainfall exceeds 500 mm (about 20 in.). Shifts between the dry season and rainy season are linked to changes in prevailing winds associated with the location of the *intertropical convergence zone (ITCZ)*, a belt of showers and thunderstorms (Figure 6.7). As the

ITCZ follows the seasonal excursions of the sun, its northward surge in spring triggers rainfall, whereas the southward shift of the ITCZ in fall brings the rainy season to an end. During the rainy season, surface winds blow from the south and southwest, transporting humid air from over both the Atlantic Ocean and Indian Ocean. During the dry season, the Sahel is under the eastern flank of the North Atlantic subtropical high and surface winds blow from the dry north and northeast.

In a summer when the ITCZ does not move as far north as usual, or arrives late, or shifts southward early, rainfall is below the long-term average. A succession of many such summers means drought. In the 20th century, the people of the Sahel endured three major long-term droughts: 1910-1914, 1940-1944, and 1970-1985. Rainfall during the 1961-1990 period was 20% to 40% lower than it was during the prior three decades, constituting the greatest 30-year negative anomaly in precipitation recorded anywhere in the world. Drought and famine claimed over 600,000 lives in 1972-1975 and about the same number in 1984-1985. The reconstructed long-term climate record (based on lake-level fluctuations and historical accounts of landscape changes) indicates that droughts lasting 1 or 2 decades are the norm in the Sahel.

Some scientists argue that the principal reason for drought in the Sahel is changes in atmospheric circulation patterns (i.e., seasonal shifts of the moisture-bearing ITCZ) that are linked to anomalies in sea-surface temperature (SST). Initial studies showed that when SST is higher than normal in the eastern tropical Atlantic Ocean, south of the equator and southwest of West Africa (e.g., the Gulf of Guinea), rainfall is below the long-term average in the Sahel. In 2003 scientists at the International Research Institute for Climate Prediction at Palisades, NY announced the results of a NASA global climate model study of rainfall in the Sahel covering the period 1930 to 2000. They found that rising sea-surface temperature in the Indian Ocean was more important than changes in Atlantic Ocean SST in simulating long-term trends in Sahel rainfall. They also found that El Niño and La Niña accounted for much of the year-to-year variability in Sahel rainfall. More recently, runs of another global climate model developed at the Max Planck Institute for Meteorology in Germany found a similar dependence of decadal trends in Sahel rainfall on Indian Ocean SST. But that is not the end of the matter. In 2005, James Hurrell of the National Center for Atmospheric Research (NCAR) and Martin Hoerling of NOAA reported on new findings regarding drought in the Sahel. In experiments in which they used five different numerical models to generate 80 simulations, Hurrell and Hoerling discovered that drought in southern Africa is linked to warming of the Indian Ocean. However, their model simulations indicated that moisture conditions in the Sahel depend on SST in the Atlantic Ocean rather than the Indian Ocean. Apparently, monsoon failure and drought in the Sahel were linked to the late 20th century cooling of the North Atlantic Ocean. A shift to wetter conditions in the Sahel during the 1990s corresponded to the post-1990 warming of the North Atlantic Ocean. Therefore the significance of Atlantic versus Indian Ocean SST in explaining Sahel rainfall patterns is still a matter of study.

Human activity (i.e., overgrazing, conversion of woodland to agriculture) may also contribute to persistent drought in sub-Saharan Africa by reinforcing dry conditions. Overgrazing and deforestation alter the regional radiation balance by denuding the soil's vegetative cover and degrading the quality and moisture holding capacity of the soil. The albedo of the soils increases, evaporation decreases, atmospheric convection weakens, and rainfall becomes less likely. What has happened in parts of the Sahel may be *desertification*, the name applied to the conversion of arable land to desert because of some combination of climate change and human land management practices. Analysis of drought in the Sahel is an example of how the Earth system perspective provides valuable insights on the environmental factors that contribute to climate change.

ESSAY: El Niño in the Past

Lengthy records of El Niño episodes of the past would provide a useful perspective on more recent events and perhaps help determine whether a connection exists between global warming and the frequency and intensity of El Niño. However, in most areas of the world, reliable instrument-based weather records that signal past El Niño events extend back only to about the mid 19th century. For information on earlier occurrences of El Niño, scientists must rely on *proxy climatic data*, that is, information inferred from documentary (e.g., logs, diaries), geological (e.g., ocean bottom sediment cores, glacial ice cores), or biological (e.g., tree growth rings, tropical corals) indicators of climate. Suppose, for example, that written records from India and Southeast Asia list agricultural losses due to prolonged drought. Meanwhile, a sediment core extracted from a lake bottom contains evidence of heavy rainfall in normally arid coastal Peru during the same time interval. These simultaneous events are consistent with a strong El Niño.

Geological evidence indicates that El Niño episodes were occurring at least as far back as late in the Pleistocene Ice Age (1.7 million to 10,500 years ago). In 1999, based on his analysis of ancient corals from Sulawesi Island, Indonesia, Harvard researcher Daniel Schrag concluded that El Niño was occurring at 3- to 7-year intervals about 124,000 years ago. Schrag used oxygen isotope analysis to distinguish between El Niño and neutral (normal) years. Living corals build their external skeletons of limestone ($CaCO_3$) that incorporates two isotopes of oxygen: O^{16} and O^{18}. The lighter oxygen isotope evaporates more readily than does the heavier oxygen isotope. Hence, during relatively dry weather, evaporation rates are high, and the coral skeleton is enriched in O^{18} relative to O^{16}. On the other hand, during rainy episodes, evaporation rates are low, and the coral skeleton is enriched in O^{16} relative to O^{18}. Corals build their skeletons in annual growth rings that can be dated so that oxygen isotope analysis permits a detailed chronology of general weather conditions that can be tied to El Niño.

David Lea of the University of California, Santa Barbara, and Sandy Tudhope of the University of Edinburgh, Scotland studied coral reef terraces in New Guinea dating back some 130,000 years. In 2001, they reported on their isotopic and chemical analyses of these corals. They determined that El Niño events were more intense over the past 100 years than at any time during the past 130,000 years. Furthermore, they concluded that El Niño was about 50% weaker during the ice age and intensified during warm episodes, again spurring speculation that the recent upturn in El Niño intensity is linked to the global warming trend.

The El Niño signal shows up in a 4000-year record of lake sediments extracted from Glacial Lake Hitchcock, which occupied the Connecticut River valley during the waning phase of the last ice age. Layers of lake sediments chronicle short-term climate fluctuations spanning the period from about 17,500 to 13,500 years ago (during the final retreat of glacial ice from New England), and apparently resolve both intense and weak El Niño events (having periods of 2.5 to 5 years).

In 2002, Geoffrey Seltzer of Syracuse University and his colleagues reported on their analysis of two 8-m (26-ft) sediment cores extracted from the bottom of Laguna (Lake) Pallcacocha high in the Andes Mountains of southern Ecuador. Rainfall governs the amount of sediment delivered to the lake but rainfall associated with a weak El Niño is not likely to reach the 4200-m (13,800-ft) high lake. Hence, the researchers interpreted anomalously thick layers of silt in the cores as indicating heavy rainfall associated with an intense El Niño. The lake sediment cores span the past 12,000 years and indicate that between 12,000 and 7000 years ago, strong El Niño episodes occurred five or fewer times per century. The frequency of intense El Niño episodes then increased and peaked during the 9th century CE when they occurred about every three years.

Using documentary evidence from explorers and early settlers of the coast of northwest South America, W.H. Quinn and colleagues were able to reconstruct the chronology of El Niño episodes back to the year CE 1525. For example, El Niño conditions prevailed during 1531-32, when Francisco Pizarro (1478-1541) conquered the Incas. Although heavy rains impeded his advance, his horses were well fed by the vegetation made unusually lush by the moist conditions. Records of the maximum discharge of the Nile River at Cairo extend back to CE 622 and are another valuable source of information on past El Niño episodes. Year to year changes in discharge are linked to variations in the summer monsoon rains in the Ethiopian highlands, near the headwaters of the Nile, and decrease during El Niño.

The long-term reconstructed climate record suggests that El Niño has occurred regularly since at least the late Pleistocene—albeit with at least one significant lull from 12,000 to 7000 years ago. However, El Niño intensity has varied over thousands of years (i.e., the tempo is roughly the same but the beat has alternately intensified and weakened). We now appear to be in a period of particularly intense El Niño events.

CHAPTER 12

THE OCEAN AND CLIMATE CHANGE

Case-in-Point
Driving Question
The Climate Record
    Marine Sediments and Climate
    Other Proxy Climatic Data Sources
    Geologic Time
    Past Two Million Years
    Instrument-Based Temperature Trends
Lessons of the Climate Past
Factors Contributing to Climate Change
    Climate and Plate Tectonics
    Climate and Solar Variability
    Climate and Earth's Orbit
    Climate and Volcanoes
    Climate and Earth's Surface Properties
    Climate and Human Activity
The Climate Future
    Global Climate Models
    Enhanced Greenhouse Effect and Global Warming
Impact of Climate Change on the Ocean
    Sea Level Fluctuations
    Arctic Sea Ice Cover
    Marine Life
Conclusions
Basic Understandings/Review/Critical Thinking
ESSAY: Climate Rhythms in Glacial Ice Cores
ESSAY: The Drying of the Mediterranean Sea
ESSAY: Sea Level Rise and Saltwater Intrusion

Polar bears on an ice floe. [NOAA Office of Ocean Exploration]

Case in Point

People and other animals living in the Arctic face an uncertain future because of a recent warming trend. The Inuit people (also called Eskimos) live around the Arctic Ocean, in Greenland, Canada, Alaska, and Siberia, one of Earth's coldest regions and among the most remote and inhospitable for humans. Here, people still depend largely on hunting seals, caribou, and polar bears, herding reindeer, and gathering berries and other foods from the land.

    Higher air temperatures are melting the *permafrost* (permanently frozen ground) weakening the foundations for homes and other structures. Warming—perhaps coupled with a change in ocean circulation—is also shrinking the Arctic sea ice cover restricting the Inuit's access to their traditional hunting and gathering grounds. Warming means more summer precipitation falling as rain instead of snow. Rainwater freezes, forming a glaze that covers the ground to a depth of several centimeters, preventing caribou, reindeer, and musk ox (all hunted by the Inuit) from reaching the lichens they normally eat. Furthermore, rainwater and higher temperatures promote the growth of toxic molds on the lichens so that these animals avoid them as a food source and eventually must migrate to other areas to feed, or face death by starvation.

Another food source for the Inuit is seriously threatened. Polar bears, the Arctic's largest land predators, face possible extinction within this century as the Arctic sea ice cover shrinks. These animals depend on sea ice floes as platforms from which they hunt seals, their principal food source. They also travel across the sea ice to reach their dens on land. In short, they are uniquely adapted to living on Arctic sea ice and are often considered to be marine mammals because they spend so much time in the ice-infested water. Should the warming trend continue, the Arctic Ocean could be nearly ice-free during summer as soon as the year 2013.

Polar bears live on the sea ice and in coastal areas of Alaska, northern Canada, northern Russia, Greenland, and Norway. Effects of the shrinking sea ice cover are especially serious in Hudson Bay in northern Canada, which is near the southern limit of the polar bears' range. They have turned to scavenging for food in garbage dumps around settlements when the lack of sea ice prevents them from hunting seals. Some bears have come to depend on humans for food and are further threatened because residents may be forced to kill nuisance bears.

> ## Driving Question:
> *How and why does climate change and how does the ocean participate in and respond to climate change?*

In this chapter, we examine the instrument-derived and reconstructed climate record. One of our primary goals is to learn more about how climate changes through time. These lessons of the climate past are useful in establishing a perspective on the present climate and how climate might change in the future. Two of the most obvious lessons of the climate past are: (1) climate changes over a broad range of temporal scales, from years to decades to centuries to millennia, and (2) many forces working together are responsible for climate variations and change.

The ocean is an important source of information on the climate record. From analysis of deep-sea sediment cores, scientists reconstruct climate variability extending back hundreds of thousands of years. The ocean's low albedo, great thermal inertia, and role as a sink and source of heat energy and gases (especially water vapor and carbon dioxide) inhibit wild swings in climate. At the same time, the ocean responds to global climate change. Sea level falls in response to cooling trends that cause glaciers to expand and sea surface temperatures to fall (contracting sea water). Sea level rises in response to warming trends that melt glaciers (with runoff draining into the ocean) and raise mean ocean temperature (expanding sea water).

Such changes in sea level have important implications for the coastal zone including the potential for storm surges, flooding, and erosion.

We begin by examining the climate record for what it tells us about climate behavior. We then identify and describe the many factors that influence the variation of climate through time and finally we summarize what is known about the climate future particularly relating to the world ocean.

The Climate Record

Climate varies from one place to another and with time. Examining the record of the climate past reveals some basic understandings regarding the nature of climate behavior and provides a useful perspective on current and future climate. In most places, however, the reliable instrument-based record of past weather and climate is limited to not much more than a century or so. For information on earlier fluctuations in climate, scientists rely on reconstructions of climate based on historical documents (e.g., personal diaries, ship's logs, weather-sensitive economic data) and longer-term geological and biological evidence such as bedrock type, fossil plants and animals, pollen, tree growth rings, glacial ice cores, and deep-sea sediment cores. In this section, we first consider some of the non-instrumental sources of information on past climates (*proxy climatic data sources*). We then summarize the climate record from geologic time through to the present.

MARINE SEDIMENTS AND CLIMATE

Cores extracted from sediments that blanket the ocean floor yield a continuous record of sedimentation going back many hundreds of thousands of years and in places, millions of years (Figure 12.1). Much of what we know about the climate fluctuations of the Pleistocene Ice Age is based on analysis of the shell and skeletal remains of microscopic marine organisms that are found in deep-sea sediment cores. Identification of the environmental requirements of these organisms plus **oxygen isotope analysis** of their remains enables scientists to distinguish between cold and mild climatic episodes of the past.

Scientists use a special property of water to reconstruct large-scale climate fluctuations of the Pleistocene Ice Age. A water molecule (H_2O) is composed of one of the two stable isotopes of oxygen, O^{16} or O^{18}. (Isotopes of a single element differ in atomic mass based on the number of neutrons in the nucleus of the atom.) In the Earth system, the lighter isotope (O^{16}) is much more abundant than the heavier isotope (O^{18}); only one O^{18} exists for every thousand or so O^{16}. Nonetheless, small but significant variations occur in the amount of light oxygen compared to heavy oxygen circulating in the global water cycle. These variations have important implications for past fluctuations in glacial ice volume on the planet.

On average, water molecules containing the lighter O^{16} isotope move slightly faster than water molecules containing the heavier O^{18} isotope and evaporate more readily. Water molecules that evaporate from the ocean (or land) are enhanced in light oxygen compared to heavy oxygen. The amount of O^{16} compared to O^{18} is also greater in cloud particles and rain and snow versus liquid water on Earth's surface. Most precipitation either falls back into the ocean directly or drains from land back to the sea, replenishing the ocean's supply of light oxygen and maintaining a relatively constant average ratio of light to heavy oxygen. However, geographical variations in the oxygen isotope ratio of seawater arise because of differences in precipitation amounts and evaporation rates. Seawater has more O^{18} at subtropical latitudes where evaporation exceeds precipitation and less in middle latitudes where rainfall is greater.

A   B   C

FIGURE 12.1
Sediment cores extracted from beneath the ocean floor provide valuable information on the geologic and climatic past. (A) A hollow pipe lined with plastic tubing and coupled to a weight at the top is lowered over the side of a ship. When within about 8 m of the bottom, the corer free-falls into the sediment while a piston suctions sediment into the tube. The coring device is recovered and the sediment core is removed and split lengthwise for analysis. (B) USGS crew on the research vessel *G.K. Gilbert* collect a 20-ft sediment core, using an electric coring system and hydraulic crane. [USGS] (C) Core racks holding a total of 72,000 m of sediment cores at the Deep-Sea Sample Repository of Lamont-Doherty Earth Observatory in Palisades, NY. [Courtesy of the Lamont-Doherty Earth Observatory]

During a glacial climatic episode, snow that accumulates on land converts to ice. Heavy water molecules condense and precipitate slightly more readily than light water molecules so that moisture plumes moving from the tropics to high latitudes lose heavy oxygen along the way. Hence, snow falling at high latitudes has less O^{18} than rain falling in the tropics. The result is that growing ice sheets sequester more and more light oxygen while ocean water ends up with less and less O^{16} proportionately. With a shift to an interglacial climate, ice sheets shrink and melt water rich in O^{16} drains back into the ocean increasing the amount of O^{16} compared to O^{18}. Hence, over time the proportion of light to heavy oxygen in ocean water decreases with increasing glacial ice cover.

Organic sediments on the ocean floor record fluctuations in the oxygen isotope ratio of seawater. Marine organisms living in the sunlit surface waters such as foraminifera build their shell-like tests from calcium carbonate ($CaCO_3$) that is dissolved in seawater. Tests formed during warmer interglacial climatic episodes contain more light oxygen than those formed during colder glacial climatic episodes. When these organisms die, their tests settle to the ocean bottom and mix with other marine sediments (Chapter 4). From specially outfitted deep-sea drilling ships, scientists extract cores from an undisturbed sequence of ocean bottom sediments, with the youngest sediments at the top of the core and the oldest sediments at the bottom. In the laboratory, the core is split open, and tests are extracted and analyzed for their oxygen isotope ratio. Variations in oxygen isotope ratio document changes in the planet's glacial ice volume and hence, past changes in climate.

Oxygen isotope analysis of deep-sea sediment cores indicates that the Pleistocene was punctuated by abrupt changes between numerous glacial and interglacial climatic episodes. Oxygen isotope analysis has also been applied to ice layers within cores extracted from the Greenland and Antarctic ice sheets. These analyses confirm the abrupt change behavior of climate back hundreds of thousands of years. For more information on climatic inferences drawn from glacial ice cores, refer to this chapter's first Essay.

OTHER PROXY CLIMATIC DATA SOURCES

On land, much has been learned about past climate from study of pollen records, tree growth rings, and glacial ice cores. Pollen is a valuable source of information on late Ice Age vegetation and climate, especially over the past 15,000 years. *Pollen* is the tiny dust-like fertilizing component of a seed plant that is dispersed by the wind and accumulates on the bottom of lakes (and in other depositional environments) along with other organic and inorganic sediments. Scientists use a corer to extract a sediment column (core) that chronicles past changes in pollen (and therefore, vegetation). Back at the laboratory, pollen grains are separated from the other sediment in the core, identified as to source vegetation, and counted to determine the dominant vegetation type. Implications for past climate are drawn assuming that (1) the pollen is of local origin and (2) climate largely controls vegetation (and pollen) type. Changes in dominant pollen type in a core signal changes in nearby vegetation, likely in response to climate change.

Tree growth rings can yield a year-to-year record of past climate variations stretching back many thousands of years. Each spring/summer, living trees add a growth-ring whose thickness and density depend on weather conditions during the growing season. A small hollow drill is used to extract a tree's growth-ring record. Although other environmental factors (e.g., soil type, drainage) can be important, tree growth rings are especially sensitive to moisture stress and have been used to reconstruct lengthy chronologies of drought prior to the era of instrument-based records.

Ice cores extracted from glaciers yield a record of past seasonal snowfall preserved as thin layers of ice (Figure 12.2). Cores extracted from the Greenland and Antarctic ice sheets provide detailed decadal-scale climate information going back roughly 420,000 years. Using the oxygen isotope technique (described earlier), scientists

FIGURE 12.2
This 6-m (20-ft) long ice core was extracted from the Greenland ice sheet and is a source of information on past variations in climate and atmospheric composition. Ice layers are made cloudy by dust particles that settled out of the atmosphere. [Photo by Mark Twickler, University of New Hampshire; National Geophysical Data Center]

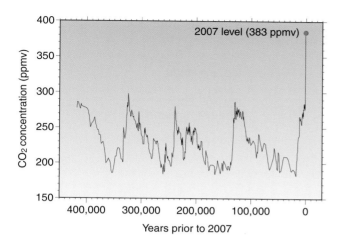

FIGURE 12.3
The concentration of atmospheric carbon dioxide in parts per million by volume (ppmv) from about 425 million years ago to 2007 based on glacial ice core analysis from the Vostok station in Antarctica. [Scripps Institution of Oceanography, University of California, San Diego]

can distinguish between cold and mild episodes in the past and through chemical analysis of tiny air bubbles trapped in the ice, determine the chemical composition of ancient air. This latter information is important in tracking long-term trends in the atmospheric concentration of greenhouse gases such as carbon dioxide (Figure 12.3). Dust layer thicknesses also allow differentiation between cold and mild episodes as well as an exact counting of annual ice layers, and precise dating, if the dust layers are volcanic in origin.

GEOLOGIC TIME

For convenience of study, the geologic past and its climate record is subdivided using the **geologic time scale**, a standard division of Earth history into eons, eras, periods, and epochs based on large-scale geological events (Figure 12.4). Throughout most of the approximately 4.5 billion years that constitute *geologic time*, information on climate is unreliable. Descriptions of early climates are suspect because of lengthy gaps in the proxy climate record and difficulties in determining the timing of events and correlating events that occurred in widely separated locations. Furthermore, plate tectonics complicates climate reconstruction efforts that focus on periods spanning hundreds of million of years (Chapter 2). Nonetheless, the available evidence supports some general conclusions regarding the climate over geologic time.

Geologic evidence points to an interval of extreme climate fluctuations about 570 million years ago, corresponding to the transition between Proterozoic and

Phanerozoic Eons. In southern Africa, along Namibia's Skeleton Coast (Atlantic Ocean) rock layers that formed in tropical seas directly overlie glacial deposits. Some scientists interpret these rock sequences as indicating abrupt changes in climate between extreme cold and tropical heat. During as many as four cold episodes, each lasting perhaps 10 million years, the continents were encased in glacial ice and the ocean froze to a depth of more than 1000 m (3300 ft). At the close of each cold episode, temperatures rose rapidly, and within only a few centuries, all the ice melted.

The Mesozoic Era, from about 245 million to 70 million years ago, was characterized by a generally warm Earth free of large glacial ice sheets. At the boundary between the Triassic and Jurassic Periods, the global mean temperature rose perhaps 3 to 4 Celsius degrees (5.5 to 7 Fahrenheit degrees), contributing to a major extinction or displacement of many animal and plant species. At peak warming during the Cretaceous Period, the global mean temperature was perhaps 6 to 8 Celsius degrees (11 to 14 Fahrenheit degrees) higher than now. Subtropical plants and animals lived as far north as 60 degrees N and dinosaurs roamed what is now the North Slope of Alaska. About 65 million years ago, a great meteorite impact threw huge quantities of dust into the atmosphere, blocking sunlight, and causing cooling that contributed to the demise of the dinosaurs (refer to the first Essay in Chapter 1). An explosion in the population of mammals followed the extinction of the dinosaurs.

The Cenozoic Era was a time of great climatic fluctuations. About 55 million years ago, near the transition between the Paleocene and Eocene Epochs, the concentration of atmospheric greenhouse gases (either methane or carbon dioxide) increased dramatically. Scientists propose that these gases were released to ocean waters during massive intrusions of basaltic magma into carbonaceous marine sediments during tectonic events related to the opening of the North Atlantic Ocean. Some scientists propose that methane was released from gas hydrates (Chapter 9). The gases escaped the ocean waters to the atmosphere, enhancing the greenhouse effect and causing an already warm planet to become even warmer. Over a period of only a few thousand years, global temperatures climbed 5 to 10 Celsius degrees (9 to 18 Fahrenheit degrees).

By 40 million years ago, however, Earth's climate began shifting toward colder, drier, and more variable conditions setting the stage for the Pleistocene Ice Age, an epoch of numerous major glacial advances and recessions. According to W.F. Ruddiman of Lamont-

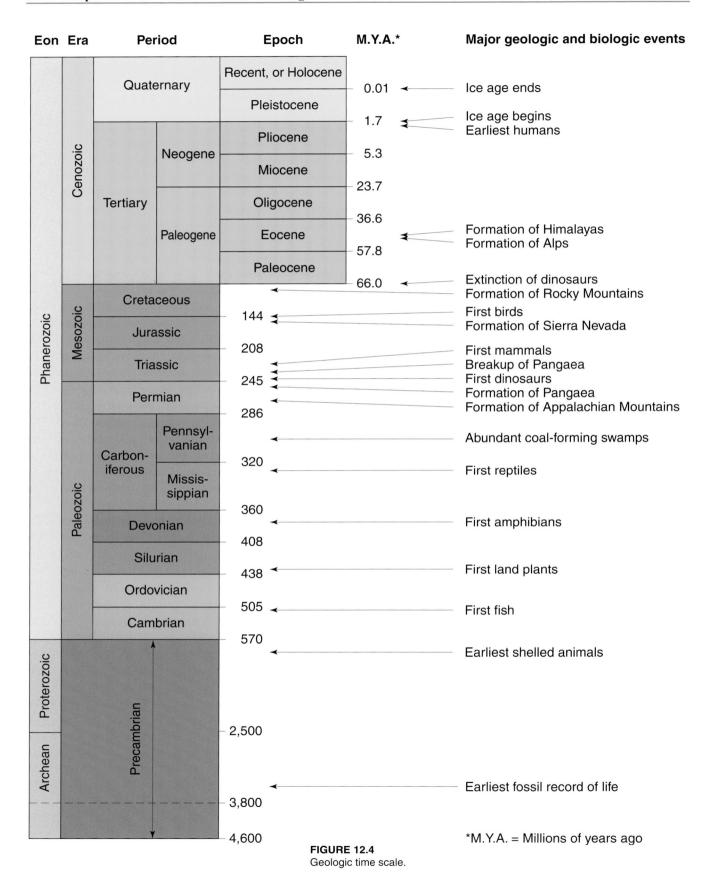

FIGURE 12.4
Geologic time scale.

Doherty Geological Observatory of Columbia University and J.E. Kutzbach of the University of Wisconsin-Madison, mountain building may explain this change in Earth's climate, specifically the rise of the Colorado Plateau, Tibetan Plateau, and Himalayan Mountains. Prominent mountain ranges influence the geographical distribution of clouds and precipitation and can alter the planetary-scale circulation. Furthermore, mountain building may alter the global carbon cycle. Enhanced weathering of bedrock exposed in mountain ranges sequesters more atmospheric carbon dioxide in sediments thereby weakening the natural greenhouse effect.

In the American West, the region from the California Sierras to the Rockies, known as the Colorado Plateau, has an average elevation of 1500 to 2500 m (5000 to 8200 ft). Although mountain building began about 40 million years ago, about half of the total uplift took place between 10 and 5 million years ago. The Tibetan Plateau and Himalayan Mountains of southern Asia cover an area of more than 2 million square km (0.8 million square mi) and have an average elevation of more than 4500 m (14,700 ft). About half of total Himalayan uplift took place over the past 10 million years. The plateaus diverted the planetary-scale westerlies into a more meridional pattern, increasing the north-south exchange of air masses and altering the climate over a broad region of the globe. Also, seasonal heating and cooling of the plateaus cause low pressure to develop in summer and high pressure in winter, enhancing the monsoon circulation over southern Asia.

PAST TWO MILLION YEARS

Climate varies over a broad spectrum of time scales so that viewing the climate record of the past two million years in progressively narrower time frames is useful. Such an approach helps to resolve the oscillations of climate into more detailed fluctuations especially over the recent past. Over the past two million years, plate tectonics was not a major factor in climate change. For example, assuming a spreading rate of 10 cm (3.9 in.) per year, in two million years the Atlantic Basin would spread a total distance of 200 km (124 mi), not very significant in a climatic sense. For all practical purposes, over the past two million years mountain ranges, continents, and ocean basins were essentially as they are today.

Compared to the climate that prevailed through most of geologic time, the climate of the last two million years was unusual in favoring the development of huge glacial ice sheets (although evidence also exists of ice ages earlier in geologic time). During much of Earth's history,

the average global temperature may have been 10 Celsius degrees (18 Fahrenheit degrees) higher than it was over the past two million years. Cooling that set in about 40 million years ago culminated in the Pleistocene Ice Age that began about 1.7 million years ago and ended about 10,500 years ago.

During the Pleistocene Ice Age the climate shifted numerous times between glacial climates and interglacial climates. A **glacial climate** favors the thickening and expansion of glaciers whereas an **interglacial climate** favors the thinning and retreat of existing glaciers or no glaciers at all. During major glacial climatic episodes of the Pleistocene, the Laurentide ice sheet developed over central Canada and spread westward to the Rocky Mountains, eastward to the Atlantic Ocean and southward over the northern tier states of the United States (Figure 12.5). At about the same time, mountain glaciers in the Rockies coalesced into the Cordilleran ice sheet, a relatively thin ice sheet covered the Arctic Archipelago, and an ice sheet much smaller than the Laurentide developed over northwest Europe including the British Isles and Scandinavia. The vast quantity of water locked up in these ice sheets caused sea level to drop by 113 to 135 m (370 to 443 ft), exposing portions of the continental shelf, including a land bridge linking Siberia and North America.

The Laurentide and European ice sheets thinned and retreated, and may even have disappeared entirely,

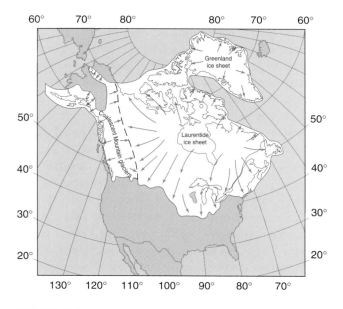

FIGURE 12.5
Extent of glacial ice cover over North America about 18,000 to 20,000 years ago, the time of the last glacial maximum. In places, the ice was as thick as 3 km (1.9 mi).

during relatively mild interglacial climatic episodes, which typically lasted about 10,000 years. Throughout these interglacials, glacial ice cover persisted over most of Antarctica and Greenland as it still does today.

During glacial climatic episodes, temperatures were lower than they are today but the magnitude of cooling was not the same everywhere. A variety of geologic evidence indicates that during the Pleistocene, temperature fluctuations between major glacial and interglacial climatic episodes typically amounted to as much as 5 Celsius degrees (9 Fahrenheit degrees) in the tropics, 6 to 8 Celsius degrees (11 to 14 Fahrenheit degrees) at middle latitudes, and 10 Celsius degrees (18 Fahrenheit degrees) or more at high latitudes. An increase in the magnitude of a climatic change with increasing latitude is known as **polar amplification**, indicating that polar areas are subject to greater changes in climate.

Oxygen isotope analysis of the deep-sea sediment cores shows numerous fluctuations between major glacial and interglacial climatic episodes over the past 600,000 years (Figure 12.6A). Shifting focus to the past 160,000 years, resolution of the climate record improves. The temperature curve in Figure 12.6B is based on analysis of an ice core extracted from the Antarctic ice sheet at Vostok. A relatively mild interglacial episode, referred to as the *Eemian*, began about 127,000 years ago and persisted for about 7000 years. In some localities, temperatures may have been 1 to 2 Celsius degrees (2 to 4 Fahrenheit degrees) higher than during the warmest portion of the present interglacial. The Eemian interglacial was followed by numerous fluctuations between glacial and interglacial episodes. The last major glacial climatic episode began about 27,000 years ago and reached its peak about 18,000 to 20,000 years ago when glacial ice cover over North America was about as extensive as it had ever been (Figure 12.5).

The global mean temperature 18,000 to 20,000 years ago was about 4 to 6 Celsius degrees (7 to 11 Fahrenheit degrees) lower than at present. A general warming trend (and rise in sea level from melting ice) followed the last glacial maximum, punctuated by relatively brief returns to glacial climatic episodes (Figure 12.7). A notable example is the relatively cold interval from about 11,000 to 10,000 years ago known as the *Younger Dryas* (named for the polar wildflower, *Dryas octopetala*, that reappeared in portions of Europe at the time). The return of glacial climatic conditions triggered short-lived re-advances of remnant ice sheets in North America, Scotland, and Scandinavia. Glacial ice finally withdrew from the Great Lakes region about 10,500 years ago ushering in the present interglacial, the **Holocene**.

FIGURE 12.6
Reconstructed records of (A) the variation in global glacial ice volume over the past 600,000 years based on analysis of the oxygen isotope ratio of shells in deep-sea sediment cores, and (B) temperature variation over the past 160,000 years derived from oxygen isotope analysis of an ice core extracted from the Antarctic ice sheet at Vostok and expressed as a departure in Celsius degrees from the 1900 global mean temperature. [Compiled by R.S. Bradley and J.A. Eddy from J. Jousel et al., *Nature* 329(1987):403-408 and reported in *EarthQuest* 5, No. 1 (1991).]

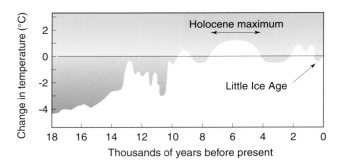

FIGURE 12.7
Reconstructed temperature variation over the past 18,000 years based on a variety of proxy climatic indicators and expressed as a departure in Celsius degrees from the 1900 global mean temperature. [Compiled by R.S. Bradley and J.A. Eddy based on J.T. Houghton *et al.* (eds.), *Climate Change: The IPCC Assessment*, Cambridge University Press, U.K., 1990, and reported in *EarthQuest* 5, No. 1 (1991).]

Events surrounding the *Younger Dryas* point to the role of the large-scale thermohaline circulation in influencing climate. About 11,000 years ago, glacial ice lobes disrupted drainage patterns, diverting melt water from the Mississippi River to the St. Lawrence River and into the North Atlantic. With the input of fresh water, North Atlantic surface waters became less saline and eventually were not sufficiently dense to sink and form deep water. This weakened the meridional overturning circulation (MOC), which in turn diminished the flow of warm water into the central and northern North Atlantic causing a marked cooling of surrounding lands. This was the beginning of the *Younger Dryas*.

At the onset of the Holocene, a warming trend caused glaciers to retreat sufficiently that fresh melt water was diverted from the St. Lawrence back to the Mississippi River. North Atlantic surface waters became saltier and denser, deep water formed, and the meridional overturning circulation strengthened. The climate of the lands surrounding the central and northern North Atlantic warmed, signaling the end of the *Younger Dryas*.

Although the Laurentide ice sheet was melting and would disappear almost entirely by about 5500 years ago, the Holocene has been an epoch of spatially and temporally variable temperature and precipitation. Cores extracted from the Greenland ice sheet and sediment cores taken from the bottom of the North Atlantic reveal that the overall post-glacial warming trend was interrupted by abrupt millennial-scale fluctuations in climate. Post-glacial warming during the Holocene gave way to a cold episode about 8200 years ago; significant cooling also occurred from about 4000 to 2400 years ago. On the other hand, at times during the mid-Holocene (classically known as the *Hypsithermal*) mean annual global temperature was perhaps 1 Celsius degree (2 Fahrenheit degrees) higher than it was in 1900, the warmest in more than 110,000 years, that is, since the Eemian interglacial. A pollen-based climate reconstruction indicates that 6000 years ago, July mean temperatures were about 2 Celsius degrees (3.6 Fahrenheit degrees) higher than now over most of Europe.

A generalized temperature curve for the past 1000 years, derived mostly from historical documents, is shown as Figure 12.8. The most notable features of this record are (1) the **Medieval Warm Period** from about CE 950 to 1250 and (2) the cooling that followed, from about CE 1400 to 1850, a period now known as the **Little Ice Age**. The Medieval Warm Period and the Little Ice Age were not episodes of sustained warming and cooling, respectively. On the contrary, sediment and

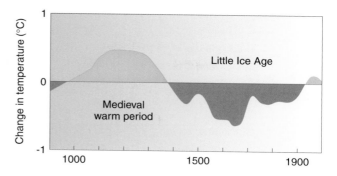

FIGURE 12.8
Reconstructed temperature variation over the past 1000 years based on analysis of historical documents and expressed as a departure in Celsius degrees from the 1900 global mean temperature. [Adapted from J.T. Houghton *et al.* (eds.), *Climate Change: The IPCC Assessment*, Cambridge University Press, U.K., 1990, p. 202.]

glacial ice core records plus historical documents point to significant decadal-scale fluctuations in temperature and precipitation. During much of the Medieval Warm Period, global temperature averaged about 0.5 Celsius degree (0.9 Fahrenheit degree) higher than in 1900. The first Norse settlements were established along the southern coast of Greenland and vineyards thrived in the British Isles. Independent lines of evidence confirm that the Little Ice Age was a relatively cool period in many regions with mean annual global temperatures perhaps 0.5 Celsius degree (0.9 Fahrenheit degree) lower than it was in 1900. Sea ice cover expanded, mountain glaciers advanced, growing seasons shortened, and erratic harvests caused much hardship for many people, including the end of the Norse settlements in Greenland.

INSTRUMENT-BASED TEMPERATURE TRENDS

Invention of weather instruments, establishment of weather observing networks around the world, plus standardized methods of observation and record-keeping made the climate record much more detailed and dependable. The most reliable temperature records date from the late 1800s with the birth of national weather services including those of the U.S. and Canada, along with the predecessor to today's World Meteorological Organization (WMO). Examination of temperature trends over the past 120 years or so is instructive as to the short-term variability of climate.

Plotted in Figure 12.9 is the 1880 to 2007 in-strument-derived record of variations in (1) global (land plus sea surface) mean annual temperature, (2) global mean sea surface temperature, and (3) global mean land

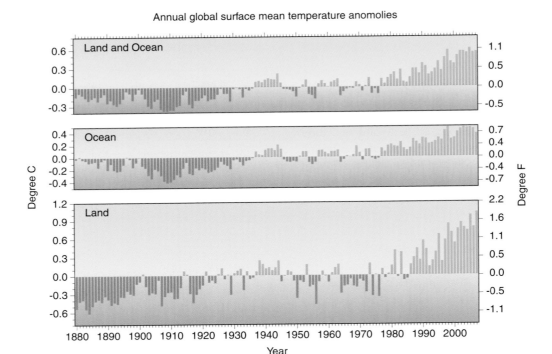

Annual global surface mean temperature anomolies

FIGURE 12.9
Instrument-derived trends in mean annual global (land plus ocean), sea-surface, and land temperatures; expressed as departures in degrees Celsius and degrees Fahrenheit from the 125-year period average. [NOAA, National Climatic Data Center]

surface temperature. In all three cases, the temperature is expressed as a departure (in Celsius degrees and Fahrenheit degrees) from the long-term (1901-2000) average. For reasons given in Chapter 3, these temperature series, assembled by NOAA's *National Climatic Data Center (NCDC)*, indicate greater year-to-year variability over land than ocean. The trend in global mean temperature is generally upward from 1880 until about 1940, downward or steady from 1940 to about 1970, and upward again through the 1990s and early 2000s. The overall temperature fluctuation is mostly ±0.5 Celsius degree (±0.9 Fahrenheit degree) about the century average. Note that this temperature record for the globe as a whole is not representative (in direction or magnitude) of all locations worldwide; that is, the trend was amplified or reversed, or both, in specific regions of the world.

In spring 2000, NOAA's NCDC reported that global warming accelerated during the final quarter of the 20th century. From 1906 to 2005, the global mean annual temperature climbed 0.74 ± 0.18 Celsius degrees. Most of this warming (0.65 ± 0.15 Celsius degrees) took place from 1956 to 2005. In terms of global mean annual surface temperature, 11 of the 12 years prior to 2007 were the warmest since 1850. Furthermore, climate reconstructions

(mostly in the Northern Hemisphere) indicate that the 20th century was the warmest in 1000 years. For example, the ice core record extracted from a glacier at 7163 m (23,500 ft) in the Himalayan Mountains revealed that the 1990s and the last half of the 20th century were the warmest of any equivalent period in a millennium.

Some critics question the integrity of hemispheric or global temperature records. They cite as potential sources of error: (1) improved sophistication and reliability of weather instruments through the period of record, (2) changes in location and exposure of instruments at most long-term weather stations, (3) huge gaps in monitoring networks, especially over the ocean, and (4) the warming influence of urbanization (*urban heat islands*). However, even when careful statistical analysis of all these potential sources of error is taken into account, a clear warming trend over the past century is evident.

A general consensus in the scientific community holds that a global-scale warming trend has prevailed since the end of the Little Ice Age. The simplest scientific explanation for the observed warming trend is the steady build-up of carbon dioxide in the atmosphere (primarily because of combustion of fossil fuels) and the consequent enhancement of the natural greenhouse effect (Chapter 5).

Continuation of the upward trend in the concentration of atmospheric CO_2 (and other greenhouse gases) inevitably will lead to global warming throughout this century and perhaps beyond. We have more to say on this topic later in this chapter.

Lessons of the Climate Past

What does the climate record tell us about the behavior of climate through time? The following lessons of the climatic record are useful in assessing prospects for the climate future and the possible impacts of climate change.

- *Climate is inherently variable over a broad spectrum of time scales ranging from years to decades, to centuries, to millennia.* Variability is an endemic characteristic of climate. The question for the future is not whether the climate will change, but how climate will change, by how much and how fast.

- *Variations in climate are geographically non-uniform in both sign (warming or cooling) and magnitude.* Some areas may experience warming while other areas experience cooling over the same period. Global- and hemispheric-scale trends in climate are not necessarily duplicated at particular locations although the tendency is for the magnitude of temperature change to amplify with increasing latitude (*polar amplification*). Partially for this reason, a large-scale change in climate is not likely to have the same impact everywhere.

- *Climate change may consist of a long-term trend in various elements of climate (e.g., mean temperature or average precipitation) and/or a change in the frequency of extreme weather events (e.g., drought, excessive cold).* Recall from Chapter 5 that climate encompasses mean values plus extremes. A trend toward warmer or cooler, wetter or drier conditions may or may not be accompanied by a change in frequency of weather extremes. On the other hand, a climatic regime featuring relatively little change in mean temperature or precipitation through time could be accompanied by an increase or decrease in frequency of weather extremes.

- *Climate change tends to be more abrupt than gradual.* In the context of the climate record, "abrupt" is a relative term. If the time of transition between climatic episodes is much shorter than the duration of the individual episodes, then the transition is considered to be relatively abrupt. Analysis of cores extracted from the Greenland ice sheet indicate that millennial-scale cold and warm climatic episodes were punctuated by abrupt change over periods as brief as a single decade. The abrupt-change nature of climate would test the resilience of society to respond effectively to climate change.

- *Only a few cyclical variations can be discerned from the long-term climate record.* Regular cycles include diurnal and seasonal changes in incoming solar radiation (the forcing) and temperature (the response). This means simply that days are usually warmer than nights and summers are warmer than winters. Quasi-regular variations in climate include El Niño (occurring about every 3 to 7 years), Holocene millennial-scale fluctuations identified in glacial ice cores, and the major glacial-interglacial climate shifts of the Pleistocene Ice Age unlocked from analysis of deep-sea sediment cores and operating over tens of thousands to hundreds of thousands of years. Study of climate cycles add to our understanding of the present climate and anthropogenic influences on climate.

- *Climate change impacts society.* History recounts numerous instances when climate change significantly impacted society. Although modern societies may be more capable of dealing with climate change than early peoples, a rapid and significant change in climate would seriously impact all sectors of modern society.

Factors Contributing to Climate Change

No one simple explanation exists for why climate changes. The complex spectrum of climate variability and change is in response to the interactions of many processes, both internal and external to the Earth-atmosphere-ocean system.

One way to organize our thinking on the many possible causes of climate change is to match a possible cause (or forcing) with a specific climatic oscillation (or response) based on similar periods of oscillation (Figure 12.10). For example, plate tectonics might explain long-term climate changes operating over hundreds of millions of years. Systematic changes in Earth's orbit about the sun

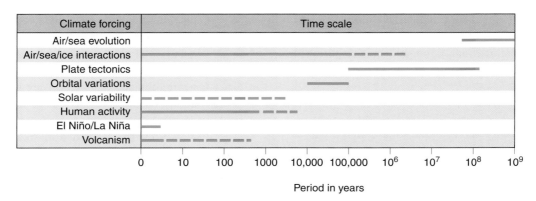

FIGURE 12.10
The potential causes of climate change operate over a broad spectrum of time scales. Dashed lines indicate uncertainty.

may account for climate shifts of the order of 10,000 to 100,000 years. Variations in sunspot number and the sun's energy output may be associated with climate fluctuations of decades to centuries. Volcanic eruptions, El Niño, or La Niña may account for climate shifts lasting several months to a few years. But matching some forcing mechanism with a climate response based on similar periods of oscillation is no guarantee of a real physical relationship.

Another way to think about the possible causes of climate change is in terms of the global energy budget. As noted in Chapter 5, **global radiative equilibrium** means that energy entering the Earth-atmosphere-ocean system (i.e., absorbed solar radiation) ultimately must equal energy leaving the system (i.e., infrared radiation emitted to space). Any change in either energy input or energy output will shift the Earth-atmosphere-ocean system to a new equilibrium and change the planet's climate. A number of factors can alter the global radiative equilibrium, including fluctuations in solar energy output, changes in Earth's orbit about the sun, volcanic eruptions, alterations in Earth's surface properties, changes in the atmospheric greenhouse gas content, clouds, and certain human activities.

In Chapter 11, we described the influence of El Niño and La Niña on inter-annual climate variability. In this section, we summarize the many other factors that may contribute to climate change over a range of time scales.

CLIMATE AND PLATE TECTONICS

Plate tectonics likely has operated on the planet for perhaps 2.5 billion years and influenced climate in many ways. Recall from Chapters 1 and 2 that Earth's solid outer skin is divided into a dozen gigantic rigid plates (and many smaller ones) drifting very slowly over the face of the planet. As plates move, continents

move, ocean basins open and close, and tectonic stresses build mountain ranges and volcanoes. Plate movements are so slow compared to the span of human existence that we can consider topography and the geographical distribution of the ocean and continents as essentially fixed controls of climate. Over the vast expanse of geologic time, however, plate tectonics was a major player in large-scale climate change.

Changes in the location of continents (*continental drift*) altered the local and regional radiation budget and the response of air temperature. Continental drift explains such seemingly anomalous discoveries as glacial deposits in the Sahara Desert, fossil tropical plants in Greenland, and coal in Antarctica. These finds reflect climate conditions millions to hundreds of millions of years ago when landmasses were situated at different latitudes than they are today. Furthermore, mountain ranges rose and eroded away, altering atmospheric circulation, the patterns of clouds and precipitation, and the concentration of atmospheric CO_2.

Opening and closing of ocean basins changed the course of heat-transporting ocean currents and altered the thermohaline circulation. About 100 million years ago, the *Tethys Sea* separated Africa from Eurasia and Central America was submerged so that warm water currents flowed around the equator connecting what are now the Pacific, Atlantic, and Indian Ocean basins. About 40 million years ago, diverging plates separated Antarctica from Australia and about 10 million years later, the Drake Passage opened between Antarctica and the southern tip of South America. The Drake Passage permitted a circumpolar current to flow around Antarctica. In addition, these plate movements eventually left the Antarctic continent situated over the South Pole. By blocking the transport of heat from the tropics to the Southern Ocean, the Antarctic circumpolar current probably led to the formation of the Antarctic ice sheets about 17 million years ago.

About 20 million years ago, the movement of Saudi Arabia northward against Asia sealed off the Tethys Sea, forming the Mediterranean Sea. About 3 million years ago, volcanic eruptions in what is now Central America formed a narrow isthmus of land, blocking the equatorial currents that previously flowed from the Atlantic through the Caribbean and into the equatorial Pacific Ocean.

For another example of how plate tectonics may have played a role in climate change, refer to this chapter's second Essay.

CLIMATE AND SOLAR VARIABILITY

Fluctuations in the sun's energy output, sunspots, or regular variations in Earth's orbital parameters are external factors that can alter Earth's climate. Satellite measurements in the 1980s and 1990s confirmed long-held suspicions in the scientific community that the sun's total energy output at all wavelengths is not constant. Furthermore, numerical global climate models predict that only a 1% change in the sun's energy output could significantly alter the mean temperature of the Earth-atmosphere-ocean system.

Changes in solar energy output are apparently related to sunspot number. A **sunspot** is a dark blotch on the face of the sun, typically thousands of kilometers

across that develops where an intense magnetic field suppresses the flow of gases transporting heat energy from the sun's interior. A sunspot appears dark because its temperature is about 400 to 1800 Celsius degrees (720 to 3240 Fahrenheit degrees) lower than the surrounding surface of the sun, the *photosphere*. A sunspot typically lasts only a few days, but the rate of sunspot generation is such that the number of sunspots varies systematically. The time between successive sunspot maxima or minima averages about 11 years with a range of 10 to 12 years (Figure 12.11). Sunspot number reached a minimum in 1996, a maximum in 2000, and a minimum in 2007.

Satellite monitoring reveals that the sun's energy output varies directly with sunspot number; that is, a slightly brighter sun has more sunspots whereas a slightly dimmer sun has fewer sunspots. The variation in total solar energy output through one 11-year sunspot cycle is less than 0.1%, with much of that taking place in the ultraviolet portion of the solar spectrum. A brighter sun is associated with more sunspots because of a concurrent increase in bright areas, known as *faculae*, which appear near sunspots on the photosphere. Faculae dominate sunspots and the sun brightens. More sunspots may contribute to a warmer global climate and fewer sunspots may translate into a colder global climate.

How reasonable is the proposed link between global climate and sunspot number? In 1893, while

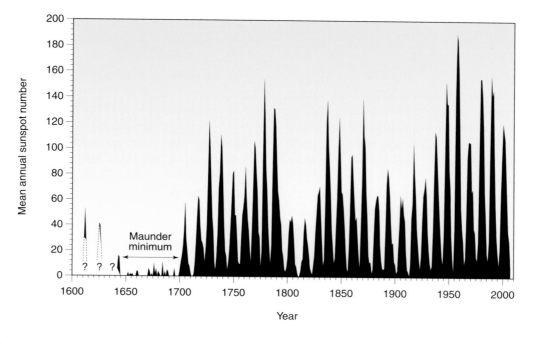

FIGURE 12.11
Variation in mean annual sunspot number since the early 17th century. [National Geophysical Data Center, Solar-Terrestrial Physics Division]

examining sunspot records at the Old Royal Observatory at Greenwich, England, astronomer E. Walter Maunder (1851-1928) discovered that sunspot activity greatly diminished during the 70-year period between 1645 and 1715, now referred to as the **Maunder minimum** (Figure 12.11). The scientific community for the most part ignored Maunder's finding until the 1970s when John A. Eddy of the University Corporation for Atmospheric Research (UCAR) in Boulder, CO reinvestigated his work. Eddy pointed out that the Maunder minimum plus a prior period of reduced sunspot number, called the *Spörer minimum* (1400 to 1510), occurred about the same time as relatively cold phases of the Little Ice Age in Western Europe. Furthermore, the Medieval Warm Period coincided with an interval of heightened sunspot activity between about 1100 and 1250.

Skeptics dismiss the significance of the match between the Maunder minimum and a cooler climate. They argue that relatively cold episodes occurred in Europe just prior to and after the Maunder minimum (i.e., 1605-1615, 1805-1815), and relatively cool conditions did not persist throughout the Maunder minimum and were not global in extent. Furthermore, some scientists argue that a 0.1% variation in total solar energy output during the 11-year sunspot cycle is much too weak to significantly impact Earth's climate. Other scientists counter that certain mechanisms operating within the Earth-atmosphere system could amplify changes in total solar output, making the slight brightening and dimming of the sun an important player in Earth's climate system.

CLIMATE AND EARTH'S ORBIT

In 1842, the French mathematician Joseph Alphonse Adhémar (1797-1862) proposed that regular variations in Earth's orbit about the sun could be responsible for climate variations that paced the glacial fluctuations of the Ice Age. Subsequently, Adhémar's ideas were expanded upon by James Croll and later by Milutin Milankovitch.

In 1864, James Croll (1821-1890), a self-educated Scottish scientist, attributed the climate changes responsible for the Ice Age to fluctuations in incoming solar radiation that accompanied regular changes in Earth's orbital parameters (eccentricity of the orbit, tilt of the rotational axis, and precession of the axis). On this basis, Croll worked out an ice age chronology, arguing that less incoming solar radiation in winter favored greater accumulations of snow. Furthermore, increases in snow cover would have a cooling effect (positive feedback) culminating in glaciation. Croll predicted multiple

glaciations, an idea that was later confirmed by the American geologist Thomas C. Chamberlain (1843-1928). However, by the close of the 19th century, Croll's theory fell into disfavor when European geologists discovered a serious discrepancy between his astronomically-based ice age chronology and field evidence.

In the second decade of the 20th century, the Serbian astronomer Milutin Milankovitch (1879-1958) revived Croll's idea and set out to calculate the latitudinal and seasonal variations in solar radiation striking Earth's surface arising from changes in Earth's three orbital parameters. For more than 25 years, Milankovitch relentlessly pursued his goal, convinced that reduced solar radiation during summer (and not winter as Croll had proposed) at high latitudes was key to initiating glaciation. In 1938, he published radiation curves for different latitudes (55 to 65 degrees N) extending back 600,000 years. In the 1930s and 1940s, support for Milankovitch's astronomical theory of the ice age was considerable, especially in Europe. However, in a dramatic turnaround, by the mid-1950s Milankovitch's views were rejected by most geologists.

Meanwhile, Willard F. Libby (1908-1980) of the University of Chicago developed the radiocarbon method of age-determination of the remains of formerly living organisms. By 1951, geologists were applying the new dating technique to organic materials associated with the last major glacial advance. (The range of radiocarbon dating was limited to about 40,000 years.) Geologists discovered that the astronomical chronology did not match the radiocarbon chronology. However, the radiocarbon chronology was derived mostly from terrestrial sources and some scientists were convinced that a more reliable chronology could be derived from deep-sea sediment cores extracted from the bottom of the open ocean.

Sedimentation rates in the open ocean are extremely slow, ranging from 1 to 3 mm per century. Hence, a relatively short undisturbed core could contain information on climatic fluctuations through much of the Pleistocene with a resolution of the order of 10,000 years. With the development of new age-dating techniques (based on reversals in Earth's magnetic field) and oxygen isotope analysis, scientists soon had the means to reconstruct past climate oscillations from analysis of deep-sea sediment cores. An international team of scientists analyzed two cores extracted from the bottom of the Indian Ocean that spanned 450,000 years. In December 1976, scientists announced that major changes in climate occurred at essentially the same frequency as variations in the eccentricity, obliquity, and precession of

Earth's orbit. Today, Milankovitch's astronomical theory is widely accepted as the explanation for the major climate fluctuations of the Pleistocene.

Milankovitch cycles are regular variations in the precession and tilt of Earth's rotational axis and the eccentricity of its orbit about the sun (Figure 12.12). These changes in Earth-sun geometry are caused by gravitational influences exerted on Earth by other large planets, the moon, and the sun. Combined, Milankovitch cycles drive climate fluctuations operating over tens of thousands to hundreds of thousands of years.

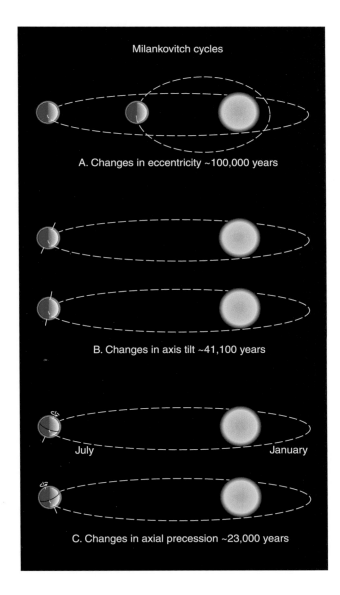

FIGURE 12.12
Milankovitch cycles likely explain the large-scale fluctuations of Earth's glacial ice cover during the Pleistocene. Note that diagrams greatly exaggerate changes in Earth-sun geometry.

Over a period of about 23,000 years, Earth's spin axis describes a complete circle, much like the wobble of a spinning top. This precession cycle changes the dates of *perihelion*, when Earth is closest to the sun, and *aphelion*, when Earth is farthest from the sun, increasing the summer-to-winter seasonal contrast in one hemisphere while decreasing the seasonal contrast in the other. At present, perihelion is in early January and aphelion is in early July. In about 10,000 years, those dates will be reversed (perihelion in July and aphelion in January) and the seasonal contrast will be greater than it is now in the Northern Hemisphere (i.e., colder winters and warmer summers) but less in the Southern Hemisphere (i.e., milder winters and cooler summers).

The tilt of Earth's spin axis changes from 22.1 degrees to 24.5 degrees and then back to 22.1 degrees over a period of about 41,000 years, the consequence of long-period changes in orientation of Earth's orbital plane with respect to its spin axis. (Presently, the tilt is 23.5 degrees.) As the axial tilt increases, winters become colder and summers become warmer in both hemispheres. Earth's axial tilt has been slowly decreasing for about 10,000 years and will continue to do so for the next 10,000 years.

The shape of Earth's orbit about the sun changes from elliptical (high eccentricity) to nearly circular (low eccentricity) in an irregular cycle of 90,000 to 100,000 years. Variation in orbital eccentricity alters the distance between Earth and sun at aphelion and perihelion, thereby changing the amount of solar radiation received by the planet at those times of the year. When Earth's orbit is highly elliptical, the difference in the amount of radiation received at perihelion versus aphelion is greater than when the orbit is less elliptical. Also, changes in eccentricity along with the precession cycle significantly influence the lengths of the individual astronomical seasons.

Milankovitch cycles do not alter appreciably the total amount of solar energy received by the Earth-atmosphere-ocean system annually, but they do change significantly the latitudinal and seasonal distribution of incoming solar radiation. The amplitude of glacial/interglacial climate cycles is not explained by the variations in solar radiation associated with the Milankovitch cycles. Feedback processes operating within the Earth System (most likely related to ocean circulation and the partitioning of CO_2 between ocean and atmosphere) amplify the climatic forcing due to orbital variations.

Milankovitch developed a numerical model based on the three cycles that calculated latitudinal differences in incoming solar radiation and the corresponding surface temperature for the time span of 600,000 years prior to the year 1800. He proposed that glacial climatic episodes began when Earth-sun geometry favored an extended period of increased solar radiation in winter and decreased solar radiation in summer at sub-polar latitudes. More intense winter radiation at these latitudes translates into somewhat higher temperatures, higher humidity, and more snowfall. Weaker solar radiation in summer means that some of the winter snow cover, especially north of 60 degrees N, would survive the summer, and a succession of many such cool summers would favor formation of a glacier. This process, according to Milankovitch, was the origin of the Laurentide ice sheet. At other times, Earth-sun geometry favored enhanced solar radiation in summer at higher latitudes, triggering an interglacial climate and shrinkage of the Laurentide ice sheet.

Milankovitch cycles do not account for the period of climate quiescence prior to the Pleistocene Epoch. Apparently, Milankovitch cycles (which likely operated throughout Earth history) were not effective in initiating continental-scale glaciation until plate tectonics provided the appropriate arrangement of oceans, continents, and mountain ranges—boundary conditions not fully achieved until onset of the Pleistocene.

CLIMATE AND VOLCANOES

The idea that volcanic eruptions influence climate has been around for more than two centuries. Benjamin Franklin (1706-1790) proposed that the eruption of Iceland's Laki volcano in the summer of 1783 was responsible for the severe winter of 1783-84. The unusually cool summer of 1816 (the so-called *year without a summer* in New England) followed the violent eruption of Tambora, an Indonesian volcano, in the spring of 1815. Several relatively cold years occurred on the heels of the 1883 eruption of Krakatau. Is the relationship between volcanic eruptions and cooling real or coincidental?

Only explosive volcanic eruptions rich in sulfur dioxide are likely to impact global or hemispheric climate and then only for a few years at most. A violent volcanic eruption can send sulfur dioxide (SO_2) high into the *stratosphere* (the atmospheric layer above the troposphere). In the stratosphere, sulfur dioxide combines with water vapor to form tiny droplets of sulfuric acid (H_2SO_4) and sulfate particles, collectively called **sulfurous aerosols**. The small size of sulfurous aerosols (averaging about 0.1 micrometer in diameter) coupled with the absence of precipitation in the stratosphere, allow sulfurous aerosols to remain suspended in the stratosphere for many months to perhaps a year or longer before they cycle to Earth's

surface. Successive volcanic eruptions have produced a sulfurous aerosol veil in the stratosphere at altitudes of about 15 to 25 km (9 to 16 mi). Sulfur dioxide emissions from clusters of volcanic eruptions temporarily thicken the stratospheric aerosol veil with implications for climate.

Sulfurous aerosols absorb both incoming solar radiation and outgoing infrared radiation warming the lower stratosphere (especially in the tropics). Sulfurous aerosols also reflect solar radiation to space. For example, NASA scientists reported that in the months following the June 1991 eruption of Mount Pinatubo (on Luzon Island in the Philippines), satellite sensors detected a 3.8% increase in the amount of solar radiation reflected to space (Figure 2.1). These interactions reduce the amount of solar radiation reaching the troposphere and Earth's surface, translating into lower air temperatures.

A violent sulfur-rich volcanic eruption is unlikely to lower the mean hemispheric or global temperature by more than about 1.0 Celsius degree (1.8 Fahrenheit degrees) although the magnitude of local and regional temperature change may be greater (Figure 12.13). The 1963 eruption of Agung in Bali lowered the mean temperature of the Northern Hemisphere an estimated 0.3 Celsius degree

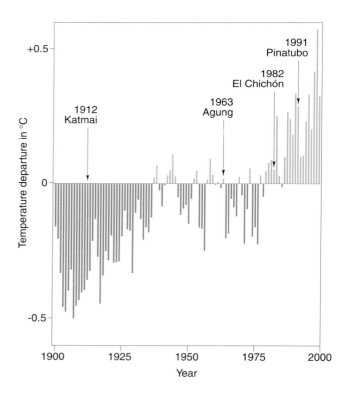

FIGURE 12.13
Large-scale cooling often followed massive volcanic eruptions that emitted sulfur dioxide into the stratosphere.

(0.5 Fahrenheit degree) for a year or two. The violent eruption of the Mexican volcano El Chichón in March-April 1982 may have produced hemispheric cooling of about 0.2 Celsius degree (0.4 Fahrenheit degree). The 1991 eruption of Mount Pinatubo injected an estimated 20 megatons of sulfur dioxide into the stratosphere, the most massive volcanic aerosol cloud of the 20th century. Cooling associated with the Mount Pinatubo eruption temporarily interrupted the post-1970s global warming trend. From 1991 to 1992, the global mean annual temperature dropped 0.6 Celsius degree (1.1 Fahrenheit degrees).

CLIMATE AND EARTH'S SURFACE PROPERTIES

Earth's surface, which is mostly ocean water, is the principal absorber of solar radiation (Chapter 5). Any change in the physical properties of Earth's water or land surfaces or in the relative distribution of ocean, land, and ice may affect Earth's radiation budget and climate.

Variations in mean regional snow cover may contribute to climate change because an extensive snow cover has a chilling effect on the atmosphere. Fresh-fallen snow typically reflects 80% or more of incident solar radiation, thereby substantially reducing the amount of solar heating and lowering the daily maximum temperature. Snow is also an excellent emitter of infrared radiation, so heat is efficiently radiated to space, especially on nights when the sky is clear. Because of this radiational feedback, a snow cover tends to be self-sustaining. An unusually extensive winter snow cover favors persistence of an episode of cold weather. On the other hand, less than the usual extent of winter snow cover raises average air temperatures.

Whereas changes in regional snow cover might impact climate over the short-term (seasonal), changes in Earth's sea ice or glacial ice coverage are likely to have longer-lasting effects on climate. Sea ice (formed from the freezing of seawater) covers an average area of about 25 million square km (9.6 million square mi), about the area of the North American continent. Terrestrial ice sheets, ice caps, and mountain glaciers cover a total area of about 15 million square km (5.8 million square mi), roughly 10% of the land area of the planet. Ice (especially snow-covered ice) reflects much more incident solar radiation than either the ocean or snow-free land so that any change in glacial or sea ice cover would affect climate. As we will see later in this chapter, the Arctic climate is particularly sensitive to changes in sea ice cover.

Changes in ocean circulation and sea-surface temperatures (SST) contribute to large-scale climate change. As described in detail in Chapter 11, changes

in SST patterns accompanying El Niño and La Niña significantly influence inter-annual climate variability. Ocean circulation includes warm and cold surface currents and the deep-ocean thermohaline circulation that transports heat energy throughout the world. Regular changes in the strength of this circulation may explain millennial-scale (1400- to 1500-year) climate cycles over the past 10,000 years. A strong thermohaline circulation brings a relatively mild climate (for the latitude) to Western Europe whereas a weakening of the thermohaline circulation triggers cooling. Such climate shifts can be abrupt, occurring in a decade or less.

CLIMATE AND HUMAN ACTIVITY

In 2007, the **Intergovernmental Panel on Climate Change (IPCC)** concluded that global warming since the mid-20th century *very likely* (estimated probability of greater than 90%) was caused mostly by human activities. In a report issued six years earlier, the IPCC described the human role in global warming as *likely* (estimated probability of higher than 66%). The IPCC, formed in 1988 by the World Meteorological Organization (WMO) and the United Nations Environmental Programme, is charged with evaluating the state of climate science as the basis for policy action.

Many human activities affect climate over broad ranges of spatial and temporal scales. Humans modify the landscape (e.g., urbanization, clear-cutting of forests) and thereby alter radiational properties of Earth's surface. Cities are slightly warmer than the surrounding countryside (the *urban heat island effect*). Combustion of fossil fuels (i.e., coal, oil, and natural gas) alters concentrations of certain key gaseous and aerosol components of the atmosphere. Of these human impacts on Earth's climate system, the final one is most likely to influence climate on a hemispheric or global scale.

Many scientists and public policy makers are concerned about the possible global climate impact of the steadily rising concentration of atmospheric carbon dioxide (CO_2) and other infrared-absorbing gases. Higher levels of these gases enhance the greenhouse effect, contributing to warming on a global scale. The *Synthesis Report of the IPCC Fourth Assessment Report*, issued in November 2007, concluded that: "Warming of the climate system is unequivocal as is now evident from observations of increases in global average air and ocean temperatures, widespread melting of snow and ice, and rising global average sea level." The Report goes on to state that: "Most of the increase in globally-averaged temperatures since the mid-20th century is *very likely* due to the observed increase in anthropogenic GHG (greenhouse gas) concentrations." This is the *Callendar effect* mentioned in Chapter 5.

In 1957, systematic monitoring of atmospheric carbon dioxide levels began at NOAA's Mauna Loa Observatory in Hawaii under the direction of Charles D. Keeling (1928-2005) of Scripps Institution of Oceanography. The observatory is situated on the northern slope of Earth's largest volcano 3397 m (11,140 ft) above sea level in the middle of the Pacific Ocean—sufficiently distant from major sources of air pollution that carbon dioxide levels are considered representative of at least the Northern Hemisphere. Also since 1957, atmospheric CO_2 has been monitored at the South Pole station of the U.S. Antarctic Program and that record closely parallels the one at Mauna Loa. The Mauna Loa record (the *Keeling curve*) shows a sustained increase in average annual atmospheric carbon dioxide concentration from about 316 ppmv (parts per million by volume) in 1959 to about 383.5 ppmv in 2007 (Figure 12.14). During the ten year period ending in 2007, the growth rate of atmospheric CO_2 was faster than over any other 10-year period since the Mauna Loa record began. Superimposed on this upward trend is an annual carbon dioxide cycle caused by seasonal changes in photosynthesis by Northern Hemisphere vegetation. Levels of carbon dioxide fall during the growing season to a minimum in October and recover over winter to a maximum in May.

The upward trend in atmospheric carbon dioxide was underway long before Keeling's monitoring and appears likely to continue well into the future.

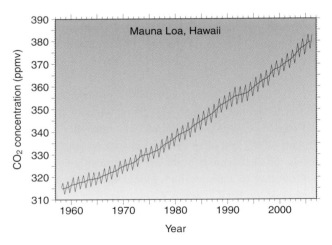

FIGURE 12.14
Trend in atmospheric carbon dioxide concentration since 1957, based on measurements made at the Mauna Loa Observatory in Hawaii. [Source of Mauna Loa data is C.D. Keeling et al., Scripps Institution of Oceanography, University of California, La Jolla, CA.]

Humankind's contribution to the buildup of atmospheric CO_2 began thousands of years ago with the clearing of land for agriculture and settlement. Land clearing contributes CO_2 to the atmosphere via burning of vegetation, decay of wood residue, and reduced photosynthetic removal of carbon dioxide from the atmosphere. By the mid-19th century, growing dependency on coal burning associated with the beginnings of the Industrial Revolution triggered a more rapid rise in CO_2 concentration. Carbon dioxide is a byproduct of the burning of coal and other fossil fuels. The concentration of atmospheric CO_2 is now about 35% higher than it was in the pre-industrial era. Fossil fuel combustion accounts for roughly 75% of the increase in atmospheric carbon dioxide while deforestation (and other land clearing) is likely responsible for the balance. With continued growth in fossil fuel combustion, the atmospheric carbon dioxide concentration could top 550 ppmv (double the pre-industrial level) by the end of the present century.

As noted in Chapters 3 and 9, the ocean, a major reservoir in the global carbon cycle, plays an important role in governing the amount of carbon dioxide in the atmosphere. Scientists were able to estimate the amount of CO_2 released to the atmosphere by human activity from the beginning of the Industrial Revolution. But in measuring the actual amount of carbon dioxide in the atmosphere, about half was missing. The "missing" carbon is distributed between sinks in the ocean and on land. According to IPCC estimates in 2007, the ocean takes up 56.2% of the carbon dioxide of anthropogenic origin (via photosynthesis and cold surface waters absorbing CO_2 and sinking) while terrestrial biomass is a sink for 13.7%. Ultimately, the rising concentration of atmospheric CO_2 is driving the net flux of carbon dioxide across the air/sea interface. Some anthropogenic carbon dioxide is transported with the oceanic thermohaline circulation and may be sequestered for 1000 years before returning to the ocean/atmosphere interface. However, oceanic uptake of carbon dioxide is likely to decline in the future as the ocean becomes more stratified in response to higher global temperatures.

Besides carbon dioxide, rising levels of other infrared-absorbing gases (e.g., methane, nitrous oxide, and halocarbons) likely will enhance the greenhouse effect. Based on analysis of air bubbles trapped in cores extracted from glacial ice sheets, the concentration of methane in the atmosphere is now greater than at any time in the past 400,000 years (Figure 12.2). In the period from 1750 through the late 1970s, the global average atmospheric concentration of methane (CH_4) increased by about 250% (up from an estimated 700 ppbv to 1745 ppbv). Since then the growth rate slowed with the concentration leveling off in 1999-2002. Methane is a product of the decay of organic matter in the absence of oxygen (*anaerobic decay*); its concentration is rising because of more rice cultivation, cattle, landfills, and/or termites, all sources of methane. The atmospheric concentration of nitrous oxide (N_2O) has increased by an estimated 46 ppb (20%) since the beginning of the Industrial Revolution, likely because of industrial air pollution, biomass burning, and fertilizer use. Although occurring in extremely low concentrations, methane and nitrous oxide are very efficient absorbers of infrared radiation.

Atmospheric aerosols that are byproducts of human activity apparently have the opposite effect on temperatures at Earth's surface as greenhouse gases. These aerosols vary in size, shape, and chemical composition. Larger aerosols tend to settle out of the atmosphere quickly whereas smaller ones may remain suspended for many days to weeks and can be transported thousands of kilometers by the wind, possibly impacting large-scale climate. Perhaps 90% of these aerosols are byproducts of fossil fuel burning in the Northern Hemisphere.

Sulfur oxides emitted from power plant smokestacks and boiler vent pipes combine with water vapor in the air to produce tiny droplets of sulfuric acid and sulfate particles. These *sulfurous aerosols* appear to raise the atmosphere's albedo directly by reflecting sunlight to space and indirectly by acting as condensation nuclei that spur cloud development. Greater reflectivity cools the lower atmosphere. Sulfurous aerosols in the troposphere have a shorter-term impact on climate than carbon dioxide and other greenhouse gases. Rain and snow wash sulfurous aerosols from the atmosphere so that the residence time of these substances is typically only a few days. On the other hand, a CO_2 molecule typically resides in the atmosphere for a much longer period before being cycled out by natural processes operating as part of the global carbon cycle. Approximately one-fifth of the carbon we release now will still be in the atmosphere after 200 years. After several thousand years, about one-twentieth will remain.

The Climate Future

What does the climate future hold? Scientists attempt to answer this question primarily by studying past and present climates and interpreting the results of experiments involving global climate models based on projections of future greenhouse gas and aerosol emissions.

GLOBAL CLIMATE MODELS

A **global climate model** is a simulation of Earth's climate system. One type of global climate model consists of dozens of mathematical equations that describe the physical interactions among the various components of the climate system, that is, the atmosphere, ocean, land, cryosphere, and biosphere. A global climate model differs from numerical models used for weather forecasting in that it predicts broad regions of expected positive and negative temperature and precipitation *anomalies* (departures from long-term averages) and the mean location of circulation features such as jet streams and principal storm tracks over much longer time scales.

Global climate models, for example, are used to predict the potential impacts on climate of rising levels of atmospheric carbon dioxide (and other greenhouse gases). Using current boundary conditions (i.e., climate controls), a global climate model simulates the present climate. Then, holding all other variables constant, the concentration of carbon dioxide (or another greenhouse gas) is elevated and the model is run to a new equilibrium state. By comparing the new climate state with the present climate, scientists deduce the impact of an enhanced greenhouse effect on patterns of temperature and precipitation.

Most modelers agree that global climate models are in need of considerable refinement. Today's models may not adequately simulate the role of small-scale weather systems (e.g., thunderstorms) or accurately portray local and regional conditions and may miss important feedback processes. A major uncertainty is the net feedback of clouds. Clouds cause both cooling (by reflecting sunlight to space) and warming (by absorbing and emitting to Earth's surface outgoing infrared radiation). The cooling effect prevails with an increase in low cloud cover whereas the warming effect prevails with an increase in high cloud cover.

Since 2001, confidence in global climate models and their predictions has grown. Today, scientists take the *ensemble* approach to climate simulation. Instead of relying on the output of only one or two models, they group together the simulations of 18 climate modeling groups from around the world. This approach enables scientists to better handle uncertainties in the simulation of climate processes that are not well understood (e.g., cloud feedback, ocean rings). A second reason for higher confidence in global climate models is their more realistic representation of climate processes (e.g., role of sea ice, aerosols).

An alternative approach to numerical global climate models in predicting future climate is to identify the various factors that have contributed to past changes in climate and to extrapolate their influence into the future. To this end, atmospheric scientists have probed climate records in search of (1) regular cycles that might be extended into the future and (2) analogs that might provide clues as to how the climate in specific regions responds to global-scale climate change. Few of the quasi-regular oscillations appearing in the climate record have much practical value for climate forecasting at least over the next century.

Although the climate record yields much useful information on how climate behaves through time, the search for analogs of future global warming has been fruitless. Proposed analogs include relatively warm episodes of the mid-Holocene and the Eemian interglacial. But those analogs are inappropriate because the mid-Holocene and Eemian warming primarily affected seasonal temperatures with only a slight rise in global mean temperature. Furthermore, boundary conditions were different. During the mid-Holocene, sea level was lower, glacial ice sheets were more extensive, and the dates of perihelion and aphelion were different than they are now or will be over the next several centuries. Although the level of atmospheric CO_2 trended upward during the mid-Holocene, the rate of increase (about 0.5 ppmv per century) was far lower than at present (more than 60 ppmv per century). Pre-Pleistocene analogs are also inappropriate because of the absence of glacial ice sheets and significant differences in topography and land-ocean distribution.

ENHANCED GREENHOUSE EFFECT AND GLOBAL WARMING

Over the next 10,000 to 20,000 years, the Milankovitch cycles favor a return to Ice Age conditions. In fact, when the connection between past ice ages and Milankovitch cycles was confirmed in the 1970s, the popular press expressed concern over a coming ice age. What about climate in the near term—over the next two decades or during the 21st century? If all other controls of climate remain fixed, rising concentrations of atmospheric CO_2 and other greenhouse gases will cause global warming to persist throughout this century and beyond. The magnitude of warming depends on projections of future emissions of greenhouse gases.

According to the 2007 IPCC Assessment Report, the climate models predict that over the next 20 years, the global mean annual temperature will increase at an average rate of about 0.2 Celsius degrees per decade. Again depending on the future greenhouse gas emission scenario, over the present century, the

climate models project that the globally averaged surface temperature will rise by 1.8 to 4.0 Celsius degrees (3.2 to 7.2 Fahrenheit degrees). Recall, however, that climate change is geographically non-uniform (in both magnitude and direction) so that this projected rise in global mean annual temperature is not necessarily representative of what might happen everywhere. For example, *polar amplification* suggests that global warming will be greater at higher latitudes. In any event, enhancement of the greenhouse effect could cause a climate change that would be greater in magnitude than any previous climate change over the past 10,000 years.

Even if greenhouse gas emissions were to stabilize at present levels, global warming would likely continue well beyond the 21st century. This considerable inertia in climate is primarily due to the dominating role of the ocean in Earth's climate system. As discussed in Chapter 3, ocean water has a high specific heat so that unusually great quantities of heat energy are involved in relatively small changes in temperature. Furthermore, the transport and mixing of heat energy and carbon dioxide throughout the deep ocean operate over time scales of millennia. Hence, a considerable length of time is required for Earth's climate system to achieve equilibrium under new environmental conditions.

Models of global warming based on an enhanced greenhouse effect assume that all other climate controls remain constant. Whether that actually happens is not known. Comparing the post-1957 trend in atmospheric carbon dioxide to the trend in mean annual global temperature strongly suggests that recent climate has been shaped by many interacting factors. The rapid rise in atmospheric CO_2 concentration was not accompanied by a consistent rise in global mean temperature over the same period. Recall, for example, that sulfurous aerosols from the June 1991 eruption of Mount Pinatubo apparently were responsible for significant global-scale cooling the following year. Also as noted earlier, El Niño and La Niña influence climate in some areas of the globe over periods of 12 to 18 months. Furthermore, analysis of the composition of tiny air bubbles in cores extracted from the Greenland and Antarctic ice sheets indicate that during the Pleistocene Ice Age, atmospheric CO_2 varied between about 200 and 280 ppmv. Although CO_2 was consistently higher during milder interglacial climatic episodes than during colder glacial climatic episodes, fluctuations in carbon dioxide levels lag reconstructed variations in temperature. For example, at the beginning of the last major glacial climatic episode, the decline in CO_2 concentration significantly lagged cooling in the

Antarctic. Hence, fluctuations in atmospheric CO_2 may have been a response to large-scale climate oscillations rather than a cause of those oscillations.

Further complicating efforts to predict the climate future are recent indications that the global radiation budget currently is not in equilibrium. In 2005, scientists reported that the planet is now absorbing about 0.85 W per m^2 more energy from the sun than it is emitting as infrared radiation to space; the imbalance is approximately 0.06% of the total incoming solar radiation at the top of the atmosphere. This conclusion is supported by measurements made by satellite sensors and instrumented buoys indicating an increase in the heat content of the ocean over the previous decade. This imbalance represents the delay in the response of Earth's climate (i.e., surface temperature) to some forcing (i.e., build up of greenhouse gases). This delay, in turn, is the consequence of considerable thermal inertia in Earth's climate system, mostly due to the ocean. On this basis, global climate models predict an as yet unrealized additional warming of 0.6 Celsius degree (1.1 Fahrenheit degrees) with no change in atmospheric composition as Earth shifts to a new state of global radiative equilibrium.

Impact of Climate Change on the Ocean

As we have seen, since the Little Ice Age ended in the mid 19th century, the global mean temperature has generally trended upward. In recent years, that warming trend has accelerated—probably the consequence of the build up of carbon dioxide and other greenhouse gases in the atmosphere. (As noted in Chapters 3 and 4, more carbon dioxide in the atmosphere also may be leading to *ocean acidification*.) If the warming trend continues, how might this climate change impact the ocean? Higher sea level is one consequence that has worldwide ramifications. In addition, warmer conditions in the Arctic may significantly reduce the sea ice cover with important implications for Earth's climate system. Furthermore, global warming is likely to impact marine life.

SEA LEVEL FLUCTUATIONS

Climate change, which was responsible for the waxing and waning of Earth's glacial ice cover during the Pleistocene Ice Age, also caused sea level to alternately fall and rise. Geological evidence such as drowned beaches and river valleys, and submarine canyons attests to periods when sea level was much lower than at present. Scientists estimate that during the last glacial maximum,

about 18,000 to 20,000 years ago, mean sea level was 113 to 135 m (370 to 443 ft) lower than it is today. More than 90% of this drop in sea level was due to a change in the global water cycle brought about by a colder climate. As noted in Chapter 1, the total amount of water on the planet is essentially constant—an assumption that likely holds throughout recent geologic time. Practically all the water locked in glaciers came from the ocean via the global water cycle. During glacial climatic episodes, glaciers on land thicken and expand, and the volume of water in the ocean basins decreases (i.e., sea level falls). Conversely, during interglacial climatic episodes, glaciers on land thin and retreat, and the volume of water in the ocean basins increases (i.e., sea level rises). Furthermore, perhaps 7% or 8% of the drop in sea level during the last glacial maximum was due to a decline in ocean temperature resulting in contraction of the ocean water and an increase in water density. Recall from Chapter 3 that seawater always contracts when its temperature drops and expands when its temperature rises.

Waxing and waning of glaciers plus ocean temperature fluctuations are two factors that govern **eustasy**, the global variation in sea level brought about by a change in the volume of water occupying the ocean basins. Another factor that contributes to sea-level change and can be important over geologic time is alterations in the size of the ocean basins brought about by tectonic movements (Chapter 2). Persistence of the global warming trend appears likely to cause sea level to rise in response to melting of land-based polar ice sheets and mountain glaciers, coupled with thermal expansion of seawater. Thermal expansion of warming seawater probably will be the greater contributor to sea level rise during the 21st century.

How did sea level respond to the global warming trend of the 20th century? For most of the century, coastal tide gauges were the principal source of data on sea level change. Care must be taken to exclude (or adjust) those tide gauge records that might be influenced by geological processes (i.e., tectonic uplift or subsidence or post-glacial rebound). Based on adjusted tide gauge records, sea level during the 20th century rose at the rate of 1.8 ± 0.3 mm per year. Since 1993, microwave altimeters onboard Earth-orbiting satellites have permitted a more precise measure of the rise in global sea level (Figure 12.15). (See the discussion of TOPEX/Poseidon and its successor Jason 1 in Chapter 11.) From 1993 to 2003, mean global sea level increased an estimated 3.1 ± 0.7 mm per year. In total, mean sea level rose about 18 cm (7.1 in.) during the 20th century.

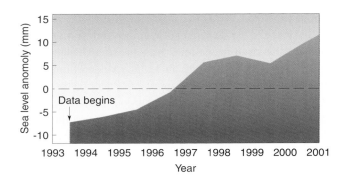

FIGURE 12.15
Annually averaged sea level variation based on TOPEX/Poseidon measurements for 1993-2000. [Adapted from C. Cabanese *et al.,* "Sea Level Rise During Past 40 Years Determined from Satellite and in Situ Observations," *Science* 294 (2001):840.]

Most mountain glaciers have been shrinking since the mid 20th century; portions of the Greenland ice sheet have shown recent signs of accelerated melting; and portions of the ocean are warming. But how much of the recent rise in sea level was due to melting of glacial ice and how much was due to thermal expansion of the warming ocean is not known.

Amplification of the warming trend at higher latitudes would threaten the Greenland and Antarctic ice sheets. About 90% of the planet's glacial ice blankets Antarctica and melting could cause a considerable rise in sea level. How likely is this to happen? Separate ice sheets cover West Antarctica and East Antarctica. The West Antarctic ice sheet sits on a former ocean bottom and is mostly below sea level whereas the East Antarctic ice sheet is situated on a continent and is well above sea level. While geological evidence suggests that the East Antarctic ice sheet has been stable for the past 15 million years and remains fairly stable today, the West Antarctic sheet has undergone episodes of rapid disintegration and may have completely melted at least once in the past 600,000 years. More than 30 years ago, recognition of the relative instability of the West Antarctic ice sheet prompted some scientists to speculate that ice streams flowing from the interior of the glacier to the Ross and Ronne ice shelves might cause a total collapse of the ice sheet in a few centuries or less. Such a catastrophic event would greatly accelerate the rate of sea level rise. (Complete disintegration of the West Antarctic ice sheet would raise sea level by about 5 m or 16 ft.)

In 2001, concerns about the possible disintegration of the West Antarctic ice sheet were alleviated with the discovery that new snowfall is keeping pace with the loss of ice from bergs breaking off the Ross Ice Shelf. In early 2002, scientists at the California Institute of Technology and the University of California-Santa Cruz reported that based on satellite-based measurements of the flow of the Ross ice streams, the West Antarctic ice sheet appears to be thickening. Meanwhile, the region of the ice sheet that feeds the Thwaites and Pine Island glaciers is thinning. These glaciers transport ice directly into the ocean (rather than adding to an ice shelf) and are responsible for about 10% of the average annual rise in sea level.

More recently, Eric Rignot of NASA's Jet Propulsion Laboratory in Pasadina, CA and colleagues used satellite imagery to measure the thickness of ice fringing the coast of Antarctica. These data along with estimates of ice stream discharge and snowfall enabled them to determine the annual loss of ice from Antarctica. They concluded that the ice loss from Antarctica (mostly West Antarctica) was about 75% greater in 2006 than in 1996. Nonetheless, the consensus of scientific opinion today is that the West Antarctic ice sheet is unlikely to catastrophically accelerate the current rise in sea level. According to some experts, long-term gradual shrinkage of the West Antarctic ice could raise sea level at a rate of about 1 m (3.3 ft) per 500 years.

Melting (and the rate of sea level rise) could accelerate if the Antarctic ice sheets begin to feel the effects of global warming. Over most of Antarctica, the mean air temperature has fluctuated very little over the past 50 years. The Antarctic Peninsula is the only part of the continent that has shown significant warming with summer mean temperatures rising more than 2 Celsius degrees (3.6 Fahrenheit degrees) over the past half century. This warming has been accompanied by considerable ice breakup along the coast.

NASA research results released in 2000 concluded that while the central interior of the Greenland ice sheet showed no sign of thinning, about 70% of the margin was thinning substantially. Two research teams—one using a Global Positioning System (GPS) to monitor ice flow and the other relying on an airborne laser altimeter to measure ice thickness—reached the same conclusion based on observations made between 1993 and 1999. The maximum melting rate at the margin was about 1 m per year. An estimated 50 cubic km (12 cubic mi) of Greenland's ice melts each year, enough to raise sea level by 0.13 mm annually.

Scientists at the University of Colorado reported that during the summer of 2002, surface melting on the Greenland ice sheet encompassed an area of about 695,000 square km (265,000 square mi)—about 9% greater than observed in 24 years of monitoring by satellite. In addition, melting in the northern and northeastern portion of the ice sheet occurred at elevations as high as 2000 m (6550 ft) where normally temperatures are too low for any melting. The duration and extent of melting at elevations above 2000 m set a new record in 2007. Researchers at the Goddard Space Flight Center monitored snow melt on the ice sheet surface using a satellite microwave sensor and computed a snow melt index by multiplying the area of snowmelt by the duration of melting. During 2007, the melting index above 2000-m elevation was about 2.5 times greater than the annual average from 1988 to 2006. It appears that winter snowfall is insufficient to offset the summer melt so that overall the Greenland ice sheet is shrinking. Furthermore, by reducing frictional resistance within the ice mass, the greater supply of melt water accelerates the flow of Greenland ice streams into the ocean and increases the rate of rise of sea level.

According to Roger G. Barry, director of NOAA's *National Snow and Ice Data Center* at the University of Colorado at Boulder, the rate of melting of most of the world's mountain glaciers accelerated after the mid-1900s and especially since the mid-1970s. Some mountain glaciers have disappeared entirely. For example, today only 26 glaciers remain of the 150 glaciers that existed in Montana's Glacier National Park a century ago. Barry estimates that runoff from melting mountain glaciers contributes about 0.4 mm to the annual rise in sea level.

Alpine glaciers are also shrinking at accelerating rates. According to Frank Paul at the University of Zurich-Irchel in Zurich, Switzerland, the combined area covered by almost 940 Alpine glaciers decreased by about 18% from 1973 to 1999. Paul's conclusion was based on analysis of satellite images, aerial photographs, and land surveys. Swiss glaciers are now shrinking at an annual rate that is more than six times the rate that prevailed from 1850 to 1973. At the present rate of shrinkage, Alpine glaciers at elevations below 2000 m (6500 ft) will likely disappear by the year 2070.

In spring 2000, NOAA scientists reported that the combined Atlantic, Pacific, and Indian Oceans warmed significantly between 1955 and 1995. The greatest warming occurred in the upper 300 m (985 ft) of the ocean and amounted to 0.31 Celsius degree (0.56 Fahrenheit degree). Water in the upper 3000 m (9850 ft) warmed by an average 0.06 Celsius degree (0.11 Fahrenheit degree). In February 2002, researchers at Scripps Institution of Oceanography reported that temperatures at mid-depths (between 700 m and 1100 m) in the Southern Ocean rose 0.17 Celsius degrees between the 1950s and 1980s. Although these magnitudes of temperature change may sound trivial,

recall that water has an unusually high specific heat so that even a very small change in temperature of such vast volumes of water represents a tremendous heat input into the ocean. Sequestering of vast quantities of heat energy in the ocean may help explain why global warming during the 20th century was less than some climate models predicted based on the concurrent buildup of greenhouse gases. That is, heating of the ocean partially offset warming of the lower atmosphere. This finding also underscores the importance of the ocean's moderating influence on global climate change.

According to the 2007 IPCC assessment, climate models predict that global warming will cause a rise in mean sea level in the range of 30 to 40 cm (12 to 16 in.) during the 21st century. Thermal expansion of ocean waters would account for more than 60% of the rise with the balance due to melting glaciers. Higher sea level would accelerate coastal erosion by wave action, inundate wetlands, estuaries and some islands, and make low-lying coastal plains more vulnerable to storm surges (Chapter 8). Globally, a 50-cm (20-in.) rise in sea level would double the number of people at risk from storm surges from about 45 million at present to more than 90 million, not counting any additional population growth in the coastal zone. Rising sea level would disrupt coastal ecosystems and could threaten historical, cultural, and recreational resources (Figure 12.16). In some coastal areas, higher sea level is likely to exacerbate saltwater intrusion into groundwater. (For more on this problem, refer to this chapter's third Essay.) According to a 1997 report by the U.S. Office of Science and Technology Policy, a 50-cm (20-in.) rise in sea level would result in a substantial loss of coastal land, especially along the U.S. Gulf and southern Atlantic coasts. Particularly vulnerable is South Florida where one-third of the Everglades is less than 30 cm (12 in.) above sea level

While higher temperatures would mean higher sea level, the level of the Great Lakes is likely to fall. Higher summer temperatures coupled with less winter ice cover on the Great Lakes are likely to translate into greater evaporation. And less winter snowfall would reduce spring runoff. Depending on the model used, forecasts call for a drop in mean water level of Lake Michigan of up to 2 m (6.5 ft) by the year 2070. Residents of the western Great Lakes may have previewed the impact of global warming from the late 1990s into the early 2000s when the levels of Lakes Michigan and Huron dropped to near historical record lows. (Refer to the first Essay in Chapter 8.)

The prospect of higher sea surface temperatures prompted some scientists to predict an upturn in the number and intensity of tropical cyclones (i.e., hurricanes and tropical storms). Recall from Chapter 8 that tropical cyclones derive their energy from evaporation of seawater. However, relatively high sea surface temperature is only one of several factors required for tropical cyclone formation. In fact, some climate models predict that stronger winds aloft will accompany a warmer climate producing wind shear that would inhibit tropical cyclone development. However, recent studies suggest that while the total number of tropical cyclones has not increased, the number of major hurricanes appears to be increasing.

ARCTIC SEA ICE COVER

A major concern associated with global warming is shrinkage of Arctic sea ice. Although melting of floating sea ice does not raise sea level, it can alter climate significantly. Shrinkage of Arctic sea ice is likely to trigger an **ice-albedo feedback** mechanism that would accelerate melting of sea ice and amplify warming (Figure 12.17). Sea ice insulates the overlying air from warmer seawater and reflects much more incident solar radiation than ocean water. The albedo of snow-covered sea ice is about 85% whereas ice-free Arctic Ocean water has an average albedo of only about 7%. As sea ice cover shrinks, the greater area of ice-free ocean waters absorbs more solar radiation, sea surface temperatures rise, and more ice melts. Furthermore, warmer water slows the formation of ice in autumn. This

FIGURE 12.16
Map of the U.S. Geological Survey's *Coastal Vulnerability Index (CVI)* for Cape Cod National Seashore, MA showing the vulnerability of the coast to changes in sea level. The CVI is based on tidal range, wave height, coastal slope, historic shoreline change rates, geomorphology, and historic rates of relative sea level change due to eustatic sea level rise and tectonic uplift or subsidence. [USGS Fact Sheet FS-095-02, September 2002]

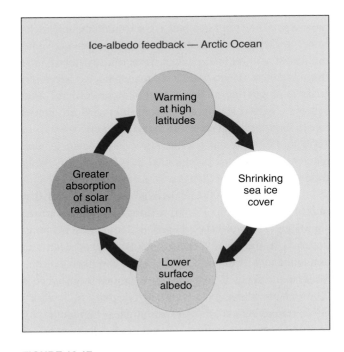

FIGURE 12.17
Positive ice-albedo feedback in the Arctic is likely to accelerate warming of surface waters and shrinkage of sea ice cover.

positive feedback mechanism could rapidly reduce Arctic sea ice cover and greatly alter the flux of heat energy and moisture between the ocean and atmosphere with possible ramifications for global climate.

Less sea ice cover on the Arctic Ocean is likely to increase the humidity of the overlying air leading to more cloudiness. As pointed out earlier in this chapter, clouds cause both cooling (by reflecting sunlight to space) and warming (by absorbing and emitting to Earth's surface outgoing infrared radiation). During the long dark polar winter, clouds would have a warming effect. In summer, the impact of a greater cloud cover depends on the altitude of the clouds. Cooling would prevail with an increase in low cloud cover whereas warming would likely accompany an increase in high cloud cover.

What is the trend in Arctic sea ice? A variety of sources provides information on the extent of Arctic sea ice cover since the early part of the 20th century. Ship and aircraft observations indicate that the multi-year Arctic ice cover remained essentially constant in all seasons through the first half of the 20th century. But beginning in the 1950s, observations by ships and aircraft detected shrinkage in the summer minimum extent of ice while the winter maximum remained nearly constant. By the mid-1970s, surveillance by satellites and submarines plus ice-core measurements found a decline in the winter maximum extent of ice as well.

Norwegian researchers reported that the area covered by multi-year ice in the Arctic decreased about 14% between 1978 and 1998. Their findings were based on satellite monitoring of the spectrum of microwave energy emitted by the ice. Comparing ice-thickness measurements made by U.S. Navy submarines from 1958 to 1976 with those made during the *Scientific Ice Expedition* program in 1993, 1996, and 1997, University of Washington scientists discovered that ice had thinned from an average thickness of 3.1 m (10 ft) to an average thickness of 1.8 m (6 ft). Thinning at the rate of 15% per decade translates into a total volumetric ice loss of about 40% in three decades. (Upward-looking acoustic sounders mounted on submarines were used to map ice depth.)

After 2000, the rate of reduction of Arctic sea ice cover accelerated. From analysis of satellite data, scientists from the Cooperative Institute for Research in Environmental Sciences (CIRES) at the University of Colorado reported that the extent of Arctic sea ice in 2002 was the lowest in the satellite record, likely the lowest since the early 1950s, and perhaps the lowest in several centuries. In September 2002, sea ice covered about 5.3 million square km (2 million square mi) compared to the long-term average

of about 6.3 million square km (2.4 million square mi). According to the IPCC, from 1979 through 2006, the extent of Arctic sea ice decreased by 2.7 ± 0.6 percent per decade in the annual average and 7.4 ± 2.4 percent per decade for the end-of-summer. Between 1981 and 2000, average ice thickness decreased by about 1.13 m (3.7 ft) or 22%.

According to scientists at NOAA's National Snow and Ice Data Center, the extent of end-of-summer (September) sea ice cover in the Arctic in 2005 was the lowest since satellite monitoring of the polar region began about 30 years ago (Figure 12.18). That record was broken two years later when the summer minimum decreased to 4.2 million square km (1.6 million square mi), 39% below the long-term average and 23% below the previous record low. This sharp decline in Arctic ice cover was attributed to a combination of factors including the long-term trend in ice thinning and shrinkage, unusually strong summer winds that created a large area of open water and thin ice in the Arctic Ocean, and less than the usual cloud cover that allowed more solar radiation to reach the ocean surface. This ice-albedo feedback accelerated the warming and melting during the summer of 2007. If current trends continue, by 2013 there may be little or no sea ice in the Arctic in summer.

Shrinkage of the Arctic sea ice may be the direct consequence of higher air temperatures or indirectly the result of changes in ocean circulation (i.e., greater input of warmer Atlantic water under the Arctic sea ice). Some scientists argue that higher air and ocean temperatures in the Arctic are natural variations in climate associated with the *Arctic Oscillation (AO)* and that the ice-cover will return to

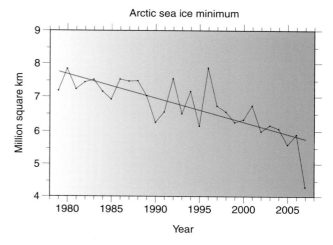

FIGURE 12.18
Arctic sea ice has been shrinking at least since the time satellite monitoring began in 1979, reaching a new end-of-season (September) record low in 2007. [Adapted from NOAA's National Snow and Ice Data Center, Boulder, CO]

normal after the AO changes phase. As noted in Chapter 11, during the present AO phase winds have been delivering warmer than usual air and seawater into the Arctic.

Mean annual air temperatures in the Arctic have climbed about 0.5 Celsius degree (0.9 Fahrenheit degree) per decade over the past thirty years. Proxy climate data indicate that present temperatures (especially in winter and spring) may be at their highest level in four centuries. In response, mountain glaciers in Alaska are shrinking at historically unprecedented rates, *permafrost* (permanently frozen ground) is beginning to thaw, and freshwater runoff into the ocean has increased. More winter precipitation combined with an increased flow of groundwater (due to melting permafrost) is likely responsible for a 7% increase in the discharge of six major Eurasian rivers into the Arctic Ocean since the 1930s.

Input of more fresh water from rivers and melting glaciers would impact the ocean thermohaline circulation by reducing the salinity and thus the density of surface ocean waters. Recall from Chapter 6 that relatively dense cold, salty water sinks at high latitudes of the Atlantic Ocean. As pointed out earlier in this chapter, changes in strength of the thermohaline circulation could alter the climate of Western Europe. Paradoxically, warming at high latitudes could lead to regional cooling due to a weaker thermohaline circulation regime.

MARINE LIFE

How might climate change impact marine life? As described in Chapters 9 and 10, marine animals and plants are components of ecosystems. An *ecosystem* is a fundamental subdivision of the Earth system in which organisms depend for their survival on other organisms and the physical and chemical constituents of their surroundings. Materials and energy flow from one organism to another via food webs within and between ecosystems. Climate change could alter the physical and chemical conditions in the ocean, perhaps exceeding the tolerance limits of organisms. If these organisms are unable to avoid these stressful conditions, they may perish.

Shrinkage of Arctic sea ice may have serious implications for organisms living on, within, or under the ice. To learn more about this extreme environment, in June/July 2005, an international team of scientists explored the Canada Basin (one of the deepest portions of the Arctic Ocean) with a variety of in situ and remote sensing techniques. The expedition, called "The Hidden Ocean,' was funded by NOAA's Office of Ocean Exploration (Figure 12.19).

Global warming could raise the sea-surface temperature sufficiently to threaten coral reefs. As noted in Chapter 10, coral polyps are sensitive to small changes in water temperature and prolonged periods of exposure

FIGURE 12.19
Mette Nielson and Rolf Gradinger are part of an international team studying the effects of diminishing Arctic ice cover on the marine community living on, within, and below the ice. Here, they are extracting ice cores for later analysis. [Courtesy of The Hidden Ocean/Arctic 2005 Exploration, NOAA-OE]

to excessively warm waters can lead to *coral bleaching* and death. Because of the interdependency of organisms (e.g., for food, habitat), loss of one species can disrupt food webs and the entire ecosystem.

Organisms are particularly vulnerable to environmental change that affects a limiting factor. A *limiting factor* is an essential resource that is in lowest supply compared to what is required by the organism. For example, a climate change may indirectly affect the supply of an essential nutrient. Concurrent shifts in atmospheric circulation may suppress upwelling in some locations or reduce the transport of micronutrients to portions of the open ocean. Furthermore, rising sea level is likely to alter marine habitats especially in the coastal zone. In some cases—where the coastline has been developed for roads and buildings—flooding may eliminate marine habitats entirely causing the demise of organisms that are dependent on those habitats.

Consider, for example, the fate of salt marshes already threatened by development. Higher temperatures will increase the rate of evaporation from the soil surface thereby elevating the soil salinity. More saline soils will cut biological production and may exceed the tolerance limits of plants. Rising sea level threatens to drown salt marshes. If plants cannot shift inland to higher ground, their fate is sealed and the marsh may be lost. Loss of salt marshes, in turn, will make the coastline more vulnerable to flooding and erosion by storm waves. Furthermore the filtration function of salt marshes will be lost so that higher levels of pollution and nutrients will enter estuaries with runoff.

A key consideration in the potential impact of climate change on marine organisms is the rate of change. Marine ecosystems can more readily adjust to gradual rather than abrupt changes in the ocean environment brought on by global scale climate fluctuations. But as noted earlier in this chapter, the climate change due to an enhanced greenhouse effect could be without precedent in the past 10,000 years.

Conclusions

Climate is inherently variable. In most places, the reliable instrument-based climate record extends back only 120 years or so. For information on prior climate regimes, scientists must rely on a variety of documentary, geological, and biological proxy climate indicators. Although the climate record loses detail, continuity, and reliability with increasing time before present, it is evident that climate changes over a broad spectrum of time scales.

The interaction of many factors is responsible for the variability of climate. Although we can isolate specific climate controls that are internal or external to the Earth-atmosphere-ocean system, our understanding of how these controls interact is far from complete. This state of the art limits the ability of scientists to forecast the climate future. We should therefore be wary of simplistic scenarios of the climate future, for not enough is known about the causes of climate change.

Continued research on climate is needed. It is reasonable to assume that physical laws govern climate change; that is, variations in climate are not arbitrary, random events. As scientists more fully comprehend the laws governing climatic change and especially the role played by the ocean in Earth's climate system, their ability to predict the climate future will improve. Meanwhile, trends in climate must be monitored closely, especially in view of the potential wide ranging impacts of climate change.

Basic Understandings

- For information on climate prior to the reliable instrument-based era, scientists rely on climate inferences drawn from historical documents, and geological/biological proxy climatic evidence such as bedrock, fossils, pollen, tree growth rings, glacial ice cores, and deep-sea sediment cores.
- Much of what is known about the climate fluctuations of the Pleistocene Ice Age is based on analysis of the shell and skeletal remains of microscopic marine organisms that are extracted from deep-sea sediment cores. Identification of the organism plus oxygen isotope analysis of remains enable scientists to distinguish between cold and mild climatic episodes of the past. Analysis of ice cores also contributes to our knowledge of past climates.
- Plate tectonics complicate reconstruction of climate over periods spanning hundreds of millions of years. In the context of geologic time, topography and the geographical distribution of continents and the ocean are variable controls of climate.
- By 40 million years ago, global climate began shifting toward cooler, drier, and more variable conditions. Scientists have implicated tectonic forces and the building of the Colorado Plateau, Tibetan Plateau, and Himalayan Mountains as

the principal causes of this climate change.

- Cooling culminated in the Pleistocene Ice Age about 1.7 million years ago. During the Pleistocene, the climate shifted numerous times between glacial climatic episodes (favoring expansion of glaciers) and interglacial climatic episodes (favoring shrinkage of glaciers).

- Cooling during the Pleistocene was geographically non-uniform in magnitude with maximum cooling at high latitudes and minimum cooling in the tropics. This latitudinal variation in temperature change is known as polar amplification.

- Notable post-glacial climatic episodes were the relatively warm mid-Holocene, the Medieval Warm Period, from about CE 950 to 1250, and the Little Ice Age, from about CE 1400 to 1850. In all cases, the temperature change was geographically non-uniform in magnitude.

- The instrument-based record of global mean temperature indicates a gradual warming trend since 1880, interrupted by cooling from about 1940 to 1970. The warming trend appears to have accelerated during the 1990s and into the 2000s.

- Analysis of the climate record reveals many useful observations about the temporal behavior of climate. Climate is inherently variable; climate change is geographically non-uniform in direction and magnitude; climate change may involve changes in mean values of temperature or precipitation as well as changes in the frequency of weather extremes; climate change tends to be more abrupt than gradual; the climate record contains few cycles that are sufficiently reliable to permit forecasting climate over the next century; and climate change impacts society.

- Matching a particular forcing mechanism with a climate response based on similar periods of oscillation is no guarantee of a real physical relationship. Factors that could alter the global radiative equilibrium and change Earth's climate include fluctuations in solar energy output, volcanic eruptions, changes in Earth's surface properties, and certain human activities.

- Changes in the sun's total energy output are apparently related to sunspot activity. Solar output varies directly and minutely with sunspot number; that is, a slightly brighter sun has more sunspots (because of a concurrent increase in faculae, bright areas), and a slightly dimmer sun

exhibits fewer sunspots.

- Milankovitch cycles drive climatic oscillations operating over tens of thousands to hundreds of thousands of years and were likely responsible for the major advances and recessions of the Laurentide ice sheet over North America during the Pleistocene. They consist of regular variations in precession and tilt of Earth's rotational axis and the eccentricity of its orbit about the sun. These same cycles also show up in deep-sea sediment cores that date from the Pleistocene Ice Age.

- Only violent volcanic eruptions rich in sulfur dioxide gases are likely to impact hemispheric or global-scale climate. Such eruptions are unlikely to lower the mean annual global surface temperature by more than about 1.0 Celsius degree (1.8 Fahrenheit degrees) for a year or two.

- Earth's surface, which is mostly ocean water, is the prime absorber of solar radiation so that any change in the physical properties of water or land surfaces or in the relative distribution of ocean and land may impact the global radiation balance and climate.

- Human activity may impact global-scale climate by elevating the concentration of greenhouse gases (causing warming) or sulfurous aerosols (causing cooling). The current upward trend in atmospheric carbon dioxide is primarily due to burning of fossil fuels and to a lesser extent the clearing of vegetation.

- The ocean, a major reservoir in the global carbon cycle, plays an important role in governing the amount of carbon dioxide in the atmosphere. According to IPCC estimates in 2007, the ocean takes up 56.2% of the carbon dioxide of anthropogenic origin while terrestrial biomass is a sink for 13.7%. Ultimately, the rising concentration of atmospheric CO_2 is driving a net influx of carbon dioxide across the air/sea interface.

- Global climate models consist of a series of mathematical equations that describes the physical laws that govern the interactions among the various components of Earth's climate system. They are used to predict broad regions of expected positive and negative temperature and precipitation anomalies.

- The climate record does not contain reliable cycles that can be used to forecast the climate over a period of several centuries. Also, no satisfactory analogs exist in the climate record that would allow scientists to predict regional responses to future global-scale climate change.

- Current global climate models predict that significant global warming will accompany a doubling of atmospheric carbon dioxide, possible by the close of this century. Warming will be greater in magnitude than any other prior climate change during the history of civilization.

- Projections of the magnitude of future global warming arising from an enhanced greenhouse effect assume that all other controls of climate remain constant. To what extent this will happen is not known.

- Global warming is likely to cause sea level to rise in response to melting of polar ice sheets and mountain glaciers plus thermal expansion of seawater. Higher sea level would accelerate coastal erosion, inundate wetlands, estuaries and some islands, and make low-lying coastal plains more vulnerable to storm surges. Rising sea level would disrupt coastal ecosystems and could threaten historical, cultural, and recreational resources.

- Shrinkage of the Arctic sea ice cover raises concerns about a possible ice-albedo feedback mechanism that would accelerate melting of sea-ice and amplify warming in the Arctic. Sea ice insulates the overlying air from warmer sea water and reflects much more incident solar radiation than ocean water. If sea ice cover shrinks, the greater area of ice-free ocean waters will absorb more solar radiation, sea surface temperatures will rise, and more ice will melt. This positive feedback mechanism could rapidly reduce the sea ice cover and greatly alter the flux of heat energy and moisture between the ocean and atmosphere with possible ramifications for global climate.

- Global warming could disrupt the functioning of marine ecosystems by exceeding tolerance limits or destroying habitats.

Review

1. What is the value of geologic time scales?
2. Distinguish between glacial climatic episodes and interglacial climatic episodes.
3. What is meant by polar amplification?
4. When did the Medieval Warm Period and the Little Ice Age occur and how did these climatic episodes influence Norse settlements in Greenland?
5. Define global radiative equilibrium and describe its significance for Earth's climate.
6. What is the potential climatic significance of the Maunder Minimum?
7. Describe the Milankovitch cycles and the general time periods over which these cycles drive climate.
8. What human activities have contributed to the significant upward trend in the atmospheric carbon dioxide level over the past three centuries?
9. Does the climate record contain regular cycles and analogs that enable scientists to accurately predict climate variations over the next century?
10. How will continued shrinkage of Arctic sea-ice cover likely influence Arctic temperatures?

Critical Thinking

1. What does analysis of deep-sea sediment cores reveal about the major climate fluctuations of the Pleistocene Ice Age.
2. What role does plate tectonics play in global-scale climate change?
3. What are some of the ways to reduce the anthropogenic contribution to global climate change?
4. How might the great thermal inertia of the ocean affect global climate change?
5. What are some of the potential impacts of rising sea level on the coastal zone?
6. Shrinking of the Arctic sea-ice cover is likely to have a positive feedback on any warming trend at high latitudes. Explain why.
7. Does climate change tend to be more abrupt or gradual? Explain your response.
8. Identify some of the limitations of proxy climatic data sources.
9. Why is climate change geographically non-uniform in direction and magnitude?
10. What is the role of the ocean in global climate change.

ESSAY: Climate Rhythms in Glacial Ice Cores

The Pleistocene Epoch, the most recent of Earth's Ice Ages, began about 1.7 million years ago and ended about 10,500 years ago. Since then, conditions in the present Epoch (the Holocene) have been reasonably mild, with relatively minor temperature fluctuations compared to the Pleistocene. In an effort to better understand climate change, scientists are collecting and analyzing climate data from the Pleistocene Ice Age with an eye toward predicting future climate (especially in view of the exploding world population and the influence of climate on energy demand and supplies of food and fresh water). Important sources of data on the climate as well as the chemical composition of air during the Pleistocene Ice Age are ice cores extracted from the polar ice sheets (Figures 1 and 2).

In 1988, Soviet and French scientists reported on their analysis of a 2200-m (7200-ft) ice core extracted at Vostok station on the East Antarctic ice sheet. The ice core spanned 160,000 years. Oxygen isotope analysis yielded a temperature record and chemical analysis of trapped air bubbles revealed trends in the greenhouse gases carbon dioxide and methane. In the mid-1990s, drilling at Vostok recovered a 3100-m (10,170-ft) ice core spanning the past 425,000 years. In 2004, the European Project for Ice Coring in Antarctica (EPICA) extracted an ice core from East Antarctica representing a time interval of 740,000 years. During the summers of 1991-93, two independent scientific teams, one American and the other European, drilled into the thickest portion of the Greenland ice sheet. The two drill sites were located within 30 km (19 mi) of each other, about 650 km (404 mi) north of the Arctic Circle. Both cores were about 3000 m (9840 ft) in length and spanned a time interval of roughly 200,000 years.

Ice cores from both Greenland and Antarctica clearly reveal an approximately 100,000 year Ice Age cycle consisting of cold glacial climatic episodes (e.g., the Wisconsinan stage) sandwiched between mild interglacial climatic episodes (e.g., the Holocene). Perhaps 16 of these long-term cycles operated over the 1.7 million years of the Pleistocene Epoch. As discussed elsewhere in this chapter, evidence from deep-sea sediment cores indicates that regular variations in Earth-sun geometry (the Milankovitch cycles) drive this approximately 100,000-year glacial/interglacial cycle.

The Greenland and Antarctic ice core records correlate well both in terms of magnitude of temperature change and the timing of events indicating that the 100,000-year Ice Age cycles were globally synchronous. However, comparison of the Greenland and Antarctic ice core data over the most recent Ice Age cycle (i.e., from about 142,000 years ago to 10,500 years ago) reveals marked differences between the Southern and Northern Hemispheres. Whereas the Antarctic record is reasonably smooth and "calm," the Greenland record shows numerous abrupt and drastic flip-flops between glacial and interglacial climatic episodes. Temperatures changed as much as 7 Celsius degrees (12.6 Fahrenheit degrees) over periods of decades or less (in some cases in only 3 years.) These abrupt temperature changes, having two basic periods of 2000 to 3000 years and 7000 to 12,000 years, occurred during the Wisconsinan stage but not during the subsequent Holocene Epoch. The periods of these temperature fluctuations are much shorter than those of the Milankovitch cycles and hence are probably unrelated to changes in Earth-sun geometry.

The most likely explanation for these short-term abrupt changes in temperature is the weakening and strengthening of the ocean's thermohaline circulation (Chapter 6). For example, as discussed elsewhere in this chapter, this may explain the occurrence of the *Younger Dryas* cold episode 11,000 to 10,000 years ago. The *Younger Dryas* began abruptly when a sudden influx of fresh water discharged by the St. Lawrence River into the North Atlantic prevented the formation of North Atlantic Deep Water (NADW). Temperatures in the North Atlantic and the surrounding lands plunged. The *Younger Dryas* ended just as abruptly as it began when the input of fresh water into the North Atlantic decreased and formation of NADW resumed. The geographic pattern of the *Younger Dryas* climatic impacts (e.g., little in western North America and only a muted response in the Antarctic ice core record) suggests that the *Younger Dryas* was not part of the larger ice age variability driven by the Milankovich cycles. Rather, the *Younger Dryas* was a regional shorter-term climatic fluctuation likely linked to changes in the Atlantic thermohaline circulation.

Changes in the thermohaline circulation that delineate the *Younger Dryas* also occurred at other times. Scientists have interpreted certain layers of lithogenous sediment in cores extracted from the floor of the North Atlantic as materials released during melting of fleets of icebergs. These icebergs surged or slid off glaciated North America and floated out onto the North Atlantic every 2000 to 3000 years as the climate flip-flopped between warm and cold episodes. Melting of the icebergs freshened the North Atlantic surface waters weakening the thermohaline circulation. With colder conditions and fewer icebergs, freshening of the surface waters ceased, the water became salty again due to wind-driven evaporation, and the thermohaline circulation strengthened. After two or three of these events, an even greater discharge of icebergs occurred at intervals of 7000 to 12,000 years. The smaller, shorter, more frequent events are called *Dansgaard-Oeschger events* (named for the paleoclimatologists Willi Dansgaard and Hans Oeschger) or "flickers" because of their relatively short period. The Greenland ice core record contains some 23 Dansgaard-Oeschger events between 110,000 and 15,000 years ago. The larger, longer, and less frequent episodes are known as *Heinrich events* (discussed in the first Essay of Chapter 4). Flickers and Heinrich events occurred during both glacial and interglacial regimes and are evident in the temperature record reconstructed from Greenland ice cores.

FIGURE 1
The Greenland Ice Sheet Project (GISP) cores in this photo show the sharp change from clear to silty ice that occurs at a depth of 3040.33 m. The transition is followed by alternating bands of silty and clear ice followed by progressively siltier ice until contact with bedrock at 3053.51 m. [Photo by J. S. Putscher, NOAA/GISP2, University of New Hampshire]

FIGURE 2
A 19-cm long section of GISP2 ice core from 1855 m, showing annual layer structure illuminated from below by a fiber optic source. Section contains 11 annual layers with summer layers (Arrows) sandwiched between darker winter layers. [Photo by Anthony Gow, United States Army Corps of Engineers]

ESSAY: The Drying of the Mediterranean Sea

The continents of Africa, Europe, and Asia surround the Mediterranean Sea, which connects to the Atlantic Ocean via the narrow Strait of Gibraltar. The Mediterranean is a remnant of the once vast *Tethys Sea* but was nearly squeezed shut during the Oligocene Epoch, 23 to 33 million years ago. The Mediterranean continues to be tectonically active and to shrink slowly in size as the African plate pushes northward, subducting under the Eurasian plate. This subduction has caused folding and uplift of marine sedimentary rocks to form the Alps along with volcanic activity at the northern edge of the Mediterranean. The Mediterranean is about 3900 km (2400 mi) long and 1600 km (1000 mi) wide. The average water depth is 1500 m (4900 ft) with a maximum depth of 5150 m (16,900 ft) off the south coast of Greece. A bathymetric sill in the Strait of Gibraltar separates the Mediterranean basin from the Atlantic Ocean basin; the maximum water depth over the sill is only 284 m (932 ft) at a point where the Strait is about 30 km (18.6 mi) wide.

In the 1960s, William Ryan of the Lamont-Doherty Earth Observatory at Columbia University made a remarkable discovery regarding the composition of sediments on the floor of the Mediterranean basin. While sailing in the Mediterranean on the *R/V Chain* from Woods Hole Oceanographic Institution, Ryan was using a new continuous seismic profiler that could penetrate sea bottom sediments. The acoustic return revealed a reflecting layer 100 to 200 m (325 to 650 ft) beneath the sea bottom, which was whimsically labeled the "mysterious layer," or M-layer. Through subsequent years of collecting M-layer data, it soon became obvious that the layer was ubiquitous in the Mediterranean and was deposited after the deep basin of the Mediterranean had already formed and had almost the same bathymetry as today.

In 1972, Ryan and Kenneth Hsü (a Swiss geologist) onboard the drill ship *Glomar Challenger* in the western Mediterranean brought up the first cores of the M-layer. The cores resembled marble and were labeled "the pillars of Atlantis." The core material turned out to be anhydrite (calcium sulfate, $CaSO_4$) and stromatolites (mats of the remains of sediment-trapping cyanobacteria). They dated from the late Miocene Epoch, about 5 million years old. These two types of sediment core material were extremely unusual in that anhydrites form only in hot, dry deserts where salty groundwater close to the desert surface evaporates causing calcium sulfate to precipitate as a solid. How is it possible for evaporites to form beneath 200 m (650 ft) of marine sediments on the bottom of the Mediterranean Sea? Stromatolites also appear to be out of place on the bottom of the present Mediterranean. Today, stromatolites form in broad, intertidal mud flats in the Bahamas and in salty bays in Western Australia and require light for photosynthesis. What are they doing on the bottom of the Mediterranean, and why are they associated with desert evaporites?

Determination of the M-layer composition points to one of the most extraordinary events in the history of the planet Earth. The atmosphere, ocean, plate tectonics, and glaciation combined to drastically alter the climate of the Mediterranean Sea. About 6 million years ago, the Mediterranean Sea became isolated from the Atlantic Ocean and almost completely dried up. For some 1 to 2 million years, the basin bottom consisted of deserts, salty lakes, and salt marshes. Then water refilled the basin pouring over the sill at the Strait of Gibraltar as a spectacular waterfall lasting about 100 years.

Several hypotheses seek to explain the drying up of the Mediterranean, most of which invoke tectonic plate movement or large-scale glaciation, plus an extended period of evaporation. The tectonic hypothesis suggests that the entire basin was uplifted and the Mediterranean Sea emptied into the Atlantic, and later dropped back down and refilled with water. This cycle may have happened not once, but several times. The driving force for uplift may have been subduction of the African plate under the Eurasian plate, which caused similar uplift in the Alps. Another hypothesis attributes the drying to large-scale glaciation that caused sea level to fall below the sill at Gibraltar, cutting off input of water from the Atlantic Ocean. This is a reasonable hypothesis considering that the sill at Gibraltar has a maximum depth of only 284 m (932 ft). When the ice sheets melted, sea level rose above the sill and refilled the Mediterranean basin. Other hypotheses propose that either the Strait of Gibraltar was squeezed closed or parts of the Atlantic Ocean floor were deformed and uplifted forming a gate that alternately closed and opened the Strait of Gibraltar.

Evaporation of the isolated Mediterranean Sea is readily explained by reconstructions of the late Miocene climate. The rock record shows that at the time, the climate in the Mediterranean region probably was as hot and arid as it is today with little input of water by rivers and streams—the type of climate that would evaporate the Mediterranean waters leaving behind anhydrite deposits.

The most reasonable explanation for the drying of the Mediterranean Sea is likely some combination of factors. In the late Miocene, tectonic stresses (causing moderate regional uplift) combined with falling sea level dropped the Atlantic Ocean below the sill at Gibraltar, cutting off the Mediterranean from the Atlantic. Over the subsequent 1000 years, the waters of the Mediterranean evaporated, eventually exposing the bottom of the basin where deserts formed among shallow hypersaline lakes, salt marshes, and salt flats. With the loss of the Mediterranean Sea, the region probably became cooler and even more arid. In the deeper eastern Mediterranean basin, a system of salty lakes, similar to North America's Great Salt Lake, was fed by salty overflow from the Black Sea to the east. Such conditions can produce both anhydrites and stromatolites together at the bottom of the Mediterranean basin. Alternating layers of biogenous sediments and evaporites suggest that over the subsequent two million years, the Mediterranean probably partial refilled and dried up between 8 and 40 times. Finally about 4.5 million years ago, tectonic forces relaxed dropping Gibraltar and/or sea level rose causing Atlantic waters to spill over the Gibraltar sill and refill the basin. Hsü calculated that the flow of water over the Gibraltar sill was about 1000 times greater than Niagara Falls and yet took a century to fill the Mediterranean basin.

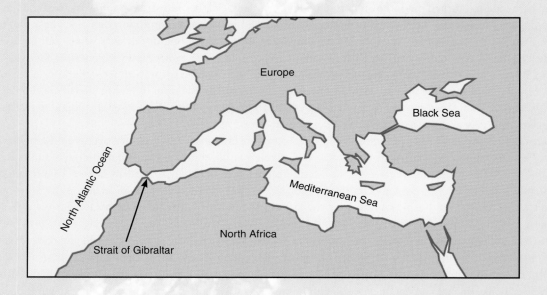

FIGURE 1
The Mediterranean Sea

ESSAY: Sea Level Rise and Saltwater Intrusion

Rising sea level threatens to exacerbate the problem of saltwater intrusion in certain low-lying coastal areas. *Saltwater intrusion* is the movement of saltwater into subsurface zones previously occupied by fresh groundwater and is most common along flat coastal plains (e.g., Florida and southeastern Georgia) and islands. Water that completely fills the openings (e.g., pore space, fractures) in sediment and rock is known as *groundwater*. An *aquifer* consists of porous and permeable earth material that is saturated with water and will yield water in usable quantities to a well or spring. In general, groundwater under land is fresh whereas groundwater under the ocean is salty. Fresh groundwater is the single most important source of potable water for humankind.

In coastal areas where fresh groundwater is situated adjacent to salty marine groundwater, excessive withdrawal of fresh groundwater can allow salt water to migrate inland. As saltwater replaces fresh water in an aquifer, coastal wells begin delivering saltwater. One of the most serious consequences of saltwater intrusion is contamination of fresh water sources so that they cannot be used for domestic purposes or irrigating crops.

The potential for saltwater intrusion is greatest in freshwater aquifers that are hydraulically connected to seawater (Figure 1). In such a system, a transition zone develops between fresh groundwater and salty groundwater. Saltwater is denser than fresh water so that a higher hydraulic head of fresh water is needed to balance the hydraulic head of saltwater and keep the interface offshore. Because the dry land surface is higher than the ocean bottom, this is usually the case. But when large amounts of water are pumped from a fresh-water coastal aquifer (without replacement), the accompanying change in hydraulic gradient encourages the flow of saltwater toward wells. That is, the interface migrates inland and upward and well water turns salty. Rising sea level increases the potential for saltwater intrusion by increasing the hydraulic head of saltwater.

Islands are particularly vulnerable to saltwater intrusion. On an island subsurface fresh water floats like a lens on the denser underlying saltwater. Excess pumping of wells on an island or rising sea level causes upward movement of saltwater in wells. Increasing withdrawal of groundwater that has accompanied the development of Hilton Head Island, SC is causing the subsurface saltwater wedge to gradually migrate toward the freshwater aquifer. The U.S. Geological Survey reports that salty groundwater is approaching the northeast side of the island at about 30 to 43 m (100 to 140 ft) per year and according to model predictions, saltwater could contaminate most of the island's wells by the year 2032.

What can be done to prevent or alleviate saltwater intrusion? Reducing the rate of groundwater withdrawal and relocating wells so that they are farther apart will help. Artificially recharging the freshwater aquifer (using injection wells) diminishes seawater encroachment. Another strategy is to drill extraction wells to remove seawater from an aquifer before it has a chance to migrate to producing wells. Prior to employing any of these strategies, however, it is important to determine the geologic and hydrologic properties of the aquifer and to install monitoring wells to locate the subsurface salt/fresh water transition zone.

FIGURE 1
Along a low-lying coastal plain, rising sea level causes the interface between salty groundwater and fresh groundwater to migrate inland. This results in saltwater intrusion of wells.

CHAPTER 13

THE FUTURE OF OCEAN SCIENCE

Case-in-Point
Driving Question
Investigating the Ocean
>   *Voyages of Exploration*
>   *Challenger Expedition (1872-1876)*
Modern Ocean Studies
>   *Technological Innovations*
>   *Remote Sensing*
>   *Scientific Ocean Drilling*
>   *Ships of Opportunity*
>   *International Cooperation*
Emerging Ocean-Sensing Technologies
>   *Autonomous Instrumented Platforms and Vehicles*
>   *Ocean Floor Observatories*
>   *Computers and Numerical Models*
Challenges in Ocean-Sensing Technologies
Conclusions
Basic Understandings/Review/Critical Thinking
ESSAY: Monitoring the Ocean with Animal-Borne
>   Instruments

NOAA and NASA dedicate a permanent survey marker on the ocean's seafloor, to be used to geo-reference coral surveys conducted by scientists striving to understand the complex mechanisms of the reef ecosystem and by astronauts training for survey missions on other planets. [NOAA]

Case in Point

Understanding the ocean, its properties and processes, as well as its role in the Earth system, requires standardized methods of observation, sampling, and analysis. Beginning with the British *Challenger Expedition* of 1872-76, the first phase of ocean exploration depended upon oceanographic ships that serve as platforms for deployment of various types of instruments and later submersible vehicles for in situ measurements of seawater and the ocean floor (Figure 13.1). However, ships are slow and follow specified routes so that vast areas of the ocean remained unexplored. Enter the third phase of ocean exploration in the late 1970s: remote sensing of the ocean by sensors onboard Earth-orbiting satellites. Satellite sensors revolutionized study of the sea because of their capability to rapidly monitor most of the ocean surface

and measure a wide variety of parameters including, for example, sea surface temperature, sea level, biological

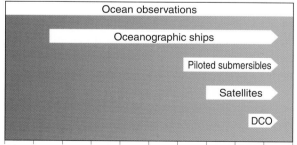

FIGURE 13.1
Principal phases of ocean exploration.

production, and wave height. However, satellite sensors are limited in that they can gather data only from surface waters. Now, many ocean scientists see on the horizon the beginnings of a fourth phase of ocean exploration: deep-sea cabled observatories.

A **deep-sea cabled observatory** is placed on the ocean floor and linked to a mainland facility by fiber-optic and power cables. The cables provide electricity to power sensors and deliver the stream of data obtained by those sensors. A power grid allows for placement of instruments on the sea floor as well as in the water column. A major advantage of a deep-sea observatory is that monitoring is continuous rather than sporadic. (Visits to specific sites of scientific interest by ship may be decades apart.) The real-time aspect of data delivery means much more rapid response time if something interesting or unexpected shows up in the data. The continuous availability of power is an advantage for power-hungry experiments and new instruments such as devices that monitor micro-seismic events or sequence the DNA of marine organisms. Because of very limited power supply, most conventional undersea instruments in use today run on batteries and cannot record or transmit large amounts of data so that data often must be archived for downloading at a later time. Deep-sea observatories will be connected to the Internet making the data stream readily available for scientists, teachers, students, and the public.

Because of high construction, operational, and maintenance costs, only a small number of deep-sea cabled observatories are currently planned. (In fact, some ocean scientists argue that projected costs are so high that less funding will be available for other areas of ocean science research.) With funding from the National Science Foundation and a target date of 2010, scientists from the University of Washington, Oregon State University, Scripps Institution of Oceanography, the Woods Hole Oceanographic Institution, and a consortium of Canadian universities plan to lay a 3000-km (1864-mi) network of cable and sensors around and across the Juan de Fuca Plate off the Pacific Northwest coast (Figure 13.2). Known as the *NEPTUNE (North East Pacific Time-integrated Undersea Networked Experiments) Ocean Observatory*, sensors will allow for real-time study of seafloor volcanism, hydrothermal vents, earthquakes, seafloor spreading, and subduction zones.

In early 2007, south of the NEPTUNE site, in Monterey Bay, CA scientists and engineers installed a 52-km (31-mi) long submarine cable equipped with sensor nodes as a part of the testing phase of new research instruments for future deep-sea observatories such as NEPTUNE. At a water depth of 891 m (2923 ft), the MARS (Monterey Accelerated Research System) Ocean Observatory Testbed features a video camera for monitoring bioluminescent organisms and a robotic microbiology laboratory. Also, sensors on a benthic rover will measure the amount of organic carbon that settles to the ocean floor.

FIGURE 13.2
The *NEPTUNE Ocean Observatory* will collect data from cable-linked sensors located around and across the Juan de Fuca plate off the Pacific Northwest coast. [Courtesy of the NEPTUNE Project and the University of Washington Center for Environmental Visualization.]

Driving Question:

How are advances in technology improving our understanding of the ocean?

The first systematic scientific observations of the ocean were made in the late 19th century from the decks of a converted sailing warship. A hundred years later, sensors onboard Earth-orbiting satellites were routinely providing ocean scientists with a unique perspective of the ocean surface that is impossible to obtain from ships at sea. Prior to remote sensing by satellite, scientists mapped the ocean by combining data from ship-borne observations often separated by thousands of kilometers in distance and decades in time. Today, satellite sensors provide ocean data instantaneously and can monitor the entire surface of the planet in just a few hours. While surface and deep ocean data still must be collected to calibrate and verify remotely sensed observations, using these modern sources of higher resolution data, ocean scientists can observe changes in major ocean currents and sea-surface temperature, map sea surface topography, and detect early signs of a developing El Niño or La Niña.

Throughout history, the ocean has commanded a prominent position in mythology, religion, and literature as a mysterious and threatening place. Today, we continue to regard the ocean with awe and treat it with respect. In this chapter, we examine humankind's efforts to learn more about the ocean, that is, to map the ocean floor, measure the properties of seawater, and monitor marine life as we seek to understand ocean's role in the Earth system.

Humankind's ability to investigate the ocean depends on the availability of appropriate observing systems. The vastness of the ocean continues to challenge the available observational technologies. For one, satellite-borne sensors are limited to observing surface waters. Even though remote sensing by satellite is developing rapidly, the ocean—especially the deep ocean—remains under-sampled so that many of its properties and processes are still poorly understood. Scientists too frequently are limited by their inability to sample and measure the properties of seawater and marine life. As one renowned ocean scientist put it, our scientific models of the ocean often have a "curious, dreamlike quality." This chapter summarizes humankind's efforts to investigate the ocean scientifically—the basic goal of oceanography. In this chapter, we also show where progress is being made, the challenges that remain, and how ocean scientists are seeking to answer questions that have so far gone unanswered. We begin by summarizing the history of exploration of the ocean.

Investigating the Ocean

From the beginning of human existence, people have been fascinated by the ocean and the mystery of what lies beyond the sea-surface horizon. From tentative forays into local waters onboard crude boats, people eventually developed ocean-going vessels capable of circumnavigating the globe.

VOYAGES OF EXPLORATION

The earliest migrations of modern humans (*Homo sapiens*) out of Africa began around 50,000 years ago. Human remains dating from 40,000 years ago were found in Australia. These early migrants apparently knew about fishing and using boats, which they needed to cross the sea separating Australia and Southeast Asia. Further evidence of human migrations via the ocean is the widespread distribution of human populations. Humans had populated all the continents except Antarctica thousands of years before Europeans began their era of ocean exploration in the 15th century. Accounts of voyages and shipwrecks 2000 years ago are found in the Bible and other works of comparable antiquity.

Little is contained in surviving written documents or charts about these ancient ocean explorations for a number of reasons. Many ancient societies had no written language. Most sailors were illiterate and thus unable to document their travels, although oral accounts were passed down from one generation to the next. Perhaps more importantly, knowledge of the sea routes that they explored were trade secrets, too valuable to be shared by the nations or companies that supported the expeditions.

One documented ancient ocean-exploring voyage was the royal trade expedition organized by the Egyptian queen and Pharaoh Hatshepsut around BCE 1450. From northern Egypt, the expedition journeyed through the Red Sea, and southward along the African coast to what is now Mozambique. Scenes from the expedition are displayed at Hatshepsut's funerary temple in southern Egypt near Luxor. The purpose of the expedition was to bring back some of the valuable resources of the region including timber, gold, ivory, and wild animals (e.g., monkeys and baboons). Commercial traffic likely had been conducted for centuries through this part of the Indian Ocean but no written accounts of such voyages have been found. The

Egyptians developed sailing ships around BCE 4000, some 2500 years earlier, but probably used them only in the eastern Mediterranean, near the mouth of the Nile River.

The earliest period of exploration and colonization of islands in the tropical Pacific Ocean took place from about BCE 1300 to 800 when the Lapita people ventured forth from coastal areas of the western tropical Pacific which they had occupied since BCE 30,000. Using simple seaworthy canoes, the Lapita sailed from Papua New Guinea at least 3200 km (2000 mi) eastward into the tropical south Pacific, settling many islands including New Caledonia, Fiji, Tonga, Samoa, and Vanuatu. Having no navigation devices, the sailors watched for signs of islands (e.g., volcanic plumes, cloud banks, seabirds, floating tree branches). After a thousand-year hiatus in exploration activity, descendants of the Lapita, known as the Polynesians, sailed eastward into the central and eastern tropical Pacific. The Polynesians reached Hawaii (CE 800-1000), Easter Island (CE 900-1200), French Polynesia (CE 500-1000), and New Zealand (CE 1200-1300).

In sailing eastward these early explorers encountered the southeast trade winds, a head wind that would have slowed their progress. However, the persistence of the trade winds also meant that if conditions deteriorated, these early sailors could turn around for a swift journey back to where they had come from. Evidence that the Polynesians reached the west coast of South America around CE 1000 suggests that El Niño may have aided their voyage. Recall from Chapter 11 that during an intense El Niño episode, the trade winds not only weaken but may reverse direction blowing from west to east. Such a circumstance would have enabled the Polynesians to sail into the eastern tropical Pacific and encounter the South American continent.

For some time prior to about BCE 1200, the Greek city state of Mycenae was at the center of a great civilization that controlled trade in the Aegean Sea and much of the Mediterranean. For about a thousand years following the decline and fall of Mycenae (at least partially because of prolonged drought), the Phoenicians, from the eastern end of the Mediterranean Sea (now modern Lebanon), dominated sea trade. They established many prosperous colonies along the shores of the Mediterranean, in Sicily, Spain, North Africa, and beyond the Strait of Gibraltar into the Atlantic Ocean and down the Red Sea into the Indian Ocean. Mythic accounts of Phoenician explorations indicate that one expedition reached Cornwall in southwestern England (then called the *Island of Tin*). Another expedition sailed along the West African coast to the mouth of the Niger River.

After the fall of the Phoenician city of Tyre to the Assyrians in BCE 640, the Greeks reestablished their dominance of Mediterranean and Black Sea trade routes. They developed more reliable methods of navigation at sea. To estimate latitude, the Greeks used a calculation based on length of daylight corrected for the time of year. About BCE 450, the Greek Herodotus published an accurate map of the world according to the Greeks. Another Greek astronomer and geographer, Pytheas, sailed out of the Mediterranean, around England and possibly even reached Iceland and the Baltic Sea around BCE 325. He also was the first to determine latitude by measuring the angular distance above the horizon of the North Star (Polaris), a technique that is still used today. About BCE 300, Alexander the Great founded a library at Alexandria, which served as a repository for scrolls from ships and land caravans. For the next 600 years, the library functioned as a maritime studies center, fostering advances in science and celestial navigation by many Greek and Egyptian scholars. About CE 150, the geographer Ptolemy produced an accurate map of the world known to the Romans that influenced geographic thinking for centuries.

The Vikings set sail from Scandinavia around CE 750 and explored and colonized lands bordering the North Atlantic, including Iceland (CE 810), Greenland (CE 980), and Newfoundland (CE 1000). The relatively mild conditions of the Medieval Warm Period (about CE 950 to 1250) and reduced sea ice cover apparently made their voyages possible. The full extent of Viking colonization of North America during this period is much debated today. Vikings who had settled along the coast of Greenland were unable (or chose not) to adapt to deteriorating climate conditions that heralded the Little Ice Age (Chapter 12). Their increasing inability to grow European style crops and livestock and to communicate with their homeland by sea (due to more widespread sea ice cover in the North Atlantic) eventually led to the collapse of the Viking settlements in Greenland.

Around CE 1420, during the Ming Dynasty (1368-1644), the Chinese embarked on seven major expeditions involving hundreds of ships technically advanced for the day (Chinese junks), using magnetic compasses. The purpose of these expeditions was to map unknown regions, obtain treasures and exotic animals for the Forbidden City (walled section of Peking containing royal palaces), and spread Chinese influence throughout the region. Some claim that the Chinese circumnavigated the world and may even have reached North America. Economic and political pressures at home terminated these voyages and began the long period of Chinese isolation.

In the 15th century, the Portuguese began the European *Age of Discovery*, an era of ocean exploration and colonization of the Americas, India, Asia, Australia, and New Zealand. In 1420, Prince Henry the Navigator (1394-1460) founded a naval observatory in Portugal, the first school for teaching navigation, astronomy, and cartography. Vasco da Gama (c. 1469-1524) sailed around Africa, reaching India in 1498 to open a lucrative trade in spices. In 1519-1522, ships under the command of Ferdinand Magellan (c.1480-1521) were credited with being the first to sail around the world, although he died in the Philippines in 1521 after reaching the eastern edge of the then known world. His crew completed the voyage back to Spain.

Oceanographic expeditions began with the three Pacific Ocean voyages of Captain James Cook (1728-1779) of the British Royal Navy over the period 1768-1780. These voyages were made onboard, at various times, the HMS *Endeavour, Resolution, Adventure,* and *Discovery.* Cook relied on the latest navigational tools (precise clocks known as chronometers) to determine longitude accurately. (Refer to the first Essay in Chapter 5.) He mapped the Southern Ocean as well as many other parts of the Pacific, "discovering" Australia, New Zealand, and the Hawaiian Islands. He was the first to circumnavigate Earth at high latitudes and sailed as far south as about 70 degrees S but did not sight Antarctica. The chief objective of Cook's voyages was not science, but to establish a British presence in the South Seas. Nonetheless, some valuable scientific information was acquired. During their exploration of New Zealand, the Great Barrier Reef, Tonga, and the Easter Islands, Cook and his crew collected samples of terrestrial plants and animals, marine life, and the ocean bottom. On his search for a Northwest Passage, Cook prepared charts of the West Coast of North America that remained very useful until World War II. He also "discovered" Hawaii although he was killed on the Big Island during a confrontation with native peoples.

Two early English explorers, Sir John Ross and his nephew Sir James Clark Ross, were interested in conditions in the deep ocean. In 1818, Sir John Ross obtained a bottom sample at a depth greater than 1900 m (6200 ft) off the coast of Greenland. Later, Sir James Clark Ross, discoverer of the Ross Sea and Victoria Land in Antarctica, reached an ocean depth of almost 4900 m (16,000 ft) in the South Atlantic using a long rope attached to a weight. They discovered abundant marine animals living on the ocean bottom at great depths of water—an extreme environment previously believed to be devoid of all life.

According to the then widely accepted **azoic hypothesis**, deep-ocean waters below 300 fathoms (550 m or 1800 ft) were barren, lacking sufficient dissolved oxygen to support marine life. The hypothesis originated in the mid-1800s with Sir Edward Forbes (1815-1854), at one time considered the father of deep-sea biology. Forbes spent more than a year on the Royal Navy ship HMS *Beacon* in the eastern Mediterranean. Dredging the sea bottom at depths as great as 230 fathoms (425 m or 1390 ft), he found that the number of marine species decreased with increasing depth. By simple extrapolation, Forbes concluded that no life existed below 300 fathoms. However, discovery of live animals on the deep-ocean floor during several British ocean expeditions debunked the azoic hypothesis and spurred scientists' interest in further exploration of the ocean basins.

From 1831 to 1836, the HMS *Beagle* undertook a voyage to study the natural science of Galápagos Islands (in the equatorial Pacific off Ecuador) as well as many other locations. Charles Darwin (1809-1882) was onboard as a naturalist. From his observations came his first major published work, *Structure and Distribution of Coral Reefs* (1842). In this treatise, Darwin correctly argued that the form and structure of reefs and atolls develop because they are living organisms growing upward in an effort to remain in the ocean's photic zone as compensation for the sinking sea floor (Chapters 2 and 10). Darwin also wrote on several other marine subjects including barnacle biology and fossils, all of which was overshadowed by his revolutionary work, *On the Origin of Species* (1859).

In 1838-42, the United States launched its Exploring Expedition, a two-pronged voyage in that it was primarily a naval expedition but had more scientific latitude than the British Challenger Expedition of 1872-76 (discussed below). Had it not been for the contentious personality of its leader, Lt. Charles Wilkes, USN, this voyage might have been as famous as those of Cook or the Challenger Expedition. The *Vincennes* was the flagship of a six-vessel fleet. Goals included showing the flag, charting, whale watching, gathering geological specimens, and general scientific observations. Exploration and charting of large parts of the Antarctic coast confirmed that Antarctica was a continent. The most unusual goal of the expedition certainly must have been to test the hypothesis that Earth was hollow with two large entry holes at the North and South Poles. The many specimens and artifacts, scientific and otherwise, collected during the voyage formed the nucleus of the collections of the recently established Smithsonian Institution in Washington, DC. Wilkes and his scientific staff produced a 19-volume final report.

Matthew Fontaine Maury (1806-73) began his naval career as a midshipman onboard the U.S. sloop-of-war *Falmouth*, serving as navigation officer (Figure 6.2). After being injured in a stagecoach accident in 1839, Maury was unable to return to sea and was assigned desk duty at home. In 1842, he was appointed Superintendent of the Navy's Depot of Charts and Instruments (later the U.S. Naval Observatory and Hydrographical Office) in Washington, DC. Maury discovered that existing ocean navigation charts were out of date, inaccurate, and supplied little useful information on winds and currents. He decided to revise the charts. Maury and his staff poured over naval logbooks stored at the Depot to glean any useful navigational information. Captains of naval vessels were ordered to supply Maury with navigational, hydrographic, and meteorological data. Later, Maury supplied captains of merchant ships with special logbooks for recording similar observations; the logbooks were mailed to the Depot at the end of a voyage. Out of this work came more accurate navigation charts of winds and currents in the world ocean. The first of Maury's "Wind and Current Charts" was issued in 1847. With these charts, sea captains could take advantage of favorable currents and winds and thereby significantly reduce sailing time on many routes. For his pioneering work on ocean navigation, Maury became known as the "pathfinder of the seas." In 1855, Maury published *The Physical Geography of the Sea*, the first textbook on modern oceanography. With the outbreak of the American Civil War, Maury resigned his position in 1861 and joined the Confederate Navy.

CHALLENGER EXPEDITION (1872-1876)

The Scottish oceanographer Charles Wyville Thomson (1830-1882) led the first voyage dedicated exclusively to marine science. The **Challenger Expedition** was underway in December 1872 and ended in May 1876 having covered 127,500 km (79,200 mi), about three times the circumference of the planet. Scientists sampled every ocean basin except the Arctic, probed the ocean and the seafloor to depths as great as 9000 m (29,500 ft), and sailed as far south as 61 degrees S before being turned back by sea ice. The Challenger Expedition laid the foundation for modern ocean science.

The Royal Society of London funded and organized the expedition while the Royal Navy provided the vessel, the HMS *Challenger*, a three-masted, square rigged wooden warship, 68.5 m (225 ft) long. The Royal Navy also supplied the captain and crew. In a forerunner of modern oceanographic practice, the captain ran the ship while a board of six chief scientists was in charge of

the scientific enterprise. Thomson and his colleague Sir John Murray (1841-1914) are credited with coining the term *oceanography*. On the ship's deck, scientific gear, a laboratory, and facilities for storage of samples took the place of all but two of the ship's original 19 guns (Figure 13.3). *Challenger* was equipped with an auxiliary steam engine for maneuvering while taking samples and scientific observations.

The Challenger Expedition tested the hypothesis that no life could exist below an ocean depth of 550 m (1800 ft) because of extreme pressure and no light. The *Challenger* was able to sample to a depth of 8185 m (26,900 ft), making 492 deep soundings, with samplers and nets at 362 stations. The hypothesis was proven false with a total of 4017 previously unknown species of marine animals and plants discovered to all depths.

Scientists onboard the *Challenger* measured air and sea temperature, winds, salinity, density, and currents.

FIGURE 13.3
Dredging and sounding equipment onboard the HMS *Challenger*. The 1872-76 Challenger Expedition laid the foundation for modern ocean science. [NOAA Photo Library]

In addition, 77 water samples were obtained and stored. Many of the Challenger Expedition's contributions are still used today; an example is the global map of marine sediment distribution (Figure 4.7). Other important contributions of the Challenger Expedition include the first systematic map of major ocean currents and water temperatures, a map of ocean bottom features (e.g., mid-ocean ridges), discovery of the *Challenger Deep* in the Mariana Trench in the Pacific Ocean, finding manganese nodules at the bottom of the North Atlantic, and documenting the great diversity of marine plants and animals, especially microscopic plankton. Probably the most important product of the voyage was the 50-volume report of the expedition's scientific findings, the *Challenger Report*, written and published between 1880 and 1895 by Sir John Murray. This report formed the foundation for the science of oceanography and is still highly valued today. In short, the Challenger Expedition marked the beginning of the modern study of the world ocean.

Some of the instruments used to collect samples on the Challenger Expedition differ little from those in use today: towed nets to gather plankton and larger organisms, bottles for collecting water samples, and coring tubes for retrieving seafloor sediment samples. Since the time of *Challenger*, winches for lowering and retrieving instruments have improved greatly and electronic instruments have largely replaced mercury thermometers and other mechanical devices. Navigation, originally done by astronomical observations, is now largely based on the Global Positioning System (described in the first Essay of Chapter 6). Furthermore, satellites and electronic computers have greatly accelerated data collection, relay, and analysis.

Modern Ocean Studies

The Challenger Expedition was a model for modern scientific study of the ocean carried out throughout the 20th century and into the present century. In this section, we examine modern initiatives and innovations aimed at developing a greater understanding of the ocean, its properties, processes, and life forms. We open with an historical perspective of technological innovations that enabled scientists to more extensively probe the sea.

TECHNOLOGICAL INNOVATIONS

The Challenger Expedition inspired two American expeditions that were directed by the naturalist Alexander Agassiz (1835-1910) on the U.S. Coast and Geodetic Sur-

FIGURE 13.4
The USS *Albatross* of the United States Fish Commission carried out many expeditions throughout the world from 1887 to 1925 and discovered hundreds of marine species using surface townets and benthic trawls and dredges. [NOAA Photo Library]

vey Ship *Blake* (1877) and later on the survey ship the *Albatross*. The USS *Albatross* sailed throughout the world ocean from 1887 to 1925, collecting hundreds of marine species using specially designed nets and benthic dredges (Figure 13.4). In the period between these two American voyages, the Russians under S.O. Makarov conducted a 3-year cruise onboard the *Vitiaz*, analyzing the physical properties of the North Pacific Ocean waters.

The first major oceanographic expedition of the 20th century was the German Atlantic Ocean Expedition of 1925-27. The Institute of Marine Research in Berlin organized the expedition and the German Navy supplied the ship, the *R/V Meteor* (the first of several German oceanographic research ships to bear that name). The primary mission of the voyage was to gather data on the physical properties of the South Atlantic Ocean using optical, acoustic, and electronic equipment. Probably the most important innovation was the use of an acoustic echo sounder to almost instantaneously measure and record the depth and profile of the sea bottom. These observations drastically changed the long-held view of the ocean floor as monotonously flat to a place of considerable topographic relief—information that would later help support the theory of sea floor spreading and plate tectonics (Chapter 2).

Since its founding in 1902, the Scripps Institution of Oceanography in La Jolla, CA has spurred the advance of oceanographic research. In 1937, the Institution's schooner, *E.W. Scripps*, began a broad research program on physical, biological, and chemical oceanography in Pacific waters off Southern California. Work at Scripps eventually led to publication of the well-known book on ocean science, *The Oceans*, in 1942.

National defense needs during World War II (1939-1945) and the subsequent Cold War (1945-1990) spurred advances in ocean science and technology by the industrialized nations of the West and the Soviet Bloc. Many nations supported multi-purpose exploration of specific areas of the ocean using ship-borne observations and backed development of observing instruments for ocean studies. Some of these studies were also aimed at improving long-range weather forecasting and detection of missile-launching submarines. The latter led to a better understanding of sound propagation in the ocean. Enormous amounts of data were collected and analyzed. Eventually these data were declassified and are now available for peacetime scientific research.

Paralleling the increasing use of ships (both military and civilian) for ocean research was the design and development of piloted submersible vehicles that enabled scientists to observe the ocean depths directly. The *bathysphere*, developed in the early 1930s by William Beebe and Otis Barton of the New York Zoological Society, was a hollow steel ball about 1.5 m (5 ft) in diameter, equipped with oxygen tanks, chemicals to absorb carbon dioxide, and portholes and a searchlight for viewing. A cable from a ship lowered and raised the bathysphere into and out of ocean waters. In 1934 just off the Bermuda coast, Beebe and Barton descended in the bathysphere to a depth of 923 m (3028 ft). They reported seeing fish and invertebrates previously unknown.

More maneuverable than the bathysphere for exploration of the deep ocean was the *bathyscaph*, designed by Auguste Piccard (1884-1962) in the late 1930s and tested in 1948. The bathyscaph was not tethered to a ship. It consisted of a thick-walled cabin suspended under a tank (float) containing less-dense-than-water petroleum. Ballast tanks attached to the float kept the bathyscaph afloat while on the surface. Flooding the ballast tanks caused the bathyscaph to dive whereas systematically releasing weights (iron pellets) slowed the descent or allowed the vehicle to surface. In the early 1950s, Piccard and his son Jacques built a new and improved version of the bathyscaph, the *Trieste*, which reached a maximum depth of 3167 m (10,392 ft) in the Mediterranean Sea. Facing high maintenance and operational costs, the Piccards sold the Trieste to the U.S. Navy in 1958. On 23 January 1960, the bathyscaph *Trieste*, piloted by Jacques Piccard and U.S. Navy Lieutenant Don Walsh, dove to a new world record depth of 10,912 m (35,800 ft) very close to the bottom of one of the deepest places in the ocean, the *Challenger Deep* in the Mariana Trench—in the Pacific Ocean about 325 km (200 mi) southwest of Guam.

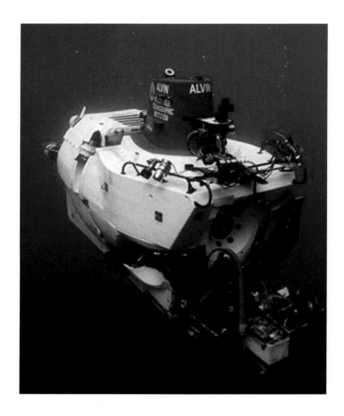

FIGURE 13.5
On 12 April 2004, the research submersible *Alvin* made its 4000th dive since christening in 1964. The dive took place on the East Pacific Rise off the coast of Mexico to a maximum depth of 2500 m (8200 ft). Operated by the Woods Hole Oceanographic Institution (WHOI), *Alvin* can transport a pilot and two passengers to ocean depths as great as 4500 m (14,765 ft). [WHOI photo by Rod Catanach]

Alvin, the world's first deep-ocean research submersible, was built in 1964 (Figure 13.5). Today, the 3-passenger (pilot plus two observers) vehicle is one of only five deep-sea research submersibles operating in the world. The National Science Foundation (NSF), NOAA, and the U.S. Navy own and fund *Alvin*; it is operated by the Woods Hole Oceanographic Institution (WHOI) in Falmouth, MA. *Alvin* is disassembled, re-built, and technologically upgraded about every 3-5 years. Considered the workhorse of submersibles, *Alvin* averages 175 dives per year (Figure 13.6). As of March 2008, *Alvin* had completed a total of more than 4200 dives, each dive lasting 6 to 10 hours, achieving a maximum depth of about 4500 m (14,765 ft). Hence, *Alvin* has direct access to about 63% of the world ocean bottom.

Alvin uses its six reversible thrusters to hover, rest on the ocean floor, or maneuver across rugged terrain. It

FIGURE 13.6
Aft view of the Research Vessel *Atlantis* moored at the Woods Hole Oceanographic Institution in Massachusetts. The 83.5-m (274-ft) *Atlantis* is the support ship for the submersible *Alvin*. [NOAA photo]

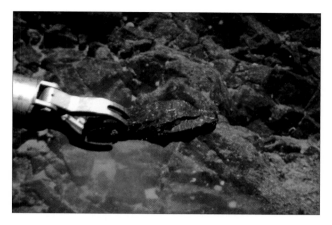

FIGURE 13.7
Alvin's arm and claw grasp a sample of pillow basalt on the ocean floor. [Courtesy of NOAA, WHOI, the Alvin Group, and the 2004 GOA Seamount Exploration Science Party]

is equipped with three 30-cm (12-in.) viewports, external lights, two robotic arms (Figure 13.7), still and video cameras, and a basket having a capacity of 680 kg (1500 lbs). *Alvin* made possible the discovery of many important deep-sea features, including the first known hydrothermal vents and associated unique biological communities in the 1970s (Chapters 2 and 9) as well as locating the wreck of the RMS *Titanic* (in 1986) and many other ships. *Alvin* was named for Allyn Vine, a WHOI engineer who helped pioneer deep submergence technology.

In the late 1980s, scientists and engineers at the Woods Hole Oceanographic Institution designed and built *JASON*, a **remotely operated vehicle (ROV)** capable of reaching a depth of 6000 m (19,685 ft). Cables (transmitting power and data) tether an ROV to a surface ship. *JASON* was used to explore and photograph hydrothermal vents along mid-oceanic ridges and to survey old shipwrecks among other activities. *JASON* was retired in 2001 and replaced by *JASON II* the following year. *JASON II* represents a significant technological upgrade with greater maneuverability and sampling capacity than

its predecessor. *JASON II* has the latest in robotics and is equipped with two mechanical arms that can reach twice as far and lift five times as much material as the single arm on the first *JASON*. *JASON II* has more power for brighter lighting and is equipped with digital cameras. Designed for routine operation at depths as great as 6500 m (21,325 ft), *JASON II* can remain on the ocean floor for days at a time. Both *Alvin* and *JASON II* are components of the National Deep Submergence Laboratory at WHOI, the only facility of its type in the nation.

In recent years, Japan and France have built research submersibles capable of diving to depths as great as 6500 m (21,325 ft). Also, the U.S. Navy has dedicated a nuclear powered submarine, the *NR-1 Deep Submergence Craft*, to scientific research. While it can dive to a maximum depth of only 700 m (2300 ft), the submarine can remain underwater for 30 days with a crew of 7 and is well suited for scientific voyages under the Arctic sea ice.

A major impetus for development of ocean instrumentation came from the offshore oil industry, which played a lead role in the design of remotely operated vehicles (Figure 13.8). Since 1970, more than 1000 ROVs have been built primarily for operational needs such as servicing oil pipelines on the ocean bottom, retrieving lost objects, and even investigating wrecked aircraft and ships on the ocean floor.

ROVs and Autonomous Underwater Vehicles (AUV) (discussed below) have greatly increased our knowledge of mid- and deep-water marine life. They are equipped with robotic arms and traps that can capture fragile, gelatinous organisms such as jellyfish

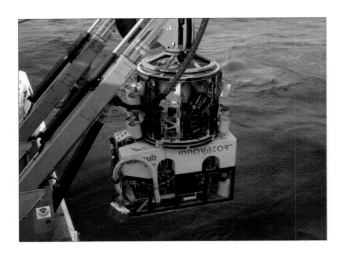

FIGURE 13.8
Launch of the ROV *Innovator*. Sample buckets are attached to the sides. [Photo by Jeremy Potter, NOAA Office of Ocean Exploration]

and ctenophores that would never survive being caught in traditional net trawls. Such organisms have been underrepresented in historical surveys of oceanic fauna but, as noted in Chapters 9 and 10, they play an important role in marine ecosystems. In early 2003, scientists from the Monterey Bay Aquarium Research Institute announced that using a ROV equipped with video cameras, they had discovered an entirely new species of red jellyfish. Nicknamed "Big Red," these animals are up to 1.0 m (3.3 ft) in diameter and live at depths of 650 to 1500 m (2100 to 4900 ft). The fact that scientists overlooked such a large animal until now underscores how little is known about the deep ocean and how modern technology enables scientists to expand our understanding.

Another method for sampling delicate drifting organisms is via a video plankton recorder (VPR). A VPR is essentially a high-powered video microscope mounted on an instrument frame towed behind a ship. The instrument is designed to illuminate and image a small volume of undisturbed water as the frame is pulled through the ocean. Cables relay the video image to the ship where it can be viewed and recorded. Image recognition software is then used to calculate census information for the different taxonomy groups.

REMOTE SENSING

Remote sensing refers to acquisition of data on the properties of some object without the sensor being in direct contact with the object. Remote sensing involves not only Earth-orbiting satellites, but also certain automated observing platforms. For example, arrays of underwater

microphones (originally intended for submarine detection) are used to measure water temperatures over great distances within ocean basins based on sound propagation (Chapter 3). Such measurements are unobtainable using ships alone. These observations are the basis for detecting and following the movements of water masses through the ocean, locating submarine volcanic eruptions, and tracking migrating whales.

Some of the most significant advances in the study of the ocean and its basins came in the final three decades of the 20th century with the development and application of remote sensing by high altitude aircraft and satellites (Chapter 1). Throughout this book, we use a variety of images processed from data acquired by sensors onboard Earth-orbiting satellites. These space platforms provide a unique global perspective of the ocean, its properties and processes. Initially, ocean scientists were limited to using satellite sensors to study only the ocean/atmosphere interface because radiation at most wavelengths cannot penetrate to great depths in the ocean. Satellite sensors remotely measure such ocean properties as sea-surface temperature, sea-level fluctuations, surface winds, sea-ice extent, and surface chlorophyll concentration.

Aquarius, a NASA satellite planned for launch in 2009, is expected to provide the first global salinity maps for ocean surface waters. Remote sensing of salinity is a major achievement in itself, but combining global satellite observations of temperature and salinity will likely yield a better understanding of the processes involved in ENSO and longer-term changes in ocean circulation. It is also possible that such data will improve long-range weather and short-term climate forecasts based on a better understanding of the Pacific Decadal Oscillation (PDO), North Atlantic Oscillation (NAO), the Arctic Oscillation (AO), and other ocean-atmosphere interactions (Chapter 11).

Paralleling advances in remote sensing by satellite was the development of computers, sufficiently powerful and fast to store and analyze vast quantities of observational data. Earth-orbiting satellites also dramatically improved communications capabilities at sea. Today, data collected in the most remote reaches of the ocean can be sent nearly instantaneously to laboratories for analysis almost anywhere in the world. Other satellite-based technologies that greatly aid ocean studies include the Global Positioning System (GPS) that enables un-piloted instrumented platforms to report their locations accurately and communications satellites that relay data to computers for analysis (Chapter 6).

SCIENTIFIC OCEAN DRILLING

Sampling marine sediments and the oceanic crust for scientific purposes began in the early 1960s when engineers demonstrated that small vessels and barges equipped with oil-field drilling rigs could be used to sample the deep-ocean bottom. The success of these experiments led to the **Deep Sea Drilling Program (DSDP)**, which operated from 1968 to 1983, using the drill ship *Glomar Challenger*. A technique known as *dynamical positioning* permitted the ship to drill in deep waters without anchoring. Powerful computer-controlled propulsion units kept the ship within a fixed distance of the spot where the drill penetrated the sea floor. The computer responds to an acoustic signal emitted by a beacon positioned on the ocean bottom. In 1983, a larger and more capable drill ship, the *JOIDES Resolution*, using essentially the same technology continued deep-sea drilling in the **Ocean Drilling Program (ODP)**. ODP operated between 1983 and 2003 and was supported by 22 nations. Newer drilling ships use GPS, rather than sea floor acoustic beacons, to fix the precise locations of the drill hole and the drill ship.

Over the past 40 years, drilling up to 1700 holes annually, scientists have recovered from the ocean floor rock and sediment cores that if laid end-to-end would have a total length of about 160 km (100 mi). Many important scientific discoveries came out of the DSDP and ODP in what is now the world's largest internationally supported Earth science program. Among the many important findings of ocean drilling was verification of sea-floor spreading from analysis of rock samples recovered from the bottom of the North Atlantic Ocean (Chapter 2). Scientists recovered thick deposits of salt underlying marine sediments in the Gulf of Mexico and the Mediterranean Sea (as described in the second Essay of Chapter 12). These deposits formed when the basins were isolated from the rest of the ocean and their waters almost completely evaporated. Furthermore, deep-sea sediment cores yield a record of climate fluctuations as far back as about 190 million years ago.

In October 2003, the **Integrated Ocean Drilling Program (IODP)** began. Sponsored initially by the U.S. and Japan, the IODP may eventually involve as many as 20 other nations. The goal of the new drilling program is to use two drill ships plus specialized drilling platforms rather than a single general-purpose ship and drill more and deeper holes on the ocean floor. The original IODP plan called for an upgraded *JOIDES Resolution* or a new similar drill ship but because of budget constraints, the U.S. sponsor (the National Science Foundation) decided to continue using an unmodified *JOIDES Resolution* at least for the foreseeable future.

By late 2006, the *Chikyu*, a new drill ship built and operated by Japan and capable of drilling 7000 m (23,000 ft) below the seabed, joined the U.S. ship. The *Chikyu* is much larger than earlier drill ships, technologically more advanced, and equipped with specialized equipment that will minimize environmental hazards (e.g., petroleum blowouts). Lacking such capabilities, DSDP and ODP drilling sites were restricted to the deep-ocean floor far from shore where the chance of encountering oil or natural gas deposits is minimal. *Chikyu's* first project was to investigate earthquake mechanisms by boring into the Nankai Trough subduction zone located offshore of Honshu, Japan—a location that was off limits to the *JOIDES Resolution* because of the potential for a petroleum blowout. Another option with IODP is the use of specialized drilling platforms for areas where drill ships could not safely or efficiently operate, such as in the Arctic multi-year sea ice.

With its unique capabilities, IODP promises to add significantly to scientific knowledge. IODP scientists can explore the oldest rocks in the ocean basins, those occurring near continental margins (Chapter 2). Gas hydrate deposits, a potential source of natural gas, can be safely sampled (Chapter 9). The deep biosphere contained in marine sediments and oceanic crust (home to perhaps two-thirds of the planet's total microbial population) can be explored at depths below that reached by DSDP and ODP drill holes; some of these microbes may one day play a role in biotechnology. The new drilling program will also add to our understanding of global climate change and earthquake generation.

SHIPS OF OPPORTUNITY

Oceanographic research ships are expensive to operate, ranging from $10,000 to over $30,000 per day. Given this cost, specialized research vessels will always be in short supply considering the vastness of the ocean. One way to expand the quantity of ocean measurements is to "piggy-back" scientific instrumentation on ships already operating in the cargo and cruise ship fleets. These *Volunteer Observing Ships (VOS)* can be outfitted with instruments that record atmospheric conditions as well as sea-surface temperature and salinity. Usually, these instrument packages are automated and do not require a scientist or technician onboard.

Some chemical properties of the ocean water are measured by VOS including, for example, the CO_2 concentration of surface waters. Measurements of ocean currents were obtained by an *ADCP (Acoustic Doppler Current Profiler)* mounted on the cargo vessel *MV Oleander* which operated a regular route between Port Elizabeth, NJ and Bermuda. The route took the ship across the Gulf Stream and more than 10 years of data document changes in the flow of this western boundary current. XBTs (expendable bathythermographs) are deployed from a VOS to gather subsurface temperature data.

Use of VOS requires hardy instrumentation which can operate in a mostly autonomous mode. It also requires cooperation and coordination with merchant fleets and the crew who operate their vessels. In general, scientific instruments must be capable of collecting data while the vessel is underway and cannot impede any of the normal operations of the ship. As more types of ocean instrumentation become automated, the opportunity to obtain global ocean measurements from Volunteer Observing Ships should continue to increase.

INTERNATIONAL COOPERATION

The need to study large, remote areas of the ocean prompted groups of nations to cooperate in international scientific studies. The high cost of conducting research at sea, including the operation of expensive research vessels, is a strong incentive for international cooperation. An early example was the scientific initiatives underway during 1957, the *International Geophysical Year (IGY)*. Among studies begun during the IGY was regular monitoring of carbon dioxide levels in the atmosphere, an important component of global climate change studies (Chapter 12). The IGY featured the first systematic hydrographic survey of the world ocean and provides the earliest baseline for large-scale changes in ocean temperature and salinity.

In the 1970s, the United Nations Educational, Scientific, and Cultural Organization (UNESCO) sponsored the *International Decade of Ocean Exploration (IDOE)*. IDOE organized the first modern systematic surveys of ocean currents and the chemical composition of seawater. IDOE also initiated field studies that eventually led to our present ability to monitor the evolution of El Niño and La Niña (Chapter 11). Subsequently, other programs were organized to marshal international support for decade-long studies of the ocean, primarily focused on specific processes such as the carbon cycle.

Thousands of scientists from about 60 nations are expected to take part in the fourth *International Polar Year (IPY)* scheduled for March 2007 to March 2009. Organized by the International Council for Science and the World Meteorological Organization (WMO), the IPY is an interdisciplinary and multilateral scientific program

focusing on the Arctic and Antarctic and covers a wide range of topics involving cutting edge physical, biological, and social research. Major themes of IPY include (1) decreasing thickness and extent of glaciers, ice sheets and sea ice cover, (2) changes in snow cover and its duration, (3) degradation of permafrost, (4) implications of these environmental changes for global sea level, freshwater supply, ocean circulation, marine ecosystems, and the people of northern lands.

Emerging Ocean-Sensing Technologies

Sending a well-equipped research vessel to sea for an extended period of time with a complete crew of sailors, technicians, and scientists is very costly. While seagoing oceanographers will not be replaced, new microelectronic instruments, better computers, and improved communications and positioning systems developed in the late 1990s have made possible new types of un-piloted ocean observing systems. These innovations have greatly expanded the range of ocean observations into areas not usually traversed by ships. We consider some of these developments in this section.

AUTONOMOUS INSTRUMENTED PLATFORMS AND VEHICLES

The need to understand the subsurface ocean on all temporal and spatial scales has led to development of new types of research platforms. They are designed to overcome the limitations of oceanographic ships, including their slow speeds, high costs, uncomfortable working conditions, and limited supply versus demand. A variety of such platforms is available and more are under development. Available now are instrumented buoys, Argo floats, Slocum gliders, and Autonomous Underwater Vehicles.

Buoys (Figure 13.9) are small floating un-piloted platforms, typically several meters in diameter that are moored at fixed locations in the ocean (such as the buoys deployed across the equatorial Pacific Ocean as components of the ENSO Observing System, described in Chapter 11.) Sensors on these buoys take continual observations of the lower atmosphere and upper-ocean. Data are then transmitted to polar-orbiting satellites for transmission to computers ashore. These platforms are sources of data at locations considered critical for improving weather and climate prediction. Many buoys have lines suspended below them with sensors attached at various depths to continually measure water temperature, currents, and salinity. A few of these buoys also have cables that connect to sensors

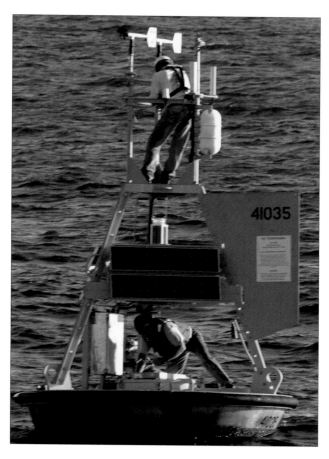

FIGURE 13.9
Two technicians repair an NDBC moored instrumented 3-m discus buoy located off North Carolina. Sensors on the buoy monitor air temperature, wind speed and direction, air pressure, sea temperature at a depth of 0.6 m, wave height, dominant wave period, and mean wave direction. [NOAA, National Data Buoy Center]

placed on the sea floor (discussed later in this chapter). Other smaller *drifting buoys* move with ocean currents and provide information on their speed and direction as well as changes in subsurface ocean properties.

Other autonomous platforms, known as *Argo floats*, are cylindrical devices equipped with sensors that augment satellite-based observations of the ocean surface as well as buoy observations of the upper ocean. As described in detail in the second Essay of Chapter 6, Argo floats obtain profiles of ocean temperature and salinity to depths as great as 2000 m (6600 ft). The array of 3000+ Argo profilers provides near real-time, three-dimensional observations of almost the entire world ocean. These data are essential for numerical models. A drawback of Argo floats is the absence of a propulsion system so that they drift passively with the ocean currents.

A more recent type of float, the *Slocum glider*, covers greater distances (a range of 1500 km or 930 mi) and has a longer sampling life span than the Argo float. Plus it is designed to follow a prescribed trajectory. The Slocum glider is named for New England Sea Captain Joshua Slocum (1844-1909). Slocum was the first person to sail solo around the world, completing the 65,000-km (40,000-mi) voyage in three years and two months (1895-98) in his 11-m (36-ft) long sailboat. The 1.5-m (5-ft) long winged torpedo-shaped glider is highly maneuverable, sinking and rising through the ocean by changing its buoyancy. As it sinks and rises, the glider's wings and rudder control horizontal movements so the vehicle moves independent of ocean currents. At a horizontal speed of about 0.5 m per sec (1 nautical mi per hr), the glider follows a saw-tooth sampling trajectory as it descends to a predetermined depth, measuring temperature, conductivity (salinity), and other water properties at various depths. At regular intervals, the glider surfaces, determines its position by GPS, and relays the stored observational data via satellite.

The Slocum glider employs the same buoyancy changing technique used in the Argo float. Hydraulic oil is pumped between an internal reservoir and an external bladder thereby changing the density of the vehicle by changing its total volume. To ascend, oil is pumped to the bladder that expands and thereby increases the volume and lowers the density of the glider. To sink, oil is pumped back to the internal reservoir, the bladder shrinks, and the overall density of the glider increases.

Until recently, the oil pump that controlled buoyancy was powered by batteries, limiting the range of the glider to the lifetime of the batteries. But scientists at Woods Hole Oceanographic Institution developed a novel engine powered by the temperature difference between surface- and deep-ocean waters that promises to extend the range of the Slocum glider. At the heart of the engine is a tube containing a wax that solidifies and shrinks at about 10 °C (50 °F). The wax melts and expands when the glider is in relatively warm surface waters but solidifies and shrinks when the glider enters the colder deep-ocean waters. Expansion and shrinkage of the wax controls the movement of a device that distributes the oil between the internal reservoir and external bladder. While the wax tube does not replace the glider batteries, it reduces the drain on them.

Gliders have been used to carry instruments that analyze and take samples of toxic algal blooms in the Gulf of Mexico (Chapter 9). Scientists at the Mote Marine Laboratory in Sarasota, FL developed a winged, robotic-controlled platform that is released at the ocean surface and glides slowly to the bottom taking either observations or water samples. The device provides a relatively inexpensive platform to work within a limited area to obtain background data on the ecosystem, detect and sample a *red tide* should one develop, and bring back water and plankton samples for laboratory analysis.

Autonomous, powered vehicles augment the capabilities of research submersibles and ROVs and move through ocean waters faster than gliders. They are called **Autonomous Underwater Vehicles (AUVs)** because they are un-piloted and do not rely on a cable tethering them to a mother ship, as do ROVs (Figure 13.10). Autonomous vehicles must be carefully programmed with simple artificial intelligence in order to carry out their mission without direct communication links with the surface operators. These vehicles have sensors that measure ocean water properties (e.g., temperature, salinity, depth, chlorophyll, light, dissolved oxygen) along trajectories that can be pre-set or controlled while the AUV is underway. The operational range of an AUV is restricted by the limited amount of power that their batteries can provide for propulsion and instrumentation. Periodically, they must return to the mother ship or shore-based facility for recharging. AUVs also have limited space and power for electronic instrument packages.

On the plus side, AUVs can observe the ocean in places and under conditions where research ships and other instrumented platforms cannot. AUVs are especially suited for studies under sea ice (such as the Antarctic ice shelves) and can be equipped with sonar to determine the

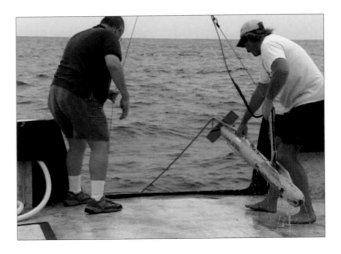

FIGURE 13.11
Recovery of a side-scan sonar towfish used to map the Pearl Harbor Defense Area. [NOAA photo by J. Smith and C. Kelley]

thickness of the ice-cover above. With side-scan sonar, they can efficiently and economically map the ocean floor in considerable detail (Figure 13.11). They can probe coastal waters at the edge of the continental shelf as well as specific locations within submarine canyons. AUVs are also useful in highly energetic ocean systems such as current rings (Chapter 6). In the future, hydrogen-powered fuel cells promise greater range and more power for AUVs.

Autonomous, ultra-light, un-piloted aircraft, once primarily used for military surveillance are also promising platforms for ocean studies. Groups of such aircraft (called drones), can fly for days or weeks over thousands of kilometers of ocean surface and observe the development of tropical cyclones, monitor sea surface temperature, salinity, and ocean color, or collect atmospheric aerosols. GPS tracks the aircraft and polar-orbiting satellites relay data back to computers ashore. Drones are especially useful in coastal and estuarine areas where satellite sensors do not provide adequate resolution for study of complex environmental processes.

OCEAN FLOOR OBSERVATORIES

As noted in this chapter's Case-in-Point, ocean floor observatories are a relatively new but powerful means of studying ocean waters, marine life, and the sea floor. An **ocean floor observatory** is an instrumented facility that can perform experiments, collect data, and communicate observations to data networks and scientists worldwide. The first generation of ocean floor observatories stored data that were retrieved during infrequent visits by surface ships or submersibles. With the next generation of *deep-*

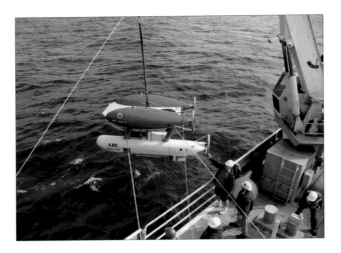

FIGURE 13.10
Launch of *ABE*, an autonomous underwater vehicle (AUV) equipped with sensors to measure temperature, conductivity, magnetics, and multibeam bathymetry. [NOAA photo]

sea cabled observatories, scientific inquiry can continue indefinitely as seafloor cables transmit in real-time a continuous stream of observational data to networks on land for widespread distribution. In this section, we describe ocean floor observatories that are precursors to the next generation of deep-sea cabled observatories.

Off the New Jersey coast just north of Atlantic City is an observatory that became operational in 1992. Instruments provide near real-time data for coastal managers, students, teachers, fishers, swimmers, surfers, and beachcombers. The undersea station, known as *LEO-15* for *Long-term Ecosystem Observatory*, is located in 15 m (50 ft) of water with two nodes located at 5 km (3 mi) and 7 km (4.4 mi) offshore on the mid-continental shelf. Observatory nodes monitor ocean currents, water temperature, salinity, light and chlorophyll levels, wave height and period, sediment transport, and phytoplankton blooms. Other data sources include an instrumented tower for atmospheric observations and Doppler radar. A small autonomous underwater vehicle is programmed to gather data from areas surrounding the station. Data obtained by undersea instruments are transmitted via electro-optic cable to the Rutgers Marine Field Station in Tuckerton, NJ.

The *Hawaiian Underwater Geo-Observatory (HUGO)*, situated at the summit of Loihi seamount south of the "Big Island" of Hawaii, was installed and began operating in1997. Loihi is the youngest volcano in the Hawaiian chain and, like the other volcanoes of the Big Island, is located over a hot spot (Chapter 2). Although its summit is more than 900 m (2950 ft) below sea level, Loihi rises more than 2700 m (8900 ft) above the sea floor—taller than Mount St. Helens was above sea level prior to its explosive eruption in 1980. HUGO is an instrumented titanium platform equipped with seismometers, an underwater microphone, and bottom pressure sensor. These instruments monitored seismic activity, volcanic eruptions, and hydrothermal venting. A 47-km (29-mi) submarine fiber-optic cable linked the observatory to a shore station at Honuapo Bay, Hawaii and provided scientists with data from the seamount. This was the first deep-water cabled monitoring system. However, the harsh conditions at the seamount disrupted the data flow and HUGO ceased operating after five years. The observatory was recovered by *JASON II*, a remotely operated vehicle out of Woods Hole Oceanographic Institution but there are no plans for re-deployment.

In 1998, the *Hawaii-2 Observatory* (or *H2O*) was installed on an abandoned AT&T submarine telephone cable that had linked Oahu, Hawaii to the California coast. Located in 5000 m (16,400 ft) of water near 28

degrees N, 142 degrees W, the Observatory was about 1000 km (620 mi) from the nearest land. A junction box on the cable provided power and communications ports for scientific instruments including a seismometer (for monitoring earthquakes), a deep-water pressure gauge (for detecting tsunamis), and a hydrophone (to listen to underwater sounds). H2O operated until 2003.

Detailed studies of seismic waves generated by earthquakes worldwide require observations that are fairly uniformly spaced but most seismometers are land-based. (The Hawaii-2 Observatory was the first seafloor station in the Global Seismographic Network but as noted above only operated from 1998-2003). The only seismometers within the ocean basins were located on islands and large portions of the ocean such as the North Pacific have few islands. About 20 deep ocean-floor seismic observatories are being planned to help fill in the gaps. Seismic instruments are installed in holes drilled into the sea floor. At some observatories ships will recover the instrument packages and retrieve their recorded data for later analysis. Others will use acoustic transmission of data to listening stations. Still others will be connected to networks on land by submarine cables providing instantaneous distribution of seismic data. These data are essential to improving our understanding of interactions between oceanic crust and the deeper parts of Earth's geosphere. These data also will aid investigations of some of the longer-term fluctuations in the Earth system such as ocean basin opening and closing (Chapter 2).

Ocean-floor seismic sensors placed in a 1000-m (3300-ft) deep borehole near Japan monitor earthquakes occurring near the Japan Trench where the Pacific Plate is subducting under the Eurasian Plate. When the plates slip past one another, seismic energy is released causing potentially destructive earthquakes, which, along with associated tsunamis (Chapter 7), can cause great loss of life and considerable property damage on the islands of Japan. Plans are underway to have the Japanese drill ship, part of the Integrated Ocean Drilling Project (IODP), install additional seismic stations. One hoped-for outcome of better earthquake surveillance is improved earthquake prediction. Initially these observatories will use replaceable data-storage units to record data but eventually fiber-optic cable will link the observatories to data networks onshore.

An innovative approach to observing remote areas of the ocean uses small, electronic instrument packages (tags) that are attached to free-swimming marine animals having strong homing instincts such as seals and whales. The tags provide information on the animals' movements as well as the environment in which they live. For more on this unique approach, refer to this chapter's Essay.

COMPUTERS AND NUMERICAL MODELS

Whereas past advances in ocean science depended heavily on sampling platforms and observing instruments, future advances will increasingly depend on access to the world's largest and fastest computers (so-called supercomputers). New high-performance computers will be necessary to assimilate the flood of observational data and to run coupled ocean-atmosphere numerical models. In this way, ocean science is following the lead of atmospheric science where even routine weather predictions require the largest and fastest supercomputers available. NOAA put the latest version of such a computer into operation early in 2003 in Gaithersburg, MD. NOAA's National Weather Service uses computer output to generate a variety of forecast and other guidance products, including some that deal with ocean conditions (e.g., sea-surface temperature, sea-ice extent, tracks of tropical cyclones). Such computers permit more accurate, longer-range forecasts.

One of the major achievements in the application of coupled air-sea numerical models is the prediction of the onset and evolution of El Niño and La Niña months in advance of the event. As noted in Chapter 11, observational data acquired by an array of moored and drifting buoys in the tropical Pacific along with satellite and tide gauge data are used to initialize these numerical models. Model-based predictions are very helpful for the many government agencies responsible for dealing with the potential impacts of extreme weather associated with El Niño and La Niña.

Challenges in Ocean-Sensing Technologies

The principal benefit of newly available ocean sensing technologies is the promise of a better understanding of how the ocean functions as part of the Earth system and hence, improved prediction capabilities. For example, more complete knowledge of the role of the ocean in Earth's climate system is fundamental to answering questions concerning global climate change (Chapter 12). New observing systems are planned to monitor the global ocean over a broad spectrum of temporal and spatial scales. Such observational data help scientists more accurately model ocean properties and processes, enabling them to predict how Earth's climate system is likely to respond to increased concentrations of greenhouse gases, issue more timely warnings of hazards such as tsunamis, and better manage marine and coastal resources.

The essential requirement for understanding the global environment and its interactions with humans is a systematic record of observations of the Earth system and its sub-systems. Among these sub-systems, the ocean is under sampled both in space and time. Furthermore, monitoring the world ocean requires international cooperation. As noted in this book, much of our knowledge of the ocean is derived from scattered observations made by instrumented buoys, floats, coastal tide gauges, and ship-based measurements. Despite recent advances in ocean observation capabilities, much more observational data are needed and many problems remain to be solved. Some of these problems and possible solutions are considered in this section.

The coastal zone is perhaps an area where substantial advances in ocean-observing technology are most needed, in part because this is where the actual and potential impacts of human population pressures are most severe (Chapter 8). Some of the observing techniques or platforms discussed in this chapter cannot be employed close to the shoreline. Yet this is the most heavily used part of the ocean and one of the most dynamic regions in the Earth system where the hydrosphere, atmosphere, biosphere, and geosphere interact. For example, the coastal zone is where storm surges and tsunamis have their greatest impact.

One emerging technology that may be useful in the coastal zone is remotely controlled ultra-light aircraft capable of flying low and making observations over extended periods. Because the most dramatic alterations of the coastal zone occur during infrequent intense storms, such aircraft in their present form cannot be the only answer. Probably an older but expensive technology will be used in the near future: instrumented towers and shallow-water sea-floor observatories.

Scientists are increasingly relying on high frequency radar to monitor surface currents in the coastal ocean. This specialized radar system, known as *CODAR* (*Coastal Ocean Dynamics Applications Radar*), uses scattered radar waves to measure ocean surface wave speed. The observed wave speed is the sum of the natural wave speed and the underlying current. By knowing the water depth, the natural wave speed can be calculated and thus the underlying current can be determined. CODAR requires stable platforms and is typically used in coastal environments where the radar antenna towers can be positioned on land. An array of CODAR stations along a coastline can determine real-time current information as far as 150 km (93 mi) offshore. In addition to benefiting basic research, maps of surface currents are useful for tracking pollution spills and in search and rescue operations conducted by the Coast Guard.

Better technologies for studying marine life are needed. As we have learned, most of the organisms living in the ocean are one-celled microbes, but many sampling techniques are designed for studying only those organisms that can be caught in nets, from large plankton up to the size of fish (Figure 13.12). One remedy is for scientists to use long tubes that pump water from ocean depths over long periods of time. In this way, they sample and filter large volumes of water to gather sufficient numbers of microbes for study. Many of the new techniques to study marine microbes will probably come from advances in biotechnology. One example is the use of new techniques to study archaea, a little understood but extremely abundant organism that

FIGURE 13.12
Crew members of the NOAA ship *McArthur* inspect a set of bongo nets used to determine the type and concentration of marine plankton. The *McArthur* conducts a range of oceanographic research missions mostly in marine sanctuaries along the U.S. West Coast. [NOAA photo]

often occupies extreme marine environments (Chapter 9). Archaea cannot be seen using standard microscopes and cannot be grown in laboratories using conventional microbiological techniques. However, techniques used to sequence the human genome in the early 21st century may assist in the study of marine life, to identify and assess its abundance. These data will aid in identifying organisms and mechanisms responsible for sequestering carbon in the ocean and in this way add to our understanding of the ocean's role in the global carbon cycle.

New microchips are needed to perform chemical analyses of compounds in seawater, including routine monitoring of essential nutrients, the fertilizers of the sea, as well as toxins released by harmful algal blooms (Chapter 9). This promising technology must overcome one of the oldest problems known to sailors, that is, **bio-fouling**. Organisms rapidly colonize any object placed in ocean water (especially warm ocean water) unless the object is pre-treated by toxic chemicals. First come bacteria and other marine microbes, then diatoms, and eventually mussels and barnacles (as any boat owner knows). Such communities will also coat and impair the functioning of any chemical-sensing chip in the ocean unless the bio-fouling problem is solved.

Better knowledge of the ocean requires more accurate maps of the ocean floor. Mapping the deep-ocean floor, begun by the Challenger Expedition, is still incomplete. Exploration of Earth's neighbors in space has produced better maps of their surfaces than we have of Earth's ocean bottom. Obtaining such maps of the ocean floor is an expensive and daunting task. Until recently, the best sea-floor maps were made by oceanographic ships equipped with GPS and state-of-the-art bottom-mapping equipment that surveys broad swaths of ocean bottom along the ship's track. NOAA's *National Ocean Survey* ships are equipped to make such maps, but about 125 ship-years would be required to complete the task of mapping the world ocean bottom at a cost of about $1 billion. Because of the high cost, to date only about 10% of the sea floor has been mapped by modern surveying techniques. As noted earlier, an economically attractive alternative for mapping the ocean floor uses autonomous underwater vehicles (AUVs) equipped with side-scan sonar.

The best global map of ocean floor topography is obtained from satellite-borne radar (microwave) altimeters. These instruments measure the shape of the sea surface which is strongly influenced by Earth's gravity field. The mountains of rock which compose the ocean floor topography affect the local gravity field and hence the shape of the sea surface (as discussed in the second Essay of Chapter 7). Combining the limited set of direct depth soundings with global coverage of satellite altimetry measurements has produced an unprecedented map of ocean floor topography. Even this map, however, is limited in fine-scale detail; the shape of the ocean surface tends to "blur" the details of very steep ocean ridges and trenches. A satellite mission, called *GRACE* (*Gravity Recovery and Climate Experiment*) consists of twin orbiting satellites which are capable of measuring fine-scale variations in Earth's gravity. Launched in 2002, the GRACE mission will provide even greater resolution of Earth's gravity field and thus the shape of the ocean floor topography.

More complete mapping of the sea floor would yield numerous benefits. These maps will permit refinement of plate-tectonic models. More precise depiction of sea-floor roughness would permit better understanding of mixing processes in the deep ocean due to tidal currents flowing over features such as volcanic ridges or seamounts. Commercial applications of deep-ocean maps include determining the optimum sites for laying optical cables for communication networks and managing fishery resources in Exclusive Economic Zones (EEZ) (Chapter 4) and the deep ocean. Tsunami prediction and hazard models would also benefit from more accurate ocean-floor maps.

A technique also exists for obtaining detailed, three-dimensional images of specific areas of the seafloor. This instrument, called *multibeam sonar*, operates from a ship somewhat like a depth sounder, but combines information received from dozens or even hundreds of sonar beams simultaneously. Images obtained this way are so detailed that in 20 m (66 ft) of water objects as small as a lobster trap can be easily seen. For objects at greater depths, less detail can be resolved, but the images still represent a remarkable step forward in identifying seafloor habitats. For example, fishing grounds can be surveyed so that gear (for example, a scallop dredge) is deployed more carefully to avoid damage to the environment.

Since the early 1990s, a global ocean-observing system has been operating under the auspices of the *Intergovernmental Oceanographic Commission (IOC)* of the United Nations' *Educational, Scientific, and Cultural Organization (UNESCO)*. However, little progress was made toward a global ocean observation system. The IOC is now working with the *Global Earth Observation System of Systems (GEOSS)* to identify ocean observation needs and to integrate it with a global system. Needed, however, is the commitment of nations to sustain an integrated ocean observing system.

Conclusions

Humankind's fascination with the sea extends back thousands of years. Sailing vessels tapped the energy of the winds and currents enabling humans to explore, discover, settle, and exploit the resources of new lands. With the development of reliable methods of navigation, ocean-going vessels provided access to all continents and commercially important trade routes were established. At first an object of mystery and curiosity, the ocean eventually became the subject of intense scientific scrutiny. Beginning with the Challenger Expedition of the 1870s, understanding of the ocean's properties and processes rapidly grew during the 20th century and into the present century. This new knowledge was partially a product of peacetime application of technologies originally developed for national defense. It was also the result of innovative technologies either adapted from other fields (e.g., deep-sea drilling) or developed specifically for probing the ocean (e.g., *Alvin*, Argo floats, Slocum glider).

Although many challenges need to be overcome and many questions remain to be answered, humankind's understanding of the role of the ocean in the Earth's system is progressing at an encouraging pace. Rock and sediment cores extracted from the ocean floor provide evidence of sea-floor spreading and confirms the hypothesis of plate tectonics, revolutionizing our understanding of Earth's large-scale geological processes. Deep-sea sediment cores unlocked the secrets of the climate fluctuations of the Pleistocene Ice Age and may provide information that is key to understanding future climate. A variety of piloted and un-piloted vehicles provide near real-time data on the physical, chemical, biological, and geological characteristics of the ocean. And sensors onboard Earth-orbiting satellites acquire a flood of valuable data from vast stretches of the ocean.

Basic Understandings

- The earliest humans to migrate from Southeast Asia to Australia around 40,000 years ago apparently knew about fishing and relied on boats for transport. Few written documents or charts refer to ancient ocean explorations because many ancient societies had no written language, most sailors were illiterate, and sea routes were trade secrets.
- The Egyptians developed sailing ships around

BCE 4000 and by about BCE 1500 a royal trade expedition traveled from northern Egypt, through the Red Sea, and southward along the African coast to what is now Mozambique. Phoenicians dominated trade in the Mediterranean for about 1000 years following the demise of Mycenae in Greece about BCE 1200. After the fall of the Phoenician city of Tyre in BCE 640, the Greeks reestablished control of Mediterranean and Black Sea trade routes and contributed significantly to the development of navigation techniques.

- The earliest period of exploration and colonization of islands in the tropical Pacific Ocean took place from about BCE 1300 to 800 when the Lapita people ventured forth from coastal areas of the western tropical Pacific. Using simple seaworthy canoes, the Lapita sailed from Papua New Guinea at least 3200 km (2000 mi) eastward into the tropical south Pacific. After a thousand-year hiatus in exploration activity, descendants of the Lapita, known as the Polynesians, sailed eastward into the central and eastern tropical Pacific.

- The Vikings set out from Scandinavia around CE 750 and later explored and colonized Iceland, Greenland, and Newfoundland.

- In the 15th century, the Portuguese began the European *Age of Discovery*, a time of ocean exploration and colonization of the Americas, India, Asia, Australia, and New Zealand. Vasco da Gama sailed around Africa and reached India; ships commanded by Ferdinand Magellan were the first to circumnavigate the globe; and James Cook mapped the Southern Ocean and many islands in the Pacific Ocean.

- In 1842, Matthew Fontaine Maury was appointed Superintendent of the Navy's Depot of Charts and Instruments in Washington, DC. By thorough scrutiny of logbooks maintained by the captains of both naval and merchant ships, Maury and his staff developed more accurate and useful navigation charts of winds and currents in the world ocean.

- The Challenger Expedition was the first voyage intended exclusively for marine scientific purposes. Between December 1872 and May 1876, the HMS *Challenger* circumnavigated the globe, sampling all ocean basins except the Arctic, probing the ocean and seafloor to depths of 9000 m (29,500 ft), and laying the foundation for modern ocean science.

- National defense needs during World War II and the subsequent Cold War spurred ocean research and technology development by the industrialized nations of the West and the Soviet Bloc. Paralleling the increasing use of military and civilian ships for ocean research was the development of piloted submersible vehicles that enabled scientists to observe directly the ocean depths. *Alvin*, the workhorse of submersibles, has operated since 1964 and made possible the discovery of many deep-sea features including hydrothermal vents.

- Another impetus for development of ocean instrumentation came from the offshore oil industry, which played a leading role in the design of remotely operated vehicles (ROVs). These un-piloted craft are tethered to a ship and can spend more time on the ocean bottom than a piloted vehicle.

- Earth-orbiting satellites provide a unique global perspective of the ocean. Initially, satellite sensors were limited to monitoring processes operating at the ocean/atmosphere interface, but recently satellite-based methods have been developed to infer the state of the ocean at some depth.

- Sampling marine sediments and ocean crust in deep waters for scientific purposes began in the early 1960s, using oil-field drilling rigs. The success of these experiments led to the Deep Sea Drilling Program (1968-83), the Ocean Drilling Program (1983-2003), and the Integrated Ocean Drilling Program (2003-). Convincing evidence for sea-floor spreading and plate tectonics is one of the major outcomes of these drilling programs.

- One way to expand the quantity of ocean measurements is to "piggy-back" scientific instrumentation on ships already operating in the cargo and cruise ship fleets. These Volunteer Observing Ships (VOS) can be outfitted with instruments that record atmospheric conditions as well as sea-surface temperature and salinity, dissolved gases, and currents..

- The need to study large, remote areas of the ocean prompted nations to cooperate in international scientific investigations. Examples include the International Geophysical Year (IGY) in 1957, the United Nation's International Decade of Ocean Exploration (IDOE) in the 1970s, and the

International Polar Year (IPY) in 2007-2009.

- New un-piloted ocean observing systems include instrumented buoys (both moored and drifting), Argo floats that profile temperature and salinity in the upper 2000 m (6600 ft) of the ocean, the Slocum glider that gathers ocean data along a predetermined trajectory, and Autonomous Underwater Vehicles (AUVs) that are highly maneuverable and can observe the ocean in places where other instrumented platforms cannot.

- An ocean floor observatory is a facility designed for long-term experiments and data gathering (e.g., seismic and volcanic activity).

- Despite recent advances in ocean-sensing capabilities, many technological challenges remain to be solved. Needed are observing methods suited to the dynamic conditions of the coastal zone, better technology for studying marine life, a solution to the problem of bio-fouling, and more accurate maps of the sea floor.

- The best global map of ocean floor topography is obtained from satellite-borne radar (microwave) altimeters. These instruments measure the shape of the sea surface which is strongly influenced by Earth's gravity field. Combining the limited set of direct depth soundings with global coverage of satellite altimetry measurements has produced an unprecedented map of ocean floor topography.

- A satellite mission, called *GRACE* (*Gravity Recovery and Climate Experiment*) consists of twin orbiting satellites which are capable of measuring fine-scale variations in Earth's gravity. Launched in 2002, the GRACE mission will provide even greater resolution of Earth's gravity field and thus the shape of the ocean floor topography.

Review

1. Why has much of the ocean—particularly the deep ocean—remained under-sampled?
2. What is the once widely held azoic hypothesis and how was it disproved?
3. Identify the major contributions of Matthew Fontaine Maury.
4. What is the role of remotely operated vehicles (ROVs) and Autonomous Underwater Vehicles (AUVs) in our understanding of marine life?
5. What is the goal of the Integrated Ocean Drilling Program (IODP)?
6. Describe the basic principle of the buoyancy changing technique used in the Argo float and the Slocum glider.
7. What is the advantage of AUVs over ROVs and other research submersibles?
8. What are some of the services provided by undersea observatories?
9. List some of the benefits of a more complete mapping of the ocean floor.
10. Why are remote sensing techniques important in investigating the properties of the ocean?

Critical Thinking

1. In investigating the ocean, what are the advantages of satellite-based remote sensing over voyages of exploration?
2. How did the 1872-76 *Challenger Expedition* serve as a model for the modern scientific study of the ocean?
3. What are the advantages of a piloted submersible vehicle for exploring the ocean and its inhabitants?
4. Why does bio-fouling pose a serious limitation to modern technologies directed at investigating the ocean?
5. What are some of the advantages of deep-water observatories in acquiring scientific data from the ocean?
6. Speculate on how the mission of near-coastal underwater observatories might differ from that of deep-water observatories.
7. In order to provide adequate advance warning of a toxic algal bloom, ocean scientists should monitor what properties of the coastal zone?
8. What natural phenomena in the ocean are regularly monitored by sensors onboard Earth-orbiting satellites?
9. In what way does in situ monitoring of ocean properties support monitoring by remote sensing techniques?
10. What are the advantages and disadvantages of ocean data acquisition by satellite versus submersible?

ESSAY: Monitoring the Ocean with Animal-Borne Instruments

An innovative approach to obtaining observational data from remote areas of the ocean uses a small, electronic instrument package physically attached or surgically implanted into free-swimming marine animals. These electronic devices, called *tags*, are attached to large, long-lived animals having strong homing instincts, such as seals and whales. (Homing is important because such animals repeat ocean transects rather than remaining in one location.) Some tags report data via Earth-orbiting satellites, providing information on the animals' movements as well as conditions of the marine environment in which they live. In some cases, the data are recovered when the animals return to their home locations. In this way, data obtained from areas outside the major shipping lanes (that are infrequently sampled by ocean survey ships) contribute to the global oceanographic database.

The most straightforward application of this technique tracks the movements of animals as they migrate and at the same time obtains other data such as water temperature, the depth at which the animal swims, and the light level. In the case of animals that dive, water temperature is obtained at various depths. The latest sensors also measure salinity. With development of smaller solid-state electronic components, the sophistication and communication range of tags increase. Among the animals that participate in this technique are seals, whales, tuna, sharks, swordfish, and sea turtles. With the future development of even smaller tags, many more animals including seabirds are likely to be used in this way to gather ocean data.

Satellite-linked electronic tags (Figure 1) enable scientists to study the travel habits of individual animals, sometimes with surprising results. For example, Barbara Bock, a marine biologist at Stanford University, and her colleagues surgically implanted tags into two bluefin tuna at about the same time off the coast of western Ireland. Nearly eight months later one of the fish was located off the coast of Portugal while the other one was swimming in waters northeast of Cuba, some 4800 km (3000 mi) apart.

FIGURE 1
Satellite tag on a narwhal. [NOAA Explorer photo courtesy of Kristin Laidre]

Instrument-bearing large marine animals were used in the world's first *Census of Marine Life*, begun in the late 1990s. The Census, a decade-long international effort, was organized to determine the regional distribution and abundance of marine organisms, as well as their relationships to each other and to their ocean habitat. These instruments were used in studies of large animals such as seals, whales, and tuna that range over vast and remote areas of the ocean.

An early application of instrumented animals in the Census involved elephant seals in the northeastern Pacific Ocean, tagged by scientists from the Southwest Center of NOAA's National Marine Fisheries Service in La Jolla, CA. A more recent study involving elephant seals was conducted by Daniel Costa and colleagues at the University of California, Santa Cruz (Figure 2). Electronic tags glued to the backs of elephant seals recorded the depth of their dives and water temperature. Another tag gave the animal's location.

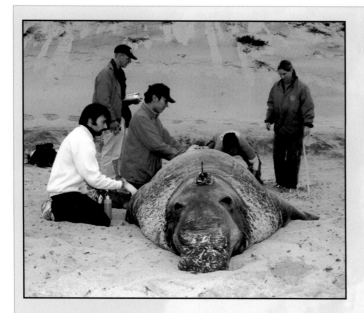

Figure 2
Scientists attach a tag to the fur of a sedated male elephant seal. [Photo courtesy of Daniel Costa/NASA JPL]

Elephant seals live in large rookeries on islands offshore from central California, where they breed and raise their pups. Information from the tags revealed that these animals leave the rookeries on regular foraging trips lasting 2 to 9 months. However, males and females follow different migration routes. Males travel along the Alaskan and Aleutian continental shelf and slope whereas females remain in the northeastern Pacific west of California. Scientists found that elephant seals make frequent dives (up to 60 per day) in search of food; an average dive lasts about 20 minutes and routinely reaches depths of about 600 m (2000 ft) but can be as deep as 2000 m (6600 ft). When elephant seals return to the surface, their electronic tags download data to polar-orbiting satellites for transmission to scientists. Costa reported that tagged elephant seals from the rookery on Año Nuevo Island near Santa Cruz, CA produced 75,000 depth profiles in only one season.

The northern elephant seal's cousin, the southern elephant seal, lives in the Southern Ocean. These animals routinely swim thousands of kilometers in the vicinity of Antarctica and off the southern tip of South America. The males go on feeding migrations that are the longest of any known marine mammal migration, except for whales. In 2004, the National Science Foundation funded a program called Southern Elephant Seals as Oceanographic Sensors. The goal is to tag 70 southern elephant seals and produce some 10,000 temperature/depth profiles annually as the animals dive and feed under the Antarctic sea ice.

Electronic tags have also been attached to wild white (beluga) whales living in the Arctic and nearby high-latitude waters where ocean data are scarce. In winter, beluga whales often enter ice-covered waters. Tagged beluga whales permit studies of oceanic processes such as sea-ice formation in northern fjords. In one study, oceanographers from the Norwegian Polar Institute captured two beluga whales from the Storfjorden, Svalbard, Arctic fjord and fitted them with tags. The small instrument package was inserted into the whale's blubber so it would not interfere with the animal's normal activities. These instruments allowed scientists to determine the whales' location and record salinity and temperature at one-second intervals as the whales ascended from their bottom feeding. The data was downloaded via satellite when the whales surfaced for air. One discovery that came out of this experiment, reported in 2003, was the presence of a thin layer of relatively warm North Atlantic water immediately under the ice. Previously, ocean scientists had assumed that the water beneath the ice was uniformly cold. This discovery may have important implications for understanding recent trends in the extent and thickness of Arctic sea-ice cover (Chapter 12).

CHAPTER 14

OCEAN STEWARDSHIP

Case-in-Point
Driving Question
Stewardship of Ocean Life
Fisheries and Sustainable Exploitation
     Overfishing
     Maximum Sustainable Yield
     Ecologically Sustainable Yield
     Bycatch
     Restoring Fisheries
     Habitat Destruction and Restoration
     Recreational Fisheries
Protecting Endangered Marine Species
     Sea Turtles
     Whales
     Water Birds
Mariculture
Marine Exotic Species
Conclusions
Basic Understandings/Review/Critical Thinking
ESSAY: Determining the Age of a Fish
ESSAY: Loss and Restoration of Coastal Wetlands

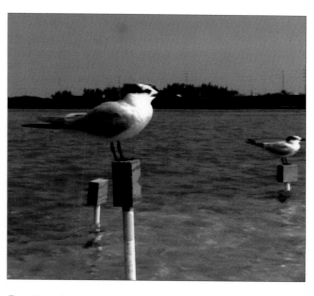

Roosting stakes promote natural fertilization by birds to enhance seagrass recovery. Once the damaged area has been stabilized , the stakes are removed to prevent over-fertilization of the site. [Courtesy Kevin Kirsch, NOAA].

Case in Point

In the 17th century, when Europeans first sailed into Chesapeake Bay, they encountered vast oyster reefs that stood above sea level at low tide and, in fact, were a navigation hazard for ships in the Bay. Native Americans and early colonists gathered oysters by hand and readily retrieved them from the shallow Bay bottom. The extensive oyster reefs also provided shelter for many fishes and other species living within the crevices between oyster shells.

Oyster production in Chesapeake Bay peaked in the 1880s and then declined. In the early 20th century, sailing vessels, known as *skipjacks* (Figure 14.1A) were largely replaced by powerboats, and the introduction of powered winches permitted oysters to be harvested from all depths. Not only were the oysters overfished, oyster reefs were destroyed in the process. With large protective reefs gone, the remaining oysters lived on the muddy Bay bottom where they were exposed to more predators and pathogens. Two oyster diseases, accidentally introduced by non-native oysters, also contributed to their decline. In the early 20th century, commercial oyster production slipped to historically low levels and "oystering" as a traditional way of life for watermen on the Bay was threatened in both Maryland and Virginia.

FIGURE 14.1
(A) Sail powered oyster dredges, known as skipjacks, operated in Chesapeake Bay. Here skipjacks are in port drying their sails. (B) Shells containing oyster spat raised by the Oyster Recovery Partnership are bagged and placed on pallets to grow before being transplanted to a designated oyster reef elsewhere in the Chesapeake Bay. [NOAA Photo Library]

Native oysters spawned and raised in hatcheries were placed on oyster beds to grow (Figure 14.1B). Unfortunately, few reached marketable size before dying from disease, especially in Virginia's more saline waters nearer the ocean. In an attempt to restore the Virginia oyster industry, sterile Asian oysters were introduced. This began on a trial basis in 2003 to test the marketability of mariculture of the non-native oyster species. These oysters are larger, faster growing, and more resistant to the diseases that killed the Bay's native oysters. They are also better adapted to living in the muddy Chesapeake Bay waters than were the native oysters.

Other efforts to restore the oyster fishery in Chesapeake Bay focus on physically rebuilding oyster reefs that stand above the muddy bottom, much as they had before Europeans arrived. These reef-building efforts, led by the *Virginia Marine Resources Commission*, continue but are limited by cost and the scarcity of appropriate materials for oyster attachment. Oyster larvae preferentially attach to clean oyster shells, which are available in relatively small quantities from oyster canneries. Shells from fossil reefs are also used but are less suitable as a substrate for juvenile oysters. Mud settling on the shells or growth of benthic organisms inhibits attachment of the larvae.

Driving Question:
How do we balance exploitation of fisheries with efforts to preserve marine species and ecosystems?

In early 2003, two Canadian fisheries scientists released the results of their 10-year study, which showed that commercial fishing has reduced the populations of as many as 90% of the world's largest fish species to such small numbers that their populations may not survive. Even more surprisingly, this population decline happened in only 50 years, the result of intensive, highly industrialized fishing practices.

The rapid decline in the populations of species such as cod, marlin, swordfish, and halibut severely impacts marine ecosystems because these fish occupy the highest trophic levels of marine food webs; most of them are **top predators** in the ecosystem. These large fish are slow growing and take a relatively long time (decades) to reach reproductive maturity. Once they become adults, the older fish tend to be the most fecund (fertile). Hence, removal of the largest fish of a species reduces the reproductive success of the population as a whole.

The United Nations *Food and Agriculture Organization (FAO)* tracks the state of the world fisheries. As of 2004, FAO estimated that since 1990, about 25% of fish stocks have been overexploited (17%), depleted (7%), or are recovering from depletion (1%). The largest number of depleted stocks is located in the Northwest and Northeast Atlantic Ocean, the Mediterranean Sea, and the Black Sea. Although the situation is serious, some fisheries management initiatives have been successful.

In this chapter we examine some examples of adverse human impacts on marine fisheries and ecosystems along with steps that are being taken to manage fisheries and protect threatened marine species. Such efforts are an essential component of **ocean stewardship**, action taken by society to protect the ocean and its living and non-living resources for now and the future.

Stewardship of Ocean Life

Components of the Earth system are highly interdependent so that disturbing one part of the Earth system can impact other parts—perhaps negatively. Thus, stewardship of the ocean and its resources involves responsibly managing all resources to benefit present and future generations. However, despite continuing advances in ocean science and technology (Chapter 13), less than 5% of the ocean bottom has been explored or mapped to the same resolution as the surface of Earth's neighboring planets, Mars and Venus. For this reason, we often lack the basic understandings needed to effectively manage and protect marine living resources and their associated ecosystems.

In the United States, the *National Oceanic and Atmospheric Administration (NOAA)* is the principal government agency charged with stewardship responsibilities for the nation's marine environment and living resources. These responsibilities include maintaining sustainable fisheries in U.S. waters, and protecting and restoring the populations of endangered marine animals, such as sea turtles and whales. NOAA also protects and maintains the viability of the nation's coastal zone. Effective stewardship requires consideration of both the biotic and abiotic components of marine ecosystems to protect living organisms, their habitats, and population sustaining interactions (e.g., predator-prey relationships). Stewardship of ecosystem components also includes managing their exploitation by commercial and recreational fishers for the benefit of people who make their living in these industries or use them for recreation.

One concept that is central to exercising wise stewardship is **sustainability**, defined by the United Nations' *World Commission on Environment and Development* as "developments that meet the needs of the present without compromising the ability of future generations to meet their own needs." Achieving sustainability requires effectively balancing environmental issues with social and economic concerns. Sustainability calls for intergenerational equity in managing resources and the environment; that is, we need to consider the needs of future generations as well as our own. It also includes the concept of maintaining a level of critical ecosystem function and biodiversity.

Fisheries and Sustainable Exploitation

Worldwide, fisheries supply about 19% of all the animal protein consumed by humans and the fishing industry employs more than 200 million people, 95% of whom live in developing nations. In coastal developing nations—especially in the tropics—almost all the protein intake comes from near-shore waters. Fishers in these waters use traditional methods (*artisanal fisheries*) and account for about half the world's marine fish production. Most of the fish they catch is eaten directly by humans. In developed nations, fishers employ technologies intended to increase the fish catch and a large amount of commercial-fish production is processed into fishmeal to feed pets and livestock, and for use in fertilizers.

In this section, we investigate overfishing, the contributing factors and the implications of overfishing for survival of top predator fish and the viability of associated marine ecosystems. We consider the advantages of a more holistic, ecologically based approach to fisheries management in order to achieve sustainable yields. Following this are discussions of fisheries and habitat restoration and recreational fisheries.

OVERFISHING

According to the authors of an international study published in *Science* magazine in 2006, worldwide an estimated one-third of all exploited fish stocks have collapsed; that is, their numbers have declined to less than 10% of their historical maximum population. **Overfishing** occurs when a fish species is taken at a rate that exceeds the maximum catch that would allow reproduction to replace the population. The two types of overfishing are known as recruitment overfishing and growth overfishing.

With **recruitment overfishing**, adult fish are taken in such great numbers that too few survive to replenish the breeding stock. A 2003 study of global fisheries spanning the previous 50 years showed that within 15 years of when a new fishery opens, about 80% of the largest fish are taken. The largest fish in a population not only have the greatest commercial value, they are also the most valuable ecologically because the largest fish in a species are the most prolific. **Growth overfishing** refers to fish that are taken too small, before the animals have grown to a size that would produce the maximum yield. Growth overfishing can reduce the value of what is caught because if left to grow, individuals would weigh more and bring a higher price in the marketplace. For example, growth overfishing may be the reason that male blue crabs taken from Chesapeake Bay have become fewer in number and smaller in size over the past several decades. (Furthermore, the recent decline in blue crab populations along the Eastern seaboard appears to be linked to changes in the weather and a parasitic infection of a dinoflagellate known as *Hematodinium perezi*.)

For more than 10,000 years, humans have taken food from the sea and for most of this time the ocean's bounty of life was considered limitless. However, even early on there were signs that this view of an inexhaustible food resource from the sea was seriously flawed. In fact, the first known human induced collapse of a marine stock occurred about 3000 years ago along the Peruvian coast. Fishers continued to harvest shellfish even after a natural disaster had greatly reduced shellfish populations.

In the years since the Industrial Revolution, a variety of technological innovations enabled fishers from developed nations to greatly increase the fish catch. These innovations included the steam and internal combustion engines that powered fishing vessels, extending their range from coastal areas to well offshore. These engines also powered heavier fishing gear such as trawls. In addition, refrigeration and factory trawlers made possible the preservation and processing of more fish. In the early 20th century, large, diesel-powered fishing boats permitted fishing on a larger scale throughout the ocean's depths. In the last half of the 20th century, freezing to preserve freshness, improved fish-locating techniques (e.g., acoustic fish finders), and precision navigational technologies (GPS) aided exploitation of fish stocks worldwide, and from all depths in the ocean. Today's factory ships can process and store upwards of 1000 metric tons of fish.

Economics is an important factor in overfishing. Governments worldwide spend billions of dollars annually subsidizing their commercial fishing industry. Consequently, many fisheries scientists and economists believe that the world fishing capacity is too large. They estimate that the world fishing fleet is about 2.5 times larger than needed to catch the ocean's sustainable fish production. Furthermore, worldwide government subsidies—totaling about $100 billion each year—support an industry that produces about $70 billion worth of fish annually. (Each year, subsidies of $15 billion to $30 billion compensate fishers whose income was lost because of government restrictions on fisheries.) In addition, trends in price structure can sometimes mask a fishery that is overexploited. It is a classic case of supply and demand. As the supply of a commercially valuable fish declines, its price rises, making the fishery more attractive for fishers. This increase in demand only hastens the decline in population and perhaps ultimately the collapse of the fishery.

Government subsidies, greater fishing efficiency, coupled with the growing demand for fish by the soaring human population drove an increase in total fish catch through the 1950s into the 1980s. The worldwide wild fish catch increased from 19.2 million metric tons (21.2 million tons) in 1950 to 88.6 million metric tons (97.6 million tons) in 1988. (Complicating matters, the People's Republic of China routinely over-reported their fish catch, significantly distorting available statistics on global fish production.) Because the rate of fish production exceeded human population growth rates, marine fisheries were thought to be the solution to the problem of feeding the world's burgeoning human population. At the time, the principal fishery management approach was to expand the areas fished and exploit newly discovered fish populations. Because many marine fishes have prolific reproductive output, ocean fisheries were assumed to be inexhaustible.

The United Nations *Food and Agriculture Organization (FAO)* reported that after many decades of steady growth, the total annual wild fish catch began to level off in the late 1980s. In 2000, the catch peaked at 87.2 million metric tons (96 million tons) and then declined to 81.7 million metric tons (90 million tons) in 2003. By then, discovery of new fisheries could no longer compensate for the decline in production. Meanwhile, the total average catch per person fell from 17 kg per year in the late 1980s to 14 kg per year in 2003.

As fishers became more adept at taking fish in larger numbers, stock collapses became more frequent forcing fishery managers to impose quotas on commercially desirable fish, limit fishing time at sea, or close fisheries altogether. The first modern day fishery collapse occurred in 1971-72 involving the Peruvian anchovy fishery. Peru's fishing industry boomed in the 1950s and 1960s and by 1970 was one of the largest in the world. At that time Peru accounted for about 20% of the total global catch of anchovies. However, overfishing combined with the effects of the 1972-73 El Niño sent the Peruvian fishery into a tailspin from which it has not recovered.

Overfishing continues to be a serious problem as shown by the collapse of the cod fishery in the North Atlantic off Newfoundland and New England, which was closed in the early 1990s and has not reopened (see the Case-in-Point at the beginning of Chapter 10). In the early years of the 21st century, cod fisheries bordering Northern Europe and in the Baltic Sea also showed signs of stress and possible pending collapse. Overfishing has led to the serial depletion of fish populations as each newly discovered stock is fished out and the fishing fleet moves on to the next stock or fishing area. Expansion of production is possible in only about one quarter of the world's fish stocks. According to NOAA's *National Marine Fisheries Service (NMFS)*, more than 60% of the 200 commercially most valuable fish stocks are either overfished or fished to the limit. One consequence is that many marine fishes in fish markets come primarily from fish farms. Wild salmon, for example, are increasingly rare in the market place, replaced by those raised in pens (see the section on mariculture later in this chapter).

Sharks are an example of an over-exploited, top predator with a relatively low reproductive capacity. Sharks are slow to mature sexually, some requiring 15 years or longer. Dusky sharks first breed when they are 20 to 25 years old. Sharks bear live young and most have long gestation periods. The spiny dogfish shark, used in British fish and chips, has a 22-month gestation period. Thus, many sharks have annual replacement rates of only 3% to 4%. As their population declines, their slow reproduction rates mean that shark species may face extinction. Even if the fishery is closed, shark populations are slow to recover. For example, in the 1960s, overfishing caused the collapse of the porbeagle fishery in the northwest Atlantic Ocean. Almost three decades passed before these sharks recovered, but when the fishery reopened, it took only about three years for the stock to be overfished again.

Between 1986 and 2000, the numbers of sharks caught in the northwest Atlantic on the long lines used to catch tuna and swordfish diminished significantly. Over the 15-year period, hammerhead shark numbers were down by approximately 89% while white and thresher shark populations declined by about 75%. The thresher shark population may have collapsed; that is, they became extinct for commercial purposes. Some areas of the ocean had no white sharks at all. Only the mako shark did not show a decline. Overall, the rates of shark decline in the northwest Atlantic Ocean indicate that the shark fishery in that area is not sustainable.

Sharks are taken for their meat; some are killed accidentally in collisions with fishing vessels whereas others are caught along with target fish and then dumped overboard. The most egregious threat to shark populations, however, is catching them just for their fins (Figure 14.2).

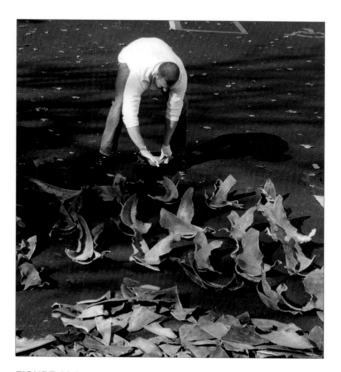

FIGURE 14.2
NOAA Office of Law Enforcement agent counting seized dried shark fins. [NOAA]

Popularity of pricey Asian shark-fin soups fuels the demand for fins that bring a much higher price than shark meat. Crews engaged in "shark finning" typically slice off the fins of a captured shark and then toss the rest of the animal overboard, a tremendous waste of food. Worldwide, fishers take an estimated 100 million sharks each year for their fins. In response to this practice, the U.S. Shark Finning Prohibition Act has been in effect since March 2002. This law bans U.S. vessels anywhere in the world ocean from possessing shark fins unless the rest of the shark carcass is also onboard. The same regulation applies to foreign vessels fishing in the U.S. Exclusive Economic Zone (EEZ), extending 370 km (200 nautical mi) offshore (Chapter 4).

While this law is well intentioned, trade in shark fins continues to be unregulated throughout most of the world ocean. In August 1992, the U.S. Coast Guard stopped and boarded the *King Diamond II* out of Honolulu in waters off of Acapulco, Mexico. Law-enforcement officials found 29 metric tons (32 tons) of fins onboard but no other shark remains. According to a NOAA official, this finding would indicate that about 30,000 sharks were taken and almost 0.6 million kg (1.3 million lbs) of shark meat was disposed of at sea.

As increasing fishing pressures cause populations of top predators to decline, organisms (e.g., other fish) at progressively lower trophic levels begin to dominate food webs in marine ecosystems. Fishers, in turn, target fish populations at these lower trophic levels. Daniel Pauly of the University of British Columbia coined the phrase "*fishing down the food web*" for this shift in targeted fishes brought about by overfishing of top predators. From an economic perspective, ecosystems are less valuable when depleted in top predators and dominated by disproportionate numbers of small fish, crustaceans, and phytoplankton.

A study of fish catches over the period 1950 to 1994 conducted by the United Nations Food and Agriculture Organization confirmed fishing down the food web. Researchers discovered a gradual shift away from food webs dominated by high trophic level fish (e.g., cod, haddock) to food webs dominated by low trophic level invertebrates and plankton-feeding fish. The FAO found that the rate of fishing down the food web was about 0.1 trophic levels per decade—likely an underestimate because of limited data from tropical fisheries.

Targeting fish at lower trophic levels initially may be accompanied by an increase in total catch. With depletion of top predators, their prey populations (smaller fish) increase in numbers. However, the greater total catch is short-lived as populations of the competitors of the top predators increase. Furthermore, smaller fish and other organisms at lower trophic levels undergo much more rapid population fluctuations than do organisms at the higher trophic levels. This implies a less reliable food supply for the limited number of remaining top predators and a less stable food web; that is, top predators are more vulnerable to environmental changes (including climate change) that impact their prey.

Fisheries scientists estimate that about 8% of the ocean's primary production is now harvested in the global fisheries (Chapter 9). That is, 8% of the total global fixation of carbon by phytoplankton is being removed from the ocean in the form of fish. (This percentage is somewhat misleading because most of the ocean is relatively unproductive.) Fisheries harvest about one quarter of the total fish biomass produced each year. Based on these findings, many scientists believe that the fish catch is already near the limit of the ocean's fish yield. This view is further supported by the apparent decline in global marine fisheries early in the 21st century. Humans are now top predator in many—perhaps most—of the world's major marine ecosystems. Unlike other top predators, however, humans return essentially nothing useful to the ecosystems from which they take their fish.

The life expectancy of a fish is an important consideration in assessing the vulnerability of a fish stock to overfishing. How scientists determine the age of a fish is the subject of this chapter's first Essay.

MAXIMUM SUSTAINABLE YIELD

Successful fisheries management requires (1) a solid scientific understanding of the exploited stock, (2) targeted fishing quotas that provide the stock size that exceeds the biomass required to produce the maximum sustainable yield, and (3) supporting regulations (e.g., prohibiting illegal fishing) that are enforceable.

To prevent overfishing of a fish stock, fishery managers typically set catch quotas. The goal is to adhere to the **maximum sustainable yield** of the fish stock; that is, limits are set on fish catches (*total allowable catch*) so that stocks are maintained at a level that will ensure the long-term viability of the target species. Quotas must take into consideration the life span, population growth rate, and reproductive capacity of a particular fish species. A fishery is sustainable if it can be fished indefinitely at reasonable levels while maintaining the ecosystem (function, structure, and diversity) on which the fishery depends, and the integrity of the habitat essential to the fish species. As we have seen, in cases where a fishery has collapsed, the fishery may be closed in order to allow its population to recover.

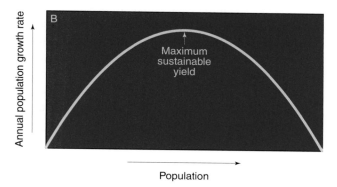

FIGURE 14.3
The maximum sustainable yield of fish is based on a model (A) that simulates the growth of the population of a fish species. The maximum population, the carrying capacity, is determined by the availability of resources in the marine habitat. The annual population growth rate (B) peaks at some intermediate population size; this is the maximum sustainable yield.

The maximum sustainable yield is based on a model that simulates the population growth of an exploited fish species. One model consists of a sigmoid (*S*-shaped) growth curve as shown in Figure 14.3A. According to this model, population growth of a fish species is slow at first and then becomes more rapid. Eventually, as the number of fish increases to the point that available food resources begin to become limiting, population growth again slows and eventually levels off at or near the carrying capacity. The **carrying capacity** is the maximum population that can be sustained by the resources of the marine habitat. In the case of fisheries, the carrying capacity is the maximum population that would exist in the absence of commercial fishing.

As shown in Figure 14.3A the population growth rate is relatively low when the population is small or when the population nears the carrying capacity. At some intermediate size, the fish population has the greatest potential for growth and reproduction. For most fish species, reducing the fish population to about half its natural size (i.e., the carrying capacity) makes available more resources per individual and produces the maximum sustainable yield (Figure 14.3B). If the fish population does not drop below this intermediate size, the fish population can be sustained by limiting the catch to no more than the annual population growth rate. Today, the populations of most fish stocks are well below that which would produce the maximum sustainable yield.

In late 2007, economists from the Australian National University and the University of Washington proposed an economics-based approach to the problem of overfishing. Using computer models, they studied four fisheries. As a fish population increases, the cost of catching the fish decreases—costs are lower because less time and fuel are needed to reach the total allowable catch. Hence, reducing the fish catch in the short term (until the population rebounds) translates into greater fishing profits in the long run. The only requirement for this scheme is that fishers who cut back on their catch must be the ones who directly benefit from the reduced cost of fishing. Furthermore, fishers who are not currently fishing cannot be allowed to participate later (after the fishery has recovered).

Also in 2007, J.R. Beddington and colleagues of Imperial College, London, argued that fisheries management strategies are more likely to achieve sustainable fisheries by (1) eliminating subsidies (described earlier), and (2) granting individual fishers a right to a portion of the total catch. In this way, fishers are no longer competing with one another and are more likely to seek to sustain the entire fishery because as the common fish stock increases, each individual's quota will increase.

ECOLOGICALLY SUSTAINABLE YIELD

Fisheries managers are reassessing the traditional approach to sustaining the populations of exploited fish stocks. This reassessment stems from the realization that fish species are components of ecosystems in which they interact with other organisms (e.g., as food sources) and the physical/chemical environment (e.g., for habitat). A decline in the population of a particular species of fish may have a ripple effect on the entire ecosystem, altering its biotic composition and reducing its stability. This is especially the case when fishers decimate the populations of commercially attractive fish such as cod, tuna, swordfish and other species that are at the top of food webs (top predators). This ecosystem perspective argues for a more holistic approach to fisheries management.

In 1993, the 24th Annual Report of the President's Council on Environmental Quality (CEQ) recommended that the President issue a directive establishing a national policy to encourage sustainable development through ecosystem management. More than fifteen years later natural resource managers still struggle with this concept. Managers accept that humans do not manage ecosystems; rather it is human activities that use and impact ecosystems which are managed. Recognizing that, ecosystem management is better referred to as *ecosystem-based management* or an *ecosystem approach to management*. Ecosystem approaches integrate ecological principles, human systems, and goals of sustainability for use in the management decision-making process.

Since the release of the CEQ report, much has been written about the ecosystem approach to management. For marine ecosystems, the concept is arguably best developed for fisheries. While opinions vary regarding what constitutes an ecosystem approach to management, most concerned parties agree that an ecosystem approach to management needs to evolve incrementally from existing approaches. Applications are becoming increasingly sophisticated in response to more intense and diverse public interest, with the use of new knowledge, and by giving explicit consideration to uncertainty. Some key challenges in advancing ecosystem approaches are to (1) improve and create processes for public participation in objective setting and in prioritizing those objectives, (2) develop operational protocols for taking into account food web complexity (recognizing that only a crude level of predictability is likely, at best) and climate change, and (3) determine the functional value of habitat related ecosystem goods (e.g., food) and services (e.g., absorption of atmospheric carbon dioxide) that benefit humanity.

Through an incremental and collaborative transition to an ecosystem approach, managers can expect to achieve healthy ecosystems with increased social and economic value of its resources as well as an informed public by which the benefits of ecosystem management can be maintained.

To be ecologically sound and effective, fisheries management must be grounded in solid scientific understanding. Consider, for example, how a better understanding of Atlantic bluefin tuna may help to head off its extinction. Bluefin tuna is a top predator that is in great demand worldwide as a food fish. Since the early 1970s, use of bluefin tuna for sushi (fish with rice and vegetables) and sashimi (sliced raw fish) has soared. Although 75% of the global catch is consumed in Japan, these foods are also popular in American supermarkets, delis, and upscale restaurants. Overfishing, inadequate catch quotas, and illegal fishing are driving Atlantic bluefin toward extinction.

Unlike most of the 20,000 species of fish that are cold-blooded, the bluefin tuna is warm-blooded. An adult bluefin grows to a maximum length of 4 m (13 ft). The largest on record weighed 679 kg (1496 lb) and was caught off the coast of Nova Scotia. The bluefin is sleek and fast, reaching speeds up to 80 km per hr, and has a ravenous appetite, eating almost any animal they encounter.

Bluefin tuna ranges over a huge area of the North Atlantic, as well as portions of the Pacific and Southern Oceans. According to a December 2007 report in *The Washington Post*, two genetically distinct populations of bluefin tuna (*Thunnus thynnus*) live in the North Atlantic Ocean. They swim side-by-side most of the year but separate for breeding; that is, the two populations do not interbreed. The spawning area is the Gulf of Mexico for one population and the Mediterranean Sea for the other population. Mixing of the two populations has resulted in inflated estimates of the western Atlantic bluefin tuna; that is, migrants from the Mediterranean give the erroneous impression of a greater western Atlantic population than actually exists.

In setting catch quotas for Atlantic bluefin tuna, the International Commission for the Conservation of Atlantic Tuna (ICCAT), a regulatory group founded in 1969, erroneously assumed that the two populations foraged for food in different portions of the Atlantic. The ICCAT treated the two populations separately and set strict quotas in the western Atlantic but relatively lenient quotas in the eastern Atlantic where overfishing has become a serious problem. Hence, the Atlantic bluefin tuna is closer to extinction than originally believed. This discovery has prompted conservationists to press NOAA's *National Marine Fisheries Service* for closure of longline fishing in the Gulf of Mexico during the spawning season (April to June) so that the Atlantic bluefin population may begin to recover. Furthermore, interest has developed in breeding bluefin tuna in captivity.

Protection of fisheries requires a thorough understanding of the entire ecosystem, not just the targeted commercial or recreational fish species. This understanding is the basis for achieving an **ecologically sustainable yield**, that is, the yield that a marine ecosystem can sustain without undergoing an undesirable change in state. New management concepts and associated policies must take into account all the species that interact with the targeted species and the habitats they depend on. Even reducing fish catches by 40% may not be enough to protect fish stocks and their ecosystems while allowing both to recover from past overfishing. Thus the goal of sustainable fisheries may be quite different from, and even incompatible with the ecologically sustainable goals of maintaining natural populations of fish and other members of the ecosystem. Furthermore, sustainability will require more extensive monitoring of the marine environment in which these ecosystems function to detect changes in conditions that might significantly alter the system. In short, humans will not only continue to be the dominant predator in marine ecosystems, but will also be responsible for managing, protecting, and restoring them if they are damaged by human activities or climate change.

BYCATCH

Many commercial fishers accidentally catch undersized fish or unwanted species in their nets or hook lines; these are discarded, either dead or dying, because they cannot be sold. Today, about one-third of the annual commercial fish catch worldwide is discarded for this reason. **Bycatch**, referring to fish and other marine animals that are taken in addition to the target species, is a major threat to many endangered species, such as sea turtles, dolphins, and other marine mammals. For example, sea turtles die in large numbers each year after swallowing floating hooks attached to long-lines intended to catch tuna or swordfish, or after they become tangled in shrimp nets. The many commercial fishing techniques are described in Table 14.1.

Ironically, the long-line fishing technique was developed to protect dolphins; it replaced nets that previously were used to catch tuna but inadvertently also killed large numbers of dolphins each year. In the late 1950s, fishers in the eastern tropical Pacific Ocean discovered that yellowtail tuna aggregated below schools

---

TABLE 14.1

Types of Commercial Fishing Gear (modified after Monterey Bay Aquarium)

Gillnetting	Netting that hangs in the ocean from floats. The head of the fish passes through the net but not its body. As the fish tries to escape its gills are caught in the net.
Harpooning	Used to catch large bluefin tuna and swordfish. The fisher stands on a shipboard platform holding an aluminum harpoon, 3 to 4.3 m long, which is attached to a long rope. The fisher uses the harpoon to spear and kill the fish and then it is taken onboard.
Longlining	A central fishing line plus smaller lines are strung with thousands of baited hooks extending distances up to 80 km. May be used to catch fish near the sea surface (e.g., swordfish and tuna) or near the ocean bottom (e.g., cod and halibut).
Pole and Line	Fishers stand on the deck shoulder to shoulder, each holding a long single pole and a short line. Fish are caught one by one and pulled out of the water and onto the ship. Target fish include tuna and mahi-mahi.
Purse Seining	A large net encircles a school of fish. A line enables the crew to close the bottom of the net (like a purse). Target species include tuna, sardines, herring, and mackerel.
Traps and Pots	Baited cages (usually attached to a line) are used to trap the catch and keep it alive until the fisher returns after several days. These traps or pots are used to catch lobster, crabs, shrimp, and sometimes bottom-dwelling fish.
Trawling/Dragging	Different types of nets are dragged behind a ship to fish in midwater (for schools of small fish such as anchovies) and along the ocean bottom (for bottom dwelling fish including cod and halibut). In some cases, nets with chain-mesh bottoms are dragged through sediment (e.g., to catch scallops).
Trolling	A boat with long rods pulls fishing lines through the water with different baits and lures.

of dolphins. Since then, the favored method of catching tuna has been to set nets around the schools of dolphin to capture the tuna beneath. For some time, on average more than 350,000 dolphins died each year when they became trapped in the fishing nets. More recently fishers have used special nets that allow dolphins to escape unharmed. Since 1998, about 2000 dolphins were killed each year in these nets, a 99% reduction in mortality. Despite this advance in protecting dolphins, three dolphin species are still listed as depleted (i.e., two species of spotted dolphin and one species of spinner dolphin). NOAA's National Marine Fisheries Service continues to work with other nations fishing in the eastern tropical Pacific to further reduce dolphin mortality.

Trawling for shrimp (also called prawns) is a major and yet little recognized contributor to the bycatch problem worldwide (Figure 14.4). Nets used to capture shrimp are dragged along the shallow sea bottom where they also catch all kinds of fishes, shellfish, and other animals, including sea turtles. An estimated 150,000 sea turtles are killed each year in shrimp-trawl nets. As noted later in this chapter, however, these turtle deaths can be reduced or avoided by using excluder devices that allow the turtles to escape shrimp nets unharmed.

Worldwide, shrimp trawling results in a bycatch of 5 to 20 kg (11 to 44 lbs) of unwanted animals and plants for every 1.0 kg (2.2 lbs) of shrimp caught. (In the past, local artisanal fishers would use unwanted fish for their own consumption.) Much shrimp trawling is conducted in shallow tropical waters and the catch is exported to European or North American food markets. The European Union is the world's largest shrimp importer, much of it coming from tropical waters near developing countries. Shrimp fishing is also heavily subsidized by the European Union, which pays nearly half the operating expenses for shrimp trawlers working off the West African (Guinea-Bissau) coast. While representing only about 2% of the global fish catch, trawling for shrimp is responsible for about one-third of the world's total bycatch. Trawl nets also damage the sea bottom (Chapter 10).

Buying farmed shrimp does little good in protecting marine fisheries. Each kilogram of farmed shrimp produced requires feeding them two kilograms of fishmeal processed from wild-fish species. Furthermore, large areas of mangrove swamps are destroyed to construct shrimp ponds, which have a relatively short productive life before disease outbreaks necessitate building new ponds and abandoning the old ones.

The bycatch problem might be partially alleviated by changing or rewriting governmental regulations to relax quotas, permitting accidental catches to be landed legally. Success in this effort may be elusive because a policy that is too relaxed on accidental catches may actually encourage such "accidents." These regulations would apply only within national waters. In open-ocean waters, beyond the boundaries of Exclusive Economic Zones (EEZ), international cooperation would be required. This policy is important for marine mammals and sea turtles.

RESTORING FISHERIES

Few marine fisheries have been restored after experiencing severe depletion. The North Atlantic herring fishery temporarily recovered after fishing ceased during World Wars I and II. Another example is striped bass, also known as rockfish, which recovered from near collapse in the 1980s when the states of Maryland and Virginia declared moratoriums on taking the species in Chesapeake Bay.

To establish sustainable fisheries for other species will require new strategies. Earlier in this chapter, we described the concept of ecologically sustainable yield. The goal of the ecosystem-based approach to fisheries management is to maintain or re-establish marine ecosystems that are home to fisheries. This would require protection of seafloor habitats (e.g., by phasing out destructive trawling practices) and expanding the areas of the world ocean designated as protected areas, called *marine reserves*, where fishing is prohibited. In these so-called *no-take zones*, fishes can grow to maturity and reach their optimal reproductive potential. The largest individual fishes are most desirable because they are the most prolific producers of eggs and sperm. For example,

FIGURE 14.4
A double-rigged shrimp trawler with one net up and the other being brought about. Trawling for shrimp is a major contributor to bycatch. [NOAA Photo Library, photo by Robert K. Bringham]

a single female red snapper weighing 12.5 kg (27.5 lb.) produces about the same number of eggs as more than 200 smaller female red snappers each weighing 1.2 kg (2.6 lb.). The resulting increased fish production could be taken in the waters surrounding marine reserves where fishing is permitted. However, existing no-take zones are small and few in number; together they cover only 0.01% of the area of the world ocean.

Within the federal waters portion of the Channel Islands National Marine Sanctuary offshore of Santa Barbara, CA, NOAA established marine reserves (110 square nautical mi) and a marine conservation area (1.7 square nautical mi). Effective 29 July 2007, all extractive activities are prohibited in the marine reserves. Within the Anacapa marine conservation area, recreational fishing for pelagic species and harvesting of lobsters is allowed. Established in 1980, the Sanctuary encompasses the waters surrounding five islands (from mean high tide to 6 nautical miles offshore) in a 1252 square nautical mi area of the Santa Barbara Channel (Figure 14.5). The primary goal of this Sanctuary is to protect the natural and cultural resources within its boundaries.

The Channel Islands National Marine Sanctuary is one of 14 national marine sanctuaries established since 1972 and administered by the NOAA National Ocean Service's *National Marine Sanctuary Program* in U.S. coastal waters and Great Lakes. In a similar vein, New York's Bronx Zoo operates a sanctuary for penguins and other sea birds on two uninhabited rocky islands near the Falkland (or Malvinas) Islands, off Argentina in the South Atlantic. (For more on marine sanctuaries and marine reserves, refer to the second Essay in Chapter 10.)

Other strategies proposed to help re-establish or protect fisheries include reducing the capacity of the global fishing fleet. As noted earlier in this chapter, the world fishing fleet is estimated to be about 2.5 times larger than needed to catch the ocean's sustainable fish production. Related to this strategy is the proposed elimination of government subsidies for unprofitable fishing operations. Furthermore, greater effort is needed to deal with the problems associated with bycatch.

HABITAT DESTRUCTION AND RESTORATION

Habitat destruction has also caused depletion or destruction of major fish stocks. Since steam-powered fishing boats began dragging heavy steel nets over the ocean bottom to catch bottom-feeding fishes (e.g., cod and haddock), benthic ecosystems and habitats have been heavily damaged. For decades the damage was ignored and fishers spoke of "plowing" the sea bottom to improve fish catches, much like farmers cultivate the land. Some fisheries scientists, however, argue that trawling the sea floor is more like clear cutting forests to improve hunting for rabbits or deer. This activity deprives adults of food and young fishes of places to hide from predators. Due to widespread damage to shallow sea bottoms, populations of cod and other long-lived, bottom-feeding fishes have experienced severe declines. Consequently, some commercial fishing operations have shifted to rapidly growing and reproducing open-water organisms, such as squid, which do not require intact benthic ecosystems and habitats for their survival.

Habitat destruction threatens oysters in coastal and estuarine waters. Tomales Bay, along the California coast about 70 km (43 mi) north of San Francisco, was originally home to a small, slow-growing, native oyster. Considered a delicacy, it was essentially destroyed as a commercial fishery in the late 1800s due to local market demand during the Gold Rush days. In an effort to restore

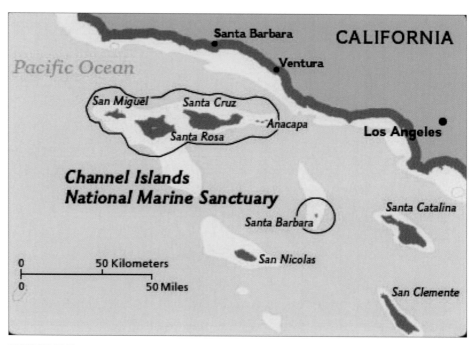

FIGURE 14.5
Map of the Channel Islands National Marine Sanctuary. [NOAA]

this native oyster in the Bay, floats with mesh bags were used to keep the oysters off the bottom so that they could grow faster and avoid predation. Part of the objective is to restore the natural filtering capacity of Tomales Bay's waters. As described in this chapter's Case-in-Point, another example of where habitat destruction resulted in the decline of oyster populations comes from Chesapeake Bay.

The sea grass beds of Chesapeake Bay provide habitat for shallow-water organisms such as blue crabs. Young crabs hide in grass beds to avoid being eaten by predators, including fish, when they are especially vulnerable after shedding their hard shells and before their new, soft shells harden. Trawling to catch blue crabs cut wide swaths and decimated sea grasses in Chesapeake Bay. Input of excess levels of nutrients from farms, cities, and industry also played a role by promoting growth of algae in the water and on the sea grass blades, depriving the plants of the light they need for photosynthesis. Efforts to restore the sea grass beds include regulation and reduction of anthropogenic nutrient discharges and planting new sea grass beds (Figure 14.6). The goal is to restore about 46,000 hectares (114,000 acres) of the nearly 240,000 hectares (600,000 acres) of submerged aquatic vegetation that originally grew on the Bay bottom providing food for ducks and habitat for many species of small fishes and invertebrates. In 1978, before restoration efforts began, only 16,000 hectares (41,000 acres) of sea grasses remained.

For more on restoration of coastal wetlands, refer to this chapter's second Essay.

RECREATIONAL FISHERIES

Recreational fisheries in the coastal ocean and in lakes are important activities worldwide. They involve large numbers of people who catch fish for sport rather than for profit. This type of fishing is part of the tourism and recreational industry, the world's largest and fastest growing economic activity. In the U.S., more than 17 million people engage in recreational fishing each year and spend more than $25 billion; the industry employs about 288,000 people. For some fish species, the value and the amount of the recreational catch equal or exceed that of the commercial fishery. Striped bass, blue fish, and flounder in the Mid-Atlantic region are examples of such prized fishes. More than half the fishes caught by recreational fishers are released alive; unfortunately many die due to the stress of "catch and release."

Important differences exist between recreational and commercial fisheries. Most recreational fishers prefer to fish near home; hence, sport fish populations are most heavily fished near major urban areas. Also recreational fisheries do not damage fish habitat as much as some commercial fishing practices. Furthermore, when the catch of popular recreational fishes declines, fisheries management agencies often resort to fish hatcheries to replenish depleted stocks. The small fishes are released into recreational waters where they grow to a size that will satisfy the sport fishing demand. Lake trout is one example of such a hatchery-raised fish released to many North American lakes; another is salmon on the Pacific coast.

FIGURE 14.6
(A) Volunteers help NOAA scientists prepare seagrass shoots for planting [NOAA]. (B) Other volunteers help restore submerged seagrass near Solomons Island in Chesapeake Bay. [Photo by Mary Hollinger, NODC biologist, NOAA]

Despite the large numbers of people involved and their associated expenditures, data for recreational fisheries are not as readily available as for commercial fisheries. Based on anecdotal accounts, recreational fisheries have followed some of the same exploitation patterns as commercial fisheries. They expand into new territories as populations of the large-bodied, slow growing but highly prized fishes decline. Like commercial fisheries, the sports fisheries shift to less desirable species and often end up with smaller, fast-growing fish. Collapse of recreational fisheries may be the culmination of a slow population decline over several decades. In time, the expectations of sport fishers change as memories of the preferred species fade.

Protecting Endangered Marine Species

Many large marine animals are protected by government regulations because their populations have been greatly depleted by commercial fishing or other human activities over the past century or so. In 1973, the U.S. *Endangered Species Act* became law providing for the protection of endangered and threatened species (and their habitats). Species determined to be in imminent danger of extinction throughout a significant portion of their range are listed as *endangered*. Species are listed as *threatened* if they are likely to become endangered in the foreseeable future. NOAA's National Marine Fisheries Service (NMFS) has authority for listing (most) marine species as threatened or endangered.

The *Convention on International Trade in Endangered Species of Wild Fauna and Flora (CITES)* is intended to control international commerce in endangered species and their products. Species listed in Appendix I of CITES are threatened with extinction; trade in these species is prohibited. Species listed in Appendix II of CITES may become threatened and their trade is restricted. At present, 67 nations are signatory to CITES. In spite of CITES, many marine species including sea turtles, whales, and water birds remain threatened or endangered.

SEA TURTLES

The large graceful marine turtles (called *sea turtles*) inhabit mostly tropical and subtropical ocean waters but are also found occasionally in bays and estuaries where they are most likely to interact with humans. While they resemble their more familiar terrestrial relatives, tortoises and freshwater turtles, sea turtles have special adaptations for the marine environment. Instead of legs, they have flippers for swimming and their shells are lighter and more streamlined to reduce water resistance. All sea turtles, except leatherbacks, have hard upper shells (*carapace*) covered with large scale-like structures (*scutes*) and a hard lower shell (*plastron*). Unlike most other animals, the carapace in turtles incorporates their backbone and ribs. The leatherback sea turtle has boney plates under the leathery skin on its back.

Sea turtles breathe air but can hold their breath for long periods when they dive or rest on the sea bottom. While swimming, they remain near the ocean surface and come up to breathe every few minutes. Some species draw water into their mouth and throat via their nasal passages and oxygen is extracted by the pharynx (similar to a gill). Like all reptiles, sea turtles are cold blooded; that is, their body temperature is the same as the surrounding water. They migrate seasonally, remaining in waters having their desired temperature range and may die if they enter waters that are too cold for their metabolic needs. One species, the leatherback turtle, apparently can create some body heat, permitting them to withstand the cold waters off Canada and Iceland, where they spend the summer. Sea turtles live in the ocean their entire lives except for adult females who come ashore during nesting season to lay eggs in beach sand (Figure 14.7).

Seven species of sea turtles are recognized worldwide. The populations of all of them are listed as either endangered or threatened. Technically, the flatback sea turtle is neither threatened nor endangered—it nests on the remote beaches of northern Australia. But because it resembles the green sea turtle, trade in its products are prohibited by CITES. Many human activities threaten

FIGURE 14.7
Federally endangered loggerhead sea turtles lay their eggs on beaches. [U.S. Fish and Wildlife Service photo]

sea-turtle populations: (1) commercial harvesting of adult turtles (e.g., for food, hides, oil) and the poaching of eggs (believed by some to be an aphrodisiac) from nests, (2) development projects (e.g., seawalls) along beaches used by turtles to nest, (3) bycatch in commercial fishing nets, especially shrimp nets, (4) collisions with ships, including recreational boats, (5) ingestion of plastic litter, especially bags, and (6) marine pollution.

Green sea turtles occur throughout the world ocean between about 35 degrees S and 35 degrees N and are considered the most commercially valuable of all sea turtles. Hawksbills prefer warmer tropical waters and have a more limited range than the other sea turtles. The shells of hawksbills ("tortoiseshell") are used for jewelry, the principal reason for its endangered status. Kemp's (Atlantic) ridley, the rarest of sea turtles, lives in the Gulf of Mexico and along the U.S. East Coast. The only known nesting beach for this species of sea turtle is Rancho Nuevo, Mexico. The olive (Pacific) ridley is found mostly in the warm waters of the Pacific Ocean but also can be found in the Atlantic and Indian Oceans. It nests along the west coast of Mexico; its status is endangered along the Pacific coast of Mexico and threatened elsewhere in its range. The loggerhead is found throughout the world with the second greatest population along the U.S. southeast coast. Loggerheads nest on beaches from Texas to New Jersey.

Leatherback turtles are the largest sea turtles (and one of the largest of all marine reptiles); they can reach a length of 2 m (6.6 ft) and weigh up to 590 kg (1300 lb). Leatherbacks have a different lifestyle from other sea turtles, living most of their lives in deep-ocean waters, between about 50 degrees N and 50 degrees S. In a single year, they can migrate from South America to Nova Scotia. They feed primarily on jellyfish, but can dive to depths of almost 1000 m (3280 ft) in search of other food. These long-lived animals take 10 to 20 years to reach sexual maturity. Like all sea turtles, leatherbacks are threatened by poachers who take their eggs from nests on beaches. Their greatest threat, however, comes from long-line fishing for tuna and swordfish. Long-lines are up to 60 km (37 mi) in length and each line has thousands of floating hooks. One scientist calculated that on any given day up to four million hooks are in the ocean for tuna and swordfish. Leatherbacks are caught when they take the bait and swallow the hook or they become entangled in the lines. In the past two decades, almost 95% of Pacific leatherback turtles have disappeared.

The population of all sea turtles declined nearly 90% between 1980 and 2000. Unless this trend is reversed, they may be extinct by 2030. Because they live primarily in open-ocean waters, protecting them will require international action. There are several ways in which the threats to sea turtles by commercial fishing can be reduced. As mentioned above, one strategy is the use of a special trap door in fishing nets that trawl the sea floor for shrimp. These low-cost devices allow turtles to escape the net easily without impeding the shrimp catch. Also, reducing the time a trawl net remains on the bottom lowers the death rate among trapped turtles. Another approach is to declare areas with high seasonal populations of turtles off limits to fishing at these times.

In the United States, NOAA's *Office of Protected Resources* within the National Marine Fisheries Service oversees activities to protect sea turtles. These efforts involve training commercial fishers to use turtle exclusion devices. Because sea turtles nest on land, the U.S. Fish and Wildlife Service co-ordinates conservation efforts on beaches.

WHALES

Hunting whales began early in human history. The first whalers used small boats and hunted close to shore, as some coastal-dwelling native peoples still do primarily around the Arctic Ocean. Around CE 1000, Basque whalers from northern Spain began hunting in the North Atlantic. In the 16th century, these whalers used larger vessels to reach North America where they established whaling stations in Newfoundland. Later, English and Dutch whalers joined them in hunting whales in the Arctic Ocean. These early whalers hunted the North Atlantic right whale, a large (45 metric ton or 50 ton), surface feeding whale. It is called the "right whale" because the animal was so easy to take, that is, it swims slowly, was easy to kill, and floated after death so it could be towed ashore for processing.

Whales provide meat for humans (especially in Japan) and for animal feed. Before petroleum became available for oil lamps in the second half of the 19th century, whale oil was used for that purpose. Other uses for whale products included baleen for corset stays, hoop skirts, and umbrellas. Spermaceti, a valuable oily substance from sperm whales, was used to make cosmetics and candles.

When Northern Hemisphere whale stocks declined markedly early in the 20th century, commercial whalers using larger steam-powered vessels moved into the untapped Southern Ocean to exploit the large whale stocks living there. Norwegians dominated commercial whaling worldwide. Initially, whales were taken to factories ashore for processing. After 1924, factory ships were developed to process whales at sea. Increased efficiency was the reason the whale catch rose from 12,000 in 1910 to 40,000 in 1940.

Like fishers, whalers focused on a single species until its numbers were so reduced that they had to hunt another (usually smaller) species. Whales are social animals and some use protected inlets for breeding, making them vulnerable to whalers, who used small boats and hand harpoons to take the whales in these close quarters. In the early 1900s, the huge blue whales were preferred and in 1930-31, 29,000 of these animals were taken. Blue whales were finally protected in 1965 but by then their numbers had dropped to an estimated 6000 in the entire world ocean. After blue whales (135 metric tons or 150 tons) were depleted, whalers took fin whales (45 metric tons or 50 tons) and then the smaller sei whales. Today, Japanese and Norwegian whalers still take the much smaller minke whales (5 metric tons or 6 tons). This is another example of serial depletion and harvesting down the food web.

In 1982, to protect the world's remaining whale stocks, the *International Whaling Commission (IWC)* declared a moratorium on commercial whaling to take effect in 1986. The IWC, founded in 1948, is the decision-making arm of the *International Convention for the Regulation of Whaling (ICRW)*. According to the ICRW charter, the International Whaling Commission was intended "to provide for the proper conservation of whale stocks and this makes possible the orderly development of the whaling industry."

As of this writing, the IWC has 73 member nations (about evenly divided between those that do or do not favor whaling). It is one of the few international regulatory bodies that set policy to protect marine animals from possible extinction. The IWC regulates whaling to conserve stocks, which were greatly depleted during centuries of uncontrolled commercial whaling.

Japan, Norway, and Iceland objected to the 1986 moratorium and continued commercial whaling. These nations claimed that the populations of smaller whales, such as the minke whale (about 8 m in length), are now at healthy levels (in the hundreds of thousands) and can sustain whaling. Another argument is that whales eat many commercially valuable fishes and must be hunted to protect those fish stocks.

Japan later withdrew its objection to the moratorium and opted to take whales for research purposes only, so-called *scientific whaling*, which is permitted under the IWC moratorium. Japan now hunts whales in the North Pacific and Southern Oceans and even intends to take humpback and fin whales in the Southern Ocean Sanctuary. The ICRW sanctions catching whales for scientific study under Article VIII. The original drafters of the document assumed that less than 10 whales would be killed for scientific purposes each year, far fewer than the hundreds of whales that Japan takes annually. Japan defends its continued whaling on cultural, historic and economical grounds. A government agency sponsors Japan's "scientific whaling" program and sells whale meat not used for research and much of it ends up in Japanese restaurants where whale meat is considered a delicacy. Many Japanese view the moratorium, strongly supported by the United States and many other nations, as a form of cultural imperialism. Cultural differences such as this make international conservation policies extremely difficult to negotiate and enforce.

Norway resumed commercial whaling in 1993, defying the IWC's moratorium. In 2005, Norwegian whalers took 639 whales. Most of the meat is eaten locally but small amounts were exported to Iceland before it too resumed whaling. Because no market now exists for whale fat (blubber), it is either burned or dumped at sea. Claiming that whale stocks had recovered sufficiently to permit commercial and scientific whaling, in 2002 Iceland announced plans to resume whaling, targeting minke and fin whales. Iceland intends to study the effect of whales on ecosystems. Many nations and organizations object to whaling, even for research purposes, arguing that it is actually commercial whaling and has little to do with scientific research.

The IWC allows aboriginal people (Inuits) in Alaska, Greenland, and Siberia to conduct small (subsistence) whale hunts for cultural reasons and for food as they had done traditionally. In 2002, their request to take 280 bowhead whales was denied by the IWC. Interestingly, opposition to the Inuit request was led by Japan, Norway and Iceland.

Whale watching is an important activity of *ecotourism*, one of the fastest growing sectors of the tourism industry. Iceland's decision to resume whaling was controversial among its citizens at least partially because whale watching is a significant part of that nation's tourism industry, earning Iceland an estimated $8 million per year. Whale watching has become so popular in many places such as Seattle, WA that there is concern that the tour boats are making so much noise that it disturbs the whales, disrupting their normal behavior.

Even after decades of protection, many whale stock populations have still not rebounded to their original numbers. Among endangered whales are the

FIGURE 14.8
Populations of humpback whales have recovered after being listed on the endangered species list. [NOAA Photo Library]

North Atlantic right whale, blue, and bowhead whales. A few whales, such as the California gray whale, have recovered to roughly historic levels; their major breeding ground in Baja California is protected by Mexico, which has banned whaling in its coastal waters thus creating the world's largest whale reserve. Some populations of fin and humpback whales have experienced a remarkable recovery (Figure 14.8).

Marine mammals and other animals, including fishes, may be adversely affected by other environmental factors, including increasing noise levels in the ocean. Noise levels in the ocean have been increasing since the beginning of the Industrial Revolution from a variety of activities including ships, petroleum exploration and production, and naval exercises. The ability of mammals to use sound pulses for communication, locating prey, and possibly even to kill prey has been known for many years. Excess noise levels at sea apparently may cause whales to beach themselves onshore where they subsequently die. Sound pulses used in acoustic thermometry to map water temperatures over entire ocean basins (Chapter 3) have also been challenged as potentially harmful, although these signals are of much lower strength.

WATER BIRDS

Restoration of some water-bird populations is among the few successes resulting from environmental policies and regulations in the late 20th century. Populations of brown pelicans were greatly depleted by commercial hunters for their feathers to decorate ladies hats and dresses in the late 19th and early 20th centuries. Brown pelicans are large, fish-eating coastal birds. In 1903,

President Theodore Roosevelt (1858-1919) designated Florida's Pelican Islands as the nation's first wildlife reserve. In 1918 the Migratory Bird Treaty gave them further protection from hunting.

Commercial fishers often killed pelicans by raiding their nests because they were thought to be voracious predators of commercially valuable fish stocks. As a result, pelican populations declined markedly. After 1940 their numbers were further reduced by the widespread use of DDT (dichlorodiphenyltrichloroethane) and other persistent organic pesticides. These compounds accumulated in the fatty tissues of the fish they ate and in the birds themselves. DDT caused pelicans eggs (and the eggs of other birds) to develop such thin shells that they broke before hatching.

Brown pelican populations began recovering after 1972 when the U.S. Environmental Protection Agency banned the manufacture and use of DDT (Figure 14.9). By 1985, brown pelican populations on the U.S. Atlantic coast had recovered to such an extent that they were removed from the endangered species list. Since then the birds have expanded their range, moving northward as far as Chesapeake Bay. However, populations of brown pelicans living on the Pacific and Gulf coasts as well as in Central and South America remain endangered. DDT is still manufactured and used in some developing countries to control mosquitoes and combat malaria.

FIGURE 14.9
While the brown pelican population on the U.S. Atlantic coast has recovered to such an extent that they were removed from the endangered species list, the larger California brown pelican (pictured above) is still endangered. [U.S. Fish and Wildlife Service]

The history of North American ospreys during the 20th century was similar to that of the brown pelican. They also are large fish-eating birds, sometimes called fish hawks. They live on rivers, lakes, and estuaries across much of North America in summer and winter in South America. Like brown pelicans, osprey populations were decimated by the egg thinning caused by DDT accumulation in their tissues. The 1972 ban on DDT greatly aided their recovery. Ospreys build their nests in dead trees near the water and also use duck blinds, power poles, or channel markers as bases for their nests. For many years, U.S. Coast Guard personnel destroyed their nests on navigational aids, thus limiting the number of available nesting sites. After the Coast Guard reversed that policy, the number of ospreys rebounded dramatically. Now they are commonly seen and heard near coasts, lakes, and rivers.

Mariculture

Wild fish stocks are increasingly stressed by overfishing and even collapsing, such as the once plentiful cod in the North Atlantic. On the other hand, **mariculture** (or *marine aquaculture*), industrial farming of fish and shellfish in the ocean is a growing industry worldwide. In 2007, mariculture was valued at $200 million in the United States. For many varieties of fish and shellfish (e.g., salmon, catfish, trout, mussels, oysters, and clams) farmed fish and shellfish dominate retail markets. They are raised within 5 km (3.1 mi) of the shore under the jurisdiction of the state although recent technological advances and soaring demand may move fish farming into the open ocean where it would be regulated by the federal government. Most of these oceanic fish farms are large-scale operations. They have huge floating pens, usually located in protected inlets, holding hundreds of thousands to millions of animals (Figure 14.10). Even marine algae are farmed in Asia, but our focus here is on fish and shellfish.

The simplest mariculture operations involve filter-feeding mollusks (i.e., mussels, oysters and clams). They are usually grown in mesh bags suspended in seawater from floating platforms. Because these animals feed by filtering plankton from the water, they do not require additional food. As they grow, mollusks must be tended to remove algae that grow on the bags and limit the circulation of oxygenated water. Periodically the bags must be replaced as the animals grow.

All fish-farming operations release large amounts of fecal matter that settle to the bottom. Decay

of these organic deposits can deplete near-bottom waters of dissolved oxygen if the currents are not sufficiently strong to disperse these materials. Some particularly large mussel, clam and oyster farms are situated in inlets along the northwest coast of Galicia in Spain but this fish farming has destroyed the original ecosystems.

The salmon-farming industry has grown dramatically since the 1960s when it began off Norway. Today, it dominates the world market for salmon, which is supplied by large farms in cold-water inlets in the coastal waters of Norway, Scotland, Atlantic Canada, British Columbia, and Chile. Wild salmon, while highly prized for its flavor, is now rare, but farmed salmon is abundant, inexpensive, and available year-round. The preferred species for these fish farms is Atlantic salmon because it grows faster, is easier to handle, and more animals can be grown in a single pen than other salmon species. The fish are grown in square steel-net pens (about 30 m or 100 ft on a side) suspended in the water from floating platforms.

Fish farms can add to water pollution problems. Carnivorous fish are fed a diet of fish oils and fishmeal; some of it sinks uneaten to the bottom along with fecal matter. Critics of fish farms compare them to floating pig farms or cattle feed lots on land in terms of the amount of waste material produced. About 1.1 kg (2.4 lb) of wild fishmeal is required to grow 0.5 kg (1.0 lb) of salmon. In addition, the fish must be inoculated against diseases that would otherwise kill them because they live in such crowded conditions, unlike the widely dispersed wild species. Pesticides are also added to their food to control infestations of fish lice. Toxic chemicals are used to treat

FIGURE 14.10
Cobia at a Puerto Rican offshore mariculture facility. Mariculture. refers to the farming of fish and shellfish in the ocean. [NOAA]

the nets to prevent algae growth that would otherwise clog them. Finally the salmon must be fed pigments with their food to make their flesh salmon-pink rather than a less appealing pale gray. In the wild, the salmon's normal color comes from eating pink krill, a variety of large zooplankton.

Salmon farms affect wild salmon and may be responsible for reducing native salmon populations in areas where the farms are located. Captive fish escape when their pens are damaged by storms or attacked by sea lions. They may breed with wild fish, reducing their genetic variability, or even replace them entirely. Wild fish coming close to the pens may also become infested by sea lice, which otherwise occur in low concentrations in the scattered low-density wild populations.

Less complex are freshwater catfish farms, often grown in converted rice fields. These herbivorous fish can feed on terrestrial grains rather than fish, thus reducing the pressure on wild stocks of anchovies, sardines, and mackerel—ingredients of fishmeal. Furthermore, catfish are more efficient than salmon in converting feed to fish proteins.

Marine Exotic Species

Exotic species, sometimes called *alien species*, are animals and plants introduced into ecosystems, usually by humans. Some introductions are intentional (new organisms used for mariculture) whereas others are unintentional (transported in ships' ballast waters). Introduction of exotic species has been taking place for centuries, especially in coastal waters. In most cases the introduced organisms do not survive because they are not well adapted to the physical or chemical conditions of their new environment or they are unable to compete in the new ecosystem. But sometimes an exotic species finds its new environment to be favorable; lacking competitors or diseases, their population expands rapidly. Such introduced species often have no predators to control its numbers. Also they often are outside the range of many of the diseases they normally encounter in their native habitat. Thus, they grow larger than normal, reproduce faster than usual, and take over—perhaps destroying—entire ecosystems. This situation develops in both coastal ocean waters and lakes. (Examples of exotic species in the Great Lakes are lamprey eels and zebra mussels.)

An example of a marine exotic species is the Asian carp, a large (50 kg or 110 lbs) fast-growing fish imported from China to the southern United States by fish farmers. Each female produces millions of eggs each year so that they can quickly overwhelm native fish species. Asian carp consumes up to 40% of their body weight daily, eating vegetation, phytoplankton, mussels and fishes, thereby decimating ecosystems. In the early 1990s, Asian carp were accidentally released into the lower Mississippi River system when floodwaters broke through the dikes surrounding fishponds holding the carp. Since then Asian carp has taken over large stretches of the Mississippi, destroying commercial fisheries on the Lower Mississippi as they migrate northward about 80 km (50 mi) per year to cooler waters, which they prefer. By 2003, they had reached Chicago where a canal connects the Mississippi River system to Lake Michigan and the other Great Lakes.

The *International Joint Commission (IJC)*, the U.S.-Canadian organization established to protect the Great Lakes that the two nations share, has proposed various schemes to prevent the further spread of Asian carp. Among these schemes is the use of an existing electrical barrier in the canal or building a new, physical barrier. Keeping Asian carp out of the Great Lakes will be difficult, however, as they have already been found in a fountain in Toronto, Ontario and in Lake Erie.

Another more recent example of a successful invasive species is the northern snakehead, an air-breathing fish that originated in the waters of eastern Asia. It first showed up in 2002 in a pond in Maryland. Concerned that heavy rain would wash northern snakeheads into a nearby river, wildlife officials drained the pond and poisoned the fish population. However, in 2004 the northern snakehead showed up in the Potomac River with officials unclear as to the long term ramifications. The northern snakehead has no natural predators and competes with the large mouth bass for the same habitat and food.

New exotic organisms may also result from subtle exchanges of genetic materials. The tall marsh grass (*Phragmites*) commonly found in the mid-Atlantic salt marshes has become a widespread and invasive species that crowds out other types of marine grasses. For many thousands of years prior to about 1910, the native form of *Phragmites* grew along with other marine grasses. Beginning in the 1970s, the plant became far more intrusive. Apparently some genetic material, perhaps only a small root fragment of a closely related grass, was brought to North America from Europe or Asia. The genetic material from this exotic variety became dominant and has supplanted the native, less invasive form. Now only plants having genetic material from the Asian form are common.

Exotic marine organisms can also cause health problems among humans. In 1993, a new strain of bacteria, native to Bangladesh and India, appeared in Peru's coastal waters and later spread throughout Central and South America. The bacteria were apparently introduced by ballast water discharged from a ship. Carried by coastal plankton, this strain is now endemic in the region and causes severe cholera-like symptoms when ingested by humans.

Conclusions

For thousands of years humans have looked to the ocean as an important source of food. In fact, the belief was widespread that the sea held an almost limitless bounty of food and inspired some to speculate that marine fisheries could meet the needs of Earth's burgeoning human population well into the future. A variety of technological innovations enabled fishers to become more and more efficient at taking the most desirable top predator fishes and as those fish stocks diminished, they typically moved on to another fishery and repeated the process. However, by 2000, the world fish catch peaked and has been declining ever since. Overfishing forced imposition of quotas and the closure of some fisheries but not before some species came to the brink of extinction. Overfishing and its associated problems (e.g., habitat destruction, bycatch) spurred fisheries managers to reassess their management schemes. The move is to shift from the traditional method of managing fisheries for maximum sustainable yield to a more holistic, ecologically based approach that emphasizes the sustainability of the marine ecosystem (structure and function) that is home to the fishery.

Basic Understandings

- Stewardship of the ocean and its resources involves responsibly managing all resources to benefit present and future generations. In the United States, the National Oceanic and Atmospheric Administration (NOAA) is the principal government agency with stewardship responsibilities for the nation's marine environment and living resources.
- Central to exercising wise stewardship is sustainability, defined by the United Nations' *World Commission on Environment and Development* as "developments that meet the needs of the present without compromising the ability of future generations to meet their own needs."
- Overfishing occurs when a fish species is taken at a rate that exceeds the maximum catch that would allow reproduction to replace the population. With recruitment overfishing, adult fish are taken in such large numbers that too few survive to replenish the breeding stock. Growth overfishing takes place when fish are taken too small, before the animals can grow to a size that would produce maximum yield.
- A variety of technological innovations enabled fishers to greatly increase the fish catch. These innovations include new engines to power larger fishing vessels, refrigeration, factory trawlers, fish-locating equipment, and GPS.
- Governments worldwide spend billions of dollars annually subsidizing their commercial fishing industry—often spending more than the fishery is worth.
- As fishers became more adept at taking fish in large numbers, the frequency of stock collapses increased, forcing fishery managers to impose quotas on commercially desirable fish, limit fishing time at sea, or close fisheries altogether.
- Sharks are an example of an over-exploited, top predator with a relatively low reproductive capacity. Sharks are taken for their meat; some are killed accidentally in collisions with fishing boats; others are unintentionally caught along with target fish and then dumped overboard. The most egregious threat to shark populations, however, is catching them just for their fins and disposing the carcasses overboard.
- As increasing fishing pressures cause populations of top predators to decline, organisms at progressively lower trophic levels begin to dominate the food webs of marine ecosystems. Fishers, in turn, must target fish populations at these lower trophic levels. This shift in targeted fishes is described as "fishing down the food web."
- To prevent overfishing of a fish stock, fishery managers typically set catch quotas. The goal is to adhere to the maximum sustainable yield of the fish stock; that is, limits are set on fish catches so that stocks are maintained at a level that will preserve the long-term viability of the target species.

- Protection of fisheries requires a thorough understanding of the entire ecosystem, not just the targeted commercial or recreational fish species. This understanding is the basis for achieving an ecologically sustainable yield, that is, the yield that a marine ecosystem can sustain without undergoing an undesirable change in state.
- The ecosystem-based approach to fisheries management requires protection of seafloor habitats (e.g., by phasing out destructive trawling practices) and expanding the areas of the world ocean designated as protected areas (called marine reserves) where fishing is prohibited.
- Many commercial fishers accidentally catch undersized fish or unwanted species; this so-called bycatch is discarded, either dead or dying, because it cannot be sold. Bycatch is a major threat to many endangered species, including sea turtles, dolphins, and other marine mammals.
- Recreational fisheries and commercial fisheries differ in important ways. Most recreational fishers prefer to fish near home; hence, sport fish populations are most heavily fished near major urban areas. Recreational fisheries do not damage fish habitat as much as some commercial fishing practices. When catches of popular recreational fishes decline, fisheries management agencies often resort to fish hatcheries to replenish depleted populations.
- Around the world, sea-turtle populations are threatened by many human activities including (1) commercial over-harvesting of adult turtles and illegal poaching of eggs from beaches, (2) development along beaches used for nesting, (3) bycatch in commercial fishing nets, especially shrimp nets, (4) collisions with ships, including recreational boats, (5) ingestion of plastic litter, especially plastic bags mistaken for jellyfish, and (6) marine pollution.
- Like fishers, whalers focused on a single species until its numbers were so reduced that they had to hunt another (usually smaller) species. To protect the world's remaining whale stocks, in 1986 the International Whaling Commission (IWC) declared a moratorium on commercial whaling. However, Japan, Norway, and Iceland continued commercial whaling, arguing that the populations of smaller whales (e.g., the minke whale) are now at healthy levels and can sustain whaling, and that whales eat many commercially valuable fishes.

- Restoration of some water-bird populations is among the successes resulting from changed environmental policies and regulations in the late 20th century. North American brown pelicans and ospreys are examples.
- Mariculture, industrial farming of fish and shellfish in the ocean, is a growing industry worldwide. For many varieties of fish and shellfish (e.g., salmon, catfish, trout, mussels, oysters, and clams), farmed fish and shellfish dominate retail markets.
- Marine exotic species are animals or plants introduced into ecosystems, usually by humans. Some introductions are intentional (new organisms used for mariculture) whereas others are unintentional (brought in with the ballast water of ships). In some cases, an exotic species finds its new environment favorable; lacking competitors or diseases, their population expands rapidly. Thus, they grow larger than normal, reproduce faster than usual, and take over—perhaps destroying entire ecosystems.

Review

1. What are the ocean stewardship responsibilities of the National Oceanic and Atmospheric Administration (NOAA)?
2. What is meant by sustainability?
3. Describe the two types of overfishing.
4. At what general size does a fish population have the greatest potential for growth and reproduction?
5. What is bycatch? Identify some of the ways bycatch occurs.
6. Identify some strategies for establishing sustainable fisheries.
7. How does shrimp trawling threaten sea turtles and what is being done to alleviate this problem?
8. Why are whales in demand by certain nations?
9. Define mariculture and describe how it can damage marine ecosystems.
10. Under what conditions are exotic species likely to infiltrate and possibly dominate a marine ecosystem?

Critical Thinking

1. How do technological innovations contribute to the problem of overfishing?
2. Why are "top predators" particularly subject to overfishing? What are some major implications for the rest of the food web?
3. How would adherence to the maximum sustainable yield help prevent overfishing?
4. What is the principal advantage of achieving ecologically sustainable yield?
5. What strategies would help alleviate the bycatch problem?
6. Why is the age of a fish an important consideration in the recovery of a fish population that has been depleted by overfishing?
7. Why is commercial fishing potentially more disruptive of marine ecosystems than recreational fishing?
8. Speculate on why an overfished stock might never recover to its original population level.
9. In what sense are invasive species "exotic"?
10. Briefly outline what is meant by an ecosystem approach to fisheries management.

ESSAY: Determining the Age of a Fish

Knowing how long a fish lives is vitally important to managing fish stocks and protecting them from overfishing by commercial or recreational fishers. As noted elsewhere in this chapter, *overfishing* is the practice of harvesting fish at a rate that causes a dramatic decline in the fish stock, perhaps to the extent that the fishery collapses. In essence, the rate of harvest exceeds the maximum harvest that would allow for replacement of the population through reproduction. Long-lived animals grow slowly, reproduce infrequently, and take a long time to recover from overfishing. Agencies responsible for protecting and regulating fish populations must therefore know the life span of fish that are being harvested.

Orange roughy, a deep-water fish caught near New Zealand, was once presumed to live no more than about 20 to 30 years and catch limits were set accordingly. Within five years, the fishery collapsed due to overfishing. Scientists discovered that the orange roughy actually lives more than 100 years (up to a maximum of about 150 years), is very slow growing, and does not reach sexual maturity until about 30 years of age. It appears likely that recovery of orange roughy stock will take decades.

A long-used indirect method of estimating the age of a fish is to measure the length of large numbers of fish of the same species caught in nets. From these data, scientists estimate age based on models of how fast the particular fish species grows. Another method of age determination is to raise fish in tanks to determine directly the relationship between size and age. Neither of these methods is entirely satisfactory, however.

A more accurate technique is to count the number of annual growth rings in a fish's ear stone, the *otolith*. This calcareous concretion is up to about the size of a nickel. Bone is deposited on the outside of the otolith as the fish grows, thereby forming a banded bone that can be sectioned and studied much like the growth rings of a tree. Some fishes produce annual bands; others take longer to form a single band. By cutting thin sections of an otolith and counting the bands, it is possible to determine a fish's age accurately. Sufficient samples of many fish of the same species provide a reasonable estimate of life span.

Furthermore, chemical analysis of the individual bands in otoliths permits scientists to determine the various environments where the fish has lived during its life cycle (e.g., lakes, estuaries, or open-ocean). Also, oxygen isotope analysis of the otoliths enables scientists to reconstruct the water temperature when the particular band formed. (Oxygen isotope analysis is discussed in Chapter 12.) Finally, these detailed analyses can be used to determine which animals lived together when the bands formed.

Another method of age determination applies to bony fishes. They have scales on their skin that grow by forming rings. The fish's age is determined by analyzing the scales under a microscope and counting the rings. This technique is especially useful in tiny tropical fishes whose otoliths are too small to study conventionally. In general, these smaller, faster-growing tropical fish have shorter life spans than larger, slower-growing fish living in colder waters.

FIGURE 1
Scientist aboard the *Gordon Gunter* removing ear bones from fish to determine its age. [NOAA photo taken by Paul Olson]

ESSAY: Loss and Restoration of Coastal Wetlands

For centuries, people have attempted to reclaim wetlands near cities and in densely populated coastal regions, such as Japan or the Netherlands. Much of Lower Manhattan's shoreline is built on such reclaimed lands, as is New York City's John F. Kennedy International Airport. The Dutch pioneered reclamation techniques, converting shallow sea bottoms to agricultural fields surrounded by dikes; such reclaimed lands are called *polders*. Other former coastal marshes were filled and are now used as landfills for solid waste.

In more recent years, studies have demonstrated the many valuable functions that wetlands perform if maintained in their natural state, including protecting coastal lands against saltwater encroachment and flooding from storm surges and heavy rainfall. Wetlands filter water flowing through as well as acting as sponges, soaking up water at high tide and during floods. Again, the Dutch are leading the way in restoring wetlands by breaking the dikes surrounding certain polders, permitting them to flood again and return to their original condition as salt marshes or shallow sea beds. On smaller scales, individual farmers have removed drains to permit low-lying fields to flood seasonally, thereby encouraging marsh plants to invade and provide habitats. These areas are used by water birds and by fish as nursery grounds during their larval and juvenile stages.

Some marshes were damaged by introduced species that destroyed the native grasses, thereby accelerating erosion as sea level rises. That happened at the Blackwater Natural Wildlife Refuge on Chesapeake Bay's Eastern Shore, which is the largest unbroken stretch of marshland on the Chesapeake. In the 1930s, the *nutria*, a beaver-sized rodent native to South America, was introduced deliberately to provide local trappers with a source of furs. Unlike its cousin the native muskrat, which eats only the top of the marsh grasses, nutria eats the plant roots. Its voracious appetite destroyed the native grasses, leaving large areas of marshland unprotected against erosion by waves and tidal currents (Figure 1). By 2001, the original 9700-hectare (24,000-acre) refuge was losing 60 hectares (150 acres) of salt marsh each year, producing large open-water areas and accelerating erosion of adjoining salt marshes.

FIGURE 1
Research biologist examining nutria damage to marsh at the Blackwater National Wildlife Refuge. [Photo by Mike Haramis, USGS]

In the 1990s, wetland restoration projects began in the Chesapeake including the Chesapeake Marsh Restoration/ Nutria Control Project to reclaim marshes in the Blackwater National Wildlife Refuge. This restoration project also helps alleviate another major environmental problem in the Chesapeake Bay, that is, the disposal of sediment dredged from shipping channels. A special dredge removes mud from channel bottoms and discharges it over the marshes. The newly deposited sediment layers are sufficiently thin that they do not kill the grasses, which grow over them, thus stabilizing the restored marsh. Each year, many thousands of migrating waterfowl as well as large numbers of bald eagles use the restored marshlands. These areas are also home to endangered fox squirrels. The shallow waters are nursery grounds for crabs, the most important commercial fishery in the Chesapeake. Furthermore, sediment trapping and nutrient retention by the marsh helps improve water quality in the nearby Chesapeake Bay.

According to the Louisiana Coastal Wetlands Conservation and Restoration Task Force, Louisiana has been losing coastal wetlands (i.e., bayous, marshes, and swamps) to the waters of the Gulf of Mexico at an alarming rate of about 65 to 100 square km (25 to 38 square mi) per year for the past several decades. This loss adversely affects fisheries in the Gulf of Mexico and makes the coastal zone more vulnerable to storm surges such as that produced by Hurricane Katrina in August 2005. Since the early 1930s, the state's coastal wetlands have shrunk by an area equivalent to the state of Delaware. According to estimates by the U.S. Geological Survey, an additional 1800 square km (700 square mi) could be lost by mid-century.

As much as 75% of the fish and other marine life in the northern Gulf of Mexico depend on Louisiana's coastal wetlands. The wetlands function as a nursery for commercially important catches of shrimp, crawfish, blue crab, and oysters. It is a food source for larger fish including yellow fin tuna, red snapper, and swordfish. In 2003, about three-quarters of the nation's fish and shellfish catch by weight came from Louisiana's waters. In addition, the wetlands are a stopover for millions of birds migrating between North America and Central/South America. Furthermore, wetlands and associated barrier islands protect the ports, buildings, and other coastal structures from storm surges. Wetlands are particularly important in buffering the levees surrounding New Orleans, much of which is below sea level.

Many factors contribute to the loss of Louisiana's coastal wetlands. Thousands of kilometers of pipelines transporting oil and natural gas through the marshes plus the extensive network of navigation canals allows saltwater to invade the wetlands. Increased salinity of the originally fresh or brackish waters kills wetland grasses, shrubs, and other vegetation that anchor the soil in place. The canals also allow tidal currents to flow further inland, accelerating erosion of wetland soils. Exacerbating the problem was the introduction of the nutria in the 1930s and as was the case in Chesapeake Bay (described earlier), the nutria soon began to devour marsh grasses. The most important factor in the loss of Louisiana's coastal wetlands, however, is the consequence of flood control structures (levees) constructed along the banks of the Mississippi River by the U.S. Army Corps of Engineers in the 1940s. Levees constrict the flow of the river so that water and suspended sediments discharge directly into the Gulf. Deprived of a continuous input of sediment and vegetation-supporting nutrients, the existing sediments compact, wetlands subside, and Gulf waters encroach upon the wetlands. With the expected continued rise in mean sea level due to global climate change, erosion of Louisiana's coastal wetlands may accelerate in the future (Chapter 12).

Plans to reverse the loss of Louisiana's coastal wetlands seek to restore the structure and function of those wetlands while protecting existing wetlands. Although public policy makers were aware of the problem in the 1960s, little was accomplished prior to 1990 when federal legislation provided the state with about $50 million annually for a variety of wetland restoration projects that, unfortunately, proved to be too small and piecemeal. Federal, state, and local officials proposed a much more ambition plan to create a "sustainable ecosystem that supports and protects the environment, economy, and culture of southern Louisiana." Known as *Coast 2050*, this proposal carried a price tag of $14 billion and would take 3 decades to complete. In 2003, the Bush Administration rejected this plan as too costly. The following year, a scaled-down plan, called the *Louisiana Coastal Area (LCA)* study, was developed calling for a budget of $1.9 billion over 10 years. Among the projects supported by the LCA study was the breaching of some levees along the lower Mississippi River. This partial diversion of the river is intended to increase the supply of sediments to the wetlands. Closing or installing locks on some navigation canals would reduce saltwater encroachment. In addition, dredged sediment would be used to restore wetlands and barrier islands.

However, much more needs to be done. An assessment of the LCA study by the National Academy of Sciences in 2005 concluded that it is "too modest an effort." According to calculations by the U.S. Army Corps of Engineers, the LCA plan would slow the rate of coastal wetland loss by only 20%.

CHAPTER 15

OCEAN PROBLEMS AND POLICY

Case-in-Point
Driving Question
Milestones in Ocean Governance
    Freedom of the Seas
    Antarctic Treaty
Human Impact in the Coastal Zone
    Human Population Trends
    Environmental Pollution
    Coastal Zone Management
Oil Spills
Dams and Marine Habitats
Restoring Chesapeake Bay
Waste Disposal in the Ocean
Deep-Ocean Carbon Storage
Obstacles to Ocean Policy Making
Conclusions
Basic Understandings/Review/Critical Thinking
ESSAY: Pathogens in the Coastal Zone
ESSAY: Predicting Oil-Spill Trajectories

Plastic debris on a reef in Guam, Mariana Islands. [NOAA's Coral Kingdom Collection photo by David Burdick]

Case in Point

In the United States, removal of even small dams on rivers and streams is a relatively new strategy intended to benefit downstream ecosystems including marine ecosystems. Hundreds of small dams were removed in the 1990s although few cases have been studied in sufficient detail to demonstrate conclusively the environmental benefits of dam removal. One of the success stories involves the breaching of the Edwards Dam on the Kennebec River in Augusta, ME on 1 July 1999. For the first time in 162 years, the river flowed freely to the ocean. At the time, the Kennebec was the largest river in the nation to have a dam removed and the Edwards Dam is still among the largest dams ever removed.

      Built in 1837, the Edwards Dam decimated local fish populations, first by flooding critical habitats and then by preventing *anadromous fish* from migrating from the ocean to their upstream spawning grounds. Removing the Edwards Dam reopened about 30 km (19 mi) of fish spawning and nursery habitat in the Kennebec River. Environmental improvements in Merrymeeting Bay (at the river's mouth), the largest freshwater tidal complex on the Atlantic coast north of Chesapeake Bay, were reported in the years after removal of the dam. Populations of 10 species of anadromous fish exhibited varying levels of recovery; among them were alewives, American shad, Atlantic salmon, striped bass, and Atlantic sturgeon. Some fish populations will require releases of hatchery-raised young fish to restore their populations to pre-dam levels. Many bird populations also increased in number (e.g., ospreys, kingfishers, cormorants, and bald eagles) and water quality improved (i.e., higher water clarity and dissolved oxygen levels). In addition, recovery of the river spurred revitalization of Augusta's waterfront and other

riverside communities as tourists, recreational fishers, and boaters returned to the area.

> ## Driving Question:
> *How does national and international ocean policy promote wise stewardship of the world ocean?*

This chapter is concerned with the impact of human activities on the ocean and coastal zone, marine ecosystems and habitats, and how society is attempting to minimize that impact, remediate past damage, and head off future problems. Throughout this book, we presented many instances of how humans adversely affect the ocean and the coastal zone. Rising sea level, coral bleaching, ocean acidification, and shrinkage of the Arctic ice cover are likely linked to our dependence on fossil fuels and the enhanced greenhouse effect. In Chapter 8, we described how humankind has attempted to stabilize the inherently dynamic coast by constructing seawalls, jetties, breakwaters, and groins often to little or no avail. In fact, we have made some of our coastlines more vulnerable to storm surges, flooding, and erosion by developing barrier islands and removing protective mangrove swamps. The discharge of excessive nutrients into coastal waters has triggered harmful algal blooms (HABs) and created oxygen depleted "dead zones." Our growing demand for fish and shellfish is responsible for overfishing, bycatch, destruction of essential fish habitat, and endangered some marine species.

In attempting to remediate these problems in the ocean and coastal zone, we have adopted *ocean stewardship* (Chapter 14). In this regard we recognize the need for an ecosystems approach to fisheries management and protection of living and non-living marine resources through federal and state sanctuaries programs and fisheries management. To a large measure, ocean stewardship arises from humankind's desire to regulate exploitation of marine resources and space to meet human needs and to achieve *sustainable development*.

While the United States is the principal focus of many of the issues discussed in this book, vast areas of the ocean are in international waters and marine ecosystems adhere to no political boundaries. Hence, in dealing with human impacts on the marine environment, a global perspective and international cooperation are essential. In this chapter, we take a closer look at the human

interaction with the ocean and coastal zone with emphasis on remediation, sustainability, and stewardship. We begin with a summary of important milestones in the national and international governance of the ocean.

Milestones in Ocean Governance

On land, humans have long divided space and resources into two categories: private property and public property held in trust for citizens of the nation in which these resources are found. The history of ocean governance, however, differs dramatically from that of land. For most of human history, the open ocean has been beyond the direct management of coastal nations or any other governments, just like outer space. As the human population soared and human exploitation of ocean resources expanded, regulations and institutions to govern the ocean were developed.

FREEDOM OF THE SEAS

In 1609, the Dutch legal scholar Hugo Grotius (1585-1645), a pioneer natural rights theorist, published his influential treatise, *The Freedom of the Seas*. In it, he argued that the ocean was open with free access to all nations; that is, no nation or group of nations has the right to monopolize either its use or access to it. For Grotius, liberty of the sea was key to maintaining communication among peoples and nations. Along with this doctrine of free access, the general consensus was that the sea was limitless and its resources inexhaustible. There was no need to control access if marine resources were essentially unlimited and therefore virtually immune to any possible damage caused by human activities.

Partitioning of the coastal ocean began in the late 1700s, when the new United States of America claimed a 5-km (3-mi) "territorial sea" off its coast. Such a narrow coastal fringe could be guarded and controlled given the range of the military cannons of the day. Authority over these territorial waters was assigned to the individual states. In 1945, the U.S. extended its national claims on coastal resources to the outer edge of the continental shelf. A major reason for this policy change was the expansion of offshore oil and natural gas production on the shallow continental shelf around the Gulf of Mexico and off the California coast. To this day, the U.S. considers waters outside national territorial waters to be international waters, open to all.

In 1976, the United States extended its jurisdiction over some marine fisheries. The *Magnuson-Stevens Fisheries and Conservation Act* (also known as the *Magnuson Act*) extended the jurisdiction of the nation's fisheries-management seaward from the shore to 330 km (200 mi), waters that were formerly heavily fished by foreign vessels. The Magnuson Act also established fishery councils to manage the fishery resources in each region of the U.S. In 1996, the *Sustainable Fisheries Act* amended the Magnuson Act imposing strict new mandates to halt overfishing, rebuild overfished stocks, reduce bycatch, and protect essential fish habitat.

The first commission to develop a national ocean policy for the United States was the *Commission on Marine Science, Engineering and Resources*, more commonly known as the *Stratton Commission* after its Chair, Julius A. Stratton (1901-94), then also Chair of the Ford Foundation. The Commission worked for two years and presented its final report, *Our Nation and The Sea, A Plan for National Action*, in January 1969. Among other recommendations, it called for creation of the *National Oceanic and Atmospheric Administration (NOAA)* by combining existing government agencies responsible for the ocean and atmosphere. Recognizing that the ocean plays an integral role in the economic, environmental, and security interests of the United States, a second *U.S. Commission on Ocean Policy* was established to make recommendations to the President and Congress for a coordinated and comprehensive national ocean policy. It began work in 2001 and issued its final report at the end of summer 2004. Recommendations called for an overhaul of ocean policy including a shift to ecosystem-based management of marine life (Chapter 14), creation of a National Oceans Council within the Executive Branch of government, and doubling of federal funding for ocean research.

Other nations, including Australia and Canada, have developed ocean policies for their Exclusive Economic Zones (Chapter 4). Such policies are tailored to the interests and priorities of the individual countries. No international ocean policy has yet been developed to deal with open-ocean areas outside the various EEZs.

In 1982, the *United Nations Convention on the Law of the Sea* expanded the narrow territorial waters 20 km (12 nautical mi) from the shoreline and authorized nations to establish *Exclusive Economic Zones (EEZs)*. The U.S. established its EEZ in 1983, extending federal jurisdiction from the seaward limits of the state-controlled territorial seas to 370 km (200 nautical mi) from the coastline. In 1996, EEZs were extended to the edge of the continental shelf when the shelf edge was more than 370 km (200 nautical mi) offshore. Within their individual EEZ, each coastal nation has the same rights and responsibilities that they exercise over their land areas. Migratory fishes, which may cross national boundaries, and range beyond the limits of an EEZ, are regulated under the *Convention on Straddling Stocks*. Cooperation on the conservation of such stocks is the responsibility of those nations where the fish live or where they are taken.

At the beginning of the 21st century, about two-thirds of the ocean was part of the **ocean commons** and beyond the control of any coastal nation. The ocean commons essentially is free to all for unlimited exploitation. Little or no regulation exists over the ocean commons, except for a few specialized treaties such as the 1972 *London Dumping Convention* that bans the discharge of wastes from land by ships or aircraft. Commercial whaling was uncontrolled until banned by the International Whaling Commission in 1986 (Chapter 14). Unregulated commercial fishing has depleted some open-ocean fish populations. An example is the overfishing and eventual collapse of the Canadian cod fishery in the early 1990s (Chapter 10).

As the global human population continues to grow and increasing demands for natural resources exceed supplies on land, ocean resources are likely to be increasingly exploited. In the future, such pressures are likely to drive human governance over more ocean space and resources. Innovative technologies could be used to enforce international regulations. As noted in Chapter 13, various technologies now provide continuous surveillance of the ocean surface and interior. Some experts argue that all ships, planes, and submarines operating in, on, and over the ocean can be tracked, and their activities monitored in various ways. For example, acoustic methods can detect whether fishing boats have nets in the water and even identify the types of nets in use.

Future governance of ocean resource exploitation may apply the *Precautionary Principle*: "When an action causes a threat to human health or the environment, precautionary measures should be taken even if some cause-and-effect relationships are not fully established scientifically." The 1992 United Nations Conference on Environment and Development held in Rio de Janeiro, Brazil adopted the Precautionary Principle. It was also included in the Rio Declaration's "Agenda 21," which was adopted by 178 nations in June 1992, and later ratified by the United States. The precautionary approach helps to overcome the enormous barrier to action posed by the inevitable scientific uncertainty about cause-effect relationships in complex systems. This is especially important in the ocean where many important sub-systems and processes, and their interactions are still poorly understood.

ANTARCTIC TREATY

Human activity in the Antarctic region includes the slaughter almost to extinction, of millions of seals and whales, and the dumping of huge amounts of garbage by explorers and scientists. However, in the last half of the 20th century, Antarctica and the Southern Ocean came under the protection of the Antarctic Treaty System. The *Antarctic Treaty System* is a complex of arrangements that regulate relations among nations near Antarctica and those conducting research and exploration there. In 1959, the Antarctic Treaty System was adopted by the dozen nations that engaged in scientific research in the Antarctic region during the International Geophysical Year (1957-58). The Treaty has since expanded to 45 nations sponsoring research in Antarctica and/or the Southern Ocean. In 2003, these countries represented about two-thirds of the world's population. The Antarctic Treaty System ensures that no national claim of territorial rights in Antarctica or the surrounding waters will ever be legally recognized and that Antarctica forever would be used exclusively for peaceful purposes.

The Antarctic Treaty System applies to waters, ice shelves, and islands in the Southern Ocean, that is, south of 60 degrees S. This is the approximate latitude of the *Antarctic convergence* where cold Antarctic waters from the south meet warmer waters from the north (Chapter 6). The Antarctic convergence acts as a biological barrier so that the Southern Ocean is essentially a separate ecosystem. The *Convention on the Conservation of Antarctic Marine Living Resources (CAMLR)* was adopted in 1982 as part of the Antarctic Treaty System. CAMLR was established in response to international concerns that increased catches of krill (a large shrimp-like zooplanktonic organism) in the Southern Ocean could threaten krill populations as well as the large whales, other marine mammals, birds, and fishes that feed primarily on krill and associated high seas fisheries.

Human Impact in the Coastal Zone

As noted in Chapter 8, the majority of the human population lives in the coastal zone where they interact with the ocean (and large lakes). It is in the coastal zone that stewardship over the ocean is most urgent and, in many cases, most challenging. People living in the coastal zone are vulnerable to certain natural hazards (e.g., flooding due to storm surge, tsunamis). They also impact the natural functioning of the coastal zone where the land, ocean, atmosphere, cryosphere, and biosphere interact.

HUMAN POPULATION TRENDS

About 80% of the land on Earth is now inhabited by people or otherwise impacted by human activities such as agriculture, pasturing animals, growing trees, mining, or urban development. Satellite images taken at night of lighted settlements combined with census data (base year 1990) show that half the world's people live within about 30 km (19 mi) of the coastline and nearly 75% within 50 km (31 mi). Population density in Earth's coastal zone is about three times that of the overall Earth average. The most densely populated coastal zones are in Europe and Asia; most of these coastal dwellers live in rural areas and small- to medium-size cities, rather than large urban areas.

In earlier chapters, we described how human habitation of the coastal zone exposes people to many natural hazards. The hazard risk is especially great for people living in low-lying coastal plains less than 100 m (330 ft) above sea level. With sea level rising, the principal problems are expected to be in low-lying delta areas, such as the Netherlands in Western Europe, Bangladesh in South Asia, and the Mississippi River delta of North America. In these areas, storm surge flooding can extend inland 100 km (62 mi) or more.

Population growth in the coastal zone during the first half of the 21st century is expected to take place in small- and mid-sized communities in developing countries. Older mega-cities, which are mostly located at shorelines and near large rivers, are expected to grow more slowly. A significant fraction of this coastal-zone population growth will likely come from people moving from inland agricultural communities to small coastal communities, filling in the space between large metropolitan areas, such as the Boston-New York-Washington, DC corridor in the United States or the Tokyo-Osaka corridor in Japan. Consequently, a larger fraction of the world's population will impact the coastal zone and risk exposure to natural hazards.

ENVIRONMENTAL POLLUTION

Increasing human population density in the coastal zone is likely to exacerbate environmental pollution. **Pollution** is defined as an intentional or unintentional disturbance of the environment that adversely affects the wellbeing of organisms (including humans) directly or the natural processes upon which they depend. The disturbance might involve the alteration of a biogeochemical cycle as when combustion of fossil fuels alters the global carbon cycle and elevates the concentration of carbon dioxide in the atmosphere (Chapter 12). In other cases, toxic and hazardous materials may be dumped or otherwise introduced into reservoirs where they may not normally occur. As described in the Case-in-Point of Chapter 4, disposal of mercury waste in Minamata Bay, Japan contaminated fish and shellfish that were subsequently consumed by humans who developed debilitating symptoms. In the U.S., all along the Mississippi River, runoff from agricultural lands is transported and eventually discharged into the Gulf of Mexico off the Louisiana coast. This results in excessive primary production off the Mississippi River delta. The subsequent decomposition of this production causes annual oxygen-deficient "dead zones" on the ocean bottom (Chapter 10).

Inevitably, all organisms (including humans) disturb their environment by exploiting and utilizing resources, as well as producing waste products. Through the years, humans have been particularly pervasive in their disturbance of the environment so that many areas of the world suffer from air and water pollution. In addition, natural physical forces such as hurricanes, floods, tsunamis, volcanic eruptions, and earthquakes disturb the Earth system. Anyone who has survived a hurricane or destructive earthquake would agree that humankind is unable to prevent such catastrophes. As noted in Chapter 8, even efforts to lessen the impact by structural means (e.g., building sea walls to protect against storm surge) have limitations and often fail in the long term. We can, however, reduce the toll of lives lost and property damaged by planning for such disasters and avoiding habitation of areas that are particularly prone to natural hazards.

On the other hand, we can do something about disturbances for which humans are responsible. For example, we can reduce the input of excess nutrients from agricultural fields into estuaries and other coastal waters, as well as freshwater lakes and systems, and stop the dumping of untreated sewage and industrial waste into rivers and streams that ultimately empty into the ocean. Most long-term efforts to control or prevent harmful algal blooms (HABs) center upon reducing the amount of nutrients in the water that stimulate algal blooms, specifically by reducing nitrogen and phosphorus discharges from wastewater treatment plants or runoff from farms, factories, and cities (Chapter 9). In addition, the presence of disease-causing microbes forces the closing of recreational beaches and contaminated shellfish beds. For more on this problem, refer to this chapter's first Essay.

If we are responsible for disturbances that reduce the quality of the coastal marine environment, then corrective action is needed. Typically, however, not everyone agrees that action is needed or on what specific steps should be taken when there is general agreement that a problem must be dealt with. Some people argue that any disturbance that harms plants, animals, or humans in any way is unacceptable. But how seriously must organisms and/or the ecosystems be impaired before the disturbance is considered unacceptable? Are we concerned about all species or just a select group of species or the ecosystem-species interaction as in ocean fisheries? What are the political and economic ramifications of our choices? There are often no easy answers to these questions.

A better understanding of the problem of pollution in the coastal zone and elsewhere in the ocean is based on the concepts of carrying capacity, assimilative capacity, and limiting factors. Waste disposal in ocean waters is an ongoing problem that can only be exacerbated by human population growth in the coastal zone. The human **carrying capacity** of a region is based on the maximum rate of resource consumption and waste discharge that is sustainable indefinitely without progressively impairing ecosystem productivity and integrity. **Assimilative capacity** is the amount of waste that an ecosystem can assimilate (via decomposition by bacteria, fungi, and invertebrates) without damaging ecosystem functions or building up waste products to levels that may cause unwanted or harmful impacts on living organisms (including humans). The growth and wellbeing of an organism is limited by the essential resource (e.g., nutrients, dissolved oxygen) that is in lowest supply relative to what is required. This most deficient resource is known as the **limiting factor** (Chapter 9).

Carrying capacity and assimilative capacity are especially important considerations for islands, which often are densely populated and lack adequate facilities to treat the wastes of large and seasonally variable populations of tourists. For example, this is a serious problem in many popular beach resorts around the Mediterranean Sea.

COASTAL ZONE MANAGEMENT

The need to balance multiple use and preservation of the coastal zone spurred the federal government to partner with states having coastlines to develop and implement plans for sustainable coastal zone management. The federal government assists coastal states in managing and protecting their coastal resources through the **Coastal Zone Management Program (CZMP)** authorized by the *1972 Coastal Zone Management Act*. Program goals are "to preserve, protect, develop, and where possible, to restore or enhance the resources of the Nation's coastal zone" and to encourage states to develop and implement plans "to achieve wise use of the land and water resources of the coastal zone." At the federal level, NOAA's Office of Ocean and Coastal Resource Management (OCRM), part of the National Ocean Service, administers the CZMP.

The CZMP promotes comprehensive management of coastal resources. This program seeks to protect those resources for future generations while balancing competing economic, cultural, and environmental issues. The federal government supports state efforts at coastal zone management by providing financial assistance (matched by state funds), mediation of conflicts, technical services, and information. Coastal states that show satisfactory progress in implementing their management plan are eligible for special federal grants (matched by state funds) to help states preserve or restore coastal areas, redevelop urban waterfronts and ports, and provide access to public beaches. Actual day-to-day coastal zone management decisions rest with the individual states.

As of this writing, all 34 eligible coastal states and U.S. territories have federally approved coastal zone management plans that apply to much of the more than 160,000 km (100,000 mi) of national coastline. All approved state coastal management plans must address a number of issues in balancing use with preservation. These issues include (1) an inventory and designation of areas of particular concern in the coastal zone, (2) a definition of permitted land and water uses that directly impact coastal waters, (3) identification of how those uses will be controlled, and (4) an outline of broad guidelines to determine priority uses in coastal areas.

Another provision of the 1972 Coastal Zone Management Act established the *National Estuarine Research Reserve System (NERRS)*. The U.S. Secretary of Commerce can authorize grants to coastal states to acquire, develop, and operate estuarine research reserves (Figure 15.1). Since 1972, the NERRS has expanded to include 27 estuarine research reserves along the Pacific,

FIGURE 15.1
This National Estuarine Research Reserve at Jug Bay, Chesapeake Bay, MD, is one of 27 sites established for long-term research, education, and stewardship of estuaries. [NOAA Photo Library, NOAA's Office of Ocean and Coastal Resource Management].

Gulf, Atlantic, and Great Lakes coasts plus Puerto Rico. The reserves were established for long-term research, education, and coastal stewardship. NOAA provides funding, national guidance, and technical assistance. Reserve staff work with local communities and public interest groups on issues such as non-point source pollution, habitat restoration, and invasive species.

Oil Spills

Releases of oil, hazardous substances, and other pollutants continue to threaten fragile coastal ecosystems. According to the *Office of Response and Restoration* of NOAA's National Ocean Service, about 200 maritime accidents collectively spill about 7.6 million liters (2 million gal) of oil each year into the coastal zone. More than 700 hazardous waste sites contaminate the U.S. coastal zone. Pollutants transported to the coastal environment by rivers and streams can kill fish and birds, destroy habitats, disrupt marine food webs, and close recreational beaches. In this section, we consider the causes and impacts of oil spills in coastal waters.

Oil is a major industrial commodity shipped in huge quantities across the ocean every day. For many reasons (shipwreck, collisions, pumping of ships' bilges, war, and terrorism), oil is spilled accidentally or intentionally into the ocean on a daily basis. Oil routinely enters the ocean from storm sewer and wastewater discharges. In addition, a large but mostly unknown quantity of oil enters the ocean naturally, leaking through the seafloor into the overlying water. All of these discharges adversely affect the ocean and its ecosystems with the exception of an unknown number of chemosynthetic ecosystems. Consider the impacts on the ocean of some of the larger oil spills of the late 20th and early 21st centuries.

One of the world's most well-known oil spills occurred in the coastal waters of Alaska in 1989. Because of navigational errors, early on 24 March 1989, the supertanker *Exxon Valdez* ran aground on a reef in Prince William Sound, ripping open the tanker's hull. Eventually nearly 42 million liters (11 million gal) of crude oil spilled into the ocean, creating the largest oil spill in U.S. history. The spill occurred in one of the world's most bountiful coastal areas, home to diverse and productive ecosystems.

During the next several weeks, in part due to inadequate planning, technology, and the ability to control and corral the leaking oil, strong currents and storm winds transported the spilled oil as a slick through the Sound and along the open North Pacific coast. Some of the oil moved westward coating beaches along about 2400 km (1500 mi.) of the Alaska Peninsula. The Exxon Corporation, the ship's owner, conducted a massive, $2 billion shoreline cleanup. Thousands of people washed beaches with hot and cold water, removed oiled sediment deposits, and spread chemical fertilizers to spur bacterial growth and decomposition of petroleum residues (Figure 15.2). Naturally occurring oil-decomposing bacteria bloomed in the near shore waters after the spill and helped to clean shorelines. Smaller cleanup crews worked during subsequent summers, removing oily sediments and recording the condition of the treated beaches.

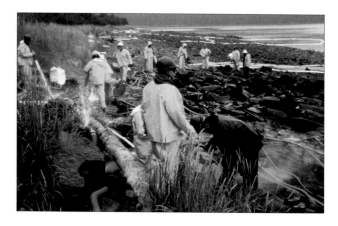

FIGURE 15.2
Cleanup in Alaska's Prince William Sound area following the 1989 *Exxon Valdez* oil spill. [EXXON VALDEZ Oil Spill Trustee Council, NOAA Photo Library]

The spilled oil devastated many communities of marine organisms, which were covered by oil and thereby exposed to many toxic constituents. Organisms living attached to the rocky upper and middle parts of the intertidal zone were severely impacted. In such areas, most seaweeds, and attached and burrowing organisms perished. Weathered oil that sank to the bottom below low tide levels killed eelgrass beds and the animals living in them. The spilled oil also decimated sea birds; an estimated half-million birds representing 90 species probably died. Sea birds that live mostly on the water's surface were especially vulnerable, including common murres and harlequin ducks. About 250 bald eagles were apparently killed, either directly by the spill or later when they ate oil-coated fish and oil-contaminated carcasses.

Marine mammal populations near the oil spill were also affected. About 2800 sea otters were probably killed immediately when their fur coats were oiled, thus depriving them of their fur's insulation and providing them with inadequate protection from the cold. Furthermore, oil slicks that spread from the spill contaminated many prime haulout-areas used by hundreds of harbor seals, just before pupping season began. Large marine mammals, such as humpback whales, apparently were little affected. However, nearly two dozen killer whales from a resident pod were missing and presumed dead.

Among commercially exploited fishes in Prince William Sound, herring and salmon were most seriously affected. Billions of salmon died. For many fish species, the cause of death probably will never be known. Their corpses likely sank to the bottom, were washed out to sea, or were eaten by scavengers. Unfortunately, many of the scavengers that ate them probably also died from the oil-contaminated meat.

A federal-state council of resource agencies planned and implemented a program of natural resource damage assessment. Together with the U.S. Environmental Protection Agency, the council developed plans for restoring Prince William Sound and its ecosystems. With the massive cleanup efforts and almost two decades of natural healing, many of the resources of Prince William Sound have recovered or are still recovering. Unfortunately, some ecosystems may take much longer to recover and some may never return to their original state.

When Prince William Sound was surveyed nearly 14 years after the spill and cleanup, the results were mixed. Six species had nearly fully recovered: murres, black oystercatchers, bald eagles, river otters, and two species of salmon. Oil still clung to the underside of rocks on beaches. Many species had not recovered to pre-spill levels, including herring (a major food source in local ecosystems), several species of seabirds (loons, cormorants, ducks), harbor seals, and killer whales. Some ecologists question whether humans can restore such a system that has been so extensively disturbed. All parties agree that more money is needed for restoration activities. Exxon settled claims for damages to the marine environment amounting to $1 billion. In addition, the company was fined billions of dollars for punitive damages. Much of the money already spent has gone into purchasing wildlife areas and studying the long-term effects of the spill.

A much smaller oil spill occurred off Cape Cod, MA on 15 December 1976, following the wreck of an oil barge. Much of the spilled oil (about 700,000 liters or 185,000 gal) was buried in the sediment of a nearby small salt marsh. After nearly three decades, the oil remained in the same location, essentially unaltered. Under certain circumstances, oil can persist and remain toxic for decades. One explanation is that, in the absence of dissolved oxygen in the interstitial waters of the marsh sediments, bacteria were relatively ineffective at degrading the oil.

One of the world's largest oil spills, this time not an accident, occurred in February 1991 when retreating Iraqi armies released 6 to 8 million barrels of oil into the shallow Persian Gulf waters, forming a slick that coated nearly 1600 km (1000 mi) of shoreline. Cleanup cost about $700 million. When these coastal areas were surveyed in 1998, marine organisms appeared to have recovered significantly, shrimp catches had returned to pre-spill levels, and coral reefs appeared to be healthy.

Another large oil spill occurred in mid-November 2002 off Galicia, Spain's northwestern province. Waves whipped by strong storm winds caused the old, single-hulled tanker *Prestige* to split in two and sink about 250 km (150 mi) offshore. The wreck slowly discharged at least 11,000 metric tons (10,000 tons) of bunker oil (a mix of different grades of petroleum) through holes in the damaged hull. The spill immediately killed sea birds (including the locally endangered murre population) and threatened beaches, rich fishing grounds, as well as mariculture operations along the Spanish and Portuguese coasts. Mariculture of mussels is Galicia's largest industry and is particularly vulnerable to oil spills that would smother the filter-feeding organisms. Fearing toxic effects, the Spanish government banned fishing and shellfish harvesting along a 300-km (186-mi) stretch of impacted coastline. The oil slick eventually

reached French Atlantic beaches coating surfaces with a gooey mess having the consistency of molasses. Economic losses and the cost of clean-up operations are expected to top $145 million. Another 74,000 metric tons (67,000 tons) of the oil went down with the ship and could adversely impact the seafloor environment for an extended period of time. The economic losses and possible cost of clean-up operations of the oil that went down with the ship (e.g., pumping out the sunken ship) are unknown.

As noted, the *Prestige* was a single-hulled tanker. Subsequent to the spill, the European Union passed legislation to ban such single-hulled tankers older than 23 years from its ports, and seeks to join with the *International Maritime Organization (IMO)* to institute such bans worldwide. In 1990, the United States banned single-hulled tankers older than 23 years from operating in its waters and ports after 2010. Use of double-hulled ships in place of single-hulled ships greatly reduces the risk of spills associated with oil transport on the high seas. A double-hulled ship is essentially a ship within a ship and costs about 15% to 25% more to build. According to the U.S. Coast Guard, double-hulled ships could eliminate an estimated 95% of all oil spills, but probably would not prevent spills in the case of major accidents, such as the one involving the *Exxon Valdez* where both hulls would have been punctured.

Much of the oil entering the coastal ocean comes from untreated storm-sewer discharges. To deal with these discharges, engineers have developed ways to use natural processes to treat these waters at low costs. The initial surge of runoff from a paved road during a heavy rain event carries the greatest pollutant loads. Unburned fuel from cars and trucks along with accumulated grease from road surfaces flows into storm drains soon after the rain starts. This water is diverted into gravel-lined trenches where suspended particles settle into the gravel and the water infiltrates the underlying soil. Bacteria in the trenches decompose hydrocarbons while metal-rich particles from brake pads and particles from tires are trapped in soils and can be extracted periodically for later disposal in a sanitary landfill. Runoff from later in the rainfall event contains fewer pollutants and flows through drainage channels directly into the ocean. Storm waters flowing through wetlands are also filtered naturally and at low cost.

Recent technological advances have made possible a more rapid and effective response to oil spills in the ocean. For more on this topic, refer to this chapter's second Essay.

Dams and Marine Habitats

A dam is a barrier constructed across a watercourse that impounds water in an upstream reservoir (Figure 15.3). Worldwide about 15% of Earth's renewable freshwater supply is stored in reservoirs behind dams (about 6000 cubic km of water). Almost 3000 of these reservoirs have a combined storage capacity of more than 94 billion liters (25 billion gal); this is equivalent to all the water in Lakes Michigan and Ontario.

Most dams and associated reservoirs are multipurpose structures. They impound water for irrigation, recreation (e.g., boating, swimming, fishing), and municipalities (e.g., drinking water supply). They are used for flood control, to generate hydroelectric power (supplying about 20% of the global electrical capacity), and to regulate water levels for navigation. No reliable statistics exist on the total number of dams worldwide although one estimate is close to 800,000. Hydrologist Catherine Reidy of Umeå University in Sweden estimates that about 45,000 dams are greater than 15 m (50 ft) tall. Together these large dams can hold back about 15% of the volume of water flowing in the world's rivers each year. In the United States, the best estimate is 75,000 dams taller than about 2 m (7 ft). The Hoover Dam, constructed on the Colorado River in the 1930s, marked the beginning of the era of so-called *superdams*, dams that are more than 150 m (490 ft) high and capable of storing one or more years of the average annual flow of a river. Today, more than 100 superdams operate worldwide.

FIGURE 15.3
Navigational dam located just upstream of Zanesville, OH on the Muskingum River. [NOAA/NWS/Advanced Hydrologic Prediction Service]

Dam construction is a big business especially in developing nations. During the 1990s, dam construction costs amounted to nearly $40 billion dollars annually. In 2003, nearly 1700 dams were under construction—nearly 500 in Brazil and more than 700 in India. At present worldwide, at least 273 large dams are either planned or under construction on 46 major rivers. Dam construction has received funding from the World Bank and the International Monetary Fund. Now, however, the environmental and human costs of dams are more widely recognized and in many developed nations such as the United States, emphasis has shifted from dam construction to floodplain management in which the uses of the floodplain are regulated to protect lives and property and preserve ecosystems. About 25% of all U.S. dams are more than 50 years old. Unfortunately, many have been abandoned, are no longer maintained, and pose safety hazards to downstream communities. Over the past decade or so in the U.S., more dams have been removed than new ones constructed. This trend is expected to continue especially for small dams.

Dams cause major dislocations among native and indigenous peoples who are forced to move from areas flooded by reservoirs, losing their homes, farms, and communities. For instance, rising water associated with the world's largest superdam, China's Three Gorges Dam, so far has displaced about 1.4 million people. Construction began in 1994 and the dam is expected to be fully operational in about 2011. This dam spans the Yangtze River, China's largest river, and primarily is intended to generate electricity and control flooding. The maximum electrical generating capacity is expected to be about 22,500 megawatts. The 700-km (430-mi) long reservoir flooded 60,000 hectares (150,000 acres) inundating 160 towns, many villages, and 1600 factories. Untreated wastes discharged from upstream cities and factories flow slowly through the reservoir, creating local pollution problems and exacerbating the already severe pollution problems in Shanghai, downstream from the dam.

Prior to construction of the Three Gorges Dam, the Yangtze was among the largest sediment-transporting rivers in the world (Chapter 4). After the dam's completion, most of the sediment carried by the river will accumulate in the reservoir. Over time, these deposits reduce the reservoir's storage capacity, thus diminishing its flood-control and hydroelectric generating capabilities. Loss of the sediment load previously carried downstream by river waters accelerates river flow and increases erosion along the river's course below the dam. Furthermore, the loss of sediment previously deposited in the Yangtze delta region during floods will halt the regular renewal of this fertile agricultural land. This situation is similar to what happened to the Nile Delta following completion of the Aswan High Dam (Chapter 4).

Dams have caused major alterations in coastal river and marine ecosystems. During the 20th century, the U.S. government extensively dammed the Columbia and Snake Rivers to produce hydroelectric power, control flooding, and allow river-barge traffic throughout the region; 14 dams were constructed on the Columbia River and 13 on the Snake River. In addition, about 4000 smaller non-federal dams were built in Oregon and Washington to provide electricity and supply water for factories, farms, and cities in the region. Dams transformed these once cold, swift-flowing rivers and streams into a series of large lakes with warmer, sluggishly flowing waters. The effect of dams on *anadromous fish* populations has been especially severe (Chapter 10); salmon populations plummeted from an estimated 16 million before the rivers were dammed to 300,000 by early in the 21st century. Some salmon stocks are now nearly extinct. (Overfishing and climate change may be contributing to some part of this population decline.)

Dams block adult salmon returning from the Pacific Ocean to spawn on upstream gravel bars and sandy river bottoms, eliminating much of the original spawning grounds for these fish populations. *Fish ladders* were built on the dams to allow fish to swim past the dams but they did not work very well (Figure 15.4). Furthermore, hydroelectric turbines kill many of the newly hatched salmon as they attempt to swim to the sea. Like a food

FIGURE 15.4
A new Alaskan Steep Pass fish ladder just prior to installation at a small dam in Byfield, Essex County, MA. The old fish ladder failed to provide anadromous fish with regular access to their spawning grounds in the Parker River. [NOAA Restoration Center, Louise Kane]

processor, turbine blades grind up the young fish and the extreme pressure changes and turbulence they encounter from the spinning blades kill an estimated 15% at each dam. Overall about 60% to 70% of juvenile salmon never reach the ocean.

The most radical proposal to protect and restore wild salmon stocks calls for removal or partial breaching of some of the large hydroelectric dams. Some water would flow through a breached dam, permitting fish to swim downstream without encountering the turbines. The problem is that either removal or breaching of dams would reduce the amount of hydropower generated. The region has already experienced electrical shortages and further loss of generating capacity would only exacerbate energy problems. The hotly debated alternative of removing dams has been proposed for the lowermost four dams on the Snake River.

Although removal of dams (Figure 15.5) can benefit marine ecosystems as described in this chapter's Case-in-Point, dam removals can also cause problems. Some problems arise from the downstream release of sediments formerly trapped in the reservoir behind the dam. The influx of sediments alters downstream habitats wiping out organisms such as insects, algae, and filter feeders.

In some cases, contaminants are mobilized along with the sediments. For example, the upper Hudson River in New York has several low dams, which previously formed large, slowly flowing pools where PCB-contaminated sediments released by manufacturing plants accumulated over several decades. Before 1973, most of these contaminated sediments were sequestered at the bottom of the reservoir behind a dam at Ft. Edward. Concern over possible failure due to the dam's age and poor structural condition led to its removal in 1973. Before another dam could be built in its place, major floods in 1974 and 1976 transported the contaminated sediments downstream where they were deposited behind the next dam. About the same time elevated levels of PCBs were detected in fish living downstream. Plans call for dredging the contaminants and storing them in an enclosed structure to prevent their further movement and pollution of the river downstream.

A smaller dam on the Patapsco River, a tributary of the Chesapeake Bay near Baltimore MD, was repaired rather than removed. In this case, the dam was needed to retain contaminated sediment deposited behind it. These deposits had high concentrations of chromium discharged by earlier industrial operations. Many small dams near older manufacturing plants and in mining districts face similar problems involving contaminated sediment deposits.

Restoring Chesapeake Bay

FIGURE 15.5
In the summer of 2004, NOAA provided funds to help the town of Henniker, N.H., remove the 18-foot-high West Henniker Dam, which blocked migratory fish and eel passage to upstream spawning and feeding grounds. Removal of the dam restored approximately eight acres of in-stream habitat and opened 15 miles of the Contoocook River that had previously been blocked. Photos show the dam before removal (A); during removal (B) and the Contoocook River after removal of the dam (C). [New Hampshire Department of Environmental Services/NOAA]

Since 1983, the Chesapeake Bay estuary has been the focus of the nation's largest federal-state environmental restoration project, the *Chesapeake Bay Program*. The Bay Program seeks to halt further degradation of the Bay, restore its water quality, and rebuild its fisheries. Program partners include the states of Maryland, Virginia, and Pennsylvania; the District of Columbia; the Chesapeake Bay Commission, a tri-state legislative body; and citizen advisory groups. The U.S. Environmental Protection Agency (EPA) represents the federal government. Federal partners are in ten departments having land-holdings in the Chesapeake Bay watershed and numerous agencies having responsibilities or programs in the Bay or its watershed, among them is the National Oceanic and Atmospheric Administration (NOAA). Total cost for the Bay's restoration is estimated at approximately $20 billion.

Following settlement by European colonists at the beginning of the 17th century, human activities greatly modified Chesapeake Bay with important consequences for the functioning of the ecosystem. Much of the original forest that covered its **watershed** (the geographical area drained by rivers and their tributaries flowing into the Bay) was cleared and converted to agricultural lands, roads, cities, and suburban developments. These modifications accelerated the influx of nutrients (i.e., compounds of nitrogen and phosphorus), sediment, biocides (i.e., pesticides, herbicides), and other pollutants into the Bay.

In essence, people converted the Chesapeake Bay watershed from a *closed system* to an *open system*. In the original climax forests, nutrients primarily cycled within the system with relatively little input into the Bay. Clearing the land for agriculture increased the area of the soil exposed to the elements and runoff from rain and snowmelt accelerated nutrient input into the Bay. Increasing levels of nutrients spur the growth of algal populations and when these organisms die (in mid-summer), their remains settle to the bottom. Decomposition of their remains reduces the dissolved oxygen in the Chesapeake's bottom water. Also, more sediment input increases the turbidity of the water, reducing sunlight penetration for photosynthesis. As described in Chapters 10 and 14, these changes in habitat have a ripple effect on the Chesapeake Bay food webs.

Today, the Chesapeake Bay watershed is home to an estimated 16.5 million people. That number is projected to increase to about 18 million by 2020. Some 150 rivers

FIGURE 15.6
Since 1983, the Chesapeake Bay estuary has been the focus of the nation's largest federal-state environmental restoration project, the Chesapeake Bay Program. [U.S. Geological Survey Photo]

and streams drain an area of approximately 166,000 square km (64,000 square mi) encompassing portions of New York, Pennsylvania, West Virginia, Delaware, Maryland, Virginia, and the District of Columbia (Figure 15.6). Forests cover about 60% of the Bay's watershed; farms and pastures cover about 30%; cities, suburbs and highways cover the remaining 10%. Point and non-point sources within the watershed discharge wastes into the Bay primarily through rivers that empty into the Bay. A **point source** of pollution is a discernible conduit, such as pipes, chimneys, ditches, channels, sewers, tunnels or vessels, which transport contaminants. A **non-point source** of pollution is a broad area of the landscape, such as agricultural fields or parking lots. In addition, some airborne pollutants (e.g., ozone, nitrogen oxides), primarily from fossil fuel fired electric power plants in the Ohio River Valley, also reach the Bay and settle or are washed by rain and snow into its waters.

Chesapeake Bay is generally shallow with deeper dredged shipping channels leading into port facilities at

Baltimore, MD to the north and Norfolk, VA near the mouth of the Bay. As described in Chapter 8, it is a moderately stratified (partially mixed) estuary with several smaller, tributary estuaries emptying into it. The northern end of the Bay is essentially the estuary of the Susquehanna River, which drains portions of Pennsylvania and New York; it contributes about half the river water flowing into the Bay. The Potomac and James Rivers flowing from the west each contribute about one quarter of the total river inflow. An unknown amount of groundwater flows into the Bay, primarily from its eastern side. Sediments enter the Bay directly from the Susquehanna River, whereas sediments transported by the Potomac and James Rivers are mostly trapped in their lower reaches and do not reach the Bay. Sands from the continental shelf enter the Bay with the flow of seawater through its mouth.

Chesapeake Bay was the first U.S. estuary selected for restoration and protection. Research on the Bay's environmental problems conducted in the 1970s identified three major problems requiring immediate attention: Over-enrichment of nutrients in Bay waters, continued loss of submerged aquatic vegetation (sea grass beds), and pollution by toxic chemicals. The Bay Program focused on restoring the Bay's living resources, especially its finfish and shellfish stocks, and sea grasses. After more than two decades, the accomplishments of the Chesapeake Bay Program are modest. Communications among federal and state agencies on a regional level have improved. Plans for fisheries management and habitat restoration have been formulated and adopted. Expansion of sea grass beds was mapped. Goals were set for reducing the amounts of nutrients entering the Bay from land-based sources. Numerical models were developed to describe the amounts and effects of nutrients discharged to the Bay. And a program was set up for monitoring water quality.

Unfortunately, the Bay Program could not prevent the decline of the oyster and blue crab fisheries, the last two commercial fisheries in the Bay. Phosphorus concentrations in Bay waters declined, but this was primarily due to government policies dating to the early 1970s banning phosphate detergents. Although reduced runoff from land cut nitrogen levels in Bay waters, the Program's goal of a 40% reduction by 2000 was not met. About 25% to 30% of the nitrogen entering the Bay and its watershed is airborne material emitted by motor vehicles and coal-fired electric power plants. On the plus side, the Chesapeake Bay Program has helped to prevent environmental conditions in the Bay from deteriorating as rapidly as they were prior to the 1970s.

The Bay's striped bass population was rescued from near collapse by a short moratorium on fishing in the mid- and late-1980s; the fishery was declared fully restored in 1995 and is again a major recreational fishery in the region. Maryland initially imposed the moratorium followed by Virginia but for a much shorter period. This is an example of successful policy action by individual states.

The efforts of *non-governmental organizations (NGOs)* have also helped to improve Bay conditions. NGOs educate and organize residents in volunteer conservation programs. They try to garner public support to influence government policies about environmental issues. The *Chesapeake Bay Foundation*, the largest NGO dedicated to restoring the Bay, worked to prevent pollutants from entering the Bay as well as to restore the Bay's natural water-filtering mechanisms: forests, wetlands, sea grass beds, and oysters. Volunteers carry out these activities. Educational programs for children and adults as well as efforts to build an environmental ethic in the watershed have been important factors in the ongoing effort to restore the Chesapeake Bay.

In December 2007, the Chesapeake Bay Foundation (CBF) issued its annual State of the Bay report and the news was not good. The CBF assigns scores representing the degree of progress in remediation of the various environmental problems afflicting the Bay. The CBF gave the Chesapeake Bay estuary an overall grade of 28, equivalent to a "D." This is slightly lower than the prior year's score. Cited as major reasons for the low score was increased phosphorus pollution, greater turbidity of the water, and the decline in blue crab populations. Failing grades were assigned to efforts to reduce input of nitrogen compounds into the Bay, restore sea grass beds, reverse the decline in oyster populations, and elevate dissolved oxygen levels. On the positive side, Maryland and Virginia are attacking the nutrient discharge problem by spending millions of dollars to upgrade their wastewater treatment plants. Also, recovery of the rockfish fishery and establishment of forest buffers received high scores.

Waste Disposal in the Ocean

The global human population will continue to grow rapidly during the next century. Population growth will increase the demand for fresh water, food, energy, consumer goods, and living space. At the same time, it will be increasingly important to find new and acceptable ways to dispose of waste generated by human activities while maintaining a satisfactory level of environmental quality both on land and in the ocean. The rate of waste production is likely to keep pace with or perhaps outpace population growth. Disposing of waste in an environmentally acceptable manner is likely to be most challenging in the coastal zone where the human population is growing at a much more rapid rate. Sanitary landfills are filling rapidly and high-tech incinerators are expensive to operate. Recycling of discarded materials is among the strategies to reduce the amount of material entering the waste stream. Some cities encourage whereas others require recycling of paper, metals, glass, and plastics. Management of toxic and hazardous waste is particularly challenging. Treaties banning the manufacture of some persistent chemicals, such as DDT, PCBs, and CFCs have been most successful in developed countries but have had less adherence in developing countries. Discharge of excess nutrients and sediments eroded from the land will likely continue worldwide.

The ocean is viewed as one possible solution to the problem of waste disposal as terrestrial options are used up. International treaties and national regulations prohibit ocean disposal of most waste. However, the ocean has been used for disposal of a great variety of wastes since humans began navigating and fishing its waters. Shipwrecks, abandoned petroleum production platforms, and other debris from human activities are common on the ocean bottom, especially near land and in shipping lanes. Many nations have directly discharged wastes at sea, including materials dredged from coastal waterways, solids (sewage sludge) from wastewater treatment plants, various industrial and construction wastes, and radioactive materials.

Deliberate discharge of these substances from ships, planes, and platforms is regulated under the *Convention on the Prevention of Marine Pollution by Dumping of Waste and Other Matter*, more commonly known as the *London Dumping Convention*, administered by the United Nations *International Maritime Organization (IMO)*. The treaty was first established in 1972 and strengthened in 1996. Dumping of some materials was banned entirely (e.g., radioactive wastes); others were regulated (e.g., dredge spoils, sewage sludge, mining wastes).

Given the population pressures on land, some people argue that waste disposal in the ocean is an attractive alternative for many waste disposal operations. The ocean is vast and the deep-ocean floor (more than 3000 m or 10,000 ft below the sea surface) covers about half of Earth's surface. Much of this deep-ocean bottom is a featureless, sediment-covered plain, seemingly monotonous physically, chemically, and biologically. Unfortunately, our knowledge of this realm is very limited. Thus, it is easy to assume that part of this region could be used for waste disposal without interfering with other uses of the sea. For example, the argument continues, dumping barge-loads of crushed rock from Indonesian gold-mine operations down a submarine canyon off New Guinea would have few, if any, adverse effects on the nearby ocean bottom. This region naturally receives huge amounts of river-borne sediment.

Other people suggest that we should use the deep ocean for disposal of nuclear wastes, or carbon dioxide from industrial chimneys (in liquid or solid form). The ocean is viewed as a potential receptacle for wastes that would be considered undesirable in a land disposal site. But most scientists point out that we do not yet know nearly enough about the chemistry, circulation processes, and marine ecosystems in the deep ocean to be sure that such disposal would be safe and secure.

In addition to scientific concerns, ethical issues are involved in ocean waste disposal. Many individuals and organizations refuse to consider using the ocean in this way; they consider it immoral to pollute the ocean and oppose all forms of waste disposal at sea. This is especially true for disposal of radioactive materials. Disposal of these wastes pose extremely difficult problems for the industries and government agencies that produce them. Radioactive wastes (e.g., from nuclear power plants) emit ionizing radiation that poses serious health hazards. As a general rule, radioactive isotopes must be kept isolated for a period equivalent to 10 half-lives before they can be safely released into the environment. (One *half-life* is the amount of time required for the radioactivity emanating from a particular radioactive substance to decrease by one-half.) For some high-level radioactive isotopes, this means isolation for hundreds of thousands of years. Because human institutions and structures are highly unlikely to survive intact for such long periods, the materials must be safely isolated. Isolation through burial in geologically stable regions is usually the preferred disposal option.

Land disposal sites proposed for radioactive wastes are bitterly opposed because of the risk of escape of radioactive materials to the groundwater or air. The "NIMBY" (not in my back yard) argument is often heard when this issue is debated. Sealing radioactive wastes in special containers and then burying them in the deep-ocean floor is one option that has been discussed. This strategy is hypothesized to keep the radioactive waste out of direct human contact for thousands, perhaps millions, of years.

Other schemes would place radioactive-waste containers in subduction zones so that they would be drawn down into Earth's mantle and presumably, out of contact with humans (Chapter 2).

Essentially these disposal plans are resisted because we know so little about the deep ocean. The basic argument is that it is unwise to put the most dangerous waste materials where they may be subjected to processes not fully understood. Furthermore, retrieving such waste from the sea floor might be difficult if not impossible if they had to be relocated. The deep ocean appears to be even more complex, with greater biodiversity, than many ecosystems on land. Some deep-ocean currents are apparently stronger than previously thought, and the ocean's thermohaline circulation operates over a time scale of ~1000 years, which is far less than the half-life of most radioactive wastes. Furthermore, new fishing techniques permit commercial fishing in deep-ocean waters so that wastes might be accidentally introduced into commercial fish catches, or trawled up.

Deep-Ocean Carbon Storage

As we have learned, levels of atmospheric carbon dioxide have been rising since at least the middle of the 19th century and are likely contributing to global climate change by enhancing Earth's greenhouse effect (Chapters 5 and 12). Burning fossil fuels and deforestation are primarily responsible for the increase in atmospheric CO_2. Schemes to remove carbon dioxide from the atmosphere or to store it directly instead of releasing it to the atmosphere have been proposed.

Replanting tropical forests has been proposed as a low-cost way to remove atmospheric carbon dioxide. Plantation costs are low in many developing countries in the tropics and rain forest vegetation grows rapidly, thus storing carbon for decades to centuries. Unfortunately, such projects do not provide enough carbon storage over the long term to be effective. Growth slows as trees mature, so the carbon uptake also diminishes. Furthermore, forests are either harvested or burned due to natural causes (e.g., lightning) every 30 to 50 years. As populations grow and more agricultural land is needed, forests will probably shrink, rather than expand.

Another potential storage place for carbon dioxide is in rock formations below the sea floor. This type of repository has been used at some offshore natural-gas production facilities where carbon dioxide is separated from methane. The methane, the chief component of natural gas, is piped ashore and the carbon dioxide is injected into bedrock fractures and pore spaces below the facility (rather than being vented to the atmosphere). Using this technique, Norway's state-controlled oil company has disposed of about 1 million tons of carbon dioxide per year since 1996 at its natural gas operation in the North Sea. Other options for sequestration of carbon dioxide include injection into aquifers, deep coal seams, or depleted oil reservoir rock.

Ocean iron fertilization (OIF) is proposed as a means of boosting the ocean's uptake of carbon dioxide from the atmosphere (Figure 15.7). Recall from Chapter 9 that broad areas of the subtropical open-ocean receive abundant sunlight and have relatively high concentrations of nitrogen and phosphorus compounds, all essential ingredients for photosynthesis by planktonic algae. Yet, primary production is meager in these high-nutrient low-chlorophyll (HNLC) areas. In the 1990s, ocean scientists demonstrated that these waters are unproductive because they lack essential micronutrients, such as iron (refer to the first Essay in Chapter 9). Clouds of iron-rich dust particles blown from the land and settling into the ocean's surface waters trigger infrequent pulses of short-lived algal blooms.

FIGURE 15.7
A large algal bloom is indicated by the swirls of green and blue in the Atlantic Ocean off the coast of Argentina. Via photosynthesis, this multitude of phytoplankton takes up carbon dioxide from the ocean and atmosphere. Adding iron to the ocean would stimulate more blooms and removal of more carbon dioxide. Scientists are trying to determine how effective ocean iron fertilization would be in offsetting Earth's enhanced greenhouse effect and global warming. [Image courtesy of NASA]

As of this writing, ocean scientists have conducted at least a dozen OIF experiments since 1993, releasing a soluble form of iron into these waters to artificially stimulate longer-term algal blooms. Thereby, carbon dioxide is taken up from the atmosphere that would not otherwise be used in photosynthesis. When the algal cells die, some sink through the surface layer and are eaten or decomposed in the deep ocean or are deposited on the ocean floor via the physical and biological pumps (Chapter 9).

Researchers continue to investigate the feasibility of OIF and any possible adverse effects it might have on marine ecosystems. Field experiments conducted in the Southern Ocean and in Pacific equatorial waters showed temporary increases in phytoplankton populations and primary production following the addition of iron. But as yet no proof exists that such a method could be used economically on a large scale to bring about long-term removal of carbon from ocean surface waters and the overlying atmosphere. In fact, it appears unlikely that ocean iron fertilization would sequester atmospheric carbon in the deep ocean for lengthy periods of the order of centuries to millennia. Most areas of the ocean where OIF would work (HNLC regions) are locales of upwelling (e.g., tropical Pacific Ocean, Southern Ocean). Models suggest that most carbon pumped to ocean depths soon would be upwelled again and re-vented to the atmosphere over a time span of only years to decades.

Furthermore, open-ocean and deep-ocean ecosystems are too poorly understood to accurately predict possible consequences of such iron releases. More field experiments are planned in other areas of the ocean and over greater temporal and spatial scales to identify possible adverse effects. For example, too much phytoplankton production might deplete dissolved oxygen as the organic matter subsequently decomposes.

Another option is to inject carbon dioxide directly into deep-ocean waters for long-term storage. The Italian energy expert E. Marchetti first proposed this idea in 1977. Marchetti proposed to separate CO_2 from the emissions of coal-fired power plants and pump it into the outgoing Mediterranean waters off Gibraltar. These relatively dense waters sink into the Atlantic Ocean carrying the carbon dioxide with it. Model studies of such injections showed that the gas must be injected at depths greater than 3000 m (9800 ft) to keep the carbon dioxide in the ocean for more than a few centuries. On the other hand, liquid carbon dioxide injected at depths below 4500 m (14,800 ft) would form lakes occupying topographic depressions on the seafloor. A thin layer of ice-like hydrate would form at the lake surface thereby slowing the escape of CO_2.

The deep-ocean injection method has several drawbacks. CO_2 injections at shallow depths were less effective. The scarcity of carbon dioxide sources near suitably deep ocean water limits the feasibility of this approach. Injections into the deep Pacific Ocean were more successful than those into the deep Atlantic Ocean, which has more vigorous deep-ocean currents. Furthermore, direct injection of carbon dioxide into the ocean is expected to cause ocean waters to become more acidic with likely adverse effects on carbonate organisms (Chapters 3 and 4). Normally, seawater is slightly alkaline.

Many scientists and conservationists argue that a more practical, economical, and less ecologically risky strategy would be to focus on reducing anthropogenic carbon dioxide emissions in the first place. Much of the technology to accomplish this already exists and is being used in several industrialized nations of Europe. In North America, however, many people do not strongly support this approach and the measures it would require, such as increasing the fuel efficiency of motor vehicles and reducing reliance on fossil fuels for generating electricity.

Obstacles to Ocean Policy Making

We have considered examples of policies designed to protect the ocean and its resources in this and the previous chapter. They include local, regional, national and international policies, forged by local, state and national governments, and implemented through international treaties and organizations. However, the agreements required to forge an acceptable environmental policy at any level of government are usually complex and fraught with obstacles and controversy. A number of problems arise repeatedly. Issues are very often divisive and opposing sides hold rigid views. For example, fishers rarely believe the warnings of scientists and government agencies that fish stocks are declining. They fish with more determination, further hastening the decline, until draconian measures, such as a complete moratorium on fishing, are necessary.

Often, as in the efforts to restore and protect the Chesapeake Bay, multiple levels of government are involved. As noted earlier, the Bay Program involves agencies in three states, the District of Columbia, and many agencies of the federal government. Political differences sometimes get in the way of forging agreements on the policies needed to achieve common goals. Various governments and organizations must respond to competing interest groups and all parties must

be invited to negotiations even when they have different agendas. Diverse sectors of society may blame each other for the damage done while failing to make progress toward remediation. The agricultural industry in rural areas surrounding Chesapeake Bay feels that it is unfairly blamed for nutrient pollution in the Bay and argues that the cities and industries should bear more of the responsibility and cost of cleanup because of their sewage and other waste discharges.

At the international level, the problems are even more complex. Industrialized nations possessing advanced technology and many resources to combat pollution dominate the Northern Hemisphere. These nations have small population growth rates (if any) and an educated, affluent society that can push governments to take action to combat environmental problems. In many cases the environmental damage was done a century or more ago and is now forgotten or at least partially repaired. Developing nations are trying to improve their economies and reduce poverty by establishing industries that will create jobs. Unfortunately, the rush to industrialize and the huge population pressures in many developing countries have resulted in enormous pollution problems and damage to ecosystems. For example, the use of dynamite or cyanide to kill coral reef fish for easier harvesting causes severe harm to the reef ecosystem. The practice is banned in much of the world, but is still common in some developing countries. DDT is still used in some areas as a cheap and effective means of combating the mosquito that carries malaria (Chapter 14).

The attitude of leaders in many developing countries is that economic development must be the top priority if they are to alleviate widespread poverty. Developed countries blame them for many pollution and environmental problems. In return the developing countries point to the damage done in the past by industrialized countries (e.g. whaling, overfishing, strip mining, clear-cut logging, pollution) and demand financial and technological assistance if they are to take action on their own environmental problems. This conflict frequently frustrates or greatly delays attempts to develop international policies to protect the ocean and marine life.

Conclusions

Humans long assumed that the vast ocean holds a bounty of virtually limitless resources that are there for the taking by almost anyone. They have also assumed that the ocean's ability to assimilate waste was limitless so that the ocean was considered an appropriate repository for a wide variety of wastes ranging from sewage sludge to construction debris. In more recent times, people have begun to reevaluate these assumptions as they become more aware of issues such as overfishing, accelerated shoreline erosion, pollution, harmful algal blooms, oxygen-deficient "dead zones," and exotic species invasions.

Guided by an Earth system perspective and the fundamental understanding that marine life depends on the orderly functioning of ecosystems, scientists and public policy makers have joined ranks to rectify past practices that disrupt marine ecosystems and to formulate new policies that promise to safeguard the ecological integrity of the ocean and coastal zone for future generations. This stewardship effort is becoming more urgent as the human population density in the coastal zone continues to increase. Individual nations have taken more control over human activities in their EEZs (e.g., closing stressed fisheries) and the international community is beginning to take steps to further regulate human activities in the ocean commons. In order for ocean policy to be appropriate and effective, however, more resources need to be directed toward developing a more complete understanding of the properties and processes of the ocean.

Basic Understandings

- The history of ocean governance differs dramatically from that of the land. For most of human history, the open ocean has been beyond the direct management of coastal nations or any other governments. As the human population soared and exploitation of ocean resources expanded, regulations and institutions to govern human activities in the ocean have developed.

- In 1609, the Dutch legal scholar Hugo Grotius argued that the ocean was open with free access to all nations. For him, liberty of the sea was key to maintaining communication among peoples and nations. Along with this doctrine of free access, the general consensus was that the sea was limitless and its resources inexhaustible. There was no need to control access if marine resources were essentially unlimited and therefore virtually immune to any possible damage caused by human activities.

- Partitioning of the coastal ocean began in the late 1700s, when the new United States claimed a 5-km (3-mi) "territorial sea" off its coasts. In 1945, the U.S. extended its claims on coastal resources to the outer edge of the continental shelf—principally because of the expansion of offshore oil and natural gas production on the shallow continental shelf.

- The U.S. established its Exclusive Economic Zone (EEZ) in 1983, extending federal jurisdiction from the seaward limits of the state-controlled territorial seas (5 km or 3 nautical mi) to 370 km (200 nautical mi) from the coastline. In 1996, EEZs were extended to the edge of the continental shelf in the cases when the shelf edge was farther offshore than 370 km (200 nautical mi).

- Future governance of ocean resource exploitation may be guided by the Precautionary Principle: "When an action causes a threat to human health or the environment, precautionary measures should be taken even if some cause-and-effect relationships are not fully established scientifically."

- In 1959, Antarctica and the Southern Ocean came under the protection of the Antarctic Treaty System ensuring no national claim of territorial rights in Antarctica or the surrounding waters will ever be legally recognized and that Antarctica would be forever used exclusively for scientific and other peaceful purposes.

- Increasing human population density in the coastal zone is likely to further exacerbate the problem of environmental pollution. Pollution is defined as an intentional or unintentional disturbance of the environment that adversely affects the wellbeing of an organism (including humans) directly or the natural processes (e.g., ecosystem) upon which it depends.

- A better understanding of the pollution problem in the coastal zone and elsewhere in the ocean is based on application of the concepts of carrying capacity, assimilative capacity, and limiting factors.

- The human carrying capacity of a region is based on the maximum rate of resource consumption and waste discharge that is sustainable indefinitely without progressively impairing ecosystem productivity and integrity.

- Assimilative capacity is the amount of waste that an ecosystem can decompose without damaging ecosystem functions or building up waste products to levels that may cause unwanted or harmful impacts on living organisms (including humans). The growth and wellbeing of an organism is limited by the essential resource that is in lowest supply relative to what is required; this most deficient resource is known as the limiting factor.

- The need to balance multiple use and preservation of the coastal zone spurred the federal government to partner with states having coastlines to develop and implement plans for sustainable coastal zone management.

- For many reasons (shipwreck, collisions, pumping of ships' bilges, war, and terrorism), oil is accidentally or deliberately spilled into the ocean. Some oil enters the ocean routinely from storm sewer discharges and an unknown quantity of oil seeps into the ocean naturally, leaking through the sea floor into the overlying water.

- Dams have caused major changes in river and ocean ecosystems. The effects of dams on *anadromous fish* populations have been especially severe to the point that some salmon stocks are now nearly extinct. Fish ladders were built to allow fish to swim past the dams but they did not work very well. Furthermore, hydroelectric turbines kill many of the newly hatched salmon as they attempt to swim to the sea. The most radical proposal to protect and restore wild salmon stocks calls for removal or partial breaching of some large dams.

- Since 1983, Chesapeake Bay has been the focus of the nation's largest federal-state environmental restoration project, the Chesapeake Bay Program. The Bay Program seeks to stop further degradation of the Bay, restore its water quality, and rebuild its fisheries.

- Within the Chesapeake Bay watershed, numerous point and non-point sources discharge wastes into the Bay waters, primarily through rivers that empty into the Bay. A point source of pollution is a discernible conduit, such as pipes or channels which transport contaminants. A non-point source of pollution is a broad area of the landscape, such as agricultural fields or parking lots.

- The vast ocean is considered by some as a possible solution to the growing problem of waste disposal as terrestrial options are used up. But most scientists argue that we do not yet know nearly enough about the chemistry, circulation processes, and marine ecosystems in the deep ocean to be sure that such disposal would be safe.

- To reduce global warming due to a build up of atmospheric carbon dioxide (a greenhouse gas), many schemes have been proposed to remove carbon dioxide from the atmosphere or to store it directly without releasing it to the atmosphere. One possibility is to store CO_2 in rock formations below the sea floor. This technique has been used at some offshore natural-gas production facilities where carbon dioxide is separated from methane.

- Fertilization of ocean surface waters (e.g., iron as a micronutrient) has been proposed as a means of increasing the ocean's uptake of carbon dioxide from the atmosphere and letting nature pump it to the ocean bottom via the biological and physical "pumps". Another option is to inject carbon dioxide directly into deep-ocean waters for long-term storage.

- It appears unlikely that ocean iron fertilization would sequester atmospheric carbon in the deep ocean for lengthy periods of the order of centuries to millennia. Most areas of the ocean where OIF would work (HNLC regions) are locales of upwelling (e.g., tropical Pacific Ocean, Southern Ocean). Models suggest that most carbon pumped to ocean depths soon would be upwelled again and re-vented to the atmosphere over a time span of only years to decades.

- Agreements required to forge an acceptable national and/or international ocean environmental policy at any level of government are usually complex and fraught with obstacles and controversy.

Review

1. How are the resources of Antarctica and the Southern Ocean protected?
2. How far does the U.S. Exclusive Economic Zone (EEZ) extend seaward from the shore?
3. What are the ocean commons?
4. Define limiting factor.
5. List the potential purposes of a dam constructed across a river.
6. How might a dam influence marine ecosystems?
7. What are the goals of the Chesapeake Bay Program?
8. Distinguish between a point source and a non-point source of pollution.
9. What does the London Dumping Commission regulate?
10. What ocean-based options are available for removal and storage of carbon dioxide?

Critical Thinking

1. How might human activities be regulated in the ocean commons?
2. How does human population growth in the coastal zone impact the quality of the marine environment?
3. What are some of the disadvantages of dams constructed across large rivers that empty into the ocean?
4. What can be done to restore a beach that was extensively eroded following construction of a dam across a river?
5. Explain why water quality specialists use a drainage-basin (or watershed) approach when inventorying pollution sources for the Chesapeake Bay.
6. Why is a federal-state partnership needed for restoration of the Chesapeake Bay estuary?
7. Why are physical and chemical properties an important consideration in regulating the type of waste materials that are dumped into the ocean?
8. What is the purpose of the *Precautionary Principle*?
9. Why is Antarctica and the surrounding Southern Ocean given special status for exploitation of marine resources?
10. What fundamental assumption underlies the concept of an *ocean commons*?

ESSAY: Pathogens in the Coastal Zone

Along with the rapid development and human population growth in the coastal zone has come more frequent contamination of beaches and shellfish beds by disease-causing micro-organisms (pathogens). These bacteria, viruses, and protozoa are derived primarily from animal and human fecal waste. The public health threat is forcing officials to close more beaches and shellfish beds for longer periods. The National Resources Council reported that in 2004, coastal states ordered a total of almost 20,000 days of closure and pollution advisories were issued for about one-third of all beaches regularly monitored by public health officials.

People are exposed to waterborne microbes by consuming contaminated shellfish or by engaging in recreational activities at the beach (e.g., swimming, surfing, waterskiing). People who eat raw or inadequately cooked shellfish may contract gastroenteritis (an unpleasant malady with vomiting and diarrhea) or other more serious illnesses. At the beach, people run the risk that waterborne microbes will enter the body through the mouth, eyes, or an open wound. Potential illnesses include gastroenteritis and infections of the eyes, ear, respiratory system, and skin (swimmer's itch). In addition, more serious diseases such as hepatitis and Guillain-Barré syndrome have been reported. In addition to the health hazards, contaminated beaches have implications for the local economy: tourism dollars decrease and real estate values decline.

What is the connection between development of the coastal zone and contamination of beaches and shellfish beds? Prior to development, a typical coastal zone was covered by soils, forests, and wetlands—surfaces through which water gradually seeps. Through this infiltration process, water is cleansed of most pathogens. With development, however, forests were clear-cut, wetlands were drained and filled, and much of the coastal zone was covered over by impervious asphalt and concrete with buildings, roads, and parking lots (Figure 1). Now, instead of seeping into the ground, most rainwater (and snowmelt) runs off and is usually conveyed by drain pipes or ditches to the ocean (or large lake). Along the way, the storm water runoff picks up animal feces and associated microbes. Added to this input may be human waste from sewage overflow or leaking septic tanks depending upon the local sewage treatment system.

FIGURE 1
The image shows the extent of impervious surfaces in and around Washington, DC and Baltimore. Red represents high concentrations of impervious surfaces. Blue represents moderate concentrations and green represents low concentrations of impervious surfaces. The map of impervious surfaces was derived with data from both Landsat and Space Imaging's high-resolution IKONOS satellite. [NASA]

Two separate networks of sewer pipes are under the streets of most U.S. cities (Figure 2). In this *separated sewer system*, the larger-diameter storm-sewer pipe collects runoff and channels it to the nearest waterway (e.g., ocean, lake, river) without any waste treatment. The smaller-diameter sanitary-sewer pipe conveys wastewater from dwellings and commercial establishments to a sewage treatment plant, where it is treated (including removal of pathogens and other contaminants) and then discharged into a waterway. In some cities, a single large-diameter pipe transports both runoff and wastewater to a sewage treatment plant; this is called a *combined sewer system*. During rainy episodes, runoff combines with wastewater and both are treated and then discharged. If the rainfall is excessive, however, the plant's capacity may be exceeded and the overflow (containing raw sewage) bypasses treatment and is discharged directly into the ocean or other waterway.

Many coastal areas are not served by a centralized wastewater treatment plant (either separated or combined systems). In that case, most residents rely on a septic tank system in which wastewater is cleansed by gravitational settling of solids, decomposition of organic materials, and seeping through soil and sediment. However, in some locales, the substrate is highly permeable (e.g., sands, fractured limestone) and very little filtration is achieved. In that case, appropriate fill must be hauled in and mounded or a holding tank is installed and periodically pumped out.

The greater runoff in a developed coastal zone also translates into more rapid erosion of stream banks, drainage ditches, and construction sites. The suspended sediments not only turns the runoff turbid, they also bind with the fecal bacteria and viruses, thereby protecting the pathogens from potentially lethal ultraviolet radiation.

What can be done about this problem of pathogens in the coastal zone? Writing in the June 2006 issue of *Scientific American*, Michael A. Mallin, an aquatic ecologist the University of North Carolina, Wilmington, calls for "smart-growth" strategies in the coastal zone. He urges developers to minimize clear-cutting of forests, draining of wetlands, use of impervious pavement, and runoff of sediments from construction sites. In addition, Mallin calls for more vegetated areas. These strategies promise to reduce runoff and increase infiltration that will remove contaminants.

FIGURE 2
Separated sewer system beneath the streets of most U.S. cities.

ESSAY: Predicting Oil-Spill Trajectories

Accidents involving spilled oil are all too frequent occurrences in coastal regions. Many factors (e.g., winds, surface currents, tides, air and water temperatures, and salinity) control the movement of spilled oil. Furthermore, the type and amount of spilled oil, and local shoreline and bottom features also influence movements of an oil slick. An effective response to an oil spill requires the input of scientists representing many different specialties plus information on the chemical composition of the spilled oil, ocean currents, and weather. All these data are needed for mathematical models that predict movements (known as *trajectory analysis*) of the oil. When combined with biological resource information, trajectory analyses can be used to identify those areas most vulnerable to damage from the oil so that equipment to contain the oil spill can be deployed to where it will be most effective. Sensitive areas requiring protection include marine sanctuaries and other unique habitats, especially those that are home to endangered species. Protection is key because oil not only causes immediate contamination but also has long-term effects on coastal ecosystems.

NOAA's *Coastal Change Analysis Program* uses remote sensing data, primarily aerial photography, to identify and classify sensitive habitats of bottom-dwelling organisms, such as sea grasses. Oil spills can affect sea grasses in many ways. Toxic materials in the spilled oil mix with sediments and enter the water and ultimately living organisms. Oil can also block sunlight from reaching the plants. Heavy oils sink and mix with sediment and can coat sea grasses. When these grasses are damaged or killed, organisms that depend upon them as a food source or for habitat are also adversely affected. This has a ripple effect on the local ecosystem and ultimately can damage economically valuable fish and shellfish, thus impacting local economies for many years.

Major sectors of Maine's economy, especially tourism and fishing, require clean coastal waters, aesthetically appealing coastlines, and functioning coastal ecosystems. Thus, the state requires timely and appropriate responses to oil spills. To demonstrate the importance of accurate oil-spill trajectory analysis and prompt response to mediate the effects of oil spills, we examine two cases separated by nearly 25 years.

In 1972, the tanker *Tamano* spilled 380,000 liters (100,000 gal) of oil into Casco Bay, near Portland in southern Maine, then the largest oil spill in the state's history. Plans for dealing with spills were antiquated and slow to be implemented. During the several days required to mobilize response teams, the oil spread along about 75 km (47 mi) of coastline, including beaches on 18 small islands, damaging commercially valuable fish and shellfish stocks. The cleanup that followed took 11 years and cost nearly $4 billion.

On 27 September 1996, the tanker *Julie N.* struck a bridge entering Casco Bay, spilling 680,000 liters (180,000 gal) of light fuel oil and much heavier bunker-C, a mix of oils. The light fuel oil evaporated quickly but left behind toxic components. The less toxic but heavier bunker-C sank to the bottom, covering vegetation and wildlife with a thick, sticky coating. The response to this incident was rapid and effective. The damaged tanker quickly docked and was immediately surrounded by floating barriers, called booms, to contain floating oil. Other booms were deployed quickly to prevent oil from reaching vulnerable biological resources or economically valuable locations. In addition, special clean-up vessels skimmed and collected oil from the water surface.

NOAA officials note that the spill occurred during the spring ebb tides, with south to southwest winds that initially kept the oil within the inner harbor. However, the following night stronger winds pushed the oil through the protection booms at the upriver side of the inner harbor. Timely response combined with successful predictions of oil movements under those circumstances meant that much of the damage that had occurred 25 years earlier in the same area was not repeated.

FIGURE 1
Oil tanker *Julie N* surrounded by booms. [Photo by S. Mierzykowski, USFWS]

APPENDIX I

CONVERSION FACTORS

	Multiply	By	To obtain
LENGTH	inches (in.)	2.54	centimeters (cm)
	centimeters	0.3937	inches
	centimeters	10000	micrometers (µm)
	feet (ft)	0.3048	meters (m)
	feet	0.167	fathoms (fm)
	meters	3.281	feet
	meters	0.547	fathoms
	statute miles (mi)	1.6093	kilometers (km)
	statute miles	0.869	nautical miles
	kilometers	0.6214	statute miles
	kilometers	0.54	nautical miles
	nautical miles	1.852	kilometers
	kilometers	3281	feet
	feet	0.0003048	kilometers
	fathoms	1.8288	meters
	fathoms	6	feet
SPEED	miles per hour (mph)	1.6093	kilometers per hour (kph)
	miles per hour	0.869	knots (kts)
	miles per hour	0.447	meters per second (m/s)
	knots	1.151	miles per hour
	knots	0.514	meters per second
	knots	1.852	kilometers per hour
	kilometers per hour	0.6214	miles per hour
	kilometers per hour	0.540	knots
	meters per second	1.944	knots
	meters per second	2.237	miles per hour
WEIGHTS AND MASS	ounces (oz)	28.35	grams (g)
	grams	0.0353	ounces
	pounds (lb)	0.4536	kilograms (kg)
	kilograms	2.205	pounds
	tons	0.9072	metric tons

	metric tons	1.102	tons
	metric tons	1000	kilograms
LIQUID MEASURE	fluid ounces (fl oz)	0.0296	liters (L)
	gallons (gal)	3.785	liters
	liters	0.2642	gallons
	liters	33.814	fluid ounces
AREA	acres (A)	0.4047	hectares (ha)
	square yards (yd^2)	0.8361	square meters (m^2)
	square miles (mi^2)	2.590	square kilometers (km^2)
	hectares	0.010	square kilometers
	hectares	2.471	acres
	hectares	10000	square meters
	square kilometers	1000000	square meters
PRESSURE/ FORCE	pounds force (lb)	4.448	newtons (N)
	newtons	0.2248	pounds
	millimeters of mercury at 0 °C	133.32	pascals (Pa; N per m^2)
	pounds per square inch (psi)	6.895	kilopascals (kPa; 1000 pascals)
	pascals	0.0075	millimeters of mercury at 0 °C
	kilopascals	0.1450	pounds per square inch
	bars	1000	millibars (mb)
	bars	100000	pascals
	bars	0.9869	atmospheres (atm)
ENERGY	joules (J)	0.2389	calories (cal)
	kilocalories (kcal)	1000	calories
	joules	1.0	watt-seconds (W-sec)
	kilojoules (kJ)	1000	joules
	calories	0.00397	Btu (British thermal units)
	calories	4.186	joules
	Btu	252	calories
POWER	joules per second	1.0	watts (W)
	kilowatts (kW)	1000	watts
	megawatts (MW)	1000	kilowatts
	kilocalories per minute	69.80	watts
	watts	0.00134	horsepower (hp)
	kilowatts	56.87	Btu per minute
	Btu per minute	0.0235	horsepower

APPENDIX II

OCEAN TIMELINE

BCE 4000   Egyptians developed shipbuilding and ocean piloting capabilities, as well as trading on the Nile.

BCE 3800   First maps showing water (river charts).

BCE 2000-500   The Polynesians voyaged across the Pacific Ocean and settled all the major islands, first inhabiting Tonga, Samoa, ca. 1000 BCE. Micronesian stick chart used.

BCE 1200-850   Phoenicians explored entire Mediterranean Sea and sailed into the Atlantic to West Africa and to Cornwall, England for trading.

BCE 900   Greeks first use the term *okeanos*, a mythical god, to describe the great river that flowed in a circle around the Earth and the root of the present word ocean.

BCE 800   First graphic aids to marine navigation.

BCE 600   The Greek Pythagoreans assumed a spherical Earth.

                      Thales of Miletus, a Greek natural philosopher, developed the origin of science as we define it today and he is alleged to have written a book on navigation.

BCE 450   The Greek Herodotus compiled a map of the known world centered on the Mediterranean region.

BCE 325   The Greek Pytheas explored the coasts of England, Norway, and perhaps Iceland. He developed a means of determining latitude from the angular distance of the North Star and proposed a connection between the phases of the moon and the tides.

                      The Greek philosopher, Aristotle, published *Meteorologica,* which described the geography of the Greek world, and *Historia Animalium* the first known treatise on marine biology—a catalog of marine organisms.

BCE 300   Library founded at Alexandria by Alexander the Great, which served as the repository for scrolls from ships and land caravans; for the next 600 years, it was a maritime studies center, fostering advances in science, celestial navigation by a variety of Greek and Egyptian scholars.

BCE 276-192   The Greek Eratosthenes, a scholar and librarian at Alexandria, calculated the circumference of a spherical Earth with remarkable accuracy using trigonometry noting the specific angle of sunlight that occurred at Alexandria and Syene (now called Aswan), Egypt. He also invented latitude and longitude lines based on landmarks.

BCE 127	Hipparchus of Nicaea, a Greek mathematician, developed a 360 degree system and arranged latitude and longitude in regular grid by degrees.
BCE 54 - CE 30	The Roman Seneca devised the hydrologic cycle to show that, despite the inflow of river water, the level of the ocean remained stable because of evaporation.
1st century CE	Chinese invent first compass.
CE 150	The Greek-Egyptian scientist, Claudius Ptolemy, added minutes and seconds to the latitude-longitude system and compiled a map of the Roman World, but erred in estimating Earth's circumference, which remained uncorrected for hundreds of years.
CE 415	The Alexandrian library with an estimated 700,000 scrolls destroyed and the last librarian, Hypatia, murdered by religious mob; Earth considered flat again.
CE 673--735	The English monk Bede published *De Temporum Ratione,* which discussed the lunar control of the tides and recognized monthly tidal variations and the effect of wind drag on tidal height.
CE 780	Viking raids begin.
CE 800-1000	Hawaii colonized by Polynesians
CE 950-1250	Medieval Warm Period
CE 982	Eric the Red, a Norse chieftain, completed the first transatlantic voyage, reaching present-day Baffin Island, Canada.
CE 995	Leif Ericson, son of Eric the Red, established the settlement of Vinland in what is now Newfoundland, Canada.
CE 1000	Norwegian colonies established in North America
1050	The astrolabe, a navigation instrument used to measure the height of celestial bodies above the horizon, first arrived in Europe from the East.
1400-1850	The Little Ice Age.
1405	Admiral Cheng Ho, the commander of the Treasure Fleet of the Dragon Throne began his voyages for Emperor Chu Ti, ultimately ruling the South Pacific and Indian Ocean until 1433.
1420	Prince Henry the Navigator of Portugal founded a naval observatory and the first school for teaching navigation, astronomy, and cartography.
1452-1519	Leonardo da Vinci, the famous Italian scientist, observed, recorded and interpreted characteristics of currents and waves and noted that fossils In Italian mountains implied that sea level had been higher in the ancient past.
1460	Prince Henry the Navigator died.
1492	Christopher Columbus rediscovered North America, sailing to the islands of the West Indies.

1497–1499	Vasco da Gama, a Portuguese navigator, journeyed to India by sea by rounding the Cape of Good Hope with four ships, thereby establishing the first European all water trade route between Europe and India.
1500	The Portuguese navigator and explorer, Pedro Alvares Cabral, traveled westward in search of a route to India, but reached and explored Brazil.
1513	Juan Ponce de Leon described the swift and powerful Florida Current.
1513-1518	Vasco de Nunez de Balboa crossed the Isthmus of Panama and sailed in the Pacific Ocean.
1515	Peter Martyr proposed an origin for the Gulf Stream.
1519-1522	Ferdinand Magellan embarked on the first circumnavigation of the globe; the crew led by Sebastian del Cano completed the voyage. On the voyage, named the Pacific Ocean.
1569	Geradus Mercator, the Flemish mapmaker, constructed a map projection of the world that was adapted to navigational charts.
1605	Bishop Resen of Copenhagen drew the first map of the Gulf Stream.
1609	Hugo Grotius, a Dutch legal scholar, published *Mare Liberum,* the foundation for all modern law of the sea.
1674	The British scientist Robert Boyle investigated the relation among temperature, salinity, and pressure of seawater with depth and reported his findings in *Observations and Experiments on the Saltiness of the Sea.*
1687	Sir Isaac Newton published *Principia Mathematica*, which includes an explanation of the operation of gravity and that tides are the result of gravitational attraction of the moon and sun.
1714	Gabriel D. Fahrenheit invents a temperature scale.
1725	Count Luigi Marsigli from Bologna, Italy compiled *Histoire Physique de la Mer*, the first book pertaining entirely to oceanography, examining the geological formation of ocean basins along with the marine life that lived in the sea.
1733	English clockmaker John Harrison invented the first of his five accurate and durable nautical chronometers for determining longitude at sea. He was awarded a cash prize for his accomplishment in 1773.
1735	George Hadley proposed an explanation for the trade wind regime that involved a consideration of the Earth's rotation.
1740	Leonhard Euler, noted Swiss mathematician, developed an approximation of the three-body problem to calculate the magnitude of the lunar and solar attractive forces that generate ocean tides.
1742	Anders Celsius invents a temperature scale.
1758	Carolus Linnaeus publishes 10th edition of *Systema Naturae*, formalizing biological nomenclature.

1760	John Harrison invented the Number Four chronometer in his quest to solve the longitude problem.
	Joseph Black proposed the concept of specific heat.
1768-1771, 1772-1775, 1776-1780	Captain James Cook commanded three major ocean voyages gathering extensive data on geography, geology, biota, currents, tides, and water temperatures of all of the principal oceans.
1769 or 1770	The American scientist, Benjamin Franklin, published the first chart of the Gulf Stream (by Folger), which was used by ships to cross the North Atlantic Ocean faster.
1779	James Cook died in Hawaii.
1802	Nathaniel Bowditch of Massachusetts published the *New American Practical Navigator*, a navigational resource that continues to be revised and published to this day.
1805	Admiral Sir Francis Beaufort of the Royal Navy developed his 12-category wind force scale to aid mariners estimate wind speed; this scale was later modified.
1807	President Thomas Jefferson mandated coastal charting of the entire United States and established the U.S. Coast and Geodetic Survey.
1811	British chemist Sir Humphry Davy made the first gas hydrates in his laboratory.
1817-1818	Sir John Ross ventured into the Arctic Ocean to explore Baffin Island, where he sounded the bottom successfully (took the first deep-water and sediment samples) and recovered starfish and mud worms from a depth of 1.8 km.
1820	Alexander Marcet, a London physician, noted that the proportion of the chemical ingredients in seawater is unvarying in all ocean basins.
1831-1836	The epic five-year journey of Charles Darwin aboard the British research ship HMS *Beagle* led to a theory of atoll formation and later the theory of evolution by natural selection.
1835	Gaspard-Gustav de Coriolis, a French mathematician, published first papers on an object's horizontal motion across the surface of the rotating Earth.
1836	William Henry Harvey, an Irish botanist, devised a taxonomy of seaweeds.
1838-1842	Departure of the United States Exploring Expedition led by Lieutenant Charles Wilkes on the flagship *Vincennes*. Six vessels mapping coastal areas, collected specimens.
1839-1843	Sir James Clark Ross led an expedition to Antarctica, recovering samples of deep-sea benthos down to a depth of 4.9 km.
1841, 1854	Sir Edward Forbes published *The History of British Star-Fishes* (1841) and then his *Distribution of Marine Life* (1854), in which he argued that sea life cannot exist below a depth of about 600 m (the so called azoic hypothesis).
1847	Hans Christian Oersted observed plankton.

1851	The first telegraph cable was laid across the Straits of Dover, stimulating new technologies to protect, raise and lower cables to the sea floor.
1853	The first international conference convened in Brussels by Lt. Matthew Fontaine Maury, USN for the purpose of establishing a uniform means of meteorological observations at sea.
1855	Matthew Fontaine Maury, USN compiled and standardized the wind and current data recorded in U.S. ship logs and summarized his findings in *The Physical Geography of the Sea*, credited as the first textbook of modern oceanography.
1859	Darwin's *Origin of Species* published.
1865	Fr. Pietro Angelo Secchi, a papal scientific advisor, perfected the Secchi disc for determination of the transparency of Mediterranean Sea water to sunlight.
1868-1870	Charles Wyville Thomson, aboard HMS *Lightning* and HMS *Porcupine,* made the first series of deep-sea temperature measurements and collected marine organisms from great depths, disproving Forbes' azoic hypothesis.
1870s	William Ferrel, an American meteorologist, drew attention to the deflecting effect of the Earth's rotation on ocean currents (the Coriolis Effect).
1871	The U.S. Fish Commission was established with a modern laboratory at Woods Hole, MA.
1872-1876	Lead by Charles Wyville Thomson, *HMS Challenger* conducted worldwide scientific expeditions, collecting data and specimens that were later analyzed in the more than 50 volumes of the *Challenger Reports.*
1872	Departure of *Challenger* Expedition.
1873	Charles Wyville Thomson published a general oceanography book called the *Depths of the Sea.*
1877-1880	Alexander Agassiz, an American naturalist, founded the first U.S. marine station, the Anderson School of Natural History, on Penikese Island, Buzzards Bay, MA.
1880	William Dittmar determined major salts in seawater.
1884-1901	USS *Albatross* was designed and constructed specifically to conduct scientific research at sea and undertook numerous oceanographic cruises.
1880s	Development of the civil time zones and the ultimate specification of the Greenwich Mean Time (GMT) as the world-wide reference.
1888	The Marine Biological Laboratory was established at Woods Hole, MA.
1890	Alfred Thayer Mahan completed *The Influence of Sea Power upon History.*
1891	Sir John Murray and Alphonse Renard classified marine sediments.
1893	Discovery of Maunder sunspot minimum by astronomer E. Walter Maunder.

1893–1896	The Norwegian Fridtjof Nansen while aboard the *Fram,* studied the circulation pattern of the Arctic Ocean and confirmed that a northern continent did not exist.
1900	On 8 September, a hurricane storm surge struck Galveston, TX. More than 8000 people died, mostly by drowning, in the most deadly natural disaster in U.S. history.
1902	Danish scientists with government backing established the International Council for the Exploration of the Sea (ICES) to investigate oceanographic conditions that affect North Atlantic fisheries. Council representatives were from Great Britain, Germany, Sweden, Norway, Denmark, Holland, and the Soviet Union.
1903	The Friday Harbor Oceanographic Laboratory was established at: the University of Washington in Seattle.
	The Laboratory that became the Scripps Institution of Biological Research, and later the Scripps Institution of Oceanography, was founded in San Diego, CA.
1905	Marconi perfected wireless telegraphy, which became important for communication on the ocean.
	The Swedish oceanographer, V.W. Ekman, published his classic work on the cause of the spiral nature of wind driven ocean currents near the surface.
1906	The first Sonar type listening device was invented by Lewis Nixon in order to detect icebergs.
	Prince Albert I of Monaco established the Muscée Océanographique.
1907	Bertram Boltwood calculated age of Earth by radioactive decay.
1911	Roald Amundsen was first at South Pole.
1912	Following the sinking of the *Titanic*, the International Ice Patrol formed to monitor icebergs.
	German meteorologist Alfred Wegener proposed his theory of continental drift in his Frankfurt lectures.
1912	Scripps Institution allied with the University of California.
1918	Vilhelm Bjerknes and colleagues at the Bergen (Norway) school formulated theories of air masses, atmospheric fronts, and midlatitude storm systems.
1921	International Hydrographic Bureau founded.
1924	Discovery of the southern oscillation by Sir Gilbert Walker.
1925-1927	A German expedition aboard the research vessel *Meteor* studied the physical oceanography of the Atlantic Ocean, using an echo sounder extensively for the first time.
1929	British geologist Arthur Holmes first proposed that convection in Earth's mantle was the driving force for continental drift. This explanation was revived in the 1960s by Harry Hess and Robert S. Dietz.

1930	The Woods Hole Oceanographic Institution was established on the southwestern shore of Cape Cod, MA.
1931	*Atlantis* launched.
1932	The International Whaling Commission was organized to collect data on whale species and to enforce voluntary regulations on whaling.
1937	*E.W. Scripps* launched.
1938	Serbian astronomer Milutin Milankovitch began work on his astronomical theory of the Ice Age.
1942	Harald Sverdrup, Richard Fleming, and Martin Johnson published the first modern oceanographic reference text, *The Oceans,* which is still consulted today.
1943	Jacques Cousteau and Emile Gagnan invented the scuba regulator and tank combination, the "aqualung" for diving underwater.
1946	On 1 April, a tsunami destroyed most of the waterfront of Hilo, Hawaii causing 159 deaths.
1949	Maurice Ewing formed the Lamont (later changed to Lamont Doherty) Geological Observatory at Columbia University in New York.
1957	Systematic monitoring of atmospheric carbon dioxide levels begins at the Mauna Loa Observatory, Hawaii, under the direction of Charles D. Keeling.
1957-1958	The International Geophysical Year (IGY) was organized as an international effort to coordinate geophysical investigations of the Earth, including the ocean.
1958	The first U.S. nuclear submarine, USS *Nautilus*, also made the first submerged transit of the Arctic ice pack, passing the geographic North Pole.
1959	Antarctic Treaty System adopted by 12 nations.
1959-1965	The International Indian Ocean Expedition was established under United Nations auspices to intensively investigate Indian Ocean oceanography.
1960	The bathyscaphe *Trieste* carrying Jacques Piccard and Don Walsh reached the bottom of the deepest (Mariana) trench (10,912 m, or 35,800 ft).
1960s	Jacob Bjerknes developed concept of teleconnections involving El Niño events and the southern oscillation.
1962	Rachel Carson's book *Silent Spring* initiated the U.S. environmental movement.
1963	F.J. Vine and D.H. Matthews of Cambridge University interpreted sea floor magnetic field anomaly patterns in support of sea floor spreading.
1964	*Alvin*, the world's first deep-ocean research submersible was launched.

	On 28 March, a tsunami struck the Seward, Alaska area, claiming more than 100 lives.
1965	Discovery of a natural deposit of methane hydrates under permafrost in Siberia.
1966	The U.S. Congress adopted the Sea Grant College and Programs Act to provide nonmilitary funding for marine science education and research.
1968	*Glomar Challenger* returns first deep-sea cores, indicating the age of the Earth's crust. The cores support theories of plate tectonics.
	The U.S. National Science Foundation organized the Deep Sea Drilling project (DSDP) to core through the sediments and crust of the ocean bottom.
1969	Santa Barbara, CA oil well blowout captured national attention.
	Stratton Commission developed the first national ocean policy for the U.S.
1970	The U.S. government created the National Oceanic and Atmospheric Administration (NOAA) to oversee and coordinate government activities related to oceanography and meteorology.
	Completion of the Aswan High Dam on the Nile River.
1970s	The United Nations initiated the International Decade of Ocean, Exploration (IDOE) to improve scientific knowledge of the ocean.
	Saffir-Simpson Hurricane Intensity Scale rated hurricanes from 1 to 5 corresponding to increasing intensity.
1970	John Tuzo Wilson, a Canadian geologist, proposed a cyclic model of tectonic revolution.
1971	Jason Morgan of Princeton University proposed hotspot volcanism.
1972	The Geochemical Ocean Sections Study (GEOSECS) was organized to study seawater chemistry and investigate ocean circulation and mixing, and the biogeochemical recycling of chemical substances.
	Marine Mammal Protection Act established a moratorium on the hunting of marine mammals in U.S. waters and by U.S. citizens on the high seas (reauthorized in 1994).
	Provisions of the 1972 Marine Protection, Research and Sanctuaries Act authorized the President to designate national marine sanctuaries in coastal waters of the continental shelf and in the Great Lakes (reauthorized in 2000).
	London Dumping Convention banned the discharge of waste from land into the ocean by ships or aircraft.
	Coastal Zone Management Act passed into law whereby the federal government assists coastal states in managing and protecting coastal resources.
1973	U.S. Endangered Species Act became law.

1974	Project FAMOUS (French-American Mid-Ocean Undersea Study) mapped and sampled the Mid-Atlantic Ridge, a zone of seafloor spreading.
	F.S. Rowland and M.J. Molina first warned of the threat of CFCs to the stratospheric ozone shield.
1975	Sinking, on 10 November, of the ore carrier Edmund Fitzgerald on Lake Superior with the loss of her 29-member crew.
1976	Scientists discover indications of Milankovitch cycles in deep-sea sediment cores.
	Magnuson-Stevens Fisheries and Conservation Act established fishery councils to manage the fishery resources in each region of the nation.
1977	The submersible *Alvin* finds hydrothermal vents in the Galápagos rift.
1978	*Seasat-A,* the first satellite dedicated to the remote sensing of the ocean, was launched.
	Coastal Zone Color Scanner (CZCS) flown aboard NASA's Nimbus-7 satellite.
1979	NOAA's SLOSH numerical model developed to predict the location and height of a storm surge.
1981	The Burgess shale declared a UNESCO World Heritage Site.
1982	The UN Convention on the Law of the Sea established.
	The UN Convention on the Law of the Sea granted jurisdiction over an exclusive economic zone (EEZ) to 151 coastal nations.
1983	The Chesapeake Bay Program became the nation's largest federal-state environmental restoration project; the nation's first estuary selected for restoration and protection.
1985	The scientific research vessel *JOIDES Resolution* replaced *Glomar Challenger* in Deep Sea Drilling Project.
	Tropical Ocean-Global Atmosphere (TOGA) commenced a 10-year experiment in the equatorial Pacific, with the deployment of the TOGA Tropical Atmosphere Ocean (TAO) Array.
	R. D. Ballard located wreck of *Titanic*.
1986	Moratorium on commercial whaling issued by the International Whaling Commission (IWC).
1987	Joint Global Ocean Flux Study (JGOFSS) founded to assess processes controlling carbon fluxes.
1988	The Intergovernmental Panel on Climate Change (IPCC) formed by the World Meteorological Organization and the UN Environmental Programme to evaluate the state of climate science as the basis for policy action.
	Heinrich layers first described by German researcher Hartmut Heinrich. Sediment released to the floor of the North Atlantic during the melting of fleets of ice bergs.

1989	On 24 March, the supertanker *Exxon Valdez* ran aground on a reef in Prince William Sound, Alaska, producing the largest oil spill in U.S. history.
1990	The *JOIDES Resolution* drilling vessel retrieved a sediment sample estimated to be 170 million years old.
1991	JOI researchers bore to a depth of 2 km (1.24 mi) beneath the seafloor near the Galápagos Islands.
	The NOAA National Weather Service Forecast Office in Miami, FL began to issue outlooks for rip currents.
1992	The U.S.-French *TOPEX/Poseidon* satellite launched to continuously monitor global ocean topography.
	The Tropical Ocean Global Atmosphere Coupled Ocean-Atmosphere Response Experiment (TOGA COARE) was conducted in western Pacific.
1993	Beginning of a series of ocean iron fertilization experiments (12 so far).
1994	The Law of the Sea Treaty entered into force.
1995	*Keiko*, a small remotely controlled Japanese submersible, sets a new depth record, reaching 10,978 m (36,008 ft) in the Challenger Deep.
1998	UN declared the "Year of the Oceans" to increase awareness of the importance of the ocean.
	Galileo spacecraft found possible evidence of an ocean on Jupiter's moon Europa.
	Scientists from 30 nations began deploying Argo profiling floats in the world ocean.
2000	Beginning of 10-year international project, *Census of Marine Life*.
2004	On 26 December, tsunami originated off the west coast of Sumatra, Indonesia; death toll is estimated at 230,000.
	U.S. Commission on Ocean Policy made recommendations for a new national ocean policy.
2005	On 28 August, Hurricane Katrina struck the Gulf coast of Louisiana and Mississippi. The death toll was estimated at 1300 in the most destructive hurricane in U.S. history.
2007-09	Fourth International Polar Year (IPY).
2007	Modern Japanese drill ship, *Chikyu*, became fully operational.
2008	As of March, 3129 Argo active profiling floats are deployed in the world ocean.

GLOSSARY

A

absorption The process whereby incident radiant energy is retained by a substance. The absorbed radiation is then converted to another form of energy (e.g., heat).

abyssal plain The flat surface of the sea floor, usually at the base of a *continental rise* and formed by the deposition of sediments that obscure the preexisting topography.

abyssal storm Unusually strong bottom current (of the order of 1.0 knot) that scours the ocean floor generating moving clouds of suspended sediment.

acid rain Precipitation with a pH of less than 5.6.

acoustic thermometry A method of determining ocean temperature by measuring the speed of sound propagating through the ocean.

adaptation A genetically controlled trait or characteristic that enhances an organism's chance for survival and reproduction in its environment.

adaptive coloration Camouflage whereby an organism's color pattern closely matches its background substrate.

aerosols Minute solid and liquid particles which are suspended in the atmosphere.

air mass A large widespread volume of air, the thermal, moisture, and stability properties of which are characteristic of its source region and modified as it moves away from its source.

air pressure The force exerted per unit area by the atmosphere as a consequence of gravitational attraction upon the molecules in a column of air lying directly above a specified location.

air pressure gradient A change in air pressure from one place to another.

albedo The ratio of the amount of electromagnetic radiation reflected by a body to the amount incident on it; commonly expressed as a percentage. Usually, albedo refers to radiation in the visible range or to the full spectrum of solar radiation.

anadromous fishes Fishes which travel from salt water to fresh water or up rivers to spawn. They include salmon, shad, sturgeon and striped bass.

Arctic Oscillation (AO) A seesaw variation in air pressure between the North Pole and the margins of the polar region. Changes in the horizontal air pressure gradient alter the speed of horizontal winds in the polar vortex.

artificial beach nourishment A process whereby sand dredged from offshore (or an inland source) is moved to badly eroded beaches with an aim of re-establishing the natural balance between sediment input and output on the beach.

assimilative capacity The amount of waste that an ecosystem can assimilate (via decomposition by bacteria, fungi, and invertebrates) without damaging ecosystem functions or building up waste products to levels that may cause unwanted or harmful impacts on living organisms (including humans).

asthenosphere A region of the upper mantle between 200 and 400 km deep which exhibits plastic-like behavior and readily deforms in response to stress; underlies the lithosphere.

astronomical tides The periodic rise and fall of sea level resulting from the gravitational interaction and motions of the moon, sun, and Earth system.

atmosphere A relatively thin envelope of gases and

suspended particles surrounding the Earth and held there by gravity.

atmospheric window Wavelength bands in which atmospheric constituents absorb very little or no electromagnetic radiation; allows the escape of Earth's heat to space.

atoll A series of coral reefs surrounding a *lagoon* that remains after a volcanic island sinks beneath the waves or erodes away.

Autonomous Underwater Vehicles (AUVs) Un-piloted, remotely controlled powered vehicles that are not tethered to a mother ship. They carry sensors that measure ocean water properties (e.g., temperature, salinity, dissolved oxygen).

azoic hypothesis The erroneous belief that deep-ocean waters (below 300 fathoms or 550 m) lacked sufficient dissolved oxygen to support marine life.

B

barrier island An elongated, narrow accumulation of sand oriented parallel to a shoreline, but separated from the mainland by a *lagoon*, *estuary*, or bay.

beach A deposit of unconsolidated sediment (usually sand and gravel), extending landward from low tide to a change in topography or where permanent vegetation begins.

beach sediment budget The sum of all sediment outputs and inputs on a beach; determines whether the beach is growing or shrinking.

benthic zone One of the two basic subdivisions of the marine biome which includes the sea floor and bottom dwelling organisms.

benthos A collective term for marine organisms which live on or near the sea floor, or *benthic zone.*

berm A platform of sand, flat-topped and sloping steeply seaward, formed near the mean high-water mark.

bioaccumulation The process by which persistent materials (that resist chemical, physical, or biological breakdown) gradually become increasingly concentrated in living tissue as one organism consumes another within a food web.

bio-fouling The undesirable accumulation of organisms on any submerged surface.

biogenous sediment Marine sediment formed from the excretions, secretions, and remains (e.g., shells) of organisms.

biogeochemical cycle Pathways along which solid, liquid, and gaseous materials flow among the various reservoirs of the Earth system.

biological pump The process whereby carbon cycles through the ocean as organic matter decomposes.

bioluminescence Production of light by living organisms. Light is generally the product of a chemical reaction that takes place in specialized cells or organs.

biosphere Consists of all living organisms on Earth; component of ecosystems.

bioturbation The churning and stirring of sediment deposits by benthic animals in the course of feeding or movement.

black smokers Substances that precipitate from hydrothermal vent waters appear as dark clouds and accumulate in the form of conical chimneys.

Bowen ratio For any moist surface, the ratio of heat energy used for sensible heating (conduction and convection) to the heat energy used for latent heating (evaporation of water or sublimation of snow or ice).

breaker The collapsing of a wave as it becomes steeper and less stable upon entering shoaling water.

breakwater A long, narrow offshore structure, usually constructed of large blocks of rock or concrete, oriented parallel to the shoreline and intended to provide calm waters for docking boats and to protect beaches from erosion.

brine rejection Salts are excluded from the ice structure as seawater freezes and the remaining unfrozen water becomes saltier and therefore freezes at still lower temperatures.

bubble injection A mechanism of gas transfer at the air/sea interface whereby breaking waves introduce a foam composed of small bubbles below the surface greatly enhancing exchange rates.

buffer A substance that causes chemical equilibrium.

bycatch Fish and other marine animals that are caught in addition to the target species; they are often disposed of.

C

calcareous oozes Deep-sea pelagic sediment containing at least 30% calcareous (calcium carbonate) skeletal remains by weight.

Callendar effect Theory that global climate change can be brought about by enhancement of the natural greenhouse effect by increased levels of atmospheric CO_2 from anthropogenic sources, principally the burning of fossil fuels. The theory is named for the British engineer Guy Stewart Callendar who investigated the link between global warming and fossil fuel combustion beginning in the late 1930s.

calving The breaking away of a mass of ice from the leading edge of a glacier forming icebergs upon entering the ocean.

capillary waves Small ocean waves with a wavelength of less than 1.7 cm (0.7 in.).

carbonate compensation depth (CCD) The depth of the ocean below which material composed of calcium carbonate ($CaCO_3$) dissolves and does not accumulate.

carrying capacity The maximum population of a species that can be sustained by the resources of the habitat.

cartilaginous fishes Also called *elasmobranchs*, these generally primitive fishes lack true bones and their skeletons consist of cartilage. Examples include sharks, skates, and rays.

catadromous fishes Fish that breed in the open ocean, but spend their adult lives in fresh water. An example is the American eel.

celerity The rate at which a surface wave progresses outward in still water from the point where the water was disturbed.

cellular respiration The process whereby food is broken down liberating energy for maintenance, growth and reproduction, while releasing carbon dioxide, water and heat energy to the environment.

Challenger Expedition The first voyage dedicated exclusively to marine exploration. Conducted from December 1872 to May 1876, scientists sampled every ocean basin except the Arctic.

chemosynthesis The process whereby marine organisms in the absence of sunlight derive energy from substances such as hydrogen sulfide (H_2S) or methane.

climate The weather of some locality averaged over some specific interval of time (e.g., 30 years) plus extremes in weather observed during the same period or during the entire period of record.

coast A strip of land of indefinite width that extends from the low-tide line inland to the first major change in landform features; transitional between land and ocean.

coastal downwelling Downward motion of warm surface waters along the coast caused by *Ekman transport* onshore.

coastal upwelling Upward motion of cold, nutrient-rich deep water along the coast caused by *Ekman transport* offshore.

Coastal Zone Management Program (CZMP) A program authorized in 1972 whereby the federal government assists coastal states in managing and protecting their coastal resources.

coastline The farthest inland extent of storm waves, in some cases marked by sand dunes or wave-cut cliffs.

coccolithophorids Single-cell photosynthesizing organisms, covered with tiny calcium carbonate plates. They are unusual in that they appear to thrive in nutrient-poor waters, forming large blooms that turn surface waters greenish blue as viewed from space.

cold-core rings Eddies having a core of relatively cold water that break off from an ocean surface current; viewed from above in the Northern Hemisphere, they rotate in a counterclockwise direction.

compensation depth The ocean depth below which no *net primary production* occurs, usually where the light level diminishes to about 1% of what it is at the surface.

condensation The process whereby water changes phase from vapor to liquid.

conservation of angular momentum For a body rotating in a plane about a point, a decrease in the radius of the orbit is accompanied by an increase in the angular velocity.

constructive wave interference The result when the crests of sets of waves coincide to form a wave of greater height.

consumer An organism that is unable to manufacture its food from nonliving materials but is dependent on the energy stored in other living things; also known as a *heterotroph.*

continental climate Characterizes a middle or high latitude locale well inland from the moderating influence of the ocean or large lake; characterized by a significant difference between mean summer and winter temperatures.

continental crust The outermost part of the lithosphere overlying the mantle and forming the solid surface of Earth's landmasses; mostly granite in composition.

continental drift The slow movement of landmasses as part of *tectonic plates.* The continents of today were once a single landmass (Pangaea) that broke apart with the various fragments moving over the surface of the planet.

continental rise The gently sloping area of the sea floor beyond the base of the *continental shelf.*

continental shelf The submerged zone between the shoreline and *continental slope* where the sea floor slopes seaward at a gradient of less than one degree.

continental slope The relatively steep downward sloping area from the shelf-slope break to the more gently sloping *continental rise* or directly into an *ocean trench.*

convergent plate boundary The boundary between two tectonic plates that are moving toward one another;

responsible for *subduction.*

copepods A diverse group of tiny crustaceans covered with an exoskeleton made of chitin.

coral atoll A ring-shaped island surrounding a seawater *lagoon.*

coral bleaching The whitening of coral colonies due to the loss of symbiotic zooxanthellae from the tissues of coral polyps; may be triggered by a rise in seawater temperature.

coral reef A calcareous reef in relatively shallow, tropical seas composed of a thin veneer of living coral growing on older layers of dead coral or volcanic rock.

Coriolis Effect An apparent force relative to Earth's surface due to Earth's rotation that causes deflection of moving objects to the right in the Northern Hemisphere and to the left in the Southern Hemisphere.

cosmogenous sediment Particles entering the Earth system from outer space, often originating from meteorite fragments.

cotidal line A line plotted on a chart connecting points at which high water (high tide) occurs simultaneously. Lines show the time lapse, in lunar-hour intervals, between the Moon's passage over a reference meridian (usually the prime meridian) and the succeeding high water at a specified location.

countershading Protective coloration found in fish whereby their dorsal (back) side is a dark color making it difficult to see them from above and their ventral (underbelly) side is a light color making it difficult to see them from below.

cryosphere The frozen portion of the *hydrosphere*, encompassing glacial ice, icebergs, sea ice, and the ice in permafrost.

D

decomposers *Consumers*, usually microscopic, that feed on dead organic matter, either on the ocean bottom or in the water column, thus aiding in recycling nutrients.

deep layer Dark, cold nearly isothermal ocean water

below the *pycnocline*; accounts for most of the ocean's mass.

Deep Sea Drilling Program (DSDP) Using the drill ship *Glomar Challenger*, this project sampled marine sediments and oceanic crust for scientific purposes from 1968 to 1983.

deep-water wave A wave on the surface of a body of water whose depth is more than one-half the wavelength.

delta A landform at the mouth of a river produced by the sudden divergence and dissipation of a stream's velocity and the resulting deposition of the river's suspended sediment load in the shape of the Greek letter *delta* when viewed from above.

density Mass per unit volume.

deposition The process whereby water changes directly from vapor to solid (ice crystals) without first becoming liquid.

destructive wave interference When the troughs of sets of waves coincide with the crests of another set of waves producing waves of reduced height.

diatoms A diverse group of minute shell-covered phytoplanktonic marine organisms having silica exoskeletons.

dinoflagellates Any of a class of single-cell marine planktonic organisms having characteristics of both plants and animals.

distillation Purification of water through phase changes (e.g., *evaporation* followed by *condensation*). When water vaporizes, all suspended and dissolved substances such as sea salts are left behind.

diurnal inequality The difference in heights between the two successive high waters (high tides) or the two successive low waters (low tides) of a tidal day.

diurnal tide An *astronomical tide* with only one high water (high tide) and one low water (low tide) occurring each lunar (tidal) day.

divergent plate boundary The zone between tectonic plates that are pulling apart with magma and new crust

moving in to fill the gap; most often occurring at a mid oceanic ridge.

doldrums An east-west equatorial belt of light and variable surface winds where the *trade winds* of the two hemispheres converge.

downwelling Downward motion of surface waters caused by *Ekman transport* onshore.

E

Earth-atmosphere system The interaction of processes operating at the Earth's surface with those of the overlying atmosphere.

eastern boundary currents Generic term for the relatively slow, broad, and shallow flow of ocean water (current) that runs along the eastern flank of a subtropical ocean gyre; the Canary Current is an example.

ebb tides Tidal currents flowing seaward with falling sea levels.

ecological efficiency The fraction of the total energy input of a system that is transformed into work or some other usable form of energy.

ecologically sustainable yield The maximum catch that a marine ecosystem can sustain without undergoing an undesirable change in state.

ecosystem Community of plants and animals that interact with one another, together with the physical conditions and chemical constituents in a specific geographical area.

Ekman spiral In response to a steady wind blowing over the ocean surface, water at increasing depths moves in directions more and more to the right (in the Northern Hemisphere) until at about 100 m depth the water is moving in a direction opposite to that of the wind; the spiral is in the opposite direction in the Southern Hemisphere.

Ekman transport The net transport of water due to the *Ekman spiral*; 90 degrees to the right of the surface wind in the Northern Hemisphere and 90 degrees to the left of the surface wind in the Southern Hemisphere.

El Niño Anomalous warming of ocean surface waters in the eastern tropical Pacific; accompanied by suppression of upwelling off the coasts of Ecuador and northern Peru and along the equator east of the international dateline. Typically lasting for 12 to 18 months and occurring every 3 to 7 years, El Niño is accompanied by changes in oceanic and atmospheric circulation plus weather extremes in various parts of the world.

elasmobranchs *Cartilaginous fishes* including sharks, skates and rays. More primitive than bony fishes, their skeletons consist entirely of cartilage.

electromagnetic radiation Energy in the form of waves that have both electrical and magnetic properties; these waves can travel through gases, liquids, and solids and require no physical medium. All objects emit all forms of electromagnetic radiation, although each object emits its peak radiation at a certain wavelength within the electromagnetic spectrum. Forms of electromagnetic radiation include gamma rays, x-rays, ultraviolet, visible light, infrared, microwaves, and radio waves.

electromagnetic spectrum The various forms of *electromagnetic radiation* arranged and distinguished by type by their wavelength (or frequency).

ENSO Contraction for El Niño/southern oscillation. The term for the coupled ocean-atmosphere interactions in the tropical Pacific Ocean characterized by episodes of anomalously high sea surface temperatures in the equatorial and tropical eastern Pacific. It is associated with large-scale swings in surface air pressure between the western and eastern tropical Pacific and is the most prominent source of inter-annual variability in weather and climate around the world.

Epifauna Organisms that live on the surface rather than within marine sediments on the ocean floor.

equatorial upwelling Upward circulation of cold, nutrient-rich bottom water toward the ocean surface; the consequence of convergence of the trade winds of the North and Souh Hemispheres plus *Ekman transport*.

erosion Removal and transport of sediments by running water, glaciers, wind, or gravity.

estuary The highly productive portion of a river affected by ocean tides; the semi-enclosed region in the vicinity of a river's mouth, in which the freshwater of the river mixes with the saltwater of the ocean.

euphausiid Larger members of the zooplankton community, including krill.

eustasy Condition of world-wide sea level and its fluctuations which may be caused by changes in the global water cycle (e.g., the waxing and waning of Earth's glacial ice sheets).

evaporation The process whereby water changes phase from a liquid to a vapor.

evaporative cooling The cooling a surface, such as Earth's surface, experiences as water evaporates, absorbing heat and transferring that heat to the atmosphere via water vapor. Evaporation of water requires the latent heat of vaporization.

exclusive economic zone (EEZ) The jurisdictional area initially established in 1983 for marine resources; the inner boundary of that zone is coterminous with the seaward boundary of coastal nations and extends seaward 370 km (200 nautical miles).

exotic species Animals and plants introduced into an ecosystem usually by humans intentionally or unintentionally; also known as invasive species.

extratropical cyclone Any *synoptic-scale* storm system that is not a *tropical cyclone*, usually referring only to the migratory low pressure systems of middle and high latitudes.

eye The roughly circular area of comparatively light winds and fair weather found at the center of an intense tropical cyclone (i.e., a *hurricane*).

eyewall The organized ring of intense thunderstorms surrounding the eye of a *tropical cyclone*, typically a *hurricane*.

F

fecal pellets Organic excrement found especially in marine sediment deposits and made up of the undigested organic matter secreted by animals.

fetch The distance the wind blows over a continuous water surface.

filter feeders Marine organisms that use tiny hairs (called *cilia*), mucous-covered surfaces or other strategies to capture food particles suspended in the water.

fjord A narrow inlet or arm of the sea bordered by steep cliffs; formed when the post-glacial rise in sea level flooded a glacially eroded river valley.

float An instrument package that obtains vertical profiles of water temperature and salinity and is used to study deep-ocean currents; an example is the *Argo profiler.*

flood tides Tidal currents directed toward land, causing water levels to rise in harbors and rivers.

food chain A sequence of feeding relationships among organisms whereby energy and biomass is transferred from one trophic (feeding) level to the next higher trophic level (i.e., from *autotrophs* to *heterotrophs*).

food web A complex of feeding relationships consisting of food chains linked together in an ecosystem.

G

geologic time scale A standard division of time on Earth into eons, eras, periods, and epochs based on occurrence of large-scale geological events; spans millions to billions of years in the past.

geosphere The solid portion of planet Earth consisting of rocks, minerals, and sediments.

geostationary satellite A satellite which revolves around Earth at the same rate and in the same direction as the planet rotates so that it always remains over the same point on the equator and monitors the same field of view. The satellite orbits Earth at an altitude of about 36,000 km (22,300 mi).

geostrophic flow Horizontal movement of surface water parallel to ocean height contours and arising from a balance between the *pressure gradient force* and the *Coriolis Effect.*

glacial climate A climate which favors the thickening and expansion of glaciers.

glacier A mass of ice that flows internally under the influence of gravity.

global climate model A simulation of Earth's climate system usually consisting of a series of mathematical equations and used to predict climatic anomalies.

global radiative equilibrium The balance between net incoming solar radiation and infrared radiation emitted to space by the Earth-atmosphere system.

global water cycle The ceaseless movement of water among its various reservoirs on a planetary scale.

greenhouse effect Heating of Earth's surface and lower atmosphere as a consequence of differences in atmospheric transparency to electromagnetic radiation. The atmosphere is nearly transparent to incoming solar radiation, but much less transparent to outgoing infrared radiation. Terrestrial infrared radiation is absorbed and radiated principally by water vapor and, to a lesser extent, by carbon dioxide and other trace gases, thereby slowing the loss of heat to space by the Earth-atmosphere-ocean system and significantly elevating the average temperature of Earth's surface.

greenhouse gases Those atmospheric gases that absorb and emit terrestrial infrared radiation and contribute to the *greenhouse effect* in the *Earth-atmosphere system.* The principal greenhouse gas is water vapor; others are carbon dioxide, ozone, methane, and nitrous oxide.

groin A low artificial structure often composed of rock rubble that is built perpendicular to the shoreline to trap littoral drift; similar to a jetty but smaller.

gross primary production The total amount of carbon fixed into organic matter through *photosynthesis* in a given unit of time; usually expressed in units of grams of carbon per square m per day or year.

guyot A flat-topped seamount of volcanic origin rising more than 1 km above the sea floor.

gyre Refers to the nearly circular motion of surface ocean currents in each of the major ocean basins centered under subtropical high-pressure systems. Viewed from above the subtropical gyres rotate clockwise in the Northern Hemisphere and counterclockwise in the Southern Hemisphere.

H

HNLC regions Portions of the ocean featuring *H*igh

Nutrients and *Low Chlorophyll*. Biological production is low even though surface waters have relatively high concentrations of nutrients (nitrogen and phosphorus compounds).

harmful algal blooms (HABs) A proliferation of a single species of phytoplankton that can cause serious harm to the environment, demise of marine organisms, economic losses, and human health problems, including illness and death; also known as *red tides*.

halocline A layer of water characterized by a relatively large change in salinity with increasing depth.

heat The name applied to a form of energy transferred between systems in response to a difference in *temperature*. Heat is always transferred from a warmer system to a colder system.

high A dome of air that exerts relatively high surface air pressure compared to the surrounding air and is usually associated with fair weather; same as an anticyclone.

high biomass bloom An excessive proliferation of phytoplankton (due to input of excessive levels of nutrients) that upon decomposition greatly depletes the dissolved oxygen supply of seawater.

Holocene The time interval since the end of the Pleistocene Ice Age (about 10,500 years ago); the current interglacial.

horse latitudes A nautical term describing the latitude belts over the ocean at approximately 30 to 35 degrees N and S where winds are usually light or the air is calm and the weather is hot and dry. These zones coincide with the location of the subtropical anticyclones.

hot spot A long-lived source of magma caused by rising plumes of hot material originating deep in the mantle. As a tectonic plate moves over a hot spot or as a hot spot moves, magma may break through the crust and form a new volcano.

hurricane An intense *tropical cyclone* originating over tropical ocean waters, usually in late summer or early fall, with a sustained wind speed of 119 km per hr (74 mph) or higher.

hydrogen bonding An attractive force whereby a positively charged (hydrogen) pole of a water molecule attracts the negatively charged (oxygen) pole of another water molecule.

hydrogenous sediment Particles which are chemically precipitated from seawater.

hydrosphere One of the major interacting subsystems of the Earth system which includes water in all three phases (ice, liquid, and vapor) that continually cycles from one reservoir to another within that system (i.e., the global water cycle).

hydrothermal vent A site where ocean water enters fractures in newly formed oceanic crust, is heated, and then surfaces again through fractures; usually located near oceanic ridge systems.

I

igneous rock A crystalline or glassy rock formed from the cooling and solidification of *magma* (or *lava*).

infauna Marine organisms that burrow into and live within marine sediments on the ocean floor.

Integrated Ocean Drilling Project (IODP) A program of ocean floor exploration underway in October 2003 with the goal of using two drill ships plus specialized drilling platforms to retrieve more cores from deeper holes in the ocean floor.

interglacial climate A climate which favors the thinning and retreat of exiting glaciers or no glaciers at all.

internal energy A measure of the molecular activity of a system or the summation of total energies of all molecules in a specific mass.

internal tides Waves generated by tides well below the sea surface and occurring at tidal frequencies.

internal waves Waves that form and propagate well below the sea surface along the boundary between layers of water that differ in density.

intertidal zone The shore area between high and low tides.

intertropical convergence zone (ITCZ) A narrow,

discontinuous belt of convective clouds and thunderstorms paralleling the equator and marking the convergence of the trade winds of the two hemispheres; this zone shifts north and south seasonally.

island arc A curved chain of volcanic islands that parallels a deep-sea trench where oceanic lithosphere is subducted causing volcanism and producing volcanic islands.

J

jetty A breakwater oriented perpendicular to the shoreline and extending seaward up to a kilometer or more; intended to protect a harbor or tidal inlet from filling by littoral drift.

K

kelp Includes various species of brown algae which grow to enormous size, found in cool waters worldwide, especially in coastal upwelling zones.

krill Shrimp-like crustaceans that are the major food source for whales and other organisms in the Southern Ocean.

L

La Niña An episode of strong trade winds and unusually low sea surface temperatures in the central and eastern tropical Pacific. Essentially the opposite of *El Niño*, La Niña is accompanied by weather extremes in various parts of the world.

lagoon A partially enclosed shallow stretch of seawater separating a barrier island from the mainland.

latent heat The heat energy that is used to change the phase of water but not the temperature of the water; hence the term *latent*, meaning hidden.

latent heat of condensation Heat released to the environment during the change in phase of water from vapor to liquid.

latent heat of deposition Heat released to the environment during the change in phase of water from vapor to solid (ice).

latent heat of fusion Heat released to the environment when water changes phase from liquid to solid.

latent heat of sublimation Heat absorbed from the environment when ice or snow vaporizes.

latent heat of vaporization Heat absorbed from the environment when water changes phase from liquid to vapor.

latent heating The transfer of heat energy from one place to another as a consequence of the phase changes of water.

law of the minimum The growth and well being of an organism is limited by the essential resource that is in lowest supply relative to what is required by the organism.

law of universal gravitation The force of attraction between two objects is directly proportional to the product of their masses and inversely proportional to the square of the distance between them.

limiting factor The most deficient of the essential resources an organism requires for growth and well being.

lithification The process whereby sediment is converted to sedimentary rock involving compaction and/or cementation; part of the rock cycle.

lithogenous sediment Marine sediment formed mostly by the weathering and erosion of pre-existing rock.

lithosphere The outer, rigid part of the Earth, consisting of the upper part of mantle, oceanic crust and continental crust.

Little Ice Age A relatively cool interval during the Holocene interglacial, from about CE 1400 to 1850, when average temperatures were lower in many areas, and alpine glaciers advanced down mountain valleys. The Little Ice Age followed the *Medieval Warm Period*.

littoral drift Sediment transport by a longshore current along a coast, either nourishing or cutting back beaches.

longshore current The component of water motion parallel to the shore and in the *surf zone*; the consequence of waves breaking at an angle to the shore.

low An area of relatively low atmospheric pressure often associated with clouds and precipitation; same as a cyclone.

M

magma Hot molten rock material formed deep in the crust or upper mantle which wells up and migrates along rock fissures; called *lava* when it flows onto Earth's surface.

manganese nodules Irregularly shaped, sooty black or brown nodules on the sea floor which contain a high concentration of manganese and iron.

mangrove Any of various coastal or aquatic salt-tolerant trees that form large colonies in swamps or shallow water.

mangrove swamp A marshy coastal wetland area with a dense growth of mangroves and other tropical plant species which tolerate salt water flooding.

mariculture Industrial farming of fish and shellfish in the ocean.

maritime climate Characterizes a middle or high latitude locale downwind from the moderating influence of the ocean or large lake; characterized by minimal contrast between mean summer and winter temperatures; contrast with *continental climate*.

Maunder minimum The period of greatly diminished sunspot activity between CE 1645 and 1715 identified by and named for E. Walter Maunder.

maximum sustainable yield The maximum catch of a fish species that will ensure the long-term viability of its population.

Medieval Warm Period A relatively mild climatic episode during the *Holocene* from about CE 950 to 1250.

meridional overturning circulation (MOC) The thermohaline circulation transports heat energy, salt, and dissolved gases (e.g., the greenhouse gas carbon dioxide) over great distances and to great depths in the world ocean and plays an important role in Earth's climate system. In the North Atlantic, for example, a warm surface ocean current flows north and eastward from the Florida Strait. At high latitudes, the surface waters cool, sink, and flow southward as cold bottom water.

mesoscale systems Weather phenomena that are so small that they influence atmospheric conditions over only a portion of a city or county; includes thunderstorms and sea breezes. These systems have dimensions of 1 to 100 km (1 to 60 mi) and last from hours to a day or so.

metamorphic rock A crystalline rock derived from other rocks that were subjected to high temperatures, high pressures, and chemically active fluids.

microbial loop A micro-food chain that works within (or along side) the classical food chain. The smallest organisms, heterotrophic bacteria, use dissolved inorganic material directly as carbon and energy sources.

microscale system Weather phenomena representing the smallest spatial subdivision of atmospheric circulation, such as a weak tornado. These systems have dimensions of 1 m to 1 km (3 ft to less than a mile) and last from seconds to an hour or so.

Milankovitch cycles Systematic variations in the precession and tilt of the Earth's rotational axis and the eccentricity of its orbit about the sun; affects the seasonal and latitudinal distribution of incoming solar radiation and influences climate fluctuations operating over tens of thousands to hundreds of thousands of years.

mixed layer The surface layer of the ocean that is mixed by the action of waves and tides so that the waters are nearly isothermal and isohaline; underlain by a pycnocline.

mixed tide An *astronomical tide* with two high waters (high tides) and two low waters (low tides) occurring during a tidal day and having a marked *diurnal inequality*.

mixotrophs Marine organisms having characteristics of both plants (*autotrophs*) and animals (*heterotrophs*).

model An approximate representation or simulation of a real system.

mud flat A nearly level area of fine silt near the shore and an intertidal habitat for submerged aquatic vegetation and benthic animals.

N

NAO Index A measure of the strength of the horizontal air pressure gradient between Iceland and the Azores in the North Atlantic; influences the climate of eastern North America and much of Europe and North Africa; varies from year to year and decade to decade.

neap tides *Astronomical tides* that have the least monthly *tidal range* occurring at the first and third quarter phases of the moon.

nekton Pelagic animals that are free-swimmers such as fish, adult squid, turtles, and marine mammals.

neritic deposits River-borne lithogenous sediment which settles along the continental margin.

neritic zone Also called the *coastal zone*, the area seaward from the shore to the *continental shelf* break at a depth of about 200 m (650 ft); includes the *intertidal zone*.

net primary production The amount of organic matter produced by living organisms within a given volume or area in a given time, minus that which is consumed through *cellular respiration* by the organisms.

net production The amount of organic matter produced during photosynthesis that exceeds the amount consumed in the process of *cellular respiration*.

neutrally stable system A system that, following a disturbance, does not return to its initial state and is easily mixed.

new production *Primary production* based on nutrients brought into the ecosystem by processes such as upwelling or winter mixing.

Newton's first law of motion An object in constant straight-line motion or a rest remains that way unless acted upon by an unbalanced force.

non-point source A broad area of the landscape that yields contaminants to the air or waterways.

nor'easter Common contraction for northeaster, an intense *extratropical cyclone* that tracks along the East Coast of North America and is named for the direction from which its most destructive winds blow.

North Atlantic Oscillation (NAO) A seesaw variation in air pressure between Iceland (the Icelandic low) and the Azores (the Bermuda-Azores subtropical high); influences the climate of eastern North America and much of Europe and North Africa over periods up to decades.

O

ocean acidification With the continuing upward trend in the concentration of atmospheric carbon dioxide, concern is focused on the potential effects on the ocean's buffering ability and the viability of certain marine organisms. CO_2 that is absorbed by the ocean participates in chemical reactions that increase the acidity (lowers the *pH*) of ocean waters.

ocean basin A large topographic depression occupied by ocean water.

ocean commons The vast portion of the ocean that is beyond the control of any coastal nation and essentially free to all for unlimited exploitation.

Ocean Drilling Program (ODP) Project that obtained samples of oceanic crust and sediment using the drill ship JOIDES *Resolution*; operated from 1983 to 2003.

ocean floor observatory A long-term facility on the sea floor designed to collect data, perform experiments, and communicate information to scientists onshore.

ocean trench A long narrow deep depression in the ocean floor caused by subduction of tectonic plates.

oceanic crust The outermost part of the lithosphere overlying the mantle and lying beneath the ocean; mostly composed of the fine-grained ferromagnesian igneous rock known as basalt.

open ocean convection The sinking of relatively dense surface-ocean waters and the ascent of less dense ocean waters.

overfishing A fish species is taken at a rate that exceeds the maximum catch that would allow reproduction to replace the population.

oxygen isotope analysis A technique used to identify

climate fluctuations of the past by examining the ratio of light and heavy isotopes of oxygen (O^{16} and O^{18}) found, for example, in shells extracted from deep-sea sediment cores.

P

pH The acidity of water (or any other liquid) is expressed in terms of the hydrogen ion concentration.

pH scale The *pH* increases from 0 to 14 as the hydrogen ion concentration decreases. Pure water has a pH of 7, which is considered neutral; a pH above 7 is increasingly alkaline whereas a pH below 7 is increasingly acidic. The pH scale is logarithmic; that is, each unit increment corresponds to a tenfold change in acidity.

Pacific Decadal Oscillation (PDO) A long-lived variation in climate over the North Pacific Ocean and North America in which sea surface temperatures fluctuate between the north central Pacific and the west coast of North America; linked to changes in strength of the Aleutian low.

partial tides Harmonic components that comprise the *astronomical tide* at any point. The periods of partial tides are derived from the tidal forces of the moon and sun.

partially mixed estuary A partially isolated body of water where fresh water from rivers and streams mixes with seawater to the extent that stratification is weak and the *salinity* typically varies by less than 10 parts per thousand from bottom to top. Mixing is greater than in a *salt-wedge estuary* but not as great as in a *well-mixed estuary*.

particulate organic carbon (POC) The carbon contained in organic particles that sink out of the ocean's surface layer and is then consumed by zooplankton or decomposed by bacteria and converted back to dissolved inorganic carbon.

pelagic deposit Fine-grained sediments that accumulate over time on the deep-ocean floor.

pelagic zone The open-ocean environment, divided into the *neritic zone* (seaward to a depth of 200 m) and the oceanic zone (depth greater than 200 m).

photic zone The upper sunlit layer of the ocean where photosynthesis takes place.

photosynthesis The process whereby *autotrophs* use light energy from the sun to combine carbon dioxide from the atmosphere with water to produce sugar, a form of carbohydrate that contains a relatively large amount of energy.

physical pump The physical process whereby carbon dioxide sinks deeply in the cold ocean water at high latitudes and is sequestered in the deep ocean for varying lengths of time.

phytoplankton Microscopic unicellular algae and photosynthetic bacteria living in the ocean and responsible for considerable biological production.

pinnipeds Marine mammals which have distinctive swimming flippers; species include seals, walruses and sea lions.

placer deposits Relatively dense and resistant metals and gemstones left behind as a lag concentrate after the mechanical sorting action of river or ocean currents remove the less dense sand grains.

planetary albedo The fraction (or percent) of incident solar radiation that is scattered and reflected back to space by the *Earth-atmosphere-ocean system*; satellite sensors indicate a planetary *albedo* of about 31%.

planetary-scale systems Weather phenomena operating at the largest spatial scale of atmospheric circulation; includes the global wind belts (i.e., trade winds, westerlies, polar easterlies) and semipermanent pressure systems (e.g., subtropical anticyclones).

plankton Plant and animal life found floating or drifting in the ocean and used as food by nearly all marine animals.

plate tectonics The process by which the massive plates of the lithosphere are slowly driven across the face of the globe by huge convection currents in Earth's mantle.

point source A discernible localized source, e.g. a conduit such as a pipe or chimney that transports contaminants to a waterway or the atmosphere.

polar amplification An increase in the magnitude of a climate change with increasing latitude.

polar-orbiting satellite Satellite in a relatively low-altitude orbit that passes near the north and south geographical poles. Earth rotates through the plane of the satellite's orbit, which is at an altitude of about 800 to 1000 km (500 to 620 mi).

poleward heat transport Meridional flow of *latent heat* and *sensible heat* from tropical to middle and high latitudes in response to latitudinal imbalances in radiational heating and cooling; brought about by air mass exchange, storms, and ocean circulation.

pollution Intentional or unintentional disturbance of the environment that adversely affects the wellbeing of organisms (including humans) directly or the natural processes upon which they depend.

precipitation Water in frozen or unfrozen forms (rain, snow, drizzle, ice pellets, hail) that falls from clouds and reaches Earth's surface.

pressure Force per unit area.

pressure gradient force A three-dimensional force operating in a fluid that accelerates the fluid from regions of high pressure and toward regions of low pressure. See *air pressure gradient*.

primary production The amount of organic matter synthesized by simple organisms from inorganic substances.

principle of constant proportions The major constituents of seawater occur in the same relative concentrations throughout the ocean system.

producers Simple marine organisms also called *autotrophs* that manufacture the food they need from the physical environment.

profiling float A free-moving instrument package that measures vertical profiles of ocean water temperature and salinity plus current velocity.

progressive wave Wind-driven waves that move through a body of water.

pycnocline Layer of ocean water in which density increases rapidly with depth (due to vertical changes in temperature and/or salinity); in low and middle latitudes situated between the mixed layer and deep layer.

R

recreational fisheries Fishing for sport rather than commercial purposes.

red tide A discoloration of surface ocean waters usually in the coastal zone caused by a high concentration of microscopic organisms (e.g., dinoflagellates); also known as a *harmful algal bloom (HAB)*.

reflection Process whereby a portion of the radiation striking the interface between two different media (e.g., atmosphere and ocean) is redirected such that the angle of reflection equals the angle of incidence.

refraction The bending of a wave in response to changing wave speed.

regenerated production Primary production using recycled nutrients.

remote sensing Acquisition of data on the properties of some object without the sensor being in direct contact with the object.

remotely operated vehicle (ROV) A data-gathering submersible tethered to a ship by cables that transmit power and data.

residence time The average length of time for a substance in a reservoir to be replaced completely.

resonance A buildup of amplitude in a physical system when the frequency of an applied force is close to the natural frequency of the system.

rings Large turbulent rotating warm-core and cold-core eddies that break off from the relatively swift western boundary currents (e.g., the Gulf Stream).

rip current Whereas the shoreward transport of water occurs over broad areas of the surf zone, the return seaward flow of water tends to concentrate in narrow widely spaced belts often corresponding to depressions in the seafloor or breaks in sand bars. The narrow seaward flow of water must balance the broad shoreward flow of water so that the offshore flow occurs as a relatively swift surface or near-surface current.

rock cycle A sequence of events/processes involving

the formation, alteration, destruction, and reformation of igneous, sedimentary, and metamorphic rocks as a result of such processes as erosion, transportation, deposition, lithification, metamorphism, melting, and crystallization.

rogue wave Unusually high wave that occurs in the open ocean as well as some coastal areas; may be the product of *constructive wave interference.*

S

Saffir-Simpson Hurricane Intensity Scale Hurricane intensity scale based on central pressure, and specifying a range of wind speed, height of storm surge, and damage potential; 1 is minimal, 5 is most intense.

salinity A measure of the quantity of dissolved salt in seawater.

salt marsh Coastal wetland consisting of salt-tolerant grasses regularly covered with seawater.

salt-wedge estuary An estuary where river inflow is swift and tidal currents are weak; the denser high-salinity seawater forms a distinct layer beneath the low-salinity river water.

sand spit A finger-like ridge of sand or gravel that projects from the shore into the ocean.

scattering The process by which small particles suspended in a medium such as air or water diffuse a portion of the incident radiation in all directions.

scientific method A systematic form of inquiry that involves observation, gathering data, critical thinking, and formulating and testing hypotheses.

schooling The characteristic behavior of many fish species to swim together in organized groups to avoid predation.

sea The state of the surface of the ocean with regard to waves or swells.

sea-floor spreading The divergence of adjacent plates on the ocean bottom; occurs along the oceanic ridge system.

sea wave An oscillation on the ocean surface that propagates along the interface between the atmosphere and the ocean.

seamounts A structure of volcanic origin rising more than 1 km above the sea floor.

seawall A concrete embankment intended to protect beaches, roads, buildings, and shoreline cliffs from erosion by storm waves.

seawater The water of the ocean, distinguished from fresh water by its higher salinity.

secondary production The organic material produced in the growth of consumers (*heterotrophs*).

sediment Particles of organic or inorganic origin that are transported from their place of origin and deposited by wind, water, or ice; typically in unconsolidated form.

sedimentary rock Consolidated rock composed of any one or a combination of compacted and cemented fragments of rock and mineral grains, partially decomposed remains of dead plants and animals (e.g. shells, skeletons), and minerals precipitated from solution.

seiche A rhythmic oscillation of water in an enclosed basin or partially enclosed coastal inlet; a type of *standing wave.*

semi-diurnal tide An *astronomical tide* with two high waters (high tides) and two low waters (low tides) occurring during a tidal (lunar) day and having a small diurnal inequality.

sensible heating Transport of heat energy from one location or object to another through conduction, convection, or both, which brings about temperature changes.

shallow-water waves Waves in water shallower than the *wave-base* (half the wave length).

shore Land exposed at low tide up to the coastline.

shoreline The boundary line between a water body and land, usually taken at mean high tide.

significant wave height The average height of the tallest one-third of the waves observed in a patch of ocean.

siliceous ooze Pelagic deposit made from the shells of silica-secreting organisms.

slack water   Periods of little or no horizontal water movement occurring between *ebb tides* and *flood tides*.

SLOSH (Sea, Lake, and Overland Surges from Hurricanes)   A numerical model which accurately predicts the location and height of a *storm surge*.

SOFAR channel   SOund Fixing And Ranging; a zone at an ocean depth of about 100 m (3300 ft) where the speed of sound reaches a minimum value.

solar altitude   The angle of the sun above the horizon; varies from 0 degree (horizon) to 90 degrees (zenith).

sorting   The dynamic process by which sedimentary particles are separated by size; well-sorted sediment has a narrow range of particle sizes whereas poorly-sorted sediment has a broad range of particle sizes.

southern oscillation   Opposing swings of surface air pressure between the western and central tropical Pacific Ocean; associated with intense *El Niño* events.

specific heat   The amount of heat required to raise the temperature of 1 gram of a substance by 1 Celsius degree.

spring bloom   A dramatic increase in phytoplankton populations in the ocean which occurs as a consequence of more sunlight and abundant nutrients.

spring tide   An *astronomical tide* occurring twice each month at or near the times of new moon and full moon when the gravitational pull of the sun reinforces that of the moon, and having an unusually large or increased *tidal range*.

stable system   A system which tends to persist in its current state without changing and, following a disturbance, tends to return to its original state or condition.

standing wave   This is in contrast to the wind-driven waves that are *progressive waves* in that they move through a body of water. With wind-driven waves, crests and troughs travel along the water surface but with standing waves, crests alternate vertically with troughs but at fixed locations; a *seiche* is an example of a standing wave.

stewardship   Action taken by society to protect resources for now and the future.

storm surge   An abnormal local rise in sea level accompanying a *tropical cyclone* or other intense storm system and whose height is the difference between the observed level of the sea surface and the level that would have occurred in the absence of the storm.

sub-polar gyres   Roughly circular surface current systems, smaller than their subtropical counterparts, occur at high latitudes of the Northern Hemisphere; the Alaska gyre in the far North Pacific and the gyre south of Greenland in the far North Atlantic. The counterclockwise surface winds in the Aleutian and Icelandic sub-polar low pressure systems drive the ocean currents in the sub-polar gyres.

subduction   The process whereby the leading edge of one tectonic plate on the ocean bottom descends beneath the margin of another plate and then into Earth's mantle.

subduction zone   A long, narrow zone at a convergent plate boundary where an oceanic plate descends beneath another plate, either oceanic or continental.

sublimation   The process by which water changes directly from a solid to a vapor without first becoming liquid.

submarine canyon   A steep-sided canyon below sea level in the continental shelf and slope.

submarine fan   A cone-shaped sedimentary deposit that accumulates on the continental slope and rise.

subpolar low   A region of low pressure found in both the Northern and Southern Hemispheres where the middle latitude westerlies converge with the polar easterlies.

subtropical anticyclone   A massive semi-permanent high pressure system that occurs in subtropical latitudes of both hemispheres; a major control of climate.

subtropical gyres   Large-scale roughly circular surface current systems in the ocean basins. Depending on location, gyres are either subtropical or sub-polar and are the dominant type of flow within the ocean's mixed layer. The trade winds, on the equatorward flank of a subtropical high pressure system, and the westerlies, on the poleward flank of a subtropical high pressure system, drive the subtropical gyres, centered near 30 degrees latitude in the North and South Atlantic, the North and South Pacific, and the Indian Ocean.

subtropical high One of the massive semi-permanent anticyclones centered over the ocean basins near 30 degrees N and S.

sulfurous aerosols The tiny droplets of sulfuric acid (H_2SO_4) and sulfate particles which form in the stratosphere when sulfur dioxide combines with moisture.

sunspot A dark blotch on the face of the sun, typically thousands of kilometers across that develops where an intense magnetic field suppresses the flow of gases transporting heat from the sun's interior.

surf A nearly continuous train of waves breaking along a shore.

surface tension The attraction between molecules at or near the surface of a liquid.

sustainability Actions that meet present needs without compromising the ability of future generations to meet their own needs.

swash Intermittent landward flow of water across a beach following the breaking of a wave.

swell Large long-period ocean waves that radiate away from the region where they were generated by strong storm winds.

symbiotic relationship A mutually beneficial association between organisms.

synoptic-scale systems Weather phenomena operating at the continental or oceanic spatial scale, including migrating *tropical* and *extratropical cyclones*. These systems have dimensions of 100 to 10,000 km (60 to 6000 mi) and last from days to a week or so.

system An interacting set of components that behave in an orderly way according to the laws of physics, chemistry, geology, and biology.

T

tektite Black fragments of glass formed from rock which has been liquefied when a meteor strikes the Earth.

teleconnection A linkage between weather changes occurring in widely separated regions of the globe.

teleost Bony fishes which have skeletons and scales.

temperature A measure of the average kinetic energy of the individual atoms or molecules composing a substance.

tephra Sediments derived from explosive volcanism.

terminal velocity Constant downward-directed motion of a particle within a fluid due to a balance between gravity (directed downward) and fluid resistance (directed upward).

thermal inertia Resistance to a change in temperature.

thermocline A layer of water in which the temperature decreases rapidly with increasing depth (e.g., between the warmer mixed layer and the colder, deep layer in a thermally stratified ocean).

thermohaline circulation Subsurface movement of water masses caused by density contrasts arising from differences in temperature and salinity.

tidal bore In some coastal areas where the tidal range is relatively large and the flood tide enters a narrow bay or channel, a wall of turbulent water, usually less than a meter in height, forms and moves upstream in a river or shallow estuary.

tidal currents Alternating horizontal movements of water accompanying the rise and fall of *astronomical tides*.

tidal day The moon-based day based on the interval of time between two successive passes of the moon over a meridian (approximately 24 hours, 50 minutes).

tidal period The elapsed time between successive high tides or successive low tides.

tidal range The difference in height between consecutive high water (high tide) and low water (low tide).

tide pool A volume of water left behind in a rock basin or other intertidal depression by an ebbing tide.

top predators Organisms that occupy a high trophic level in a marine food web.

trade winds The wind system, occupying most of the

tropics, which blows outward from the *subtropical highs* toward the equatorial trough or *intertropical convergence zone*; a major component of the planetary-scale circulation of the atmosphere. Trade winds blow from the northeast in the Northern Hemisphere and from the southeast in the Southern Hemisphere.

transform plate boundary The region where adjacent tectonic plates slide laterally past one another.

transitional wave A wave entering water having a depth of between one-twentieth and one-half of the wavelength.

transpiration The process whereby water that is taken up from the soil by plant roots eventually escapes as vapor through the tiny pores (stomates) on the surface of green leaves.

trophic level The feeding position of an organism within a *food chain* or *food web*.

tropical cyclone Generic term for a non-frontal synoptic-scale cyclone originating over warm tropical or subtropical ocean waters with cyclonic surface wind circulation (e.g., hurricane, tropical storm).

tropical depression A *tropical cyclone* in which the sustained surface wind is at least 37 km per hr (23 mph) but less than 63 km per hr (39 mph); an early stage in the development of a *hurricane*.

tropical disturbance A discrete system of organized convection in the tropics or subtropics with a detectable center of low air pressure; the initial stage in the development of a *hurricane*.

tropical storm A *tropical cyclone* having a sustained surface wind speed of 63 to 118 km per hr (39-73 mph).

troposphere The lowest thermal layer of the atmosphere; where the atmosphere interfaces with the ocean, cryosphere, lithosphere, and biosphere and where most weather takes place.

tsunami A rapidly propagating shallow-water ocean wave that develops when a submarine earthquake, landslide or volcanic eruption disturbs deep ocean water; known to build to tremendous wave height in shoaling coastal areas.

turbidites Sedimentary deposits produced by turbidity currents.

turbidity current A sediment-water mixture denser than normal seawater that flows down slope to the deep-sea floor.

turbidity maximum The area in an estuary where sediments are most concentrated.

twilight zone The intermediate zone of the ocean, below the photic zone, but above the greater depths where there is less biologic activity.

U

unstable system A system which following a disturbance tends not to return to its original state or condition.

upwelling Upward circulation of cold, nutrient-rich bottom water toward the ocean surface; may occur along the coast or equator.

V

vertical migration The daily migration of zooplankton from deep waters to the surface zone to feed on phytoplankton.

W

warm-core rings Eddies having a core of relatively warm water that break off from an ocean surface current; viewed from above in the Northern Hemisphere, they rotate in a clockwise direction.

water mass A large, homogenous volume of ocean water featuring a characteristic range of temperature and salinity.

watershed The geographical area drained by a river and all its tributaries.

wave A regular oscillation that occurs in a solid, liquid, or gaseous medium as energy is transmitted through that medium.

wave-base A depth of about one-half wavelength, where the diameter of the orbits of water particles in waves is essentially zero; the depth below which water is not affected by surface waves.

wave crest The highest point reached by an oscillating water surface.

wave frequency The number of waves passing a fixed point over an interval of time.

wave height A measurement of the vertical distance between *wave crest* and *wave trough*.

wave interference The interaction among *progressive waves* of different origins; may be constructive or destructive.

wave period A measurement of the time needed for two successive wavelengths to pass a fixed point.

wave trough The lowest point in an oscillating water surface.

wavelength The distance between successive *wave crests* (or equivalently, the distance between successive *wave troughs*).

weather The state of the atmosphere at some place and time, described in terms of such variables as temperature, precipitation, cloud cover, and wind speed.

weathering The physical disintegration, chemical decomposition, or solution of exposed rock which takes place where the lithosphere (mainly the crust) interfaces with the other Earth subsystems.

well-mixed estuary An *estuary* where strong tidal currents dominate the inflow from rivers and thoroughly mix the fresh water and saltwater.

western boundary current Generic term for a relatively strong and narrow flow of ocean water (current) that runs along the western edge of a major ocean basin; the Gulf Stream is an example.

wetland Low-lying flat areas that are covered by water or have soils that are saturated with water for at least part of the year.

wind-waves Sea waves that are the produced as the kinetic energy of the wind is transferred to surface waters.

Wilson cycles Cycles of ocean basin spreading and closing operating over hundreds of millions of years.

Z

zooplankton Single-celled and multi-cellular animals that drift passively with ocean currents.

INDEX

A

abiotic, ecosystems, 236

absorption, 119
abyss, 263
abyssal plain , 39
abyssal storms, 100
abyssopelagic zone, 263
Aceh Province, Sumatra, 187
acid rain, 74
acid snow, 74
Acoustic Doppler Current Profiler, 364
acoustic fish finders, 380
acoustic thermometry, 17, 79, 160
active continental margin, 39, 47
adaptation, 264, 287
adaptive coloration, 267
ADEOS, 194
Adhémar, J.A., 330
Advanced Very High-Resolution Radiometer
 (AVHRR), 249
aerobic decomposers, 234
aerosols, 7
Afghanistan drought, 305
Africa,
          Sub-Saharan drought, 314-315
Agassiz, A., 359
Age of Discovery, 357
agricultural runoff, 289, 405
Agulhas Current, 152, 156, 157, 172
Agung, Bali, 332
ahermatypic corals, 275
air masses, 127
          exchange of, 127-128
          source region, 128
air pressure, 129
air pressure gradient, 130, 298
air pressure gradient force, 130
Alaska, 321

Alaska Current, 153
Alaska sub-polar gyre, 152, 153
albatross, 282
albedo, 119, 340
          of the ocean, 119-120
          planetary, 120
Aleutian low, 133, 151, 310
Alexander the Great, 356
Alexandria, Egypt, library at, 356
Alexandrium catanella, 234
algae, 269, 273
algal bloom, 264, 289
alien species, 394
Alpine glaciers, 339
Alps, 349
Alvin, 58, 360, 370
Amazon River, 184, 211
American eel, 279
Amery ice shelf, 287
amnesic shellfish poisoning, 233
anadromous fish, 11, 279, 401, 410
anaerobic bacteria, 289
anaerobic decay, 335
anaerobic decomposers, 234
anaerobic organisms, 102
anchovies, 301
Andes Mountains, 316
anemometer, 193
angiosperms, 271
animal-borne instruments, 374-375
Año Nuevo Island, 374
Antarctic Bottom Water, 161, 246
Antarctic Circle, 118
Antarctic Circumpolar Current, 35, 153, 155, 162, 196
Antarctic Convergence, 404
Antarctic Intermediate Water, 162
Antarctic Treaty System, 404
Antarctic ozone hole, 143
anticyclone (high), 130
anti-esuarine circulation, 212

antinode, 177
APEX, 169
aphelion, 182, 330, 336
apogee, 182
Aquarius, 362
aquifer, 351
archaea, 245, 369
Arctic Circle, 118, 347
Arctic Oscillation (AO), 287, 294, 309, 310, 311, 340-342, 362
Arctic sea ice cover, 318, 340, 341, 342, 402
    albedo of, 340
    shrinkage of, 341-342
Argo float, 17, 18, 159-160, 169, 364, 365, 370
armor (beach), 208-210, 232
Array for Real-time Geostrophic Oceanography, 159,
artificial beach nourishment, 209, 210, 232
artisanal fisheries, 379
Asian carp, 394
assimilative capacity, 405
Assyrians, 356
asteroid, 12, 27-28
asthenosphere, 37
astronomical tides, 178-186
    currents, 183-185
    generating force, 179-180
    in ocean basins, 182-183
    in open ocean, 185-186
    types of, 180-182
Aswan High Dam, 99, 410
Atlantis, 34
atmosphere, 6-8, 113-135
    circulation of, 123-135
    composition of, 7-8
    evolution of, 30-31
    scales of motion, 131
    temperature profile, 6-7
atmospheric aerosols, 7
atmospheric fixation, 31
atmospheric window, 122
atoll, 49, 275
Australia, 273, 355, 357
Autonomous Profiling Explorer (APEX), 169
Autonomous Underwater Vehicles (AUV), 366
autotrophs, 11, 236
Azam, Farooq, 245
azoic hypothesis, 357

B

backwash, 205

Bacon, Francis, 42
bacteria, 236, 237, 238, 239
Baja California, 265, 392
bald eagles, 401, 407
Baltic Sea, 356
Bangladesh, 404
barnacles, 270
barrier islands, 206-207
barrier reef, 49, 273-275
Barringer Crater, AZ, 27
Barry, Roger G., 339
Barton, Otis, 360
bathypelagic zone, 263
bathyscaph, 360
bathysphere, 360
bathythermograph (BT), 169
Battisti, David, 296-297
Bay of Fundy, Nova Scotia, 183, 184, 198
beach contamination, 405, 420-421
beach drift, 205
beach nourishment, 209, 210 beach sediment, 204-206
beach sediment, 204-206
beach sediment budget, 205
beaches, 204, 405
Beaufort, Francis, 193
Beaufort Scale, 193
Beddington, J.R., 383
Beebe, William, 360
benthic ecosystems, 263, 276
benthic organisms, 268-277
    selective feeders, 276
    unselective feeders, 276
benthic zone, 263, 268
benthos, 268
Bering Sea, 244
Bering Strait, 162
berm, 204
Bermuda-Azores subtropical high, 132, 133, 309
Bermuda Triangle, 172
bio-fouling, 369
bioaccumulation, 240-241
biogenous sediment, 94-96
biogeochemical cycles, 12-14
biological fixation, 31
biological pump, 247-249
bioluminescence, 266, 267
biomass, 11, 240
biosphere, 9
biotic ecosystems, 236
bioturbation , 276

Bishop Resen of Copenhagen, 145
bivalves, 264
Bjerknes, Jacob, 298
Black, Joseph, 66
black oystercatchers, 407
Black Sea, 289, 350, 356
black smokers, 49-50
Blackwater National Wildlife Refuge, 399-400
blue crab, 271, 400, 412
blue whales, 392
bluefin tuna, 384
Board of Longitude, 139
Bock, B., 374
bomb (cyclone), 222
bony fish, 277, 278-279, 398
bottom waters, 161-162
Bowen ratio, 127
bowhead whales, 392
Brazil Current, 152
breaker, 176
breakwater, 209, 402
Briggs, Derek, 111
brine, 287
brine rejection, 75, 161, 287
brown algae, 269, 273
brown mud, 99
brown pelicans, 392
brown seaweed, 269-270
bubble injection, 72-73
buffer, 73
buoy, 306, 364-365
Burgess Shale, 110-111
Burkino Faso, 314
Bush, George W., (U.S. President), 291
bycatch, 385-386

C

calcareous oozes, 99-100
California Current, 152, 296
California gray whale, 265
Callendar effect, 123, 334
calorie, 65
calving, 93, 108
Cambrian explosion, 110
Canada, Atlantic fishery, 379, 403
Canary Current, 152, 155
Cape Cod, MA, 339, 340, 408
Cape Cod National Seashore, 339, 340
Cape Hatteras, NC, 153, 156, 222
Cape Hatteras Lighthouse, 232

Cape Horn, 153
Cape Mendacino Fracture Zone, 45
capillary waves, 174
carapace, 389
carbon cycle, 12-14
carbon dioxide, 6-8, 12-14, 71-73, 123, 333-334
carbon fixation, 238
carbonate compensation depth (CCD), 99-100
Carboniferous Period, 13, 322
caribou, 317, 318
carnivores, 11, 236
carnivorous fish, 393
carrying capacity, 383
cartilaginous fishes, 277-278
Casco Bay, ME, 422
cast, 159
catadromous fishes, 279
catfish, 393, 394
Cathedral Escarpement, 110
celerity, 175
cellular respiration, 10, 73, 240
Celsius, Anders, 65
Celsius temperature scale, 65
Cenozoic Era, 321, 322
Census of Marine Life, 263, 374
Center for Operational Oceanographic Products and Services (CO-OPS), 184
central waters, 161
Centre National d'Etudes Spatiales, 307
cetaceans, 280
Chad, 314
Challenger Deep, 46, 359, 360
Challenger Expedition (1872-1876), 358-359
Challenger Deep, 46, 359, 360
Chamberlain, T.C., 330
Channel Islands National Marine Sanctuary, 291, 292, 387
Chapman, D.S., 37
chemosynthesis, 10, 50, 238
Chengjiang, 111
Chesapeake Bay, 271, 377-378, 388, 399-400, 411-413, 416
　　blue crab fisheries, 271, 411-413
　　oyster fisheries, 377-378, 411-413
　　sea grass ecosystem, 271, 411-413
　　striped bass population, 271
Chesapeake Bay Foundation, 413
Chesapeake Bay Program, 411-413, 416
Chesapeake Marsh Restoration/Nutria Control Project, 400

Chicxulub crater, 27
Chikyu, 57, 58, 363
Chinese junks, 356
Chisso Chemical Plant, 88
chitons, 270
chlorofluorocarbons (CFCs), 141-143
chlorophyll, 236, 237, 259-260
cilia, 238
ciliates, 245
circumpolar deep water, 161, 162, 246-247
circumpolar vortex, 143
clams, 393
climate, 115
    and the ocean, 67-68, 295-297
    continental, 67-68, 118
    controls, 295-297
    glacial, 323
    interglacial, 323
    maritime, 67-68, 118
climate change, 317-351
    and Earth's orbit, 330-332
    and Earth's surface properties, 333
    and human activity, 333-335
    and marine life, 342-343
    and plate tectonics, 328-329
    and solar variability, 329-330
    and volcanoes, 332-333
    causes of, 327-335
    impact on ocean, 337-343
climate controls, 295-297
climate future, 333-337
Climate Prediction Center (CPC), 305
climate record, 318-327
    lessons of, 327
climate system, 295-297
Clinton, William J, (U.S. President), 292
closed system, 411
cloud condensation nuclei, 124
clouds, 124-126, 335, 341
coal, 13-14
Coale, Kenneth, 254
coast, 201
Coast 2050, 400
coastal armor, 208-210
coastal downwelling, 157
Coastal Ocean Dynamics Applications Radar, 368
coastal upwelling, 157, 299
coastal zone, 263, 404-406
    evacuation, 220-222
    human population trends, 201, 404

management, 406
    natural hazards of, 186-189, 212-214, 219-220
    pollution in, 405
Coastal Zone Color Scanner (CZCS), 259
coastal zone management, 406
Coastal Zone Management Act (1972), 406
Coastal Zone Management Program (CZMP), 406
coastline, 202
    features, 204-210
    formation, 202-203
    human alterations, 208-210
coccolithophoids, 94, 95, 237
coccoliths, 94, 95
cod, 61, 261, 262, 393
CODAR, 368
cold-core rings, 155-156
cold phase (ENSO), 294, 304-305
Cold War, 360
collection bottles, 168
Colorado Plateau, 323
Columbia River, 410
combined sewer system, 421
comets, 29
Commission on Marine Science, Engineering and Resources, 403
Commission on Ocean Policy, 403
compensation depth, 242
conceptual model, 21
condensation, 14, 66
conduction of heat, 126
Congo River, 98
Connecticut River, 316
conservation of angular momentum, 154
conservative properties, 69, 73
constructive wave interference, 172, 175
continental climate, 67-68, 118
continental crust, 37
continental drift, 42, 328
continental margins, 37, 38-40
continental rise, 39
continental shelf, 39
continental slope, 39
convection, 42, 126
Convention on International Trade in Endangered Species of Wild Fauna & Flora (CITES), 389
Convention on Straddling Stocks, 403
Convention on the Conservation of Antarctic Marine Living Resources (CAMLR), 404
Convention on the Prevention of Marine Pollution by Dumping of Waste & Other Matter, 413

convergent plate boundary, 46-47
Cook, Captain James, 357
Cooperative Institute for Research in Environmental Sciences (CIRES), 341
copepods, 238
coral atoll, 49, 275
coral bleaching, 274, 301
coral polyps, 274, 301, 342
coral reefs, 273-275
corals, 49, 273-275, 316
    ahermatypic, 275
    hermatypic, 275
Coriolis Effect, 130-131, 149, 154, 155, 158, 182, 212, 217, 228, 300
Coriolis, Gaspard-Gustave de, 130
Cork, Ireland, 114
cormorants, 282, 401, 408
Cornwall, England, 356
cosmogenous sediment, 97
cotidal line, 183
countershading, 267
coupled model, 305
coupled phenomenon, 298
covalent bonding, 63
crabs, 289
crawfish, 400
Cretaceous Period, 102, 321, 322
critical current velocity, 92
Croll, J., 330
crust, 36-38
crustaceans, 287
Crutzen, P.J., 141
cryosphere, 5
crystal lattice, 63
ctensphores, 362
Cullen, Heidi M., 305
cumulonimbus clouds, 126, 300
cumulus clouds, 126
Curie, Pierre, 42
Curie temperature, 42
current rings, 155-157
currents, 145-147, 149-158, 183-184
    boundary, 154-155
    equatorial, 153-154
    ring, 155-157
    tidal, 183-184
    western boundary, 154-155
    wind-driven, 151-158
cutoff anticyclone, 304
cyanobacteria, 237-238

cycling rate, 12
cyclone (low), 128, 130, 217

D

dams, 99, 401-402, 409-411
    and dislocation of human populations, 409
    impact on ecosystems, 99, 401-402
    removal of, 401-402, 409-411
Dansgaard-Oeschger events, 348
Dansgaard, Willi, 348
Danube River, 289
DART, 188, 189
Darwin, Charles, 274, 357
    On the Origin of Species, 357
    Structure and Distribution of Coral Reefs, 357
    voyage on the HMS Beagle, 357
Davis, R.E., 223
Davy, Humphry, 256
daylight, 115-119
DDT (dichlorodiphenyltrichloroethane), 392-393, 416
Dead Sea, 61
dead zone, 264, 289, 417
decibar, 77
declining stage, 51, 52
decomposers, 11, 239
deep layer, 148
Deep-Ocean Assessment and Reporting of Tsunamis (DART), 188, 189
deep-ocean carbon storage, 414-416
deep scattering layer (DSL), 266
deep-sea cabled observatory, 354, 366-367
Deep-Sea Drilling Program (DSDP), 57, 363
deep-sea mud, 98
deep sea sediment cores, 319-320, 330-331
deep-water waves, 175-176
Deep Water Boundary Current, 160
deeps, 46
delta, 97-98
demersal fishes, 278
density, 75-77
    fresh water, 75-76
    saltwater, 76-77
deposition, 15, 66
desalination, 83-84
desertification, 315
destructive wave interference, 175
dentritivores, 11, 239
detritus, 237, 276
Deuterium (D), 29
diatoms, 95, 237, 264

Dietz, Robert S., 42
diffusion, 73
dinoflagellates, 237, 267, 380
dinosaurs, 27-28
dissolved gases, 71-73
dissolved organic carbon (DOC), 245
dissolved oxygen, 71-73
distillation, 15, 83-84
distributary, 97
Dittmar, William, 69
diurnal inequality, 181
diurnal tide, 181
divergent plate boundary, 44-46
Dolan, R., 223
Dolan-Davis wave power index, 223
doldrums, 153
dolphins, 265, 280, 292, 385-386
dominant wave period, 193
domoic acid, 233-234
double-hulled ships, 408
downwelling, 157-158
drainage basin, 16
Drake Passage, 35, 153, 328
drifting buoys, 365
drones, 366
drought, 293-294, 301-302, 305, 314-315
Dry Tortugas Islands, 292
Dryas octopetela, 324
dugongs, 281
dust (wind-blown), 93
dynamic model of tides, 183
dyamical model, 305
dynamical positioning, 363

E

Earth-atmosphere system, 114, 329
Earth system, 5-12
    origin of, 30-31
Earth system perspective, 2
earthquakes, 405
East Antarctica ice sheet, 347
East Greenland Current, 152, 153
East Pacific Rise, 45, 49
Easter Island, 356, 357
eastern boundary currents, 154-155
ebb tide, 183
Ebbesmeyer, Curtis, 170
echo sounder, 78
ecological efficiency, 240
ecologically sustainable yield, 384

ecosystem, 10, 235, 236, 342
    based management, 384
ecotourism, 391
Ecuador, 293, 294, 300, 301
eddies, 175
Eddy, John A., 330
edge wave, 229
Edmund Fitzgerald, 172, 230
Edwards Dam, 401
eelgrass, 407
Eemian interglacial, 324, 325, 336
Ekman pumping, 170
Ekman spiral, 149-150
Ekman transport, 149-150, 157-158, 217, 229, 243-244, 299
Ekman, V. Walfrid, 149
El Chichón volcano, 294, 333
El Niño, 293-294, 297-299, 300-304, 305-308
    frequency of, 307-308
    historical perspective, 297-299
    observing, 305-307
    predicting, 305-307
El Niño of 1972-73, 301
El Niño of 1982-83, 293-294, 302
El Niño of 1997-98, 301, 302-304, 305, 307
elasmobranchs, 277-278
electromagnetic radiation, 18, 19
electromagnetic spectrum, 18, 19
electron, 63
elephant seals, 374
embryonic stage, 52
Emperor Seamounts, 59-60
empirical model, 305
ENSO, 298, 362
ENSO cycle, 298
ENSO Observing System, 306, 364
endangered species, 389
Endangered Species Act, 389
energy, 12
EPA, 411
epifauna, 276
epilimnion, 229
epipelagic zone, 263
equatorial countercurrent, 153, 154
equatorial currents, 153-154
equatorial tides, 181
equatorial under currents, 153
equatorial upwelling, 158, 299
equilibrium model of tides, 180
equinox, 115-118

erosion, 9, 91
Eskimos, 317
estuary, 11, 210- 212, 271-272
ethanol, 289
eukaryotes, 245
euphausiids, 238
European ice sheet, 323
European Project for Ice Coring in Antarctica (EPICA), 347
European Union, fishery, 386
eustasy, 337
eutrophic waters, 264
evacuation (coastal), 220-222
evaporation, 14, 66
evaporative cooling, 66
Everglades, 339
E.W. Scripps, 359
exclusive economic zone (EEZ), 103, 104, 370, 382, 403
exotic species, 394-395
expendable bathythermograph (XBT), 169
expendable conductivity-temperature-depth profiler (XCDT), 169
Exploring Expedition (US), 357
extent of sea ice, 86
extratropical cyclone, 213, 222-223
extreme environments, 10
Exxon Corporation, 408
Exxon Valdez, 407, 408
eye (hurricane), 216
eyewall (hurricane), 216

F

faculae, 329
Fagatele Bay, American Samoa, 291
Fahrenheit, Gabriel Daniel, 65
Fahrenheit temperature scale, 65
fair-weather cumulus, 126
Falkland (Malvinas) Islands, 387
fall turnover, 229
Falmouth, 358
fast ice, 86
fast-spreading ridge, 45
fathom, 56
fathometer, 56
fecal pellets, 94
Federal Emergency Management Agency (FEMA), 222
feeding strategies, 268, 276
FEMA, 222
ferromagnesium silicate minerals, 92
fertilizers, 289

fetch, 175
Fiji, 356
filter feeders, 238, 268, 277, 408
first law of thermodynamics, 12
first-year ice, 77, 85
fish, 277-280
    isomotic, 278
    viviparous, 278
fish farms, 240, 393, 394
fish finder, 78
fish hatcheries, 388
fish ladders, 410
fisheries, 379-389
    artisanal, 379
    bycatch, 385-386
    ecologically sustainable yield, 383-385
    maximum sustainable yield, 382-383
    overfishing, 380-382
    recreational, 388-389
    restoring, 386-387
fishing gear, 385
fjord, 211
flat calm, 173
flatfishes, 278-279
flatworms, 287
flickers, 348
float, 159-160
    Argo floats, 17, 18, 169, 364, 365, 370
Floatees, 170
flooding, 293, 294, 405
flood tides, 183
floodgate, 200-201
Florida Current, 152
Florida Keys National Marine Sanctuary, 292
flotsam, 170
fluid resistance, 90
fluorescence, 267
Folger, Timothy, 146
Folly Beach, SC, 210
Food & Agriculture Organization (FAO), 379, 381
food chain, 11, 239
food web, 11, 239, 411
foraminafera, 320
Forbes, Sir Edward, 357
Forbidden City (China), 356
force, 129
forced waves, 175, 178
fortnightly tides, 182
fossil fuels, 13, 326, 333
Fram, 149, 150

Franklin, Benjamin, 145, 146, 332
Franklin-Folger map, 146
frazil ice, 85
free waves, 175
Freedom of the Seas, 402
French Polynesia, 293, 356
frequency, 18, 19, 173
fringing reef, 49, 274
Frobisher, Martin, 145
front, 135
frost, 66
frustule, 237, 264

G

Gakkel Ridge, 46
Galápagos Islands, 254, 281, 357
Galápagos Rift, 49
Galicia, Spain, 408
Galveston, Texas, 214
Gama, Vasco da, 357
Ganges River, 97
gas hydrates, 256-258
geoid, 196
geologic time (climate), 321
geologic time scale, 321
Geological Survey of Canada, 111
geosphere, 8-9
GEOSS, 370
geostationary satellite, 20
geostrophic flow, 150-151, 196, 229
geosynchronous satellite, 20
German Atlantic Ocean Expedition of 1925-27, 359
giant squid, 266
Gibralter, 349
Gill, J., 301
gillnetting, 385
glacial climate, 323
glacial ice cores, 320-321, 347-348
Glacial Lake Hitchcock, 316
glacier, 5, 339
Glacier National Park (Montana), 339
global carbon cycle, 12-14
global climate change, 318, 364
global climate models, 335-336
Global Earth Observation System of Systems (GEOSS), 370
global positioning system (GPS), 140, 147, 166-167, 307, 338, 359, 362
global radiative equilibrium, 121, 127, 328
Global Seismographic Network, 367

global warming, 326, 337, 342
global water budget, 15, 16
global water cycle, 14-16
Glomar Challenger, 56, 349, 363
GLONASS, 166
Goddard Space Flight Center, 339
Gondwanaland, 42
Gould, Stephen J., 111
grab sampler, 56
GRACE, 370
Grand Bahama Canyon, 39, 40
Grand Banks fishery, 261
graphical model, 21
gravitation, 179
gravitational attraction, 179
gravity, 90, 174
Gravity Recovery & Climate Experiment, 370
grease ice, 85
Great Barrier Reef, 273, 274, 357
Great Bear Lake, 357
Great Lakes (of North America), 157, 227-231, 324, 339, 387, 394
Great Lakes of the World (GLOW), 227
Great Slave Lake, 227
greenhouse effect, 121-123, 295-296, 336-337
greenhouse gases, 121-123, 295, 333-335
Greenland, 320, 325, 328, 356, 357
    Viking colonization of, 325, 356
Greenland ice sheet, 325, 338-339, 347
Greenwich, England, 330
groin, 209, 402
gross primary production, 242
Grotius, Hugo, 402
groundwater, 16, 351
growth overfishing, 380
Gulf dead zone, 289, 290
Gulf of Mexico, 102, 152, 156, 289, 290, 302, 363, 400, 403
Gulf of Venice, 199-200
Gulf Stream, 101, 114, 145-147, 154-155, 160, 222, 269, 296
guyot, 48
gyres, 150-151, 152-153

H

habitat destruction and restoration, 387-388
half-life, 414
halite, 68
halocline, 147-148
Hansa Carrier, 170

Hanseatic League, 61
Happelius, 145
Haracan, 216
harbor seals, 408
harlequin ducks, 407
harmful algal blooms (HAB), 234-235, 402, 405
harpooning, 385
Harrison, John, 139-140
Hasterok, D., 37
Hatshepsut, 355
Hawaii, 218, 274-275, 302, 356, 357
Hawaii-2 Observatory (H20), 367
Hawaiian-Emperor Seamount Chain, 59, 60
Hawaiian Underwater Geo-Observatory (HUGO), 367
heat, 65
heat source, 129
heat sink, 129
Heinrich event, 108-109, 348
Heinrich layers, 108
Henry the Navigator, Prince of Portugal, 357
herbivores, 11, 236
hermatypic coral, 275
Herodotus, 356
herring, 279, 407
Hess, Harry, 42
Hess-Dietz model, 42
heterotrophs, 11, 236
high, 132, 133-135
high biomass bloom, 234
Hilton Head Island, SC, 351
Himalayan Mountains, 47, 323, 326
Hirondale, 170
Hjulström diagram, 92
HMS Adventure, 357
HMS Beacon, 357
HMS Beagle, 49, 357
HMS Challenger, 69, 358-359
HMS Discovery, 357
HMS Endeavor, 357
HMS Resolution, 357
HNLC regions, 244, 254-255, 415
Hoerling, M., 301, 315
holdfasts, 268, 272
Holmes, Arthur, 42
Holocene interglacial, 324, 325, 327, 347
Homo sapiens, 355
Hoover Dam, 409
horse latitudes, 133
hot spot, 9, 45, 59
Hsü, Kenneth, 349

Hudson Bay, 53, 108
Hudson Canyon, 40
Hudson River, 211
HUGO, 367
humpback whales, 392, 407
Hurrell, J., 315
Hurricane Andrew, 218, 223
Hurricane Beulah, 220
Hurricane Camille, 214
Hurricane Floyd, 221-222
Hurricane Hugo, 210, 223
Hurricane Iniki, 218
Hurricane Isabel, 232
Hurricane Katrina, 214-216, 219
hurricanes, 213, 214-222
    characteristics, 216
    evacuation from, 220-222
    hazards, 212-214, 219-220
    life cycle, 218-219
    where and when, 216-218
hydrogen bonding, 62-63
hydrogenous sediment, 96
hydrosphere, 3-6
hydrothermal circulation, 49-50
hydrothermal mineral deposits, 103
hydrothermal vent, 49-50, 277
hypolimnion, 229
Hypsithermal, 325

I

ice-albedo feedback, 340, 341
ice algae, 287
ice/atmosphere interface, 287
ice bacteria, 287
ice cores, 320-321, 342, 347-348
ice floe, 85
ice keel, 86
ice lattice, 65
ice/seawater interface, 287
ice sheets, 3-6
    East Antarctica, 3-6, 337-340
    Greenland, 3-6
    Laurentide, 323-325, 330-332
    West Antarctica, 3-6, 337-340
ice shelves, 5
ice worms, 258
icebergs, 5, 6
Iceland, 356
    whaling, 391-392
Icelandic low, 133, 151, 309

igneous rock, 36
iguanas, 281
India, 297, 301-302
Indian Deep Water, 161,162
Indian monsoon, 297
Indonesia Through-flow, 151
Industrial Revolution, 100, 259, 334-335, 380, 392
inertia, 228
inertial circle, 228
infauna, 276
infiltration, 16, 420-421
infrared radiation, 18, 19, 121-123
infrared window, 122
Ingraham, W.James, Jr., 170
instrument-based climate record, 325-327
Integrated Ocean Drilling Program (IODP), 57, 363, 367
interglacial climate, 323
Intergovernmental Oceanographic Commission (IOC), 370
Intergovernmental Panel on Climate Change (IPCC), 333
intermediate waters, 162
internal energy, 65
internal geological processes, 9
internal tides, 186
internal waves, 178
International Commission for the Conservation of Atlantic Tuna (ICCAT), 384
International Convention for the Regulation of Whaling (ICRW), 391
international dateline, 139, 299, 300
International Decade of Ocean Exploration (IDOE), 364
International Geophysical Year of 1957-58, 298, 364, 404
International Great Lakes Datum (IGLD), 230
International Joint Commission (IJC), 394
International Maritime Organization (IMO), 408
International Polar Year, 364
International Whaling Commission (IWC), 391, 403
intertidal zone, 202, 263, 269
intertropical convergence zone (ITCZ), 153, 297, 314- 315
Inuit people, 317, 391
ion, 68
IPCC Assessment Report, 333, 336
iron fertilization, 254-255, 415
island arc, 46
Island of Tin, 356
isobar, 130
isomotic fish, 278
isotacy, 37

J

James River, 412
Japanese whaling industry, 391
Jason1 (satellite), 196, 307
JASON, 186, 361
JASON II, 361, 367
Java, 34
Jeddah, Saudi Arabia, 83
jellyfish, 264-265, 362
jet stream, 133, 302
jetsam, 170
jetty, 209, 402
JOIDES, 57, 58
JOIDES *Resolution*, 363
Joint Global Ocean Flux Study (JGOFS), 249
Joint Oceanographic Institutions for Deep Earth Sampling (JOIDES), 57, 58
joule, 65
Juan de Fuca plate, 202, 354
Juan de Fuca Ridge, 202
Julie N., 422
juvenile stage, 52
Jurassic Period, 102, 111, 321, 322

K

karenia brevis, 234
katabatic wind, 86
Katmai, 34
Keeling, Charles D., 334
Keeling curve, 334
kelp, 272-273
kelp forest, 272-273
Kelvin waves, 229
Kennebec River, 401
Key Biscayne, FL, 292
keystone species, 238
Kilauea, 59
Kill Devil Hills, 83
kinetic energy, 64, 90, 147, 172, 174
kinetic molecular energy, 64
King Diamond II, 382
kingfisher, 401
Kircher, Athanasius, 145
Kiritimati (Christmas Island), 294
Krakatoa, eruption of, 34, 187, 332
krill, 238, 287, 404
Kure Islands, 275
Kuroshio Current, 152, 222
Kutzbach, J. E., 323

mixed tide, 180-181

mixotrophs, 237

model, 21

Molina, M.J., 141

mollusks, 264, 269, 270, 393

Monaco, Prince Albert I, 170

monsoon, 297

Monterey Bay, CA, 291, 354

Monterey Bay Aquarium Research Institute, 362

Montreal, Canada, 233-234

Montreal Protocol on Substances that Deplete the Ozone Layer, 141

Mora, C., 301

moray eels, 281

Morgan, J., 59

Morris, Simon Conway, 111

Moses Project, 201

Moss Landing Marine Laboratories, 254

Mote Marine Laboratory (Florida), 365

Mount Pinatubo, 34, 332-333, 336

Mount St. Helens, 35

Mozambique, 355

mud flat, 269

multi-year ice, 77, 85

multibeam sonar, 370

multistage flash distillation, 83

Murray, Sir John, 358, 359

murres, 407

musk ox, 318

mussels, 393, 394, 408

Mycenae, Greece, 356

N

Namibia, 321

Nankai Trough, 363

Nankai Trough subduction zone, 257

Nansen, Fridtjof, 149, 178

NAO Index, 309

NASA Jet Propulsion Laboratory, 338

National Center for Atmospheric Research (NCAR), 305, 315

National Centers for Environmental Prediction (NCEP), 305

National Climatic Data Center (NCDC), 326

National Data Buoy Center (NDBC), 193

National Deep Submergence Laboratory, 361

National Estuaries Research Reserve System (NERRS), 406

National Hurricane Center, 219, 220

National Marine Fisheries Service, 262, 281, 374, 381,

384, 386, 389

National Ocean Survey, 369

National Oceans Council, 403

National Oceanic and Atmospheric Administration (NOAA), 104, 379, 403, 411

    Atlantic Oceanographic and Meteorological Laboratory, 160

    Coastal Change Analysis Program, 422

    Deep-Ocean Assessment & Reporting of Tsunamis (DART), 188

    National Marine Fisheries Service (NMFS), 262, 281, 374, 381, 384, 386, 389

    National Marine Sanctuary Program, 291, 387

    National Ocean Service CO-OPS, 184, 406

    National Ocean Survey, 369

    National Snow & Ice Data Center, 339, 341

    National Weather Service, 208, 368

    Office of Ocean Coastal Resource Management (OCRM) 406

    Office of Ocean Exploration, 342

    Office of Protected Resources, 281, 390

    Office of Response and Restoration, 406

    Pacific Marine Environmental Laboratory, 169

    Physical Oceanographic Real Time Services (PORTS), 184, 307

    Tropical Prediction Center/National Hurricane Center, 219, 220

National Park Service, 232

National Resources Council, 420

National Science & Technology Council, 289

National Science Foundation (NSF), 354, 363

National Tsunami Hazard Mitigation Program, 188

National Weather Service (NWS), 208, 368

natural gas, generation of, 403

nautilus, 265

Navistar satellites, 166

Nazca plate, 46

NCAR, 305, 315

neap tides, 182

nebula, 29

nekton, 263, 265-266

NEPTUNE, 354

neritic deposits, 97

neritic zone, 263

net primary production, 242

net production, 242

neutral ocean/atmosphere conditions, 299

neutrally stable system, 149

New Caledonia, 356

new ice, 85

New Orleans, LA, 216, 400
new production, 243
New York Bronx Zoo, 387
New York Zoological Society, 360
New Zealand, 356, 357
Newfoundland, 153, 262, 356
    cod industry, 261-262
Newton, Sir Isaac, 179
Newton's first law of motion, 90, 130, 180, 228
Niger, 314
Niger River, 356
nilas, 85
Nile River, 97-98, 316, 356
Nile River delta, 97-98, 410
nitrates, 289
nitrogen cycle, 14
nitrous oxide, 122, 335
no-take refuge, 292
no-take zones, 386
nodal cycle, 185
node, 177
non-conservative properties, 69
non-governmental organizations (NGOs), 413
non-point source, 412
nonferromagnesium silicate minerals, 92
nonrenewable resources, 38
nor'easter, 222-223
North Atlantic Current, 153, 296
North Atlantic Deep Water, 161, 246, 347
North Atlantic Equatorial Current, 152
North Atlantic Oscillation (NAO), 294, 308, 309, 311, 362
North Atlantic right whale, 392
North Atlantic subtropical gyre, 150-151, 152-153
North East Water, 86
North Equatorial Current, 152
North Pacific Intermediate Water, 161, 162
North Pacific Trash Vortex, 170
North Pole, 149, 357
North Sea, 102
North slope of Alaska, 321
North Water, 86
northern snakehead, 394
Norwegian Current, 152, 153
Norwegian Dawn, 171
Norwegian Polar Institute, 375
Norwegian whaling industry, 390-391
NR1-Deep Submergence Craft, 361
NSCAT/NASA Scatterometer, 194
numerical model, 22

nutria, 399

O

ocean,
    and carbon storage, 246-249, 414-416
    and climate, 295-297, 319-320, 337-343
    and nuclear waste, 413-414
    and waste disposal, 413-414
    and water cycle, 14-16
    circulation of, 149-158
    color, 259-260
    forces acting on, 149-151
    modeling, 21-22, 368
    profiling, 168-169
    remote sensing of, 18-21
    structure of, 147-149
ocean acidification, 74, 100, 337, 402
ocean albedo, 295
ocean basin, 41
    and plate tectonics, 41-53
Ocean City, MD, 209
ocean currents, 151-158
ocean commons, 403
ocean drilling, 56-58
Ocean Drilling Program (ODP), 256
ocean floor observatories, 366
ocean governance, 402
ocean iron fertilization, 254, 415
ocean policy, 402-404
ocean rings, 155-157
ocean stewardship, 379, 402
ocean trench, 46, 47
ocean water, 68-71
    properties of, 68-77
oceanic crust, 37
oceanic life zones, 263-264
oceanography, 358
octopus, 265
Oeschger, Hans, 348
oil-decomposing bacteria, 407
oil, formation of, 102
oil production, offshore, 403
oil spills, 406-407, 422
Okushiri, Japan, 186
Old Royal Observatory, 330
oligotrophic waters, 264
omnivores, 11, 236
On the Origin of Species, 357
oolith, 96
oozes, 99-100

open ocean convection, 160

open system, 411

orange roughy, 398

Ordovician Period, 102, 322

ospreys, 393, 401

otolith, 398

Our Nation and the Sea, A Plan for National Action, 403

Outer Banks (North Carolina), 83, 232

outgassing, 30, 247

overfishing, 292, 380, 381, 384, 393, 395, 398, 403

       growth, 380

       recruitment, 380

oxygen, origin of, 30-31

oxygen isotope analysis, 319, 320, 324, 347

oysters, 289, 377-378, 387-388, 393, 400, 412

ozone, 7, 141-143

ozone shield, 7

P

Pacific Decadal Oscillation (PDO), 294, 308, 310, 311, 362

Pacific Deep Water, 161, 162

Pacific Marine Environmental Laboratory (PMEL), 307

Pacific Ring of Fire, 47, 52

Pacific Tsunami Warning Center, 188

pack ice, 86

Padre Island, TX, 206

PALACE, 169

pancake ice, 85

Pangaea, 9, 42, 45

Panthalassa, 52

Papahânamokuâkea Marine National Monument (Hawaii), 291, 292

Papua, New Guinea, 356

paralytic shellfish poisoning, 234

partial tides, 185

partially mixed estuary, 211

particulate organic carbon (POC), 247

passive continental margin, 39

Patapsco River, 410

pathogens, 420-421

Paul, Frank, 339

Pauly, Daniel, 382

PCBs, 410

pelagic deposit, 99

pelagic fish, 266, 279

pelagic zone, 263, 264, 268

pelagos, 263

Pelamis Wave Energy Converter, 198

Pelican Islands, Florida, 392

pelicans, 282, 392

penguins, 282

perigee, 182

perihelion, 182, 330, 336

permafrost, 3, 317, 342

Permian Period, 102

Persian Gulf, 102, 408

Peru, 294, 300, 301, 307

Peru-Chile Trench, 46, 47

Peru Current, 152, 154

Peruvian anchovy fishery, 301, 381

pH, 73-74

pH scale, 73

Phanerzoic Eon, 321

Phillipine Islands, 357

Phoenicians, 356

phosphorescence, 267

photic zone, 73, 121, 264, 299

photocytes, 267

photodissociation, 14

photosphere, 329

photosynthesis, 10, 30, 73

phragmites, 394

physical model, 21

Physical Oceanographic Real Time Services (PORTS), 184, 307

physical pump, 246-247

phytoplankton, 236, 276, 301, 310

Piazza San Marco, Venice, Italy, 199-201

Piccard, Auguste, 360

Piccard, Jacques, 360

Pikaia, 110

pillow basalt, 44

Pine Island Glacier, 5, 6

pinnipeds, 280, 292

Pizarro, Francisco, 316

placer deposits, 102

planetary albedo, 120

planetary-scale circulation, 131, 132, 133

planetary-scale systems, 131, 132, 133

planetesimals, 29

plankton, 236, 263, 264

plate boundaries, 44

plate tectonics, 9, 41, 328, 349

       and climate, 328-329

       evidence for, 41-43

Pleistocene Ice Age, 40, 227, 254, 316, 319, 321, 323, 330, 337, 347

Point Lobos, CA, 291

point source, 412

polar amplification, 324, 336
polar bears, 280, 288, 317, 318
polar easterlies, 131
polar front, 133
polar molecules, 63
polar-orbiting satellite, 20, 307
polar stratospheric clouds, 143
polar vortex, 310
Polaris, 115
Polarstern, 287
polders, 399
pole and line fishing, 385
poleward heat transport, 127
pollen, 320
pollution, 405
polychlorinated biphenyls (PCBs), 240-241, 410
Polynesians, 356
polynyas, 86
polyps (coral), 274, 342
porpoises. 280
Port Valdez, AK, 407-408
Portuguese man-of-war, 265
Potomac River, 412
practical salinity units (psu), 70
Precambrian Era, 110
Precautionary Principle, 403-404
precipitation, 15
pressure, 64, 77
pressure gradient force, 151
pressure ridge, 86
Prestige, 408
primary production, 236
prime meridian, 139
Prince William Sound, AK, 407-408
principle of constant proportions, 69
prochlorococus, 245
producers, 11, 236
Profiling Autonomous Lagrangian Circulation (PALACE), 169
profiling float, 17, 18, 159-160, 169, 364, 365, 370
progressive wave, 177
prokaryotes, 245
Proterozoic Eon, 321
protista, 237
protoctista, 237
protozoa, 245
proxy climatic data, 318-321
pseudo-nitzschia, 233, 235
pteropods, 94
Ptolemy, 139, 356

Puerto Rico, 187
Puget Sound, 21
purse seining, 385
pycnocline, 147
Pytheas, 356

Q
Qiantang, River, 184
Queen Elizabeth 2, 171
Queensland, Australia, 273
QuikSCAT, 194
Quinn, W.H., 316

R
radar altimeter, 196
radioactive material, disposal of, 414
radiocarbon dating, 330
radiolaria, 95
radiation, 18, 19
rafting, 86
ram ventilation, 278
Rapid Climate Change Program, 129
recreational beaches, 405
recreational fisheries, 388-389
recruitment overfishing, 380
red algae, 269, 273
red clay, 99
Red Sea, 83, 355
Red Sea Intermediate Water, 161, 162
red snapper, 400
red tide, 93, 234, 366
reef-building coral, 274
reference ellipsoid, 196
reflection, 119
refraction (wave), 203
regenerated production, 242
Reidy, Catherine, 409
reindeer, 317, 318
remineralization, 248
remote sensing, 18-21, 362
    active, 18
    passive, 18
remotely operated vehicle (ROV), 361, 362
Resen, Bishop, 145
reservoir rock, 102
residence time, 12, 227
resonance, 177, 183
resources, of the seafloor, 102-104
respiration, 10
reverse estuaries, 212

reverse osmosis, 83

reversing thermometers, 168

ridge, 296

rift valley, 52

Rignot, E., 338

rings, 101, 155-157

rip current, 207

rip tide, 207-208

river-dominated delta, 97

river otters, 407

rockfish, 386

rocks, 36-38

rock cycle, 37, 101

Rocky Mountains, 323

rogue waves, 171-172

Ronne Ice Shelf, 338

Roosevelt, Theodore, 292, 392

Ross, Sir James Clark, 357

Ross, Sir John, 357

Ross ice shelf, 338

Ross Sea, 161, 357

rotifers, 287

Rowland, F.S., 141

Royal Navy, 358

Ruddiman, W. F., 321

rule of ecological efficiency, 240

runoff, 289

runoff component, 16

Rutgers Marine Field Station, 367

R/V Chain, 349

R/V Meteor, 359

R.V. Melville, 254

Ryan, William, 349

S

Saffir, H. S., 220

Saffir-Simpson Hurricane Intensity Scale, 220

Sahara Desert, 314, 328

Sahel (Africa), 314-315

Saint Lawrence River, 325, 347

salinity, 65, 68, 287

salmon, 279, 393, 394, 401, 407, 410

salmon farming, 393-394

salt, 62

salt cod, 262

salt marsh, 208, 271, 399

saltwater intrusion, 351

salt-wedge estuary, 211

Samoa, 356

San Andreas fault, 47

San Francisco Bay, 387-388

sand dunes, 206-207

sand spit, 206

sanitary landfill, 413

Santa Barbara, CA, 292

Santa Barbara Channel, 387

Santorini, 33-34

sardines, 279

Sargasso Sea, 155, 170, 217, 248, 268, 279

sargassum, 269-270

sashimi, 384

Saskatoon, Saskatchewan, 114

satellite remote sensing, 18-21, 362

saturation horizon, 99

Saudi Arabia, 329

scattering, 119

scatterometer, 193

schooling, 280

Scientific Committee of Oceanic Research (SCOR), 249

Scientific Ice Expedition, 341

scientific whaling, 391

Scotch Cap Lighthouse, AK, 188

Scripp's Institution of Oceanography, 160, 245, 354, 359

scutes, 389

sea, 175

sea breeze, 132

sea ducks, 282, 408

sea grass beds, 388, 411-413

sea ice, 85, 287

    extent of, 77-78

    first-year ice, 85

    multi-year ice, 85

    new ice, 85

    old ice, 85

    second-year ice, 85

    terminology, 85-86

    young ice, 85

sea level fluctuations, 337-340

    and saltwater intrusion, 351

sea lily, 276-277

sea lion, 280

Sea of Okhotsk, 162

sea otters, 273, 407

sea salts, 68-71

sea snakes, 281

sea state, 193-195

sea surface temperatures (SST), 113, 274, 297, 300, 302, 304, 314, 315, 333, 339

sea turtles, 281, 374, 389-390

sea urchins, 273

sea wave, 173

sea-floor spreading, 44-46

Sea-viewing Wide Field-of-view Sensor (SeaWiFS), 249, 259

seabirds, 282, 294, 408

seafloor resources, 102-104

Seager, Richard, 296

seals, 268, 280, 288, 317, 374, 404

seamounts, 48

SEASAT-A Satellite Scatterometer (SASS), 194

seasons, 115-116

seawall, 210, 402

seawater, 68

    alkalinity of, 73-74

    chemical properties of, 68-75

    conservative properties of, 69

    dissolved gases, 71-73

    non-conservative properties of, 73

    physical properties of, 75-79

    pH of, 73-74

    standard, 69

seaweed, 269-270

SeaWiFS, 249, 259

Secchi disk, 168

second-year ice, 85

secondary production, 236

sediment, 19, 89-97

    size classification, 89-90

sediment cores, 319-320, 325

sedimentary rock, 36

seiche, 176-177

selective feeding, 276

Seltzer, Geoffrey, 316

semi-diurnal tide, 180

Senegal, 314

sensible heating, 126. 178

separated sewer system, 421

Severn River, 184

sewage treatment, 420-421

shad, 279

shallow-water waves, 176

shark fin soup, 382

sharks, 277, 374, 381-382

    finning (for soup), 382

    overfishing of, 381-382

    viviparous reproduction of, 278

    shellfish, 289, 402, 405, 408, 412, 420, 422

shore, 202

shoreline, 202

shrimp, 386, 400

shrimp trawling, 386

Siberia, 265

significant wave height, 172, 193

siliceous ooze, 100

silicon-oxygen tetrahedron, 92

Simpson, R. H., 220

single-hulled ships, 408

Skeleton Coast, Namibia, 321

skipjacks, 377, 378

slack water, 183

Slocum, Josiah, 365

Slocum glider, 364, 365, 370

SLOSH (Sea, Lake, and Overland Surges from Hurricanes), 213, 220

slow-spreading ridge, 45, 49

Smithsonian Institution, 111, 357

Snake River, 410

snow ice, 186

snow melt index, 339

SOFAR, 78

SOFAR channel, 78, 268

soil, 9

solar altitude, 116

solar radiation, 115-121, 329-332

    budget of, 119-120

    and the ocean, 120-121

solar still, 83

solar variability and climate, 329-330

solstices, 115-118

solubility pump, 246-247

SONAR (Sound Navigation and Ranging), 78, 266

sorting, 89

sound, 78-79

    transmission of, 78-79

sounding, 159

source region, 127-128

South Atlantic gyre, 152

South Equatorial Current, 152, 154

South Pacific Bare Zone, 100

South Pole, 357

Southern Ocean 287, 404

southern oscillation, 297- 298

southern oscillation index (SOI), 297

Southwest India Ridge, 46

specific heat, 66-67

specific heat of water, 66-67

spermaceti, 390

Spörer minimum, 330

spreading plates, 49

spring bloom, 243

spring tides, 182
spring turnover, 230
squall line, 223
squid, 263, 265-266, 267
stability, 148-149
stable system, 148-149
standard atmospheric pressure, 77
standard seawater, 69
standing wave, 177
state of the sea, 193-195
Steele, John, 245
stewardship, 379
storm-sewer discharge, 408
storm surge, 212-214
Strait of Gilbralter, 349
strategic retreat, 209, 210, 232
stratosphere, 7, 31, 332
stratospheric ozone shield, 31, 119, 141
        and marine life, 141
Stratton, Julius A., 403
Stratton Commission, 403
striped bass, 279, 386, 401, 413
stromatolites, 349
sturgeon, 279, 401
subduction, 46-47
subduction zone, 46-47
sublimation, 14, 66
submarine canyon, 39
submarine fans, 40
submarine landslides, 258
submerged aquatic vegetation (SAV), 271
sub-polar gyres, 151
subpolar lows, 133, 151
Sub-Saharan Africa, 314-315
Subsurface Acoustic Doppler Current Profilers, 307
subtropical anticyclone, 133
subtropical gyres, 101, 151
subtropical highs, 132, 133
Suess, Eduard, 42
Suiko seamount, 60
Sulawesi Island, 316
sulfurous aerosols, 34, 332, 335
Sumatra, 34
sunspots, 329-330
superdams, 409
superplume, 48
surf, 176
surf zone, 207
surface geological processes, 9
surface tension, 174

sushi, 384
Susquehanna River, 412
sustainability, 379
sustainable development, 402
Sustainable Fisheries Act of 1996, 403
sustainable yield, 379-385
sustained wind speed, 216
suturing stage, 52
swash, 205
swell, 175
swordfish, 374, 400
symbiotic relationship, 274
Synthesis Report of the IPCC Fourth Assessment Report, 333
synoptic-scale systems, 131, 133-135
                highs, 134
                lows, 134
system, 3

T

tags, 374
Tahiti, 297
tai-fung, 217
Tamano, 422
Tambora, eruption of, 34, 332
TAO, 306
TAO/TRITON, 169, 306
Tardino, J.A., 60
Taylor, Frank B., 42
tectonic processes, 44-53
tektite, 97
teleconnections, 302
teleosts, 278, 279
temperature, 64
temperature gradients, 8, 287
tephra, 92
terminal stage, 52
terminal velocity, 90
terns, 282
territorial waters, 402-403
tests of foraminifera, 94
Tethys, 50
Tethys Sea, 328, 349
thermal inertia, 67
thermocline, 147, 229, 299, 301
thermohaline circulation , 129, 160, 347
thermosphere, 7
Thomson, Charles Wyville, 358
threatened species, 389
Three Gorges Dam, 409

Thunder Bay National Marine Sanctuary and Underwater Preserve, 291
Tibetan Plateau, 323
tidal bore, 184
tidal currents, 183-184, 399
tidal day, 180
tidal period, 178
tidal power, 198
tidal range, 177, 178
tidal wave, 178
tide (astronomical), 178-186
    diurnal, 181, 183
    ebb, 183
    equatorial, 181
    flood, 183
    fortnightly, 182
    in ocean basins, 182-183
    internal, 186
    mixed, 181, 183
    neap, 182
    observing, 184-185
    open-ocean, 185-186
    partial, 184-185
    predicting, 184-185
    semi-diurnal, 180, 181, 183
    spring, 182
    tropic, 181
tide cracks, 86
tide generating forces, 179-180
tide pool, 270
tide prediction, 184-185
Titanic, RMS, 5, 361
Tomales Bay, CA, 387-388
tombolo, 206
Tonga, 356, 357
top predators, 266, 379
TOPEX/POSEIDON, 196, 307, 337
tornado, 220, 305
total allowable catch, 382
toxic algal blooms, 233-235, 365
trace elements, 236
trade winds, 131, 300
trajectory analysis, 422
transform faults, 45
transform plate boundary, 47
transitional wave, 176
transpiration, 14, 125
trap and pot fishing, 385
trawling/dragging, 385
tree growth rings, 320

trench, 46-47
Triassic Period, 321
Trieste, 360
trilateration, 166
TRMM Microwave Imager (TMI), 307
TRMM satellite, 307
trolling, 385
trophic level, 11, 239
Tropic of Cancer, 117, 181
Tropic of Capricorn, 180, 181
tropic tides, 181
tropical cyclone, 212-222, 302, 339-340
    and El Niño, 302
    evacuation, 220-222
    hazards, 212-214, 219-220
    life cycle, 218-219
    where and when, 216-218
Tropical Cyclone Nargis, 214
tropical depression, 219
tropical disturbance, 218
Tropical Atmosphere/Ocean (TAO) array, 169, 306
Tropical Ocean Global Atmosphere (TOGA), 169, 306
Tropical Prediction Center/National Hurricane Center, 220
Tropical Rainfall Measuring Mission (TRMM), 299, 307
tropical storm, 219
troposphere, 6, 7
trough (atmospheric), 133, 296
trout, 393
tsunameter, 188, 189
tsunami, 1-2, 186-189, 405
Tsunami Warning Centers, 188
tubeworms, 277
Tudhope, S., 316
tuna, 279, 374, 384, 400
turbidites, 98
turbidity current, 39, 98
turbidity maximum, 212
Twain, Mark, 159
twilight zone, 121, 247, 266
typhoon, 217

U
UCAR, 330
UN Conference on Environment & Development, 404
UN Convention on the Law of the Sea, 403
UN Environmental Program, 333
UN Food & Agriculture Organization (FAO), 379, 381, 382
UN International Maritime Organization (IMO), 413

UN World Commission on Environment and Development, 379
UNESCO, 188, 364, 370
UNESCO World Heritage Site, 112
U.S. Army Corps of Engineers, 400
U.S. Coast & Geodetic Survey ship "Blake", 359
U.S. Coast Guard, 393
U.S. Commission on Ocean Policy, 403
U.S. Environmental Protection Agency, 393
U.S. Fish and Wildlife Service, 390
U.S. Geological Survey, 351
U.S.-Japanese Tropical Rainfall Measuring Mission (TRMM), 307
U.S. McMurdo Station, Antarctica, 143
U.S. Naval Observatory & Hydrological Office, 358
U.S. Navy Depot of Charts and Instruments, 147, 358
U.S. Office of Science and Technology, 339
USS Albatross, 359
USS Monitor, 291
USS Ramapo, 171
ultraslow spreading, 49
ultraslow spreading boundaries, 45
universal solvent, 62, 68
unselective feeding, 276
unstable system, 149
upwash, 205
upwelling, 157-158
urban heat island, 326, 333
urban runoff, 289
UV radiation, 19, 141
UVB, 141

V

Vanuatu, 356
vector, 149
Venice, Italy, 199-201

Venice Organic Soil Subsidence Project, 200
vertical migration, 266
Victoria Land, Antarctica, 357
video plankton recorder (VPR), 362
Vikings, 325, 356
Vincennes, 357
Vine, F. J., 43
Virginia Marine Resources Commission, 378
viruses, 245
visible light, 19, 120-121, 259
visible window, 122
Vitiaz, 359
volcanic eruptions, 30-31, 33-35, 48-49, 328, 405

and climate, 332-333
volcanic plumes, 356
Volunteer Observing Ships (VOS), 363, 364
Vostok, Antarctica, 347

W

Walcott, Charles D., 111
Walker Circulation, 300
Walker, Sir Gilbert, 297, 298
walrus, 280
Walsh, Don, 360
warm phase, 294, 310
warm-core rings, 155-157
wastewater treatment, 405
water
    origin of, 29
    phases, of, 63-64, 65-66
    as a solvent, 68
    specific heat of, 66-67
water birds, 389, 392
water cycle, 14-16
water mass, 161-162
water molecule, 62-63
water vapor, 64,66
watershed, 16, 290, 411
wave, 173
    capillary, 174
    deep-water, 175
    forced, 175
    generation, 173-175
    internal, 178
    progressive, 177
    rogue, 171-172
    sea, 175
    shallow-water, 176
    standing, 177
    swell, 175
    transitional, 176
    tsunami, 186-189
wave crest, 173
wave-dominated delta, 97
wave frequency, 173
wave height, 173
wave interference, 175
wave period, 173
wave power index, 223
wave refraction, 203
wave trough, 173
wave-base, 174
wavelength, 18, 173

weather, 115
weathering, 9, 30, 91
Weddell Sea, 161, 246
Wegener, Alfred, 42
well-mixed estuary, 212
Welland Canal, 227
Wentworth Classification, 89
West Antarctica ice sheet, 338
West Coast and Alaska Tsunami Warning Center, 188
westerlies, 131, 132
western boundary currents, 101, 154-155
wetlands, 98, 399, 400
whale fat (blubber), 391
whale oil, 390
whale watching, 391
whales, 268, 280, 288, 292, 374, 389, 390-392, 404
    blue, 280, 392
    bowhead, 392
    California gray, 265
    grey, 280
    humpback, 392, 407
    hunting of, 390-392
    killer, 280, 407, 408
    North Atlantic right, 392
    right, 390
    sperm, 280
    white (beluga), 374
whaling, commercial, 390-392
White Cliffs, of Dover, 237
Whittington, Harry, 111
Wilkes, Lt. Charles, 357
Wilson cycles, 50-53
Wilson, J. Tuzo, 50
Wind and Current Charts, 358
wind belts, 131, 132
wind shear, 218
wind-blown dust, 93
wind-driven currents, 149-158
wind-driven waves, 173-176
wind waves, generation of, 173-175
Wisconsinan Stage (Holocene), 347
Woods Hole Oceanographic Institution, 58, 160, 245, 248, 254, 349, 354, 360, 361, 365, 367
World Meteorological Organization (WMO), 85, 325, 333, 336, 364
XBT, 169, 364
Yangtze River, 97, 409
Year without a summer, 34
yellowfin tuna, 384
Yellowstone National Park, 60

Yoho National Park (Canada), 111
young ice, 85, 324, 325, 347
Younger Dryas, 324-325
Yucatán Peninsula, 27-28
zebra mussel, 394
zooplankton, 238, 264, 265, 266, 276, 310
zooplankton bloom, 243, 287
zooxanthellae, 274, 301